OPTICS

This book is in the

ADDISON-WESLEY SERIES IN PHYSICS

OPTICS

by

BRUNO ROSSI

Department of Physics

Massachusetts Institute of Technology

ADDISON-WESLEY PUBLISHING COMPANY, INC.

READING, MASSACHUSETTS · PALO ALTO · LONDON · DALLAS · ATLANTA

PREFACE

The purpose of this book is to acquaint the reader with the most significant facts concerning light phenomena, and with the basic physical concepts that underlie their interpretation.

The book is based on the wave model of light. It deals in succession with various groups of optical phenomena, whose study leads step by step to the discovery of the kinematic properties and of the physical nature of light waves. Chapters 1 and 2 introduce the laws of rectilinear propagation, reflection, and refraction, which explain the vast majority of the most obvious optical effects. A wave model describing light waves as a succession of very short pulses, without specifying in more detail the shape and character of such waves, is found to be adequate for the interpretation of these laws. Chapters 3 and 4 deal with the phenomena of interference and diffraction, whose analysis results in the identification of monochromatic light with sinusoidal waves. After a short digression on the velocity of light (Chapter 5), Chapter 6 discusses the phenomena of polarization and double refraction, which prove the transverse character of light waves.

This completes what may be termed the "kinematic" description of optical phenomena, and leads to the "dynamical" problem, or the problem of the physical nature of light waves, which is taken up in Chapter 7. Here it is shown how the numerical value of the velocity of light as well as the transverse character of light waves lead naturally to the conclusion that these waves are an electromagnetic phenomenon. In Chapter 8 the optical properties of matter are interpreted on the basis of the electromagnetic theory of light and of a simple model describing atoms as microscopic oscillators.

Chapter 9 explores the limits of validity of the classical electromagnetic description of light waves and, using light as an example, illustrates the complementary character of the wave description and of the particle description of all radiation phenomena.

Several reasons have led to the choice of the logical order outline above in preference to one in which light is treated from the outset as an electromagnetic phenomenon.

In the first place, it happens that the most common optical phenomena, such as the shadow cast by an opaque object, are the most difficult to explain on the basis of the rigorous theory of electromagnetic waves, whereas they can be easily interpreted, at least in the semiquantitative manner, from the general principles that apply to all wave phenomena.

In the second place, I feel that the subject of optics offers an almost unique opportunity to illustrate the value and the limitations of physical models, which play such an essential role in the development of scientific thought. The book strongly emphasizes this aspect of the scientific method, presenting first a very general model of light waves which can be easily visualized in terms of concrete mechanical analogies, and then proceeding to increasingly specific models which involve increasingly abstract and sophisticated physical concepts, At each step it is shown how the introduction of a new model does not invalidate the results obtained previously, but sets definite limits to their field of applicability.

In the third place, I believe that an order of presentation following broadly the historical development of the scientific thought on a specific subject may help the reader to appreciate the aims and limitations of the scientific method. It may clarify the ever-changing significance of scientific "truths" by presenting a dynamic rather than a static picture of the subject matter, and thus emphasizing the evolutionary character of science.

It is assumed that the reader has some knowledge of elementary calculus. Simple differential equations are used occasionally, but are presented in such a way as to be understandable to a reader who is not already acquainted with them. Slightly more advanced mathematical procedures are used only in some of the starred sections, which can be omitted without loss of continuity. An introductory course in electromagnetism, leading up to the four Maxwell equations in their integral form, is a prerequisite for Chapters 7 and 8, which deal with the electromagnetic theory of light, but not for the remainder of the book.

I have not allowed myself to use the limitations of the mathematical means at my disposal as an excuse for avoiding difficult but fundamentally important subjects. An example in point is Huygens' principle, which is the foundation of the whole kinematic theory of light. Without a clear understanding of Huygens' principle such basic optical phenomena as rectilinear propagation, diffraction, and double refraction remain a mystery. Yet many authors dispose of Huygens' principle with a few sentences, and do not attempt to justify it mathematically or to explain its deep and far-reaching significance. In this book, on the contrary, Huygens' principle is discussed in great detail from a logically rigorous point of view, and is then consistently used, in its various forms, for the explanation of different groups of optical phenomena. I have endeavored to minimize the mathematical difficulties and have gone to great lengths to clarify and illustrate with examples the subtle physical concepts underlying this principle. Nevertheless, a certain amount of effort will be needed on the part of the reader to fully appreciate its significance and its implications. I do not see why the student should be spared this rewarding effort.

Other examples are the propagation of electromagnetic waves and the radiation from an accelerated charge. The theory of these phenomena provides the solution of the dynamical problem of optics and forms the basis for the interpretation of the interactions between light and matter.

Here again I have avoided the use of complex mathematics but I have not recoiled from the labor which is necessary to fully clarify the nature of physical processes and to obtain their exact mathematical description.

The problems form an essential part of the book. They range in difficulty from simple numerical examples, aimed at developing a quantitative feeling for the phenomena under discussion, to questions designed to probe the depth of understanding of the theories underlying the interpretation of these phenomena. In the problems the reader will also find many of the practical applications of optics which are omitted from the text for the sake of brevity and coherence.

It is a pleasure to express my warm appreciation to the many colleagues and students who have helped in the preparation of this book by offering their suggestions and their constructive criticism.

Cambridge, Massachusetts   Bruno Rossi
December, 1956

CONTENTS

Starred sections may be omitted without loss of continuity.

ix

CHAPTER 1

HUYGENS' PRINCIPLE AND THE APPROXIMATION OF GEOMETRICAL OPTICS

1–1 The three laws of geometrical optics. A house or a tree casting a shadow on a sunny day; a mirror or the quiet surface of a pond returning the image of the onlooker; the broken appearance of a straight pole partially immersed in water; the illusion of water on a hot asphalt pavement; the rainbow stretching across the sky after a rainstorm; the glitter of a jewel; the image appearing on the screen of a movie theater, on the film of a photographic camera, on the retina of the eye; the beam of a searchlight reaching into the depths of the night sky; the structure of a living cell revealed by a microscope—these and countless other visual experiences are accounted for by three simple empirical laws.

These three laws form the basis of what is called *geometrical optics*. They are the law of *rectilinear propagation*, the law of *reflection*, and the law of *refraction*.

The law of rectilinear propagation, as the name implies, states that *in a homogeneous medium* light travels along straight paths. Thus an opaque object A, placed between a *point source* of light S and a screen Σ, will cast a shadow with a sharply defined boundary (Fig. 1–1): the boundary line is the intersection of the screen with the conical surface that touches the surface of the obstacle and has its apex at the source. A point source, however, is merely a mathematical abstraction, whereas a real light source always has finite dimensions, so that the transition from a region of complete shadow to a region of full light is not sharply defined. Between the two lies a region of partial shadow, the *penumbra*, which receives light from only a portion of the source (Fig. 1–2).

An eclipse of the sun occurs when the earth enters the shadow cone of the moon, and the moon is eclipsed when it enters the shadow of the earth. These are demonstrations of the validity of the law of rectilinear propagation on an astronomical scale.

The rectilinear propagation of light explains, among other effects, the operation of the *pinhole camera*. An opaque screen with a small hole (Fig. 1–3) lies between a brightly illuminated object and a white screen (or a photographic film). Light rays emanating from the various points of a luminous object and passing through the hole project on the white screen (or the photographic film) an inverted image of the object.

To formulate the laws of reflection and refraction, consider a ray of light impinging upon a plane surface of separation between two trans-

1

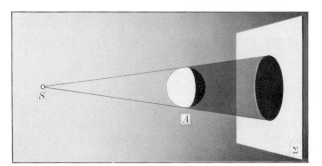

FIG. 1–1. Shadow of an opaque object with a point source of light.

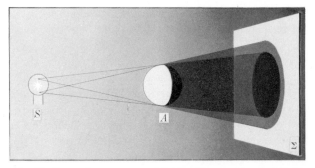

FIG. 1–2. Shadow of an opaque object with an extended light source.

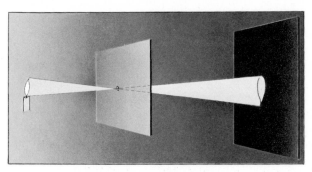

FIG. 1–3. Pinhole camera.

parent substances, 1 and 2; for example, air and water (Fig. 1–4). Assume that each of the two substances is *homogeneous* and *isotropic*, the latter qualification meaning that its properties are the same in all directions. (The propagation of light in nonisotropic media, such as crystals, will be discussed in Chapter 6.) We find, in general, that the incident ray splits into two: a *reflected* ray, which goes back into the medium from which the incident ray came, and a *refracted* ray that penetrates the other medium. We also find that:

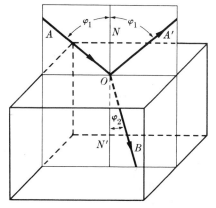

Fig. 1–4. Reflection and refraction of a light ray at the boundary between two different transparent media.

(1) The incident ray AO, the reflected ray OA', and the refracted ray OB lie in a plane perpendicular to the boundary surface, called the *plane of incidence*.

(2) The incident ray and the reflected ray form equal angles with the normal NN' to the boundary surface.

(3) If φ_1 is the angle between the incident ray and NN' (angle of incidence), and φ_2 is the angle between the refracted ray and NN' (angle of refraction), the ratio $\sin \varphi_1 / \sin \varphi_2$ is independent of the angle of incidence φ_1, and is thus a constant characteristic of the two media.

The last statement, called *Snell's law*, has the analytical expression

$$\frac{\sin \varphi_1}{\sin \varphi_2} = n_{12}. \tag{1–1}$$

The constant n_{12} is called the *index of refraction* of the second medium relative to the first.

Experiment has shown that the index of refraction of substance 1 relative to substance 2 is the reciprocal of the index of refraction of 2 relative to 1; that is, $n_{12} = 1/n_{21}$. This amounts to saying that if a light ray can follow the path AOB in passing from the first medium to the second, it could also follow the inverse path BOA in passing from the second to the first.

Notice that refraction brings a ray closer to the normal or farther from it depending on whether n_{12} is larger or smaller than unity. If $n_{12} < 1$, the angle of refraction becomes equal to $\pi/2$ when $\sin \varphi_1 = n_{12}$. For such an angle of incidence, the refracted ray goes off at a grazing angle. For a larger angle of incidence, Eq. (1–1) cannot be satisfied by any value of φ_2. The refracted ray no longer exists and the light ray is completely reflected back into the medium from which it came. This phenomenon is known as *total reflection*. For example, the index of refraction of water relative to air is (about) 1.33, and that of air relative to water is (about) 1/1.33. The angle whose sine equals 1/1.33 is 49°. Thus rays coming from a source under water are totally reflected at the surface of the water if their angles of incidence are greater than 49°.

Total reflection explains the peculiar effects observed when lights are placed under the spout of a fountain. The light rays remain trapped in the rising column of water until the column breaks into droplets, so that the droplets are brightly illuminated by the emerging light rays. Similarly, a rod of glass or of some transparent plastic material performs effectively as a "light pipe"; light entering from one end at a sufficiently small angle undergoes multiple total reflections at the walls and eventually emerges from the other end without loss except that due to absorption. The rod need not be straight; it will still hold the light if it is bent in any arbitrary shape, provided the curves are not too sharp.

Total internal reflection in a glass prism is often used to deflect a light ray through an angle of 90° without appreciable loss of intensity (Fig. 1–5). The cross section of such a prism (called a *totally reflecting prism*) is a right isosceles triangle. The light ray enters the prism perpendicularly through the face *a*, and strikes the hypotenuse face *b* at an angle of 45°, which is greater than the limiting angle for total reflection for all kinds of glass. Total reflection at the hypotenuse surface causes the light ray to emerge from the prism perpendicularly through the face *c*.

Note that total reflection at the boundary surface between two media can take place only if the second medium has a certain minimum thickness (of the order of several thousandths of a millimeter). For example, a very thin air film between two pieces of glass will partially transmit a beam of light incident upon the film even if the angle of incidence is greater than the limiting angle for total reflection. We refer the reader to Section 8–7 for a quantitative discussion of this phenomenon.

Experiments show that the index of refraction is usually slightly different for light of different colors, a phenomenon known as *dispersion*. For example, a ray of blue light entering water from air undergoes a slightly greater deflection than a ray of red light, and hence the index of refraction of water relative to air is greater for blue light than for red. A ray of white light gives rise, upon refraction, to a fanlike bundle of

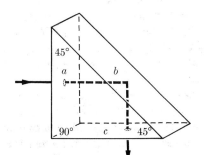

FIG. 1–5. The total reflection prism.

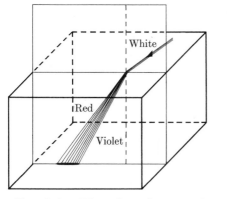

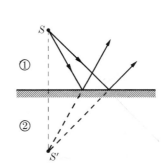

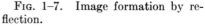

FIG. 1–6.   Dispersion of a ray of white light.

FIG. 1–7.   Image formation by reflection.

colored rays (Fig. 1–6), indicating that white light results from the superposition of light of different colors. We shall return to this phenomenon later; for the moment we shall assume that we are experimenting with *monochromatic* light (that is, light of a single color), so that we may neglect dispersion.

Consider again two media, 1 and 2, separated by a plane surface, as in Fig. 1–7. It follows from the law of reflection that light rays emanating from a point source S in medium 1 and partially reflected at the boundary surface would, if extended beyond the surface, intersect at the point S' in medium 2 (S and S' are symmetrically placed with respect to the reflecting surface). To the eye of an observer, these reflected rays appear to be diverging along straight lines from a light source at S'. The point S' is called the *specular image* of S.

It is well known that reflection occurs not only at the boundary between two transparent substances, but also at the boundary between transparent substances and certain opaque substances. Indeed, the polished surfaces of many metals reflect almost 100% of the incident light. A highly reflecting surface is often referred to as a *mirror*.

1–2 The corpuscular model and the wave model of light. Two models have been suggested for interpretation of the empirical properties of light mentioned in the preceding section.

In the corpuscular model, light is considered to be a multitude of minute particles emitted with great speed from the light source. In transparent homogeneous substances, the particles are not subject to forces of any kind and thus travel along straight lines. Near the boundary between two media, short-range repulsive and attractive forces acting upon the particles cause reflection and refraction; to explain why some particles of the same

light beam are repelled (and thus reflected) while others are attracted
(and thus refracted) requires a number of artificial assumptions.

The wave model was probably
suggested by the familiar observation of ripples on the surface of a
body of water, which spread in ever-
widening circles from a point where
a disturbance has occurred. According to this model, a point source

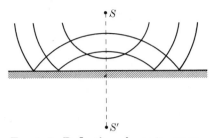

Fig. 1–8. Reflection of a water wave at a solid wall.

of light is considered to be the origin of a disturbance which (in a
homogeneous medium) sets up spherical waves.

As is illustrated in Fig. 1–8, a circular water wave, upon reaching a
solid plane wall, is reflected as a wave whose shape is the arc of a circle.
The center S' of the reflected wave and the origin S of the original disturbance are symmetrically located with respect to the wall; an observer
looking at only a portion of the reflected wave would not be able to distinguish it from a portion of a circular wave emanating from S'. This
phenomenon bears an obvious analogy to the formation of the image of a
point source by a mirror.

It appears difficult, at first, to account for the rectilinear propagation
of light by means of the wave model; indeed, we know that waves of water
bend around small obstacles in their paths. Two observations point the
way out of this difficulty: (1) an obstacle placed in the path of a water
wave does actually cast a "shadow" *if its dimensions are large compared
with the distance between two successive crests*, although the boundary of this
shadow is considerably blurred, and (2) on close inspection, it is seen that
the optical shadow of an opaque object does not have an infinitely sharp
boundary, no matter how small the dimensions of the light source (see
Chapter 4). The second observation shows that the law of rectilinear
propagation of light is not rigorously correct, and the first suggests that
we may be able to account for the approximate validity of the law by
assuming that light waves consist of a succession of very short pulses.
It will be seen that this can actually be done. Moreover, it turns out that
the wave theory of light, when properly developed and expanded, accounts
for all optical phenomena, whereas the corpuscular model becomes useless
outside the field of geometrical optics. In this book, therefore, we shall
base our study of light on the specific assumption that light is a wave
phenomenon.

1–3 A digression on mechanical waves in one dimension. As we have
pointed out, the concept of light waves was first suggested by certain

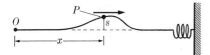

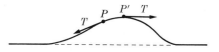

Fig. 1–9. Wave on a string.   Fig. 1–10. Forces acting on the element PP' during the passage of a wave.

similarities between the behavior of light and the behavior of mechanical waves. The mechanical wave model played an important role in the historical development of the theory of light, and did not lose its usefulness even after it became apparent that light is not a mechanical phenomenon. Indeed, many of the concepts of optics are common to all wave phenomena, and can be most easily understood by considering mechanical waves. It is thus useful to review briefly here some of the facts concerning mechanical waves.

(a) *Transverse waves in a string.* To begin with a familiar example, suppose that a long, flexible, and inextensible string is held at one end O and is kept under a constant tension, exerted, for example, by a spring attached to the other end. When, by means of an external force, we rapidly displace the endpoint O in a direction perpendicular to the direction of the string, and then bring it back to its original position, we find that a disturbance originates at O and travels with a certain velocity v along the string. We can describe the disturbance by specifying, at any given time, the *displacement* s of each point of the string from its equilibrium position (Fig. 1–9). If the deformation of the string is sufficiently small, the displacement is very nearly *perpendicular* to the direction of propagation. Hence the disturbance is described as a *transverse wave.*

The displacement s of an arbitrary point P of the string is a function of two variables: the distance x of the point P from the fixed point O, and the time t:

$$s = s(t, x). \tag{1–2}$$

For a given value of t, s becomes a function of x alone, describing the instantaneous deformation of the string. For a given value of x, s becomes a function of t alone, describing the motion of a given point of the string. In what follows, the shape of the curve representing this function will be referred to as the *shape of the wave* at the point x.

If we consider an element PP' of the string (Fig. 1–10), we find that the portion of the string to the left of P acts upon PP' with a certain force tangent to the string and pointing to the left, whereas the portion of the string to the right of P' acts upon PP' with a force tangent to the string and pointing to the right. Each of the two forces is equal in magnitude to the tension T of the string. However, the forces are not exactly opposite to each other, because the element PP' has a certain curvature. Therefore the two forces have a resultant different from zero, which produces an *acceleration* of the element PP'. These considerations form the basis for the theory of the wave phenomenon discussed here [see Appendix 2(a)]. Under the specific assumption that the displacements from the equilibrium position are small, the theory shows that (a) the *string propagates waves of any arbitrary shape without changing their shape*, and (b) *the velocity of propagation v is a constant, related to the mass per unit length μ of the string and to the tension T by the equation*

$$v = \sqrt{\frac{T}{\mu}}.   \tag{1-3}$$

Statement (a) means that two points of the string, located at $x = x_1$ and $x = x_2$, perform identical, although not simultaneous, motions. Statement (b) means that the motion of the point at $x = x_2$ occurs with a time delay equal to $(x_2 - x_1)/v$ with respect to the motion of the point at $x = x_1$.

We may formulate the above results in mathematical language by saying that the displacement s obeys an equation of the form

$$s = f\left(t - \frac{x}{v}\right),   \tag{1-4}$$

where the symbol $f(t - x/v)$ indicates an arbitrary function of the difference $(t - x/v)$. To prove this statement, let us consider two instants of time, t_1 and t_2, related to each other and to the abscissas x_1 and x_2 by

$$x_2 - x_1 = v(t_2 - t_1).   \tag{1-5}$$

If we rewrite this equation as

$$t_2 - \frac{x_2}{v} = t_1 - \frac{x_1}{v},$$

we immediately recognize that

$$f\left(t_2 - \frac{x_2}{v}\right) = f\left(t_1 - \frac{x_1}{v}\right),$$

that is, that

$$s(t_2, x_2) = s(t_1, x_1).$$

This last equation expresses mathematically the fact that the displacement of point x_2 at time t_2 equals the displacement of point x_1 at the earlier time $t_1 = t_2 - (x_2 - x_1)/v$.

We may draw another conclusion from Eq. (1–4). If we plot the displacements

$$s(t_1, x) = f\left(t_1 - \frac{x}{v}\right) \quad \text{and} \quad s(t_2, x) = f\left(t_2 - \frac{x}{v}\right)$$

as functions of x (Fig. 1–11), we obtain two curves representing the actual deformations of the string at the times $t = t_1$ and $t = t_2$. From our previous considerations, it follows that the displacement of the point P_2 at the time t_2 is identical to the displacement of the point P_1 at the time t_1, provided the distance $x_2 - x_1$ between P_1 and P_2 is related to the time interval $t_2 - t_1$ by Eq. (1–5). In other words, we obtain the curve representing the deformation of the string at the time t_2 from the curve representing the deformation of the string at the time t_1 by performing a rigid translation of length $v(t_2 - t_1)$ in the direction of the positive x-axis. This is another way of saying that the disturbance travels with uniform velocity v in the direction of the positive x-axis.

A similar argument shows that if $g(t + x/v)$ is an arbitrary function of the quantity $(t + x/v)$, *the equation*

$$s = g\left(t + \frac{x}{v}\right) \tag{1–6}$$

describes a disturbance that travels with uniform velocity v and without change of shape in the direction of decreasing x. In other words, Eqs. (1–4) and (1–6) represent waves traveling in *opposite directions* along the string; each of these equations describes a possible disturbance.

Moreover, the theory shows that the most general solution of the problem is a function of the type

$$s = f\left(t - \frac{x}{v}\right) + g\left(t + \frac{x}{v}\right), \tag{1–7}$$

which represents *two disturbances traveling simultaneously along the string, one in the positive direction, one in the negative direction.*

The special form of the function $s(t, x)$ corresponding to a given physical situation depends on the manner in which the disturbance has been produced. Suppose that, as in our original example, we excite the wave by forcing the endpoint of the string at $x = 0$ to perform a certain motion in the direction perpendicular to the x-axis, so that $s(0, t)$ is a *given* function of time. Until the time when the disturbance reaches the other end of the string, there will be only a

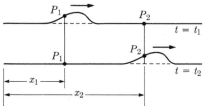

Fig. 1–11. Shape of the string at two different instants of time.

wave traveling in the positive direction, and the solution will be of the type represented by Eq. (1–4). Since $f(t - x/v)$ reduces to $f(t)$ for $x = 0$, the form of the function f describing the wave will be determined by the condition

$$f(t) = s(0, t). \tag{1-8}$$

(b) *Sound waves in a cylindrical pipe.* As a second example, we discuss the propagation of a sound wave along a cylindrical pipe containing a fluid. Viscosity and frictional forces at the wall are neglected. The passage of the wave causes each element of the fluid to move back and forth in a direction parallel to the axis of the pipe, which we take as our x-axis. It also causes the *pressure* of the fluid to change. We may assume that all the points which lie on a given perpendicular section of the pipe undergo simultaneous and identical displacements. Likewise, we may assume that the instantaneous value of the pressure is a function of x only.

Consider now the points which, in the unperturbed condition, are at a distance x from a fixed origin and denote by $s(x, t)$ the *displacement* of these points at the time t relative to their unperturbed position. Denote by $p(x, t)$ the *difference* between the actual pressure at x and t, and the pressure in the unperturbed condition. Thus, in the absence of a disturbance, both $s(x, t)$ and $p(x, t)$ are zero. Note that in the present case the displacement s is parallel to the direction of propagation. Hence the disturbance is described as a *longitudinal wave*.

If we consider an element PP' of the fluid (Fig. 1–12), we find that this element is acted upon by two opposing forces, arising from the pressure at its two end surfaces. If, for a fixed value of t, the pressure varies along the pipe (i.e., if p changes with x), the two forces are not equal in magnitude, and their resultant produces an acceleration of the element PP'. Expressing this physical fact in mathematical language, we arrive at a differential equation analogous to

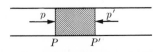

Fig. 1–12. Pressure forces acting on an element of fluid in a pipe.

that describing the disturbance in a string [see Appendix 2(b)]. We then conclude that sound waves travel along the pipe with a constant velocity v and without change of shape. As we have seen, this means that the pressure change p is represented by one of the following equations:

$$p(t, x) = F\left(t - \frac{x}{v}\right), \tag{1-9}$$

for a wave traveling in the positive direction;

$$p(t, x) = G\left(t + \frac{x}{v}\right) \tag{1–10}$$

for a wave traveling in the negative direction; or

$$p(t, x) = F\left(t - \frac{x}{v}\right) + G\left(t + \frac{x}{v}\right) \tag{1–11}$$

for the simultaneous propagation of two waves in opposite directions. We also find that if ρ_0 is the density of the fluid in the unperturbed condition and K is the compressibility of the gas (i.e., the fractional change in volume divided by the corresponding change in pressure), the velocity of propagation is given by

$$v = \sqrt{\frac{1}{K\rho_0}}. \tag{1–12}$$

The above results hold under the stated conditions, i.e., that viscosity and frictional forces may be neglected, and under the assumption that the pressure changes are small compared with the static pressure.

(c) *Energy in waves.* To generate a wave requires a certain amount of energy, which is subsequently associated with the wave itself. The energy travels with the wave and, at any given instant, is located in the disturbed region of the medium. The energy of the wave is partly potential [corresponding, for example, to the deformation of the string in the wave motion discussed in (a)], and partly kinetic (corresponding to the velocity of the various elements of the string). In the case of waves in one dimension, such as those considered above, the theory shows that the *total* energy stored in a given element of the medium at any given time is *twice* the kinetic energy of the element [see Appendix 2(c)]. This means that the kinetic and potential energies of a traveling wave are equal, a result which can be verified by direct computation.*

---

*A word of caution regarding the potential energy may be appropriate. We can deform a string subject to a uniform tension by applying additional external forces to various points of the string. If these forces are slowly and gradually changed, the string can be brought from the initial unperturbed state to any desired shape through a series of intermediate states of near equilibrium. The total work done by the external forces depends only on the final state of the string, and thus can be defined as the potential energy of the deformed string. However, the work done on *an individual element* depends on the intermediate states through which the final deformation is reached. Hence, in the case considered here, we cannot speak of the potential energy of the individual elements of the string. In the case of a traveling wave, on the other hand, it is possible to ascribe a perfectly definite meaning to the total wave energy contained in a single element of the string, and this turns out to be equal to twice the kinetic energy. For further details, see Appendix 2(c).

It should be pointed out explicitly that the above result applies only to individual traveling waves, such as those represented, for example, by the equation $s = f(t - x/v)$ or by the equation $s = g(t + x/v)$. It does not apply to the most general case of wave motion, represented by the equation $s = f(t - x/v) + g(t + x/v)$, which, as we know, corresponds to the superposition of two waves traveling in opposite directions.

For the case of a wave traveling along a string, let $u(t, x) = \partial s/\partial t$ represent the instantaneous transverse velocity of the point having abscissa x (this velocity should not be confused with the velocity of propagation v of the wave), and let $U(t, x)\, dx$ represent the energy present at time t in the element dx of the string. This element has a mass $\mu\, dx$, its kinetic energy is $\frac{1}{2}(\mu\, dx)u^2$, and its total energy is

$$U\, dx = 2(\tfrac{1}{2}\mu\, u^2 dx).$$

We thus obtain the expression

$$U = \mu u^2, \tag{1--13}$$

which relates the *energy per unit length* U to the mass per unit length μ and to the velocity u of the particles of the medium through which the wave passes. A similar equation holds for sound waves.

Another important quantity is the *energy flux*, i.e., the energy per unit time passing through a point of the string or through a section of the pipe. If Φ is the energy flux, then the amount of energy passing through a point at x in the time interval from t to $t + dt$ is $\Phi\, dt$. Since the wave travels with velocity v, at the time t this energy was located in the element between x and $x - v\, dt$. Thus $\Phi\, dt$ must be equal to $Uv\, dt$, and we obtain the following relation between energy flux and energy per unit length:

$$\Phi = Uv. \tag{1--14}$$

(d) *Absorption, dispersion, polarization, and birefringence.* So far we have discussed examples of waves in one dimension that travel without change of shape. In the case of the string, the deformation moves along the string from one portion to another, but its profile remains the same at all times, that is, all points of the string successively perform identical motions. For these waves the velocity of propagation has a perfectly definite value which does not depend on the shape of the wave, i.e., on the form of the function describing the motion of a given point of the string.

However, this is not always the case. For example, a wave traveling along a string *immersed in a viscous medium* is gradually *damped*, because part of the wave energy is changed into heat. Such a wave may be regarded as a mechanical model of a light wave traveling in an *absorbing* medium.

There are also cases in which no loss of energy occurs but the wave changes shape as it travels, so that the motions of different points are represented by functions of different forms. For example, we can construct mechanical systems that will propagate only *sinusoidal waves* without change of shape, i.e., waves in which the disturbance is a sinusoidal function of time [Appendix 2(d)]. In these systems (which may be regarded as mechanical models of the *optically dispersive* media, discussed in Sections 2–14 and 8–4) the velocity of propagation is different for different frequencies.

In discussing transverse waves on a string, we have assumed that a given point of the string moves along a fixed straight line perpendicular to the direction of propagation. We then found that the other points of the string move along parallel lines, so that at any given time they all lie in one plane that does not change with time. Waves of this kind are called *linearly polarized waves*, and the plane in which the displacements lie is called the *plane of vibration*.

The various planes passing through the string in the undisturbed position are physically equivalent, and therefore the string propagates, with equal velocities, linearly polarized waves with arbitrary planes of vibration. However, we can also construct mechanical systems in which the various directions perpendicular to the direction of propagation are not physically equivalent [see Appendix 2(e)]. Any such system can transmit a linearly polarized wave only if the plane of vibration of the latter coincides with one or the other of two mutually perpendicular planes. The velocities of propagation of the waves vibrating in these two planes are different. Systems of this kind may be regarded as mechanical models of *optically birefringent* media (see Section 6–5).

(e) *Reflection and transmission.* Consider two pieces of string of different masses per unit length, joined at a point O and kept under constant tension. An external agency produces a disturbance that travels from left to right on the first string (Fig. 1–13). Experiment shows that upon reaching the point O where the two strings join, the disturbance splits into two disturbances, one traveling in the backward direction toward the point of origin (*reflected wave*), the other traveling in the forward direction into the second string (*transmitted wave*). The reflected and transmitted waves have the same shape as the incident wave, but

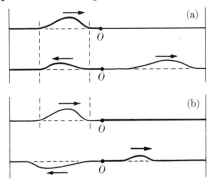

Fig. 1–13. Transmission and reflection of waves at a point of discontinuity.

are of different magnitudes; that is, the functions describing the time dependence of the displacement in the reflected and transmitted waves bear constant ratios to the function describing the time dependence of the displacement in the incident wave. Moreover, it is found that the transmitted wave always has the same sign as the incident wave, whereas the signs of the reflected and incident waves are equal or opposite depending on whether the disturbance proceeds from the heavier to the lighter string (Fig. 1–13a), or vice versa (Fig. 1–13b).

A mathematical analysis of this effect appears in Appendix 2(f). Here we wish to emphasize that similar phenomena always occur wherever there is an abrupt change in the physical properties of the medium through which a wave travels.

1–4 A digression on mechanical waves in space. (a) *Plane waves.* The simplest example of a wave in three dimensions is the *plane wave.* In a plane wave, by definition, the disturbance at any given instant of time has the same value at all points of any given plane perpendicular to a given direction, which is the direction of propagation. If we use a cartesian frame of reference, with the x-axis in the direction of propagation (Fig. 1–14), we can say that the disturbance is independent of y and z, and is thus a function only of x and t.

In the case of a plane sound wave traveling in the positive x-direction, for instance, the pressure change p is given by an equation analogous to that describing the propagation of a sound wave in a pipe (Eq. 1–9); that is,

$$p(t, x, y, z) = F\left(t - \frac{x}{v}\right), \qquad (1\text{–}15)$$

where the velocity of propagation v is again defined by Eq. (1–12).

Instead of the energy per unit length considered in the case of one-dimensional waves, we must consider here the energy per unit volume, or *energy density.* We find again, as for the case of one-dimensional waves, that the wave energy contained in a given portion of the medium is twice the kinetic energy of the medium.* We also find that

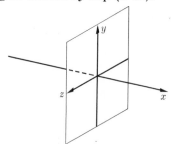

Fig. 1–14. Plane wave in space.

---

*It is hardly necessary to point out that the kinetic energy here considered corresponds to the macroscopic motions of the fluid caused by the passage of the wave and does not include the kinetic energy corresponding to the random thermal motion of the individual molecules.

the *energy flux per unit area* (i.e., the energy per unit time and per unit area crossing an area perpendicular to the direction of propagation) equals the energy density multiplied by the velocity of propagation.

The concept of a plane wave extending to infinity in all directions perpendicular to the direction of propagation is obviously a mathematical abstraction. However, there are waves which, for all practical purposes, behave like plane waves in limited regions of space.

(b) *Spherical waves.* As a second example, consider an infinite volume of fluid containing a pulsating sphere, i.e., a sphere whose surface expands and contracts radially. The sphere is the source of a *spherical sound wave*, which we may again describe by giving the pressure change p, the displacement s, and the velocity u of the various points of the fluid as functions of time and position. For reasons of symmetry, the displacement will occur at all points in the radial direction. If we denote by r the distance of the sphere from the center O, then p, s, and u will be functions of r and t alone.

As we might expect, the wave travels with the same velocity $v = 1/\sqrt{K\rho_0}$ which characterizes the propagation of a plane sound wave. The disturbance, however, will become progressively weaker as the distance from O increases. Indeed, consider two spherical surfaces of radii r_1 and r_2 centered at O $(r_2 > r_1$; see Fig. 1–15). If there is no absorption, the energy that traverses the first surface in a given time interval dt must also, at some later time, traverse the second surface in an interval of the same duration dt. Thus the energy flux per unit area is inversely proportional to the area of the spheres, i.e., inversely proportional to the square of their radii. On the other hand, we found that in a plane wave the energy flux per unit area is proportional to the density of kinetic energy, and therefore proportional to u^2. The same must be true also in a spherical wave, at least for sufficiently large values of r, because a spherical wave of very large radius should behave practically like a plane wave. This means that u^2 must vary as $1/r^2$, and therefore u must vary as $1/r$. The same results apply to the displacement s and to the **pressure change p, and we thus** conclude that in a spherical wave the magnitude of the disturbance decreases in inverse proportion to the distance from the center.

To restate this conclusion in more precise terms, let us consider an observer who travels along with the wave, with velocity v. In the case of a plane wave, the quantities u, s, and p appear to this observer as constant. In the case of a spherical

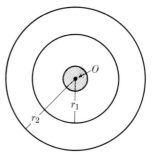

FIG. 1–15. Spherical wave.

wave, however, the quantities u, s, and p, as seen by the observer, decrease in inverse proportion to r. Thus the equations giving, for example, p and s as functions of r and t, are of the following form:

$$p = \frac{F(t - r/v)}{r}, \tag{1-16}$$

$$s = \frac{f(t - r/v)}{r}. \tag{1-17}$$

A justification of the above results will be found in Appendix 2(g). From the more rigorous theory developed there it follows that the expression for s contains an additional term that varies as $1/r^2$ and thus, for large values of r, becomes negligible compared with the term proportional to $1/r$. No similar term appears in the expression for p.

So far we have assumed a spherically symmetric source. Consider now the case where the source is not spherically symmetric, but has very small dimensions compared with the distance from the point of observation, so that it may be regarded as a point source. A disturbance emitted at a given instant of time from O, the location of the source, will simultaneously reach all points on a sphere with center at O. However, the disturbance will not have the same value at all points of this sphere. In other words, the quantities (such as p and s) describing the disturbance will be functions not only of the distance r from O, but also of the angles that determine the direction of the line connecting O with the point of observation.

It can be shown that if these functions change slowly with direction, they can be written as products of a factor q depending on the direction alone, times the functions of r and t that describe a symmetric spherical wave [Eqs. (1–16) and (1–17)]. Thus, for example, p will be given by an expression of the form

$$p = \frac{F(t - r/v)}{r} q. \tag{1-18}$$

1–5 The optical disturbance. The superposition principle. We may use the examples of mechanical waves discussed in the two preceding sections to illustrate several general concepts that apply to all wave phenomena, and therefore also to light waves. Any wave phenomenon implies the existence of a medium whose physical state is altered by the passage of the wave. Mathematically, a wave is described by a change in some property of the medium, such as, for example, the displacement s or the pressure change p. Thus, to describe a light wave, we shall introduce a quantity representing some sort of disturbance of the medium responsible for the propagation of light. Without inquiring, for the time being, into the nature of this quantity, we shall refer to it by the generic name of *optical disturbance*.

The rate of change of the physical properties at a given point of the medium that carries a wave is determined exclusively by conditions existing at neighboring points. Thus, in the example of the sound wave in the tube, the acceleration of the infinitesimal volume of fluid between P and P' (Fig. 1–12) is determined by the difference between the pressures existing at the two ends of this volume. In the example of the wave on the string, the acceleration of an infinitesimal segment is determined by the resultant of the two forces of equal magnitude T, but with different directions, acting at the two ends of the segment (Fig. 1–10).

It follows that waves are propagated progressively from point to point of the medium, each point receiving the perturbation from its immediate neighbors on one side, and transmitting it to its immediate neighbors on the other side. To clarify this point, let us consider a deformation that travels along a string from left to right, and let us focus our attention on a point A of this string (Fig. 1–16). As the deformation passes through A, this point executes some sort of oscillatory motion and then comes to rest again. We can regard the motion of A as the origin of the disturbance that propagates beyond A. In fact, we can produce exactly the same disturbance in the portion of the string to the right of A by forcing point A to move back and forth in the same manner as it actually does during the passage of the wave. In this case, however, there would also be a wave proceeding from A to the left, whereas in the previous case the portion of the string to the left of A was left unperturbed after the wave had gone through A. The reason for this difference is easy to understand. At the moment when A is reached by the progressing wave (see Fig. 1–16) the point A' immediately to the left of A is displaced upward and has an upward velocity; whereas the force exerted by A' on A displaces A from its equilibrium position, the reaction of A on A' opposes the motion of the point A'.

We might take the view that any arbitrary point A of the string, when reached by the disturbance, becomes the origin of two waves traveling in opposite directions. The wave traveling in the forward direction repre-

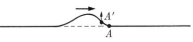

Fig. 1–16. An illustration of the propagation of a disturbance from point to point.

sents the continuation of the incident wave, whereas the wave traveling in the backward direction cancels the disturbance carried by the incident wave and brings the string back to its rest position. Note, however, that if the physical properties of the string change abruptly at A (for example, if A is the point where two strings are joined), complete cancellation between the backward wave and the incident wave no longer occurs. If the second string has a smaller mass per unit length than the first, there is only partial cancellation, and a reflected wave appears, with the same sign as the incident wave. If, on the other hand, the second string has a greater mass per unit length than the first, there is over-compensation, and a reflected wave appears, with a sign opposite to that of the incident wave [see Section 2–3(e)].

The mechanical model illustrates another important property of wave phenomena. This is the *superposition principle*, which states that when several waves are propagated simultaneously in the same medium, the resultant disturbance at a given point at a given time is the sum of the disturbances corresponding to the individual waves. The sum, of course, is a scalar or vector sum depending on whether the disturbance is a scalar quantity (like the pressure change) or a vector quantity (like the displacement). For example, consider two disturbances starting simultaneously from the two ends of a string and traveling in opposite directions (Fig. 1–17). The two disturbances will meet at the midsection of the string and will then continue beyond the region of crossing, each unaffected by the existence of the other. In the region where the two disturbances overlap, the displacement, at any instant of time, is the sum of the displacements that would be produced by the two disturbances separately.

The superposition principle is a consequence of the fact that the differential equation of the wave is linear [Appendix 2(a)]. If two functions separately satisfy a given linear differential equation, the sum of the two functions is also a solution of the same equation. Note that the differential equation describing a mechanical wave is a linear equation only in the limit of very small disturbances; hence the superposition principle has only approximate validity in the case of mechanical waves. Light waves, on the other hand, are exactly described by a linear differential equation, as we shall see in Chapter 7. Therefore the superposition principle is rigorously correct for the case of light.

1–6 Huygens' principle. Very considerable and often insurmountable mathematical difficulties stand in the way of any attempt to rigorously compute the propagation of a light wave in a medium that is not homogeneous, or one that is partially obstructed by opaque bodies. Moreover, the exact solution of such a problem requires a detailed knowledge of the physical nature of light waves, such as we shall acquire only at a later stage of our study. However, in most cases of practical importance, it is possible to find an approximate, yet perfectly adequate, answer to the

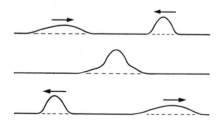

FIG. 1–17. An illustration of the superposition principle.

problem by the use of methods that
require only some general assumptions about the character of light
waves and that do not entail serious
mathematical difficulties.   Such
methods are based on a principle
known as *Huygens' principle*, which
was formulated for the first time in
the 17th century. Because of its fun-

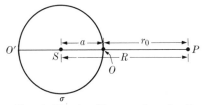
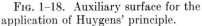

Fig. 1–18. Auxiliary surface for the
application of Huygens' principle.

damental importance, we shall discuss this principle here in some detail.

Huygens' principle originated from the general notion that waves
spread gradually from point to point of a medium, as explained in the
preceding section. Hence if a source S is surrounded by a closed surface σ
(Fig. 1–18), the disturbance produced by S can reach the region of space
beyond the surface σ only by traversing this surface. It is thus natural to
consider the disturbance in the outer region as *caused* by the disturbance
at the surface σ; that is, to take the view that *the various points of the
surface σ, when reached by the wave, become the origin of secondary waves, and
the disturbance observed beyond the surface σ results from the superposition of
these secondary waves.* This is a statement of Huygens' principle in its
most general form.

It remains to be shown that the viewpoint here adopted is a valid one,
in the sense that we can actually construct the known wave beyond the
surface σ by combining the effects of a suitable set of secondary waves
emanating from the various elements of σ. The general and rigorous proof
of Huygens' principle was given by Kirchhoff, and is known as *Kirchhoff's
theorem*. To avoid mathematical difficulties, we shall here limit ourselves
to an approximate treatment, valid under certain simplifying conditions
that will be specified below.

As our auxiliary surface σ we take a sphere of radius a and center at the
source S (Fig. 1–18). Let P be a point at any arbitrary distance $R > a$ from
S, O and O' the points of intersection of the line PS with the surface σ,
and $r_0 = \overline{OP} = R - a$ the minimum distance of P from σ. We assume S
to be the source of a spherical wave, which we shall specifically consider
as a light wave.

Let $E(R, t)$ represent the optical disturbance at the time t and at the
point P. At a given instant, E has the same value at all points of the sphere
σ, so that we may write

$$E(a, t) = f(t), \qquad\qquad (1\text{–}19)$$

where f is a given function of time alone. The general expression for $E(R, t)$
in a spherical wave is of the form indicated by Eqs. (1–16) and (1–17):

$$E(R, t) = \frac{\varphi(t - R/v)}{R}.$$ (1-20)

When $R = a$, (1-20) becomes

$$E(a, t) = \frac{\varphi(t - a/v)}{a},$$

and, with (1-19), we obtain .

$$\varphi\left(t - \frac{a}{v}\right) = af(t).$$

The above equation holds for all values of t. We can thus replace t on both sides by $(t - r_0/v)$, and we obtain

$$\varphi\left(t - \frac{r_0}{v} - \frac{a}{v}\right) = af\left(t - \frac{r_0}{v}\right),$$

or (since $r_0 + a = R$)

$$\varphi\left(t - \frac{R}{v}\right) = af\left(t - \frac{r_0}{v}\right).$$

Equation (1-20) then yields

$$E(R, t) = E(a + r_0, t) = \frac{a}{a + r_0} f\left(t - \frac{r_0}{v}\right).$$ (1-21)

We now assume that the disturbance at the surface σ lasts for a short time interval from $t = 0$ to $t = t_1$, and is represented, for example, by a curve of the type shown in Fig. 1-19(a). Then, at any given instant of time, the disturbance is confined to a spherical shell of thickness vt_1 which we assume is small compared with both a and r_0:

$$vt_1 \ll a \quad \text{and} \quad vt_1 \ll r_0. \quad (1\text{-}22)$$

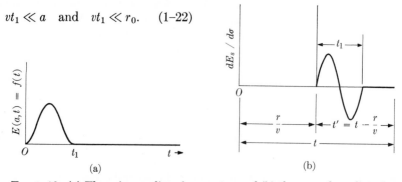

FIG. 1-19. (a) The primary disturbance at σ, and (b) the secondary disturbance from an infinitesimal zone at P.

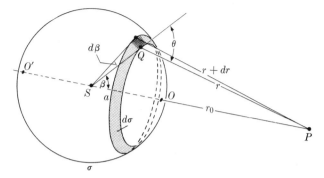

FIG. 1–20. Construction of an elementary zone on a Huygens surface.

In accordance with Huygens' principle, we take the view that each element $d\sigma$ of the surface σ emits a secondary wave during the time interval from 0 to t_1. Let dE_s represent the disturbance produced by this secondary wave at the point P. It is natural to assume that dE_s is proportional to $d\sigma$. Since there is no reason why the disturbance emanating from an element of area (in contrast to a point) should have the same intensity in all directions, we shall represent dE_s, as a function of time and position, by an equation similar to Eq. (1–18), which describes a spherical wave from an asymmetric source. However, we shall assume that the directional factor q appearing in this equation depends only on the angle θ between the perpendicular to the element of area $d\sigma$ and the line connecting this element to P (Fig. 1–20). Thus, letting r be the distance of $d\sigma$ from P, we tentatively choose for dE_s an expression of the following form:

$$dE_s = \frac{\psi(t - r/v)}{r}\, q(\theta)\, d\sigma. \tag{1–23}$$

We shall refer to the factor $q(\theta)$ as the *obliquity factor*. Without loss of generality, we may define q so that it becomes equal to unity in the forward direction, i.e., so that

$$q(0) = 1. \tag{1–24}$$

We must now show that it is actually possible to determine the functions ψ and q so that the superposition of the secondary disturbances described by Eq. (1–23) will reproduce the disturbance represented by (1–21); i.e., so that

$$\int_{\sigma} dE_s = E(a + r_0, t). \tag{1–25}$$

For this purpose we begin by noting that if r is the distance from P of a point Q of the surface σ, and β is the angle between SQ and SP (Fig. 1–20), the following equation holds:

$$r^2 = a^2 + (a + r_0)^2 - 2a(a + r_0) \cos \beta.$$

Differentiation of this equation yields

$$r \, dr = a(a + r_0) \sin \beta \, d\beta. \tag{1-26}$$

Consider now the circular zone intercepted upon the surface σ by the cones of half-apex angles β and $\beta + d\beta$, and let r and $r + dr$ be the distances from P of its two boundary circles (Fig. 1–20). The area of this zone is

$$d\sigma = (2\pi a \sin \beta) \cdot (a \, d\beta) = 2\pi a^2 \sin \beta \, d\beta = 2\pi \frac{a}{a + r_0} r \, dr. \tag{1-27}$$

Apart from infinitesimal quantities, the distance r and the angle θ are constant over the infinitesimal zone just described. Thus we can compute the contribution of the zone to the disturbance observed at P by simply substituting the area of the zone [as given by Eq. (1–27)] for the quantity $d\sigma$ appearing in (1–23). We obtain

$$dE_s = 2\pi \frac{a}{a + r_0} \psi \left(t - \frac{r}{v} \right) q(\theta) \, dr. \tag{1-28}$$

The next step is to add the contributions of the various infinitesimal zones such as the one considered above. As already mentioned, the emission of the secondary waves begins at $t = 0$ and ends at $t = t_1$; mathematically, this means that ψ is zero except for $0 < t - r/v < t_1$. Since the waves travel with finite velocity v, and since various regions of σ are at different distances from P, this point, at any instant of time, will receive secondary waves from only a limited portion of σ, which we will call the *active region*. In adding the contributions of the various infinitesimal zones which make up the active region, we shall find it convenient to consider separately five periods of time.

(a) *First period.* Consider an instant of time $t < r_0/v$. At this time neither the primary wave nor any of the secondary waves originating from the various points of σ has yet reached the point P. Equation (1–25) then represents a trivial identity, since both of its terms are identically zero.

(b) *Second period.* Consider the time interval $r_0/v < t < r_0/v + t_1$, during which the primary wave passes through the point P. In this time interval, P receives secondary waves from a portion of the sphere in the neighborhood of O (the "active region" defined above; see Fig. 1–21) whose boundary is the circle determined by the equation

$$r_1 = vt. \tag{1-29}$$

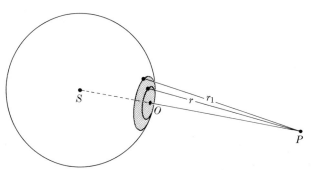

FIG. 1–21. The active region for $r_0/v < t < r_0/v + t_1$.

Setting the original disturbance equal to the sum of the disturbances received from the various infinitesimal zones included in the active region, we obtain

$$E(a + r_0, t) = 2\pi \frac{a}{a + r_0} \int_{r_0}^{r_1} q(\theta)\psi \left(t - \frac{r}{v} \right) dr. \qquad (1\text{–}30)$$

Because of the small value of t_1 [see the inequalities (1–22)], the active region is a very small portion of the spherical surface σ. Therefore the angle of emission θ of the secondary waves is close to zero for all points of the active region. Since the obliquity factor is a slowly varying function of θ and becomes unity at $\theta = 0$, we can put $q(\theta) = 1$ in Eq. (1–30).

Let us now change the variable of integration from r to t', taking

$$t' = t - \frac{r}{v}. \qquad (1\text{–}31)$$

Note that here t is the (fixed) time at which the secondary wave reaches P, and t' is the (variable) time at which this wave leaves the point of the surface σ at the distance r from P (see Fig. 1–21). Considering that $dr = -v\, dt'$, that $t' = 0$ for $r = r_1$ [see Eq. (1–29)], and that $t' = t - r_0/v$ for $r = r_0$, we obtain from (1–21) and (1–30):

$$\frac{a}{a + r_0} f\left(t - \frac{r_0}{v} \right) = E(a + r_0, t)$$

$$= 2\pi \frac{a}{a + r_0} \int_{t - r_0/v}^{0} \psi(t')(-v\, dt')$$

$$= 2\pi \frac{a}{a + r_0} v \int_{0}^{t - r_0/v} \psi(t')\, dt',$$

or

$$f\left(t - \frac{r_0}{v} \right) = 2\pi v \int_{0}^{t - r_0/v} \psi(t')\, dt'. \qquad (1\text{–}32)$$

Since f is known, this equation *uniquely determines the function* ψ. Indeed, differentiation with respect to t yields*

$$\psi\left(t - \frac{r}{v}\right) = \frac{1}{2\pi v}\dot{f}\left(t - \frac{r}{v}\right), \tag{1-33}$$

where we have indicated by $\dot{f}$ the derivative of the function f with respect to its argument, and have written this argument as $t - r/v$ instead of $t - r_0/v$.

We conclude that in the time interval $r_0/v < t < r_0/v + t_1$, it is possible to regard the original disturbance as the resultant of secondary waves originating from the various elements of the spherical surface σ. These secondary waves are described by

$$dE_s = \frac{1}{2\pi vr}\dot{f}\left(t - \frac{r}{v}\right) q(\theta)\, d\sigma, \tag{1-34}$$

or by the equivalent equation

$$dE_s = \frac{1}{2\pi vr}\left(\frac{\partial E(a, t)}{\partial t}\right)_{t - r/v} q(\theta)\, d\sigma. \tag{1-34a}$$

(c) *Third period.* During the subsequent time interval

$$r_0/v + t_1 < t < (r_0 + 2a)/v,$$

the active region of the surface σ is a zone (Fig. 1–22) whose outer and inner boundaries are the circles defined, respectively, by

$$r_1 = vt, \qquad r_2 = v(t - t_1). \tag{1-35}$$

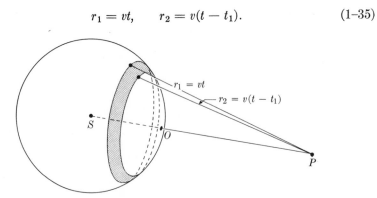

FIG. 1–22. The active region for $r_0/v + t_1 < t < (r_0 + 2a)/v$.

---

*The reader will remember that the derivative of an integral with respect to the upper limit of integration equals the value of the integrand at this limit.

According to Huygens' principle, it should be possible to represent the disturbance at P by an equation of the following type:

$$E(r_0 + a, t) = 2\pi \frac{a}{a + r_0} \int_{r_2}^{r_1} q(\theta)\psi\left(t - \frac{r}{v}\right) dr. \tag{1–36}$$

[Note that in this equation ψ is no longer an unknown function, but is the function previously determined; see Eq. (1–33).] On the other hand, we know that at all times greater than $r_0/v + t_1$ the disturbance at P is zero (that is, $E(r_0 + a, t) = 0$ for $t > r_0/v + t_1$). Thus, if Huygens' principle holds, the integral on the right side of (1–36) must vanish.

To show that this is the case, we again consider the slowly varying function $q(\theta)$ to be constant and change the variable of integration from r to t' [Eq. (1–31)], noting that $t' = 0$ for $r = r_1$ and $t' = t_1$ for $r = r_2$ [Eqs. (1–35)]. We obtain

$$\int_{r_2}^{r_1} q(\theta)\psi\left(t - \frac{r}{v}\right) dr = q(\bar{\theta})v \int_0^{t_1} \psi(t') \, dt', \tag{1–36a}$$

where $\bar{\theta}$ is some average value of θ for the zone defined by $r_1 > r > r_2$ (Fig. 1–22). When written in this form, the integral is clearly seen to be zero, because, from the definition of ψ (Eq. 1–33) and from the fact that $f(t)$ differs from zero only for $0 < t < t_1$, it follows that

$$\int_0^{t_1} \psi(t') \, dt' = \frac{1}{2\pi v} [f(t_1) - f(0)] = 0.$$

(d) *Fourth period.* The secondary disturbance from the "antipole" O' arrives at P at the time $(r_0 + 2a)/v$, and lasts until the time $(r_0 + 2a)/v + t_1$. Thus, in the time interval $(r_0 + 2a)/v < t < (r_0 + 2a)/v + t_1$, the active region includes the point O'; the boundary of this region is the circle defined by

$$r_2 = v(t - t_1) \tag{1–37}$$

(Fig. 1–23). Huygens' principle yields the following expression for the optical disturbance at P:

$$E(r_0 + a, t) = 2\pi \frac{a}{a + r_0} \int_{r_2}^{r_0 + 2a} q(\theta)\psi\left(t - \frac{r}{v}\right) dr.$$

A procedure similar to that used in the previous cases changes the above equation to

$$E(r_0 + a_1 t) = 2\pi \frac{a}{a + r_0} q(\pi)v \int_{t - (r_0 + 2a)/v}^{t_1} \psi(t') \, dt', \tag{1–38}$$

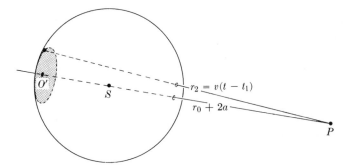

FIG. 1–23. The active region for $(r_0 + 2a)/v < t < r_0 + 2a/v + t_1$.

where $q(\pi)$ represents the value of the obliquity factor $q(\theta)$ at $\theta = \pi$. We know that in the time interval here considered, $E(r_0 + a, t) = 0$. On the other hand, the integral on the right side of (1–38) is, in general, different from zero. Thus, in order to satisfy (1–38), we must take

$$q(\pi) = 0. \tag{1–39}$$

(e) *Fifth period.* For $t > (r_0 + 2a)/v + t_1$, the point P no longer receives secondary waves from any portion of the sphere σ. The equation (1–25) expressing Huygens' principle again becomes a trivial identity, since both of its terms are identically zero.

We have now shown that Eq. (1–25) is satisfied for all values of t if we take for dE_s the value given by (1–34) or (1–34a) and if we assume that the obliquity factor $q(\theta)$ appearing in these equations is a slowly varying function of θ, whose value is unity at $\theta = 0$ and zero at $\theta = \pi$. This result proves the validity of Huygens' principle (at least for the case of the short disturbances here considered) and determines the character of the secondary waves. Our approximate treatment does not enable us to determine the obliquity factor $q(\theta)$ completely. Knowledge of the exact form of the function $q(\theta)$ will not be needed for any of the problems to be discussed in the present volume. However, it may be mentioned that a more rigorous theory yields the following simple expression for $q(\theta)$:

$$q(\theta) = \frac{1 + \cos \theta}{2}. \tag{1–40}$$

As a summary of our results, we state the following:

While the primary wave passes through the surface σ, during the time interval from zero to t_1, the various elements of σ emit secondary spherical waves, represented either by Eq. (1–34) or by (1–34a), where the obliquity factor $q(\theta)$ decreases gradually from 1 to 0 as θ increases from 0 to π.

The shapes of the functions describing the time dependence of the primary disturbance E at σ, and of the secondary disturbance dE_s at P, are compared in Fig. 1–19(a) and (b). Since dE_s is proportional (Eq. 1–34a) to the time derivative of E, and since $E(a, t) = 0$ for $t = 0$ and $t = t_1$, the total area under the curve representing dE_s is zero. Hence the secondary disturbance is sometimes positive and sometimes negative, even if the primary disturbance has the same sign at all times.

At any given instant of time, a point P at a distance $r_0 \gg vt_1$ from the surface σ receives secondary waves from a small portion of the surface σ, which we have called the "active region." The active region begins to appear at the time $t = r_0/v$ when the secondary wave emitted by O reaches P. From this time to the time $t = r_0/v + t_1$, the active region spreads to a disk whose outer boundary is a distance $r_0 + vt_1$ from P. During this interval, the superposition of the secondary waves emitted by the various points of the active region gives rise to a finite resultant disturbance. For $t > r_0/v + t_1$, the active region acquires the shape of an annular zone which moves gradually from the vicinity of the pole O to the vicinity of the antipole O' as t increases. The resultant disturbance is now zero because the negative disturbances received at P from a portion of the active region cancel the positive disturbances received from another portion of this region. At the time $t = (r_0 + 2a)/v$, the point P begins to receive the secondary wave emitted by the antipole O', which means that by this time the outer boundary of the active region has reached the point O'. For $t > (r_0 + 2a)/v$, the active region becomes a disk centered at O'. The radius of the disk decreases as t increases and vanishes at $t = (r_0 + 2a)/v + t_1$ when the tail end of the wave emitted by O' reaches P. During the time interval from $t = (r_0 + 2a)/v$ to $t = (r_0 + 2a)/v + t_1$ the positive and negative portions of the active region do not balance. However, the resultant disturbance at P is zero because the intensity of the secondary waves emitted in the backward direction is zero.

As already mentioned, it can be proved that Huygens' principle has general validity. However, our conclusions about the form of the secondary waves (Eq. 1–34) are based on the assumption that the disturbance lasts for only a short time, so that the thickness of the spherical shell in which the disturbance is located at any one instant of time is small compared with the distance from the auxiliary surface σ to the point of observation. We might also expect these conclusions to hold when the disturbance consists of a sequence of short pulses. Detailed analysis shows that this is actually the case, provided that the pulses are alternately positive and negative so that the time average of the function f over several pulses vanishes. In particular, the results obtained in this section can be applied to *sinusoidal waves*, as we shall verify by direct computation in Section 4–2.

As indicated at the beginning of this section, Huygens' principle provides a convenient and powerful method for the study of the phenomena that occur when the propagation of waves is partially blocked by "opaque" obstacles. Suppose, for example, that part of the surface σ is covered by an obstacle that does not transmit the incident disturbance. To an excellent approximation, we can assume that the secondary waves arriving at P from the unobstructed portion of σ are not modified by the presence of the obstacle. We can then compute the optical disturbance at P by adding contributions of these secondary waves.

EXAMPLE 1. *Consider a plane wave producing on a plane σ an optical disturbance represented by the function $f(t)$, where*

$$
\begin{array}{ll}
f(t) = 0 & \text{for } t < 0, \\
f(t) = (2A/t_1)t & \text{for } 0 < t < t_1/2, \\
f(t) = (2A/t_1)(t_1 - t) & \text{for } t_1/2 < t < t_1, \\
f(t) = 0 & \text{for } t > t_1
\end{array}
$$

(Fig. 1–24a). *By means of Huygens' principle, compute the optical disturbance E at the point P, beyond the plane σ* (Fig. 1–25).

The optical disturbance produced at P by the secondary waves originating from an element of area $d\sigma$ at the distance r from P [Eq. (1–34)] is

$$
dE_s = \frac{1}{2\pi vr} \dot{f}\left(t - \frac{r}{v}\right) q(\theta)\, d\sigma.
$$

Thus

$$
dE_s = 0 \qquad \text{for } t - \frac{r}{v} < 0,
$$

$$
dE_s = \frac{A\, d\sigma}{\pi v t_1 r}\, q(\theta) \qquad \text{for } 0 < t - \frac{r}{v} < \frac{t_1}{2},
$$

$$
dE_s = -\frac{A\, d\sigma}{\pi v t_1 r}\, q(\theta) \qquad \text{for } \frac{t_1}{2} < t - \frac{r}{v} < t_1,
$$

$$
dE_s = 0 \qquad \text{for } t - \frac{r}{v} > t_1,
$$

(Fig. 1–24b).

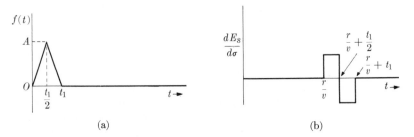

(a)   (b)

FIG. 1–24. (a) The primary and (b) the secondary disturbance in Example 1.

If $r_0 = \overline{OP}$ is the distance of P from σ (Fig. 1–25), an active region begins to appear at the time $t = r_0/v$, when the secondary disturbance emitted from O at the time $t = 0$ reaches P. Thus, for $t < r_0/v$,

$$E_P = 0.$$

At a later time t, let r_1 be the distance of P from the circle representing the outer boundary of the active region. Note that the secondary disturbances reaching P from the points of this circle are emitted at the time $t = 0$, therefore $r_1 = vt$ [(Eq. (1–29)]. On the other hand, the time of departure from the point O of a secondary disturbance reaching P at the time t is $t - r_0/v$. If $t - r_0/v < t_1$, the active region includes the point O. If, moreover, $t - r_0/v < t_1/2$ (Fig. 1–25a), the times of departure of the secondary disturbances reaching P from all points of the active region lie between zero and $t_1/2$. Thus [with $q(\theta) = q(0) = 1$] we have $dE_s = A\,d\sigma/\pi v t_1 r$. Noting that for a plane surface Eq. (1–27) yields $d\sigma = 2\pi r\,dr$, we obtain

$$E_P = \frac{A}{\pi v t_1} \int_{r_0}^{r_1} \frac{d\sigma}{r} = \frac{2A}{v t_1} \int_{r_0}^{r_1} dr$$

$$= \frac{2A}{v t_1}(r_1 - r_0) = \frac{2A}{t_1}\left(t - \frac{r_0}{v}\right).$$

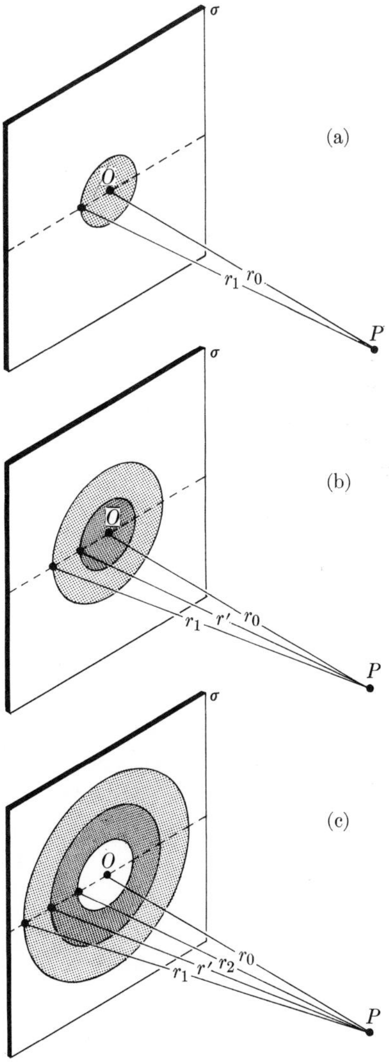

Consider next the case where $t_1/2 < t - r_0/v < t_1$. Divide the active region into two parts by means of the circle at the distance $r' = r_1 - vt_1/2$ from P (Fig. 1–25b). The times of departure $t - r/v$ of the secondary dis-

Fig. 1–25. The "positive" and the "negative" active regions in Example 1, shown at three different times.

turbances originating from points between the outer edge of the active region and the circle defined by $r = r'$ lie between zero and $t_1/2$. On the other hand, the times of departure of the secondary disturbances originating from points between this circle and the point O lie between $t_1/2$ and t_1. The first subregion contributes a positive term and the second subregion a negative term to the resultant disturbance. Again putting $q(\theta) = q(0) = 1$, we obtain

$$E_P = \frac{2A}{vt_1}(r_1 - r') - \frac{2A}{vt_1}(r' - r_0).$$

Since

$$r_1 - r' = \frac{vt_1}{2},$$

$$r' - r_0 = r_1 - \frac{vt_1}{2} - r_0 = vt - \frac{vt_1}{2} - r_0,$$

the above equation yields

$$E_P = \frac{2A}{t_1}\left[t_1 - \left(t - \frac{r_0}{v}\right)\right].$$

For $t - r_0/v > t_1$, the active region no longer contains O; its inner boundary is the circle at the distance $r_2 = r_1 - vt_1$ from P. We again divide the active region into two subregions, by means of the circle at the distance $r' = r_1 - vt_1/2$ from P (Fig. 1–25c). We find that in this case the negative contribution of the inner subregion cancels the positive contribution of the outer subregion. Thus

$$E_P = 0.$$

Finally, we obtain

$$E_P = 0 \qquad\qquad \text{for } t < \frac{r_0}{v},$$

$$E_P = \frac{2A}{t_1}\left(t - \frac{r_0}{v}\right) \qquad\qquad \text{for } \frac{r_0}{v} < t < \frac{r_0}{v} + \frac{t_1}{2},$$

$$E_P = \frac{2A}{t_1}\left[t_1 - \left(t - \frac{r_0}{v}\right)\right] \qquad \text{for } \frac{r_0}{v} + \frac{t_1}{2} < t < \frac{r_0}{v} + t_1,$$

$$E_P = 0 \qquad\qquad \text{for } t > \frac{r_0}{v} + t_1,$$

and therefore, for all values of t,

$$E_P(t) = f\left(t - \frac{r_0}{v}\right).$$

This, of course, is the well-known equation of a plane wave.

EXAMPLE 2. *Refer to the previous example and assume that the plane surface σ is covered by an opaque screen with a circular hole. Compute the optical disturbance E_P at a point P on the line perpendicular to σ through the center O of the hole (Fig. 1–26).*

As in the previous example, the disturbance at P begins to appear at the time r_0/v. If r_3 is the distance of the edge of the hole from P, no part of the active region is covered by the screen until the time r_3/v. Thus from $t = r_0/v$ to $t = r_3/v$ the disturbance at P is exactly the same as in the absence of the screen.

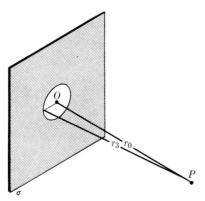

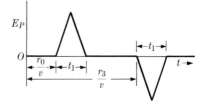

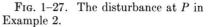

FIG. 1–26. Propagation of a disturbance beyond a screen with a circular hole.

FIG. 1–27. The disturbance at P in Example 2.

Assume, for example, that $r_3 - r_0 > vt_1$. Then E_P rises linearly from zero to A in the time interval $r_0/v < t < r_0/v + t_1/2$, and falls linearly from A to zero in the time interval $r_0/v + t_1/2 < t < r_0/v + t_1$ (Fig. 1–27).

At the time $t = r_3/v$, however, the outer edge of the active region reaches the boundary of the hole, and the "positive" subregion begins to be blotted out. Consequently, a *negative* disturbance appears at P and reaches its maximum absolute value when the boundary circle between the "positive" and the "negative" subregions coincides with the edge of the hole. This happens at the time $t = r_3/v + t_1/2$. Subsequently, the "negative" subregion, too, becomes progressively obscured. After the time $r_3/v + t_1$ the whole of the active region lies behind the screen and therefore the resultant disturbance at P is zero. An easy computation shows that the fall and subsequent rise of the resultant disturbance are linear, so that E_P is represented by a function of the type shown in Fig. 1–27. Note that if the hole is sufficiently small so that the obliquity factor may be regarded as constant, the positive and the negative pulses have the same absolute amplitude.

1–7 Rectilinear propagation of light. As pointed out in Section 1–2, certain observations suggest that a light wave is a sequence of pulses of very short duration. It is thus natural for us to begin our study by investigating the general properties of waves *in the limiting case of infinitely short pulses*. We shall find, in this limit, that the propagation of the waves obeys the three laws of geometrical optics stated in Section 1–1. It will thus become apparent that these laws describe optical phenomena to an acceptable approximation whenever the experimental conditions are such that the finite duration of light pulses may be neglected.

In this section we propose to investigate the propagation of light in the presence of opaque obstacles. Let S be a point source, and σ a spherical surface of radius a with center at S. Assume that part of the surface σ is

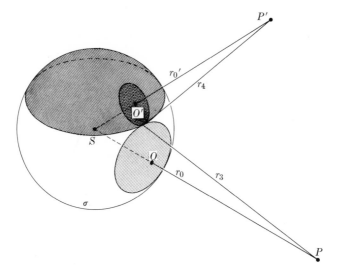

FIG. 1–28. Propagation beyond an opaque obstacle.

covered by an opaque screen. We wish to determine the illumination at a point such as P' that lies in the region of geometrical shadow, and at a point such as P that lies outside this region (see Fig. 1–28).

(a) *Point outside the region of geometrical shadow.* We first compute the disturbance at P, following step by step the method developed in Section 1–6; i.e., considering the disturbance at P to be due to the secondary waves originating from the active region of the surface σ in the short time interval from 0 to t_1. Let r_3 be the minimum distance of P from the edge of the opaque screen. For $t < r_3/v$, no portion of the active region of σ is obstructed, hence at all times before $t = r_3/v$ the optical disturbance at P is exactly the same as in the absence of the screen. Let $r_0 = \overline{OP}$ be the minimum distance of P from σ. In the absence of the screen, we know that the optical disturbance at P begins to appear at the time $t = r_0/v$ and ceases at the time $t = r_0/v + t_1$. The presence of the screen does not alter this result because t_1 is arbitrarily small, and we may thus assume that $t_1 < (r_3 - r_0)/v$; that is, that the disturbance at P ceases before the outer boundary of the active region reaches the edge of the screen.

For $t > r_3/v$ the active region is in the shape of an annular zone, which is now partly blocked by the screen (Fig. 1–29). Let us assume that the function f representing the optical disturbance on σ has the shape shown in Fig. 1–19(a), reaches a maximum at $t = t_1/2$, and drops to zero again at $t = t_1$. The function ψ describing the secondary wave then has the shape shown in Fig. 1–19(b), being positive for $0 < t' < t_1/2$ and negative for $t_1/2 < t' < t_1$. The front half of the active region contributes a positive term to the disturbance observed at P, while the other half contributes a

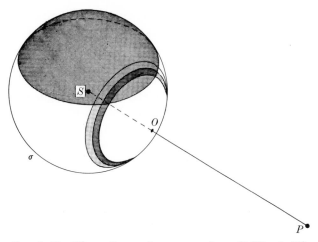

FIG. 1–29. The active region as seen from P (Fig. 1–28).

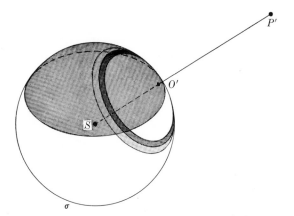

FIG. 1–30. The active region as seen from P' (Fig. 1–28).

negative term. In the absence of the screen, the positive and the negative terms exactly cancel. With the screen partially obstructing the active region, there is no longer exact cancellation because, in general, the screen will not blot out the same fraction of the "positive" and of the "negative" regions. However, the *fractional difference* between the exposed portions of the two regions tends to zero for $t_1 = 0$, and therefore the resultant disturbance vanishes at the limit for an infinitely short pulse. In this limit, the optical disturbance at P is thus at all times the same as in the absence of the screen.

(b) *Point inside the region of geometrical shadow.* Consider now the disturbance at P', inside the region of geometrical shadow. If r_4 is the minimum distance of P' from the edge of the opaque screen (Fig. 1–28), no portion of the active region is exposed at any time before $t = r_4/v$. Thus until this time the optical disturbance is identically zero. For $t > r_4/v$, the active region is in the shape of an annular zone, part of which appears through the opening (Fig. 1–30). For a pulse of finite length, the secondary waves originating from the exposed part of this region produce a finite disturbance at P'. However, with exactly the same argument presented previously, we can show that the disturbance vanishes when the duration of the pulse tends to zero. We conclude that at the limit for infinitely short pulses, the wave theory predicts the same distribution of light and shadow beyond the screen that follows from the law of rectilinear propagation.*

EXAMPLE. *A plane wave is incident perpendicularly upon a plane opaque screen bounded by a straight edge. Assume that, in the plane of the screen, the optical disturbance consists of a "triangular" pulse of duration t_1, as in Example 1, Section 1–6 (see Fig. 1–24). Study the propagation of the disturbance beyond the screen and show that the law of rectilinear propagation is fulfilled at the limit $t_1 = 0$.*

Consider a point P beyond the screen (Fig. 1–31) and construct the active region relative to this point at the time t. This active region consists of a "positive" portion [between the circles $r = r_1 = vt$ and $r = r' = v(t - t_1/2)$] and a "negative" portion [between the circles $r = r'$ and $r = r_2 = v(t - t_1)$]. Consider the circle at the distance r from P, and let α be the angle subtended at the center

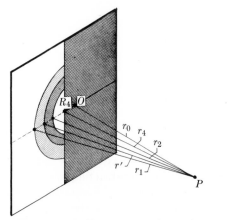 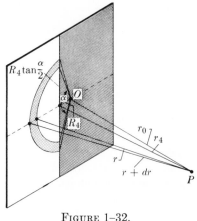

FIG. 1–31. Propagation beyond a plane opaque screen with a straight edge; point of observation in the region of geometric shadow.

FIGURE 1–32.

*This agreement breaks down for points on the axis of a perfectly circular screen or perfectly circular opening when the light wave is a spherical wave with its origin on the axis or a plane wave traveling in the direction of the axis (see Example 2, Section 1–6).

by the arc of this circle which is not covered by the screen (Fig. 1–32). Suppose first that P is in the region of geometric shadow, at the distance R_4 from the edge of the shadow and r_4 from the edge of the screen (Figs. 1–31 and 1–32).

The angle α is determined by the equation

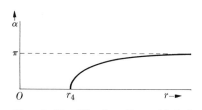

FIG. 1–33. The function $\alpha(r)$ (schematic).

$$R_4^2 \tan^2 \frac{\alpha}{2} = r^2 - r_4^2 .$$

When $r - r_4 \ll r_4$, α is a small angle and the above equation yields, to a good approximation,

$$\alpha(r) = 2\sqrt{2} \frac{\sqrt{r_4}}{R_4} \sqrt{r - r_4}.$$

At the limit $r = \infty$, α becomes equal to π. Thus $\alpha(r)$ is a function of the type represented in Fig. 1–33.

Neglecting the obliquity factor, we find that the contribution of the infinitesimal zone between r and $r + dr$ (Fig. 1–32) has the following values:

if the zone belongs to the "positive" portion of the active region,

$$dE_s = \frac{A}{\pi} \frac{d\sigma}{vt_1 r} \frac{\alpha(r)}{2\pi} = \frac{A}{\pi vt_1} \alpha(r) \, dr \, ;$$

if the zone belongs to the "negative" portion of the active region,

$$dE_s = -\frac{A}{\pi vt_1} \alpha(r) \, dr \, ;$$

if the zone does not belong to the active region,

$$dE_s = 0.$$

The disturbance at P is zero until the time r_4/v. Since t_1 is arbitrarily small, we can choose a time interval T such that $t_1 \ll T \ll r_4/v$. For $r_4/v < t < r_4/v + T$, the inequality $r - r_4 \ll r_4$ holds for all points of the active region, and the approximate expression for $\alpha(r)$ written above is applicable. For $r_4/v < t < r_4/v + t_1/2$, only a portion of the "positive" subregion is exposed, and the resultant disturbance at P is

$$E_P = \frac{A}{\pi vt_1} \int_{r_4}^{r_1} \alpha(r) \, dr = 2\sqrt{2} \frac{A}{\pi vt_1} \frac{\sqrt{r_4}}{R_4} \int_{r_4}^{r_1} \sqrt{r - r_4} \, dr$$

$$= \frac{4}{3} \sqrt{2} \frac{A}{\pi vt_1} \frac{\sqrt{r_4}}{R_4} (r_1 - r_4)^{3/2}.$$

If we introduce the variable

$$\tau = \frac{t - r_4/v}{t_1} = \frac{r_1 - r_4}{vt_1},$$

we can express the disturbance as

$$E_P = \frac{4}{3}\sqrt{2}\,\frac{A}{\pi}\,\frac{r_4^{1/2}(vt_1)^{1/2}}{R_4}\,\tau^{3/2}.$$

In the subsequent time interval $r_4/v + t_1/2 < t < r_4/v + t_1$, we have $r_2 < r_4 < r'$, and the optical disturbance at P is

$$E_P = \frac{A}{\pi vt_1}\left[\int_{r'}^{r_1}\alpha(r)\,dr - \int_{r_4}^{r'}\alpha(r)\,dr\right] = \frac{A}{\pi vt_1}\left[\int_{r_4}^{r_1}\alpha(r)\,dr - 2\int_{r_4}^{r'}\alpha(r)\,dr\right]$$

$$= \frac{4}{3}\sqrt{2}\,\frac{A}{\pi vt_1}\,\frac{\sqrt{r_4}}{R_4}\left[(r_1 - r_4)^{3/2} - 2\left(r_1 - \frac{vt_1}{2} - r_4\right)^{3/2}\right],$$

or

$$E_P = \frac{4}{3}\sqrt{2}\,\frac{A}{\pi}\,\frac{r_4^{1/2}(vt_1)^{1/2}}{R_4}\left[\tau^{3/2} - 2\left(\tau - \frac{1}{2}\right)^{3/2}\right].$$

For $t > r_4/v + t_1$ we have $r_2 > r_4$, and E_P is given by the expression:

$$E_P = \frac{A}{\pi vt_1}\left[\int_{r'}^{r_1}\alpha(r)\,dr - \int_{r_2}^{r'}\alpha(r)\,dr\right]$$

$$= \frac{A}{\pi vt_1}\left[\int_{r_4}^{r_1}\alpha(r)\,dr - 2\int_{r_4}^{r'}\alpha(r)\,dr + \int_{r_4}^{r_2}\alpha(r)\,dr\right]$$

$$= \frac{4}{3}\sqrt{2}\,\frac{A}{\pi vt_1}\,\frac{\sqrt{r_4}}{R_4}\left[(r_1 - r_4)^{3/2} - 2\left(r_1 - \frac{vt_1}{2} - r_4\right)^{3/2} + (r_1 - vt_1 - r_4)^{3/2}\right],$$

or

$$E_P = \frac{4}{3}\sqrt{2}\,\frac{A}{\pi}\,\frac{r_4^{1/2}(vt_1)^{1/2}}{R_4}\left[\tau^{3/2} - 2\left(\tau - \frac{1}{2}\right)^{3/2} + (\tau - 1)^{3/2}\right].$$

Let us define the function $F(\tau)$ such that

$$
\begin{array}{ll}
F(\tau) = \tau^{3/2} & \text{for} \quad 0 < \tau < \tfrac{1}{2}, \\[4pt]
F(\tau) = \tau^{3/2} - 2(\tau - \tfrac{1}{2})^{3/2} & \text{for} \quad \tfrac{1}{2} < \tau < 1, \\[4pt]
F(\tau) = \tau^{3/2} - 2(\tau - \tfrac{1}{2})^{3/2} + (\tau - 1)^{3/2} & \text{for} \quad \tau > 1.
\end{array}
$$

We then see that, for $t < r_4/v + T$, E_P is given by

$$E_P = \text{const.} \; (vt_1)^{1/2} F(\tau). \tag{1–41}$$

On the other hand, it follows from the condition $t_1 \ll T$ that at all times greater than $r_4/v + T$, the function $\alpha(r)$ changes by only a small amount as r varies from r_2 to r', or from r' to r_1. Hence we can develop $\alpha(r)$ in a Taylor series in the neighborhood of r', retaining only the linear term. We then obtain for E_P the expression

$$E_P = \frac{A}{\pi v t_1} \left[\int_{r'}^{r_1} \alpha(r') + (r - r') \left(\frac{d\alpha}{dr} \right)_{r=r'} dr - \int_{r_2}^{r'} \left[\alpha(r') + (r-r') \left(\frac{d\alpha}{dr} \right)_{r=r'} \right] dr \right.$$

$$= \frac{A}{\pi v t_1} \left(\frac{d\alpha}{dr} \right)_{r=r'} \left[\frac{(r_1 - r')^2}{2} + \frac{(r' - r_2)^2}{2} \right],$$

or

$$E_P = \frac{A}{\pi} \left(\frac{d\alpha}{dr} \right)_{r=r'} \left(\frac{vt_1}{4} \right). \tag{1–42}$$

From Eqs. (1–41) and (1–42) it follows that E_P is represented by a function of t of the type shown in Fig. 1–34. From the same equations, it also follows that E_P vanishes as t_1 tends to zero, for both $t < r_4/v + T$ and $t > r_4/v + T$). We conclude that at the limit for an infinitely short pulse, the disturbance at P is zero at all times.

Assume next that P lies outside the region of geometric shadow, at the distance R_3 from the edge of the shadow and r_3 from the edge of the screen. Consider again the active region relative to P, and its "positive" and "negative"

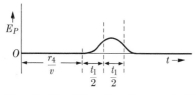

FIG. 1–34.   The disturbance at P
(Fig. 1–31.)

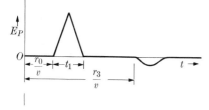

FIG. 1–36.   The disturbance at P
(Fig. 1–35.)

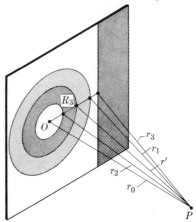

FIG. 1–35.   Propagation beyond an opaque screen with a straight edge; point of observation outside the region of geometric shadow.

subregions extending from r_1 to r' and from r' to r_2, respectively (Fig. 1–35). Until the time $t = r_3/v$, when r_1 becomes equal to r_3, the disturbance is the same as in the absence of the screen. Hence E_P increases from zero to A in the time interval $r_0/v < t < r_0/v + t_1/2$, decreases again from A to zero in the time interval $r_0/v + t_1/2 < t < r_0/v + t_1$, and remains zero until the time r_3/v (Fig. 1–36). ·

As the active zone expands further, the "positive" subregion becomes partially obscured, and a *negative* disturbance appears at P. Subsequently part of the "negative" subregion, too, is covered by the screen. At all times greater than r_3/v, the disturbance at P is equal in magnitude and opposite in sign to that which would be observed if the transparent and opaque portions of the screen were interchanged. From the results obtained previously, we thus conclude that E_P is represented by a function of the type shown in Fig. 1–36, and that the negative pulse beginning at $t = r_3/v$ vanishes as t_1 tends to zero. Thus, at the limit of an infinitely short pulse, the disturbance at P is at all times identical to that observed in the absence of the screen.

1–8 The Huygens construction. Let us re-examine the results obtained so far from a slightly different point of view.

(a) *Free propagation of a spherical wave.* Consider first the *free propagation* of a spherical wave diverging from a point source S that has emitted a very short pulse of radiation. At a certain instant, which we arbitrarily take as $t = 0$, the wave front has reached a certain sphere σ of radius a. The optical disturbance is then confined to a layer of very small thickness δ behind the surface σ (Fig. 1–37). In the short time interval from $t = 0$ to $t = t_1 = \delta/v$, the disturbance passes through the surface σ. During this time interval the various points of σ act as sources of secondary waves. At some later time t, the secondary wave fronts are spheres of radius vt. The optical disturbance corresponding to each secondary wave is confined

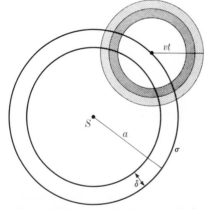

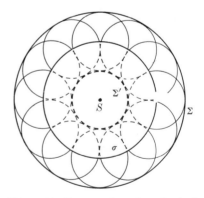

FIG. 1–37. An illustration of the Huygens construction.

FIG. 1–38. Propagation of a spherical wave according to the Huygens construction.

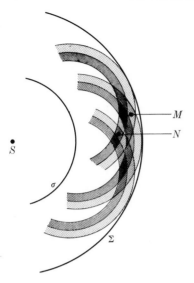

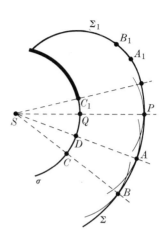

FIG. 1–39. Demonstration of how the secondary waves reinforce at M and cancel at N.

FIG. 1–40. Rectilinear propagation deduced from the Huygens construction.

to a spherical shell of thickness δ; it is positive in some parts of this volume, negative in others. For example, if the primary wave consists of a single positive pulse, the secondary disturbance is positive in the front part, negative in the rear part of the shell.

At the time t, the secondary wave fronts form a family of spheres whose geometrical envelope consists of two spheres: Σ, of radius $a + vt$, and Σ', of radius $a - vt$ (Fig. 1–38). The volume between these two spheres is the region of space where the secondary waves overlap.

In a shell of thickness δ behind the surface Σ the superposition of the secondary waves gives rise to a disturbance representing the primary wave at the time t. A disturbance would also arise in a shell of thickness δ adjacent to Σ', were it not for the fact that the intensity of the secondary waves vanishes in the backward direction. In all the rest of the volume between Σ and Σ' the positive and negative contributions of the secondary waves exactly cancel.

The following argument helps us to understand the reason why cancellation occurs everywhere except in the immediate vicinity of Σ. Since Σ is tangent to all secondary wave fronts, a point such as M, which lies an infinitesimal distance behind Σ, is also infinitely close to the fronts of all secondary waves that are active at M (Fig. 1–39). Hence, at the given instant, these waves contribute disturbances of the same sign. However, a point such as N, which lies at a finite distance from Σ, receives an equal number of positive and negative disturbances from the various secondary waves that overlap at this point.

(b) *Propagation of a spherical wave obstructed by a screen.* Consider next the case where the spherical surface σ is partially covered by an opaque screen (Fig. 1–40). Only points on the uncovered portion of σ are now active centers of secondary emission. As in the previous case, they give rise to secondary spherical waves whose radii at the time t are equal to vt. Consider the sphere with center S and radius $a + vt$. Let Σ be the portion of this sphere that lies outside the region of geometrical shadow (Fig. 1–40). The surface Σ represents the geometrical envelope of the secondary wave fronts at the time t. In other words, to each point P of Σ there corresponds a point Q on the exposed region of σ such that the secondary wave front originating at Q is tangent to Σ at P at the time t.

Inside the region of geometrical shadow, the portion of space reached by the secondary waves at the time t is bounded by a surface Σ_1 which is tangent to the spherical wave fronts originating from the points at the boundary of the opaque screen. Note that each of these fronts touches Σ_1 along an arc of a circle.

The following argument may be used to justify the fact that in the limiting case of an infinitely short pulse, the magnitude of the optical disturbance on Σ_1 vanishes, while the magnitude of the optical disturbance on Σ remains finite. Consider two finite areas, one on Σ and one on Σ_1 (in Fig. 1–40 these areas are represented by the arcs AB and A_1B_1). The disturbance on the area AB originates from a portion of the surface σ whose dimensions remain finite as the duration of the pulse tends to zero (it is represented by the arc CD in Fig. 1–40). The disturbance on the area A_1B_1, however, originates from a portion of the surface σ that reduces to a single line (represented by the point C_1 in the figure) in the limit of an infinitely short pulse. It is thus understandable that the ratio between the magnitudes of the disturbances on the area A_1B_1 and on the area AB, respectively, should go to zero for an infinitely short pulse.

The above considerations establish a direct connection between the fact that Σ is the geometrical envelope of the secondary waves and the fact that only along this surface does the superposition of the secondary waves produce a finite optical disturbance. They suggest a general method, known as the *Huygens construction*, for the study of the propagation of light within the approximation of geometrical optics. This method may be formulated as follows:

The various points of an arbitrary surface, as they are reached by the wave front, become the centers of secondary waves. The geometrical envelope of these waves at any given later time represents the instantaneous position of the wave front. The volume swept by the wave front thus defined determines the illuminated region of space.

Note that in the above formulation we have removed the unnecessary restrictions that the wave front must be spherical and that the auxiliary surface σ, from which the secondary waves originate, must coincide with a wave front. This is an important generalization, for the shape of the auxiliary surface is often determined by the nature of the problem, as will become clear from the examples to be discussed later.

1–9 Light rays. The laws of reflection and refraction derived from Huygens' principle. In the previous sections we have seen how the rectilinear propagation of light can be explained on the basis of wave theory. The Huygens construction shows that we may regard light as being propagated along straight lines perpendicular to the wave front. We are therefore entitled to call these lines *light rays*, even though they do not have the concrete meaning of particle trajectories assigned to them in the corpuscular model. The law of rectilinear propagation applies, of course, only to homogeneous media, where the velocity of propagation is everywhere the same. In such media, a point source generates spherical waves and the corresponding rays are straight lines diverging from the source. A portion of a spherical wave at a very large distance from the source is approximately a plane wave: the corresponding rays are parallel to each other and perpendicular to the wave surface.

We now proceed to show that the laws of *reflection* and *refraction* can also be derived from the Huygens construction.

Consider a plane wave impinging upon the plane surface of separation σ between two homogeneous media. We assume the two media to have different optical properties. More specifically, we assume that light travels in each of them with a different velocity. According to Huygens' principle, the points of the surface σ, as they are reached by the light wave, become centers of secondary wavelets. Analogy with the mechanical case [see Section 1–3(e)] suggests that since the optical properties of the medium change discontinuously across the surface σ, the secondary wavelets are propagated both forward and backward, giving rise to a refracted and a reflected wave.

First we propose to investigate the reflected wave. The wavelets are propagated in the backward direction with a velocity equal to that of the incident wave. In Fig. 1–41, AB is the intersection of the incident wave front with a plane perpendicular to the wave front itself and to the reflecting surface σ. It is pictured at the instant when the wave front intersects the reflecting surface σ along a straight line perpendicular to the plane of the figure and passing through A. At this moment the wave front is still a distance BC from the point C of σ. When the wave front reaches C, the wavelets originating from A and from the other points on the straight line passing through A and perpendicular to the plane of the figure have

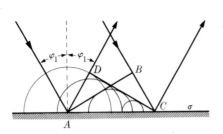

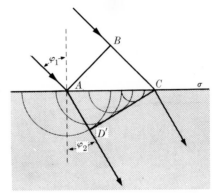

FIG. 1–41. The law of reflection deduced from the Huygens construction.

FIG. 1–42. The law of refraction deduced from the Huygens construction.

radii equal to BC. The wavelets originating from points intermediate between A and C have radii proportional to their distances from C. The envelope of all these wavelets, i.e., *the reflected wave*, is a plane surface perpendicular to the plane of the figure and intersecting this plane along the line CD. The two triangles ABC and CDA are congruent. Therefore the angles which the incident and the reflected waves form with the reflecting surface are equal ($\angle BAC = \angle DCA$). The angle BAC is also equal to the angle between the incident ray (perpendicular to AB) and the normal to the reflecting surface; i.e., $\angle BAC$ represents the angle of incidence, φ_1. Similarly, $\angle DCA$ represents the angle of reflection. We conclude that the angle of incidence equals the angle of reflection. Moreover, we see from the construction that the incident and the reflected rays lie in a plane perpendicular to the reflecting surface. Thus the law of reflection follows from Huygens' principle.

To interpret the phenomenon of refraction, we again consider a plane wave AB incident upon the plane surface of separation σ between two transparent media, and construct the wavelets propagated from the points of σ into the second medium (Fig. 1–42). We have assumed that the velocity of light is different in the two media. Let v_1 be the velocity in the first medium and v_2 the velocity in the second medium.

At the moment when the wave front reaches the refracting surface at A, it is still a distance BC from point C. While the incident wave travels this distance, the point A and the other points on the straight line passing through A perpendicular to the plane of the figure give rise to secondary wavelets whose radius AD' bears to BC the same ratio as v_2 bears to v_1:

$$\frac{\overline{AD'}}{\overline{BC}} = \frac{v_2}{v_1}. \tag{1–43}$$

Wavelets originating from points intermediate between A and C have radii proportional to their distances from C. Thus the envelope of the secondary wavelets is a plane surface CD' perpendicular to the plane of the figure. It follows that the incident ray (perpendicular to the incident wave front AB) and the refracted ray (perpendicular to the refracted wave front CD') lie in a plane perpendicular to the refracting surface σ. Moreover, note that the angle of incidence φ_1 equals the angle BAC, and that the angle of refraction φ_2 equals the angle ACD'. From the figure, we find that

$$\overline{BC} = \overline{AC} \sin \varphi_1, \qquad \overline{AD'} = \overline{AC} \sin \varphi_2. \qquad (1\text{--}44)$$

From these equations and Eq. (1–43), it then follows that

$$\frac{\sin \varphi_1}{\sin \varphi_2} = \frac{v_1}{v_2}. \qquad (1\text{--}45)$$

Thus the ratio of the angle of incidence to the angle of refraction is a constant, in agreement with the empirical law of refraction. Furthermore, wave theory, as embodied in Huygens' principle, specifies that this constant, which is by definition the index of refraction n_{12} of the second medium relative to the first, equals the ratio of the velocity of light in the first medium to the velocity of light in the second:

$$n_{12} = \frac{v_1}{v_2}. \qquad (1\text{--}46)$$

It is interesting to note that the corpuscular model yields a completely different result. According to this model, refraction occurs because, in the neighborhood of the refracting surface, light particles experience forces perpendicular to the surface itself. These forces cannot modify the component of the velocity parallel to the refracting surface. Therefore

$$v_1 \sin \varphi_1 = v_2 \sin \varphi_2,$$

or

$$\frac{\sin \varphi_1}{\sin \varphi_2} = \frac{v_2}{v_1}. \qquad (1\text{--}47)$$

We see that, according to the corpuscular model, $\sin \varphi_1 / \sin \varphi_2$ is still a constant, but now represents the ratio of the velocity of light in the *second* medium to the velocity of light in the *first* medium. For example, since in passing from air to water a light ray is refracted toward the normal to the refracting surface, the wave model predicts that the velocity of light in air is greater than in water, whereas the corpuscular model predicts that the velocity of light is greater in water than in air. These results suggest a direct experimental test of the two models. As we shall see later (Section 5–6), the measurements are in agreement with the prediction of the wave model.

For visible light, it turns out that the index of refraction of all transparent materials relative to vacuum is greater than 1 (for gases, it is very close to 1). This means that the velocity of light in any material is smaller than in vacuum. The index of refraction of a material relative to vacuum is usually called its *index of refraction,* without further qualification. It is defined by

$$n = \frac{c}{v},\tag{1–48}$$

where c is the velocity of light in vacuum and v is the velocity in the material under consideration. The index of refraction n_{12} of a medium 2 relative to a medium 1 can then be expressed in terms of the indices of refraction of the two media as follows:

$$n_{12} = \frac{n_2}{n_1}.\tag{1–49}$$

1-1. The diameters of the sun, earth, and moon, respectively, are $D_1 = 864,000$ mi, $D_0 = 7,920$ mi, and $D_2 = 2,160$ mi. Let R_1 be the distance of the earth from the sun and R_2 the distance of the earth from the moon. R_1 and R_2 are not exactly constant because of the eccentricity of the orbits of the earth around the sun and of the orbit of the moon around the earth. (a) Compute the relation between R_1 and R_2 that must be satisfied for a total solar eclipse to occur somewhere on the earth. (b) A solar eclipse occurs when the distance of the earth from the sun is 92,900,000 mi and the distance of the earth from the moon is 226,000 mi. Compute the diameters of the zone of complete shadow and of the zone of penumbra on the surface of the earth, and compare these diameters with the diameter of the earth.

1-2. A man of height h stands a distance d from a plane vertical mirror. How high must the mirror be for the man to see his full image?

1-3. Two plane mirrors, M and N, are placed at right angles to each other. A point source S lies 3 ft from M and 6 ft from N (Fig. 1–43). (a) Find the positions of the images of S due to single or multiple reflections on the mirrors.

(b) Trace the rays reaching a point P 6 ft from M and 8 ft from N after one or two reflections (assume that S and P lie in a plane perpendicular to the mirrors).

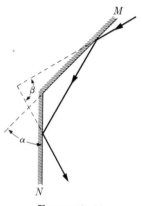

FIGURE 1–44.

1-4. Two plane mirrors M and N form an angle α (Fig. 1–44). A ray of light incident in a direction perpendicular to the intersection of the two mirrors is reflected first at one mirror, then at the other. Compute the angle β between the incident and the second reflected ray.

1-5. The rotating coil of a galvanometer carries a small mirror whose plane contains the axis of rotation. A beam of light incident in a direction perpendicular to the axis of rotation is reflected by the mirror upon a scale at a distance of 2 m. (a) Prove that if the coil rotates through an angle α, the reflected beam rotates through an angle 2α. (b) Compute the angle of rotation corresponding to a displacement of the beam on the scale by 1 cm.

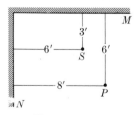

FIGURE 1–43.

1–6. Compute the lateral displacement of a light ray traversing a glass plate 1 in. thick if the angle of incidence is 45° and the index of refraction of the glass is 1.55.

1–7. A square raft, 10 ft on a side, floats on the surface of a quiet pond. Describe the volume under the raft in which a fish can swim without being seen by anyone looking into the pond from above the water. The index of refraction of water is 1.33.

FIGURE 1–45

1–8. A ray of light is incident at an angle φ on the upper horizontal face of a cube made of a transparent material of index of refraction n (Fig. 1–45). (a) For what values of φ will the ray undergo total reflection at the vertical face of the cube? (b) What is the maximum value of n for which a ray falling upon the horizontal face at grazing incidence will emerge from the vertical face? (Assume that the plane of incidence is perpendicular to the intersection between the horizontal and the vertical faces.)

1–9. Figure 1–46 illustrates the principle of an accurate method for the measurement of the index of refraction. The transparent material to be investigated (e.g., in the form of a liquid drop) is placed on the face of a glass prism whose index of refraction n relative to air is known. A convergent beam of light is focused upon a point A of the face a so that some of the rays strike the prism at grazing incidence. On the

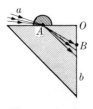

FIGURE 1–46.

face b through which the light beam emerges from the prism we observe at B a sharp boundary between light and dark. Assume that the cross section of the prism is a right triangle. (a) Compute the index of refraction n' of the substance in terms of the index of refraction n of the glass and of the distances $x = \overline{OA}$, $y = \overline{OB}$. (b) For a given value of n, what is the minimum value of n' for which rays entering the prism at grazing incidence through the face a will emerge through the face b?

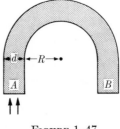

FIGURE 1–47.

1–10. A glass rod of rectangular cross section is bent into the shape shown in Fig. 1–47. A parallel beam of light falls perpendicularly on the plane surface A. Compute the minimum value of the ratio R/d for which all light entering the glass through this surface will emerge from the glass through the surthe surface B. The index of refraction of the glass is 1.5.

1–11. A fish looks at the sky through the water of a quiet pond. There are in the sky four stars, at angles of 25°, 45°,

65°, and 85° to the zenith. Compute the apparent zenith angles of these stars, as seen by the fish.

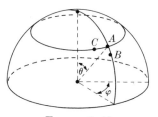

FIGURE 1–48.

1–12. Write the equations giving the apparent zenith angle θ' and the apparent azimuth φ' of a star seen from below the surface of a pond, as functions of the actual zenith angle θ and the actual azimuth φ (Fig. 1–48). Consider two stars at a small angular distance $\Delta\alpha$ from each other, and let $\Delta\alpha'$ be their apparent angular distance as perceived by an underwater observer. Compute the ratio $\Delta\alpha'/\Delta\alpha$ in terms of θ and the index of refraction n of water for the two following cases: (a) the two stars have the same azimuth but slightly different zenith angles (like A and B in Fig. 1–48); (b) the two stars have the same zenith angle but slightly different azimuths (like A and C in Fig. 1–48). Show that in case (a), when one of the stars is at the horizon, the equation $\Delta\alpha' = (\Delta\alpha)^2/(2\sqrt{n^2 - 1})$ holds.

1–13. The sun has a diameter of 864,000 mi and is 92,900,000 mi distant from the earth. Making use of the results of the previous problem, describe the appearance of the solar disk to an underwater observer (a) when the sun is at the zenith, (b) when the sun is at 40° to the zenith, (c) when the sun is at 80° to the zenith, (d) when the lower edge of the solar disk touches the horizon. In all cases, determine the apparent angular height and width of the solar disk.

1–14. A long string of mass of 1 g per meter is held under tension in a horizontal position by means of a pulley and a weight M of 1.02 kg, as shown in Fig. 1–49. The end point O is moved upward and then brought back to its original position; its displacement s_0 is represented by the following function of time: $s_0 = 0$ for $t < 0$, $s_0 = 10^{-2}[1 - \cos(200\pi t)]$ for $0 < t < 1/100$, $s_0 = 0$ for $t > 1/100$, where s_0 is measured in meters and t in sec.

(a) Determine the velocity of propagation of the disturbance. (b) Write the equation of the wave. (c) Sketch the shape of the string at $t = 0.1$ sec and $t = 0.2$ sec. (d) Compute and plot the transverse velocity u of the various points of the string as a function of the distance x from O at $t = 0.1$ sec and $t = 0.2$ sec.

FIGURE 1–49.

1–15. With reference to the previous problem, compute and plot as a function of t the energy flux per unit time through a point A, 10 m distant from O.

1–16. Consider the waves on a string described by the following equations:

(a) $\quad s_a = A \exp\left[-\frac{(t - x/v)^2}{t_1^2}\right],$

(b) $\quad s_b = A \exp\left[-\frac{(t + x/v)^2}{t_1^2}\right],$

(c) $s_c = \frac{1}{2}A \left(\exp\left[-\frac{(t - x/v)^2}{t_1^2} \right] \right.$

$\left. + \exp\left[-\frac{(t + x/v)^2}{t_1^2} \right] \right),$

(d) $s_d = \frac{1}{2}A \left(\exp\left[-\frac{(t - x/v)^2}{t_1^2} \right] \right.$

$\left. - \exp\left[-\frac{(t + x/v)^2}{t_1^2} \right] \right).$

Compute the corresponding transverse velocities. For each wave make a rough plot of s vs. x at $t = 0$ and $t = 3t_1$, with arrows indicating the directions and magnitudes of the transverse velocities of the various points of the string.

1–17. Consider, in a fluid, a spherical pressure wave emanating from a point source S, with velocity of propagation v. The pressure at a distance r_1 from the source is given by $p = p_0 + p_1 \sin \omega t$, where p_0 is the pressure in the undisturbed condition and $p_1 \ll p_0$. Compute the pressure as a function of time at a distance $r_2 > r_1$ from the source.

1–18. Consider a plane wave traveling with velocity v in the direction of the x-axis, and assume that the disturbance on the yz-plane ($x = 0$) is represented by the following equations:

$E(t, 0) = 0,$
  for $t < 0,$

$E(t, 0) = 1 - \cos\left(2\pi \frac{t}{t_1} \right),$
  for $0 < t < t_1,$

$E(t, 0) = 0,$
  for $t > t_1.$

(a) Write the equations describing the free propagation of the wave. (b) Assume that the yz-plane is covered by an infinitely extended opaque screen with a circular hole of radius R centered at the origin. Compute the disturbance at the point P of coordinates $x = x_0$, $y = 0$, $z = 0$, assuming $R \ll vt_1$, $x_0 \gg vt_1$.

1–19. Refer to Problem 1–18.

(a) Assume that, instead of a hole, the opaque screen has an opening in the shape of a narrow circular zone centered at the origin. Let R be the inner radius of the zone, ΔR its thickness, and assume that $R \ll x_0$ and that $\Delta R \ll vt_1$. Compute the disturbance at P under these new conditions (neglect the obliquity factor).

(b) Compute the disturbance when the central hole and the circular zone are open simultaneously. Take $x_0 = 10^4 vt_1$. Assume that the central hole has a radius equal to $vt_1/20$, and that the circular zone has an inner radius $R = 100 vt_1$ and a thickness $\Delta R = 1.25 \times 10^{-5} vt_1$.

1–20. Refer to Problem 1–18. Compute the disturbance at P in the absence of a screen by considering this disturbance as the resultant of the secondary waves arising from the various points of the yz-plane. Discuss separately the time intervals (a) $t < x_0/v$, (b) $x_0/v < t < x_0/v + t_1$, and (c) $t > x_0/v + t_1$.

1–21. Refer to Problem 1–18. Compute the disturbance at P, assuming that an opaque circular screen of radius $R \ll x_0$ with center at the origin lies on the yz-plane.

1–22. Refer to Problem 1–18, and assume that the yz-plane is covered by an infinitely extended opaque screen, with a circular hole of radius R centered at the origin. Compute and plot the disturbance at P for the following values of R: (a) $R = \sqrt{4x_0vt_1}$, (b) $R = \sqrt{2x_0vt_1}$, and (c) $R = \sqrt{x_0vt_1}$.

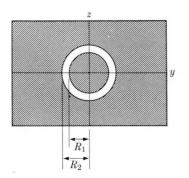

(a)

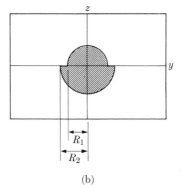

(b)

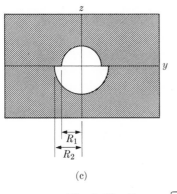

(c)

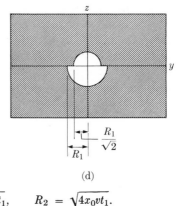

(d)

Fig. 1-50. $R_1 = \sqrt{2x_0 v t_1}$, $R_2 = \sqrt{4x_0 v t_1}$.

1-23. Consider a plane wave traveling with velocity v in the direction of the x-axis, and assume that the disturbance on the yz-plane is represented by the equations:

$$E(t, 0) = 0,$$
for $t < 0$,

$$E(t, 0) = (2\, A/t_1)t,$$
for $0 < t < t_1/2$,

$$E(t, 0) = (2\, A/t_1)(t_1 - t),$$
for $t_1/2 < t < t_1$,

$$E(t, 0) = 0,$$
for $t > t_1$.

(see Example 1 in Section 1-6). Compute and plot the disturbance at the point P of coordinates $x = x_0$, $y = 0$, $z = 0$, when various opaque screens, as shown in Fig. 1-50, are placed in the yz-plane. Assume $x_0 \gg v t_1$. Show that the sum of the disturbances observed with the two "complementary" screens (b) and (c) equals the disturbance observed in the absence of any screen.

CHAPTER 2

SOME APPLICATIONS OF GEOMETRICAL OPTICS

A systematic study of the many problems that can be treated within the framework of geometrical optics lies beyond the scope of the present volume. The reader will find a simple but exhaustive treatment of such problems in the volume on *Optics*, by F. W. Sears (Reading, Mass.: Addison-Wesley Publishing Company, Inc., 1949); for a discussion of the same problems on a more advanced level he may consult *Fundamentals of Optics*, by Francis A. Jenkins and Harvey E. White (New York: Mc-Graw Hill Book Company, Inc., 1950) or *Applied Optics and Optical Design*, by A. E. Conrady (New York: Oxford University Press, 1929). Here we wish to consider only a few applications of geometrical optics that have a particular intrinsic interest or are essential for the understanding of optical phenomena that we shall encounter later in our study.

2–1 Reflection and refraction of a wave at a surface of arbitrary shape. We begin by investigating the reflection of a spherical wave at a surface of arbitrary shape, as illustrated in Fig. 2–1, where S is the source of a wave incident on the reflecting surface σ. According to Huygens' principle, as

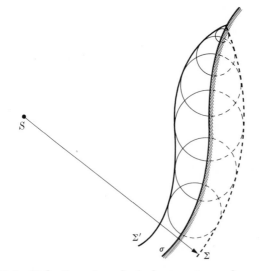

FIG. 2–1. Reflection of a spherical wave at a surface σ of arbitrary shape.

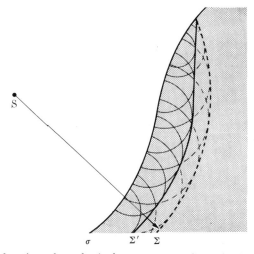

FIG. 2–2. Refraction of a spherical wave at a surface of arbitrary shape.

the points of σ are reached by the advancing wave front, they become centers of secondary spherical wavelets; at any time t after the wave front has passed σ, its position is given by the envelope of these wavelets. Evidently there are two possible envelopes which can be constructed. One, which we shall call Σ, lies on the far side of σ from S, and corresponds to the wave front which would exist if σ were an imaginary surface and the medium were homogeneous throughout. The other, Σ', corresponds to the actual reflected wave front.

The above suggests a method for finding Σ' at any instant of time: first, we neglect σ and construct the spherical wave front Σ; then, about each point of σ which has been reached by the advancing wave front, we draw a spherical wavelet tangent to Σ; and finally we construct Σ', the second envelope of these wavelets.

We can treat in a similar manner the refraction of a spherical wave at a surface of arbitrary shape that separates two homogeneous media with different indices of refraction. Let us consider an incident wave which diverges from a point source S located in the first medium (Fig. 2–2) and is refracted at the surface σ. To determine the shape of the wave front in the second medium at the time t, we imagine that the first medium occupies the whole space, and construct the spherical wave front Σ at the time t. The portion of Σ that lies beyond the surface σ may be regarded as the envelope of the secondary wavelets that originate from the various points of σ and travel with an assumed velocity c/n_1, where n_1 is the index of refraction of the first medium. Actually, however, the velocity of propagation in the second medium is c/n_2, where n_2 is the index of refraction of the second medium. Accordingly, we change the radius of each wavelet by a scale factor n_1/n_2, and obtain a new family of spherical wavelets whose envelope Σ' is the refracted wave front at the time t.

2-2 Propagation of light in nonhomogeneous media.

In a nonhomogeneous medium the velocity of propagation of light waves varies from point to point, so that we must describe the optical properties of the medium by giving the index of refraction n as a function of position: $n = n(x, y, z)$. If we assume that n varies in a continuous fashion, we may consider it to be constant in any infinitesimal volume, and it follows that a wave emitted by a point source has a spherical shape in the immediate neighborhood of the source. In general, however, the wave will acquire a different shape as it continues to spread, and although we will still be able to use the Huygens construction, we must now proceed step by step between wave fronts at infinitesimal distances from one another.

As an example, in Fig. 2–3 let Σ be the wave front at the time t, and around each point of Σ construct a hemispherical wavelet of radius $v\, \Delta t = (c/n)\, \Delta t$ in the direction of propagation. Since n (and therefore the velocity c/n) varies from point to point, these wavelets will have different radii at different points. Their envelope represents the wave front Σ' at the time $t + \Delta t$. In a similar way, we can determine the wave fronts Σ'', Σ''', etc., at later times. The light rays form a family of lines intersecting the wave surfaces at right angles and are, in general, curved; hence the. law of rectilinear propagation does not apply to nonhomogeneous media. Figure 2–3 illustrates the propagation of an initially plane wave in a medium in which the index of refraction increases gradually from left to right; we see that the rays are concave toward the region where the index of refraction is greater.

Two important results follow from application of the Huygens construction. The first is the *principle of optical reversibility*. If, in the time Δt, a wave front moves from Σ to Σ' (Fig. 2–3), we find, upon reversing the direction of propagation, that during the same time interval a wave front moves from Σ' to Σ. In fact, if Σ' is the envelope of the spheres of radii $(c/n)\, \Delta t$ with centers on Σ, then Σ is the envelope of the spheres of radii $(c/n)\, \Delta t$ with centers on Σ'. Therefore, light travels along the same paths in opposite directions. In Section 1–1 we have already discussed a special case of optical reversibility as applied to the passage of light rays across the surface of separation between two homogeneous media.

The second principle, which is self-evident, states that equal times are required for light to travel from one

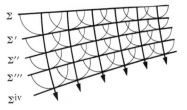

FIG. 2–3. Propagation of a light wave in a nonhomogeneous medium.

wave front Σ_1 to another wave front Σ_2 along any two paths. We can express this principle in a different way by introducing the concept of *optical length*, which is often useful in discussing optical problems. The optical length from a point A to a point B along a given path, which we shall denote by l, represents the distance that light would travel in vacuum during the time it needs to cover the distance from A to B along the given path. The mathematical expression for the optical length is

$$l = \int_A^B \frac{c}{v}\, ds = \int_A^B n\, ds, \tag{2-1}$$

where ds is the line element along the path. Making use of the concept of optical length, we may now restate our second principle as follows: all rays connecting two wave fronts Σ_1 and Σ_2 have equal optical lengths.

The fact that light rays in nonhomogeneous media are curved explains several interesting optical effects in the atmosphere. Under normal conditions, the density of the atmosphere decreases gradually with altitude above sea level, and the index of refraction decreases correspondingly. Hence a ray of light coming from a distant star follows, in the atmosphere, a slightly curved path, with the concavity in the downward direction (Fig. 2–4). An observer at the earth's surface "sees" the star in the direction of the tangent to the light ray as it enters the eye of the observer (or the telescope) and, to this observer, the star will appear closer to the zenith than it actually is. The effect, of course, is greatest for a star near the horizon (where it amounts to approximately 0.5°) and becomes zero at the zenith.

Occasionally, when the surface of the earth is strongly heated by the sun's radiation, the layers of air in the immediate vicinity of the earth become much warmer than those at a somewhat greater height. This situation produces a condition of unstable equilibrium in which, instead of decreasing, the density of air increases with increasing height, at least

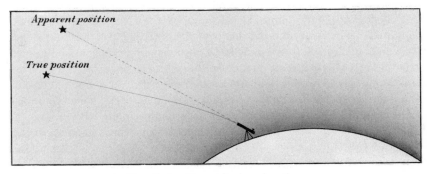

FIG. 2–4. Atmospheric refraction.

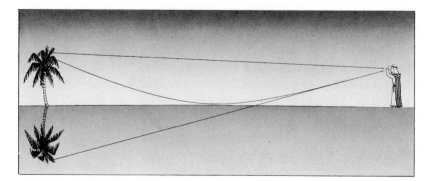

FIG. 2–5. The mirage.

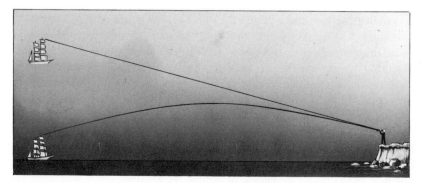

FIG. 2–6. Looming.

over a certain distance. The index of refraction then also increases with height, and consequently light rays are curved upward near the earth's surface. Under these conditions, light from an object some distance above the surface of the earth may reach the eye of an observer either along a more or less straight path, which does not approach the earth's surface, or along a curved path which passes near this surface (see Fig. 2–5). Thus the observer will see the object approximately in its correct position, and, in addition, will see an inverted image of the object as if it were reflected by a water surface. This phenomenon, known as *mirage*, is commonly seen in the desert, where it may create the illusion of a body of water. The illusory puddles of water that are occasionally seen on a hot pavement are often due to the same phenomenon.* A similar effect, called *looming*, occurs when the density of air decreases much more rapidly with increasing height than it does under normal conditions, as sometimes happens in the

---

*Specular reflection of light at grazing incidence may also create the impression of a wet pavement.

vicinity of the cold surface of the sea or of a lake. Light rays are then curved downward, and an object floating on the water may appear to be suspended in mid-air (Fig. 2–6).

It is easy to write the differential equation of the rays in a medium whose index of refraction changes in only one direction. Let us take this direction as the x-axis of a cartesian frame of reference, so that n becomes a function of x alone, and let us divide the medium into thin slices perpendicular to the x-axis. If the index of refraction is considered constant in each slice, any given ray will be approximated by a number of short straight segments. From the laws of refraction it follows that the ray lies in a plane, which we shall take as the xy-plane (Fig. 2–7). It also follows that as the ray passes from a slice whose index of refraction is n_1 to a neighboring slice whose index of refraction is n_2, its direction changes in such a way that

$$\frac{\sin \varphi_1}{\sin \varphi_2} = \frac{n_2}{n_1},$$

where φ_1 and φ_2 are the angles that the segments of the ray in the first and second slices, respectively, form with the x-axis. The above equation indicates that the quantity $n \sin \varphi$ remains constant as we go from one infinitesimal slice to the next; this remains true at the limit for infinitely thin slices. Hence, if n is the index of refraction at an arbitrary point of the ray and φ is the angle which the tangent to the ray at that point makes with the x-axis, and if n_0 and φ_0 are the values of n and φ at a fixed point P_0 of the ray (Fig. 2–8), the following equation holds:

$$n \sin \varphi = n_0 \sin \varphi_0. \tag{2–2}$$

Let ds be the length of an element of the ray, so that

$$ds^2 = dx^2 + dy^2, \quad \text{or} \quad \left(\frac{ds}{dy}\right)^2 = \left(\frac{dx}{dy}\right)^2 + 1. \tag{2–3}$$

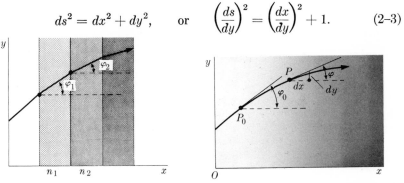

FIG. 2–7. Trajectory of a light ray in a stratified medium.

FIG. 2–8. Trajectory of a light ray in a medium whose index of refraction is a function of x.

Since $\sin \varphi = dy/ds$, Eq. (2–2) is equivalent to

$$n \frac{dy}{ds} = n_0 \sin \varphi_0, \tag{2–4}$$

which, together with (2–3), yields

$$\left(\frac{dx}{dy}\right)^2 + 1 = \frac{n^2}{n_0^2 \sin^2 \varphi_0}. \tag{2–5}$$

The solution of (2–5) gives the equation of the ray that passes through the point P_0 of the medium and forms, at this point, an angle φ_0 with the x-axis.

Differentiation of Eq. (2–5) with respect to y yields

$$2 \frac{dx}{dy} \frac{d^2x}{dy^2} = \frac{1}{n_0^2 \sin^2 \varphi_0} \frac{d(n^2)}{dx} \frac{dx}{dy},$$

$$\frac{d^2x}{dy^2} = \frac{1}{2n_0^2 \sin^2 \varphi_0} \frac{d(n^2)}{dx}, \tag{2–6}$$

which may be used as an alternate starting point for the computation of the equation of the ray.

EXAMPLE. *Derive the equation of the rays in a medium in which the index of refraction is given by*

$$n^2 = h + kx,$$

where h and k are constants.

With the above expression for n, Eq. (2–6) yields

$$\frac{d^2x}{dy^2} = \frac{1}{2 \sin^2 \varphi_0} \frac{k}{n_0^2}.$$

By successive integrations, we obtain

$$\frac{dx}{dy} = \frac{1}{2 \sin^2 \varphi_0} \frac{k}{n_0^2} y + a.$$

$$x = \frac{1}{2 \sin^2 \varphi_0} \frac{k}{n_0^2} \frac{y^2}{2} + ay + b,$$

where a and b are constants of integration, n_0 represents the index of refraction at a given point P_0 of the ray, and φ_0 is the angle between the tangent to the ray and the x-axis at P_0. Let us take our x-axis through P_0, and let x_0 be the abscissa of this point. From the condition $x = x_0$ for $y = 0$, we obtain $b = x_0$. From the condition $n = n_0$ at $x = x_0$, we obtain $n_0{}^2 = h + kx_0$. The definition of φ_0 yields

$$\cot \varphi_0 = \left(\frac{dx}{dy}\right)_{y=0} = a.$$

Thus the equation of the ray passing through P_0 at an angle φ_0 to the x-axis becomes

$$x = \frac{1}{\sin^2 \varphi_0} \frac{k}{h + kx_0} \frac{y^2}{4} + (\cot \varphi_0)y + x_0.$$

∗2–3 General equations for the propagation of light in nonhomogeneous media. To write the general equation describing the propagation of a wave front in a nonhomogeneous medium, let us assume that the wave front at the initial instant of time is represented by a given surface Σ_0, and define a function L of x, y, z, such that the value of L at a given point P equals the optical length from Σ_0 to P of the ray passing through P. The equation of an arbitrary wave front is then

$$L(x, y, z) = l = \text{const.} \tag{2–7}$$

At a given point, let ds be the distance between the two wave fronts corresponding to l and $l + dl$ (Fig. 2–9). Equation (2–7) then yields

$$|\text{grad } L| \, ds = dl,$$

where $|\text{grad } L|$ is the magnitude of the vector grad L [see Appendix 1(a)]. Since, from Eq. (2–1), $dl/ds = n$, we obtain

$$|\text{grad } L|^2 = n^2, \tag{2–8}$$

or, in cartesian coordinates,

$$\left(\frac{\partial L}{\partial x}\right)^2 + \left(\frac{\partial L}{\partial y}\right)^2 + \left(\frac{\partial L}{\partial z}\right)^2 = n^2. \tag{2–9}$$

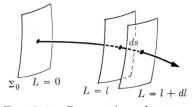

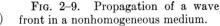

FIG. 2–9.   Propagation of a wave front in a nonhomogeneous medium.

∗Starred sections may be omitted without loss of continuity.

This partial differential equation is the mathematical formulation of Huygens' principle. Its solution, subject to the boundary condition that the equation $L(x, y, z) = 0$ represents the initial wave front Σ_0, determines the wave front at all subsequent times. Indeed, the equation of the wave front at time t is

$$L(x, y, z) = ct. \tag{2–10}$$

The light rays are the normal trajectories of the surfaces $L = $ const.

The equation satisfied by the light rays can also be derived directly, in the following manner. Let τ be a unit vector tangent to the light ray, and consider the vector $n\tau$, where n, as usual, is the index of refraction. From Snell's law it follows that when a light ray passes across the surface of separation between two different media, it changes direction in such a way that the component of $n\tau$ parallel to the surface remains unchanged. Assume that we have two surfaces corresponding to two constant values of n which differ by a very small amount Δn, and consider a light ray crossing these surfaces at the points P and P' (Fig. 2–10). From the obvious identity

$$(n\tau) \cdot (n\tau) = n^2, \tag{2–11}$$

we obtain by differentiation

$$(n\tau) \cdot \Delta(n\tau) = n \, \Delta n = n \, \text{grad} \, n \cdot \Delta \mathsf{s} = n \, \Delta s \, \text{grad} \, n \cdot \tau,$$

where $\Delta\mathsf{s}$ is the vector PP', Δs is the magnitude of this vector, and $\Delta(n\tau)$ represents the vector difference between the vectors $n\tau$ at P' and P, respectively. The above equation yields

$$\frac{d(n\tau)}{ds} \cdot \tau = \text{grad} \, n \cdot \tau. \tag{2–12}$$

Equation (2–12) indicates that the vectors $d(n\tau)/ds$ and grad n have equal projections along the tangent to the ray. Moreover, grad n is perpendicular to the surface $n = $ const., and so is the vector $d(n\tau)/ds$, because, as we have mentioned, the component of $n\tau$ parallel to a refracting surface is the same on both sides of this surface. Therefore we obtain

$$\frac{d(n\tau)}{ds} = \text{grad} \, n. \tag{2–13}$$

This is the differential equation of the light ray, in vector form.

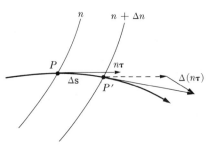

Fig. 2–10. Trajectory of a ray in a medium of variable n.

It is interesting to compare the equations that describe the propagation of light in a nonhomogeneous medium with the equations that describe the motion of a mass point in a potential field. Let us assume, for the sake of simplicity, that we are dealing with a field such that the potential energy U depends only on x. Then only the x-component of the force is different from zero, and if the initial velocity of a particle lies in the xy-plane, the particle remains in this plane. The y-component of the velocity is a constant, so that we may write

$$\frac{dy}{dt} = v_0 \sin \varphi_0, \tag{2–14}$$

where v_0 is the velocity at a given point P_0 on the trajectory of the particle, and φ_0 is the angle that the trajectory makes with the x-axis at this point. The velocity v is given by

$$\left(\frac{dx}{dt}\right)^2 + \left(\frac{dy}{dt}\right)^2 = v^2,$$

which can also be written as

$$\left(\frac{dx}{dy}\frac{dy}{dt}\right)^2 + \left(\frac{dy}{dt}\right)^2 = v^2,$$

or, making use of Eq. (2–14), as

$$\left(\frac{dx}{dy}\right)^2 + 1 = \frac{[v(x)]^2}{v_0^2 \sin^2 \varphi_0}. \tag{2–15}$$

Here we have written $v(x)$ to emphasize that v is a known function of x. We can obtain this function from the equation expressing the law of conservation of energy,

$$\tfrac{1}{2}mv^2 + U = \tfrac{1}{2}mv_0^2 + U_0, \tag{2–16}$$

where U_0 represents the value of U at P_0. The solution of Eq. (2–15) yields the trajectory of the particle. Note that (2–15) becomes identical to (2–5) if we put

$$\frac{n(x)}{n_0} = \frac{v(x)}{v_0}, \tag{2–17}$$

or, making use of (2–16),

$$\frac{[n(x)]^2}{n_0^2} = 1 + 2\,\frac{U_0 - U(x)}{mv_0^2}. \qquad (2\text{–}18)$$

Thus, with a given refracting medium whose index of refraction is defined by the function $n(x)$, we can always associate a field of force, described by the function $U(x)$, in such a way that the paths of the rays in the refracting medium are identical to the trajectories of the material particles in the field of force.

The discussion above is an illustration of the far-reaching similarity that exists between the problem of tracing rays in a medium with variable index of refraction and that of determining the trajectories of material particles in a field of force. The similarity is by no means accidental, and, in fact, was the starting point for the formulation of wave mechanics.

2–4 Fermat's principle. We can state the law of rectilinear propagation of light in a homogeneous medium by saying that light travels from a point A to a point B along the shortest possible path between these two points; that is, along the path that requires the least time, or has the shortest optical length. The laws of reflection and refraction can be similarly formulated; we shall verify this fact with some particular examples.

In Fig. 2–11, a ray goes from A to B after being reflected at D by the plane surface σ. Consider another point E of the reflecting surface, and the path consisting of the two straight segments AE, EB. As we have seen in Section 1–1, the reflected ray DB, when continued backward on the other side of the reflecting surface, passes through a point A' such that A and A' are symmetrically located with respect to the reflecting surface σ. From the figure, we readily recognize the validity of the following relations:

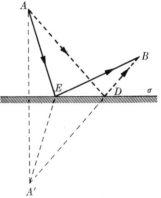

$$\overline{A'E} + \overline{EB} > \overline{A'B},$$

$$\overline{A'E} + \overline{EB} = \overline{AE} + \overline{EB},$$

$$\overline{A'B} = \overline{A'D} + \overline{DB} = \overline{AD} + \overline{DB},$$

from which we obtain

$$\overline{AE} + \overline{EB} > \overline{AD} + \overline{DB};$$

thus we have shown that the path followed by the light in going from A

Fig. 2–11. Application of Fermat's principle to reflection at a plane surface.

to B is shorter than any other path connecting the same two points and touching the reflecting surface.

The situation for the case of refraction is illustrated in Fig. 2–12, which shows two media with indices of refraction n_1, n_2, separated by the plane surface σ. Suppose that a light ray from point A in the first medium to point B in the second medium passes through the point D of σ. The optical length of the path is, by definition,

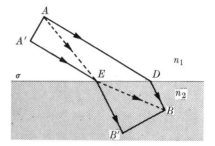

Fig. 2–12. Application of Fermat's principle to refraction at a plane surface.

$$l = n_1\overline{AD} + n_2\overline{DB}.$$

Consider now a different path between A and B, such as AEB. The optical length of this path is

$$l' = n_1\overline{AE} + n_2\overline{EB},$$

and we want to prove that $l < l'$. For this purpose we focus our attention on the incident plane wave front passing through the point A; let A' be its intersection with a ray paralell to AD and passing through E. Similarly, let B' be the intersection of the refracted wave front passing through B, with the ray parallel to DB and passing through E. As we have seen in Section 2–2, the optical distance between the two wave surfaces AA' and BB' is the same whether measured along the ray ADB or $A'EB'$; therefore

$$n_1\overline{AD} + n_2\overline{DB} = n_1\overline{A'E} + n_2\overline{EB'}.$$

On the other hand, it is obvious that

$$\overline{AE} > \overline{A'E}; \quad \overline{EB} > \overline{EB'},$$

and therefore

$$n_1\overline{AD} + n_2\overline{DB} < n_1\overline{AE} + n_2\overline{EB},$$

or

$$l < l'.$$

Thus the path of the light ray is again that with the smallest optical length, although in this case not necessarily the one with the smallest geometrical length.

We conclude that whether it is propagated through a homogeneous medium, reflected at a plane surface, or refracted at a plane surface, light follows the path of minimum optical length. These are special examples of a general principle of geometrical optics known as *Fermat's principle*, which states that in all cases (including reflection and refraction at curved surfaces, and propagation in nonhomogeneous media), light traveling from one fixed point to another traverses a path whose optical length is either a minimum or a maximum compared with neighboring paths.

In more rigorous language, the above statement means that the optical distances between two points, measured first along the actual path traversed by the light and next along another path which is everywhere infinitely close to it, differ by an infinitesimal quantity of a higher order than the separation between the two paths. Mathematically, Fermat's principle is expressed by the equation

$$\delta \int nds = 0,$$

which can be proved to be equivalent to the differential equation for the light ray (Eq. 2-13). We shall omit this proof; however, we shall illustrate by the

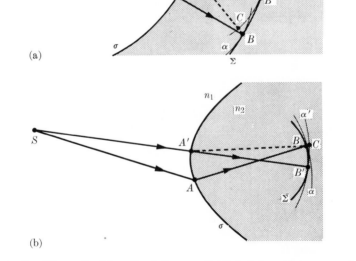

Fɪɢ. 2-13. The optical length of the ray SAB is (a) a minimum and (b) a maximum.

following example the close relationship between Fermat's principle and the Huygens construction.

Consider the refraction of light from a point source S at the curved boundary surface σ between two media of indices of refraction n_1 and n_2 (Fig. 2–13). As the various points of σ, such as A and A', are reached by the incident wave, they become centers of secondary wavelets whose envelope Σ at a given time represents the instantaneous position of the refracted wave front. Let B and B' be the points of contact between Σ and the secondary wavelets α and α' centered at A and A', respectively. SAB and $SA'B'$ are actual rays whose optical lengths are equal. Let C be the intersection of $A'B$ with α'. Then $\overline{A'C} = \overline{A'B'}$, and we have

$$(n_1\overline{SA} + n_2\overline{AB}) - (n_1\overline{SA'} + n_2\overline{A'B}) = (n_1\overline{SA} + n_2\overline{AB}) - (n_1\overline{SA'}) + (n_2\overline{A'B'})$$

$$- (n_2\overline{A'B} - n_2\overline{A'C}) = \mp n_2\overline{CB}.$$

We conclude that $n_2\overline{CB}$ represents the difference between the optical lengths of the paths SAB and $SA'B$. This difference can be negative (Fig. 2–13a) or positive (Fig. 2–13b). In either case, since the wavelet α' is tangent to Σ at B', $\overline{CB}$ is an infinitesimal distance of higher order than $\overline{AA'}$. Hence the ratio $n_2\overline{CB}/\overline{AA'}$ goes to zero as A' approaches A.

2–5 Real and virtual images. The eye "sees" a luminous point when part of the spherical wave emitted by this point enters the eye (see Section 2–15). It sometimes happens that a portion of a spherical wave diverging from a point source S, after undergoing a certain number of reflections and refractions, is changed into a portion of another spherical wave

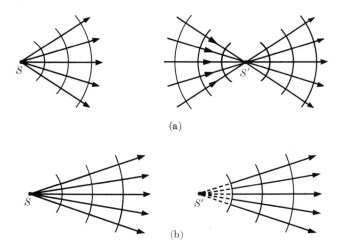

Fig. 2–14. Formation of (a) a real image and (b) a virtual image.

centered at a different point S'. If the wave is concave, it will converge to S' and then diverge again (Fig. 2–14a); an eye receiving the divergent wave will "see" a point source at S', and if we place a screen through S', a luminous point will appear on it. The apparent source at S' is called the *real image* of the point source at S. On the other hand, the wave centered at S' may be convex (Fig. 2–14b), in which case the eye will still "see" a point source located at the center S' of the divergent wave, but nowhere in space will the light wave converge to a point. In this case, the apparent source at S' is called the *virtual image* of the point source S.

If we wish to speak of rays instead of wave surfaces, we say that an optical system forms an image whenever it changes a bundle of rays diverging from or converging to a point S into another bundle of rays passing through a different point S'. The image is real if the rays emerging from the optical system form a convergent beam, virtual if they form a divergent beam.

We can use the principles stated in Section 2–2 to derive some obvious but important facts about the formation of real images. From the principle of optical reversibility, it follows that if a point source at S (Fig. 2–15) has a real image at S', then a point source at S' has a real image at S; two points such as S and S' are said to be *optically conjugate*. Since we can regard the point source at S and its image at S' as two spherical wave fronts of infinitely small radii, we conclude from the second principle stated in Section 2–2 that the optical lengths of all rays connecting S with S' are equal and, further, that if Σ is any position of the wave front intermediate between S and S', the optical lengths of all rays connecting Σ with S' are equal.

If the source at S is not a point source but has finite dimensions (Fig. 2–16), we define its image to be the ensemble of the point images, such as C', corresponding to all the points, such as C, of the source. Such an image can be real or virtual; in general, its size and shape will be different from those of the source. In the sections which follow we shall investigate the characteristics of the images formed by optical systems of various types.

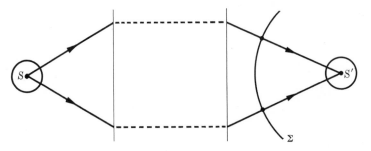

FIG. 2–15. The optical lengths of all rays from S to S' are equal.

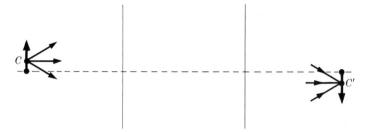

FIG. 2–16. Image of an extended object.

2–6 Formation of images by plane, parabolic, elliptical, and hyperbolic mirrors. We begin by considering the reflection of a spherical wave by a plane mirror (Fig. 2–17). Applying the method of Section 2–1, we find that the reflected wave is also spherical, and that the centers S and S' of the incident and reflected waves are symmetrically located with respect to the mirror. Thus *a plane mirror forms a virtual image of a point source located anywhere in front of the mirror.* If a point source S describes a figure of arbitrary shape ST, the image S' describes an identical figure $S'T'$, where, however, left and right are interchanged. These results are identical to those obtained in Section 1–1 by considering the reflection of rays diverging from a point source.

We consider next the reflection of a plane wave incident upon a concave mirror in the shape of a paraboloid of revolution (Fig. 2–18). Let us assume that the incident wave travels in the direction of the axis of the paraboloid; it is then easy to show that the reflected wave is spherical and converges toward the focus F. To prove this statement, we recall that there exists a plane Π perpendicular to the axis of a paraboloid, such that

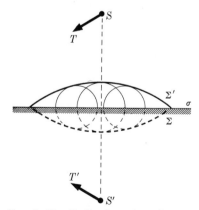

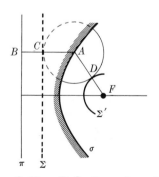

FIG. 2–17. Reflection of a spherical wave by a plane mirror.

FIG. 2–18. Reflection of a plane wave by a parabolic mirror.

each point of the paraboloid is equidistant from this plane and from the focus F. Let Σ be the position which the wave front would occupy at the time t if the mirror were not there, and consider a secondary wavelet with center at A, tangent to Σ at C and intersecting the segment AF at D. Let B be the intersection of AC with Π. From the property of the paraboloid stated above, it follows that $\overline{AB} = \overline{AF}$; since obviously $\overline{AC} = \overline{AD}$, we conclude that $\overline{DF} = \overline{CB}$. Now consider the spherical surface Σ', centered at F, whose radius is equal to the distance $\overline{CB}$ of Σ from Π. The surface Σ' is tangent at D to the wavelet centered at A; it is also tangent to all other secondary wavelets originating from the various points of the reflecting surface σ. Therefore Σ' represents the reflected wave front.

We may express this result by saying that rays parallel to the axis of a concave parabolic mirror are reflected as rays passing through its focus. In other words, *at its focus, the parabolic mirror produces the real image of a point source located at a very great distance along its axis.* For this reason, parabolic mirrors are used in the construction of astronomical telescopes. From the principle of optical reversibility it follows that a parabolic mirror reflects rays diverging from a point source located at its focus into rays parallel to its axis. This property is used in the construction of searchlights.

In a similar way, it can be shown that a concave mirror in the shape of an ellipsoid of revolution around the major axis changes a spherical wave diverging from one of its foci, F_1, into a spherical wave converging toward the other focus, F_2 (Fig. 2–19). In other words, *a point source located at one of the foci of an elliptical mirror has a real image at the other focus.* The proof is based on the fact that the sum of the distances from the two foci is a constant for every point of an ellipse. The details are left to the reader.

Finally, we state without proof that *a convex mirror in the shape of a hyperboloid of revolution around the axis passing through the foci produces at the inner focus F_2 a virtual image of a point source located at the outer focus F_1* (Fig. 2–20).

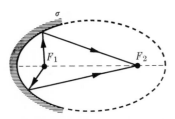

FIG. 2–19. Elliptical mirror.

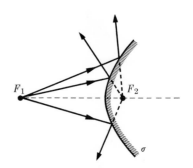

Fig. 2–20. Hyperbolic mirror.

2–7 Spherical mirrors. Parabolic, elliptical, and hyperbolic mirrors produce an image only if the point source is located at one or the other of two given conjugate points. They differ in this respect from the plane mirror, which produces images of arbitrarily located sources. In a rigorous sense, only a plane mirror has more than one pair of conjugate points; thus only a plane mirror can produce an image of an extended object. However, in certain circumstances, a curved mirror of sufficiently small dimensions will reflect a portion of a spherical wave originating from any point within a limited region of space into a wave that is still approximately spherical. For all practical purposes, the mirror is then capable of producing images of extended objects.

Of the various types of curved mirrors, spherical mirrors are the most important from a practical standpoint; in the next few sections we shall investigate in some detail the images formed by these mirrors. Consider first the case in which the reflecting surface σ is a *large portion* of a sphere. In Fig. 2–21, let S be the position of the source, O the center of curvature of the mirror (that is, the center of the sphere of which the surface of the mirror is a part), and A the intersection of the line SO with the surface of the mirror. The construction of the reflected wave Σ' is shown in the figure. With the exception of the case in which the source S is located at the center of curvature O, the reflected wave is *not* spherical; in other words, the reflected rays will not intersect at a common point. However, if the reflected wave is concave, the rays will converge before they diverge again, and there will be a surface on which the reflected light reaches a maximum of concentration. This surface is called the *caustic*.

The caustic may be more precisely defined as follows. Consider the intersection of the surface σ of the mirror with a plane containing the point source at S and the center of curvature O (Fig. 2–22). Assume that the portion of spherical surface σ is symmetric about the straight line SO which intersects σ at A. The reflected wave is then likewise a surface of revolution about this line. Now consider two rays in the plane of the drawing incident upon the surface of the mirror at two points P and P', separated by a very small distance. The two corresponding reflected rays intersect at a point C. All rays reflected at points of the mirror intermediate between P and P' will intersect at practically the

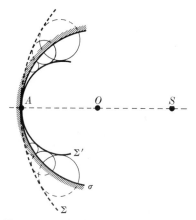

FIG. 2–21. Reflection of a spherical wave by a spherical mirror.

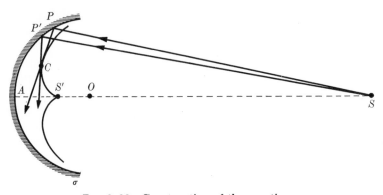

FIG. 2–22. Construction of the caustic.

same point C. (Rigorously speaking, these rays pass within a distance ϵ of C that is an infinitesimal quantity of higher order than the distance $\overline{PP'}$; i.e., the ratio of ϵ to $\overline{PP'}$ tends to zero as P' approaches P.) As the pair of neighboring points PP' is moved along the arc representing the intersection of σ with the plane of the drawing, the point C describes a curve with a singular point at S'.* The caustic is the surface of revolution obtained by rotating this curve about the straight line SA.

We now proceed to investigate what happens when the reflecting surface is limited to a *small portion* of a sphere. For this purpose, we imagine Fig. 2–22 to be rotated through a small angle $\Delta\varphi$ about the line SA. The small arc PP' traces out a "rectangular" element of the spherical surface (Fig. 2–23). The dimensions of the rectangle are $\overline{PP'}$ and $y\,\Delta\varphi$, where y represents the distance of P from SA. At the same time, the point C describes a small arc of a circle, which, for practical purposes, may be regarded as a straight segment perpendicular to the plane of Fig. 2–22. If z is the distance of C from SA, the length of this segment is $z\,\Delta\varphi$. The rays reflected by the rectangular element generated by PP' intersect along this segment. Suppose that only this small portion of the spherical surface is reflecting; then, on a screen passing through C, there will appear a short bright straight segment of length $z\,\Delta\varphi$. As the element of reflecting surface moves toward the point A, the length of this segment decreases toward zero, i.e., the segment reduces to a point. This means that, for practical purposes, a wave reflected from an element of surface close to the axis SA may be regarded as spherical. We express this conclusion by saying that *a spherical mirror will form a point image of a point source if*

---

*This curve may be alternatively defined as the geometrical locus of the centers of curvature of the line along which the reflected wave front Σ' intersects the plane of the figure (see Fig. 2–21).

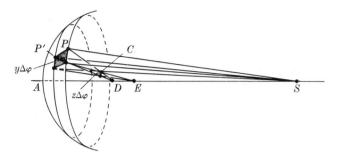

FIG. 2–23. Reflection of rays from a point source by a spherical surface.

the dimensions of the mirror are small compared with its radius of curvature, and if the source is so located that reflection occurs at nearly perpendicular incidence. The image lies at the point occupied by the cusp of the caustic surface previously described.

2–8 Construction of the images produced by spherical mirrors. In what follows we assume that the conditions for the production of an image are satisfied, and proceed to determine the position of this image.

Suppose first that the mirror is concave, and that the point source lies at S, between the center of curvature O and the reflecting surface (Figs. 2–24, 2–25). In this case, the first point of the mirror to be reached by the incident wave is A, the point of intersection of the line SO with the surface of the mirror. At some later time, the wave will have reached all the points in a region of the mirror bounded by a circle of a certain radius $h = \overline{HK}$; this circle is the intersection of the spherical surface Σ (which would represent the wave front if the mirror were absent) with the mirror σ and also with the surface Σ' (which represents the reflected wave front). If h is sufficiently small, we may consider Σ' to be part of the surface of a sphere, as explained in the last section. The center, S', of this sphere is the image of S, and S, S', and O are clearly collinear. Depending on the position of the source, Σ' may be concave (Fig. 2–24) or convex (Fig. 2–25), and hence the image may be real or virtual. In either case the following equations hold:

$$\overline{BK} \cdot (2\overline{SB} - \overline{BK}) = h^2,$$

$$\overline{AK} \cdot (2\overline{OA} - \overline{AK}) = h^2,$$

$$\overline{B'K} \cdot (2\overline{S'B'} - \overline{B'K}) = h^2,$$

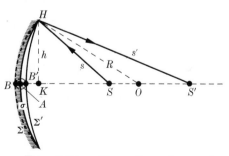

FIG. 2–24. Formation of a real image by a concave spherical mirror.

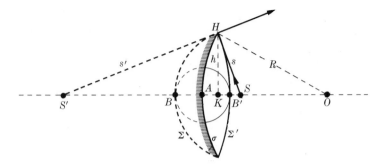

FIG. 2–25. Formation of a virtual image by a concave spherical mirror.

where B and B' are the intersections of Σ and Σ' with OA [these equations are a consequence of the "sagitta theorem"; see Appendix 1(d)].

We have assumed that the mirror is a small fraction of a spherical surface. If we further assume that S is not too close to the mirror, the distances $\overline{BK}$, $\overline{AK}$, and $\overline{B'K}$ are very small compared with $\overline{SB}$, $\overline{OA}$, and $\overline{S'B'}$. Therefore the above equations can be written, to a sufficiently good approximation, as

$$2\overline{SB} \cdot \overline{BK} = h^2,$$

$$2\overline{OA} \cdot \overline{AK} = h^2, \qquad (2\text{--}19)$$

$$2\overline{S'B'} \cdot \overline{B'K} = h^2.$$

Since $\overline{AB} = \overline{AB'}$, we find that in the case of a real image (Fig. 2–24), the following equation holds:

$$\overline{BK} + \overline{B'K} = \overline{AK} + \overline{AB} + \overline{AK} - \overline{AB'} = 2\overline{AK}, \qquad (2\text{--}20)$$

while in the case of a virtual image (Fig. 2–25), we have

$$\overline{BK} - \overline{B'K} = \overline{AK} + \overline{AB} - \overline{AB'} + \overline{AK} = 2\overline{AK}. \qquad (2\text{--}21)$$

If we now denote by R the radius of curvature $\overline{OA}$ of the mirror, by s the radius $\overline{SB}$ of the incident wave, and by s' the radius $\overline{S'B'}$ of the reflected wave (to be considered positive or negative depending on whether the reflected wave is concave or convex), we find, after taking Eq. (2–19) into consideration, that both (2–20) and (2–21) yield

$$\frac{1}{s} + \frac{1}{s'} = \frac{2}{R}. \qquad (2\text{--}22)$$

Since the distances of B and B' from the mirror are very small compared with s and s', we can *consider s and s' to be the distances of the source and the image from the surface of the mirror.*

We can use Eq. (2–22) to determine how the position of the image varies with the position of the source. Thus for $s = R$, (2–22) yields $s' = R$, which means that, as we already know, the rays diverging from the center of curvature of the mirror are reflected back to the same point. As s decreases from R to $R/2$, s' remains positive and increases without limit; that is, the image is *real* and moves away from O along the line SO. For $s = R/2$, we obtain $s' = \infty$, which means that rays coming from a source located halfway between the spherical mirror and its center of curvature are reflected by the mirror as a parallel beam. From the principle of optical reversibility, we conclude that a concave spherical mirror reflects a parallel beam of light into a bundle of rays converging to a point F halfway between the center of curvature and the surface of the mirror (Fig. 2–26). This point is called the *focal point* of the mirror corresponding to the given direction of the incident beam; its distance from the surface of the mirror is called the *focal length*. Denoting this distance by f, we have

$$f = \frac{R}{2},\qquad\qquad(2\text{–}23)$$

and we can rewrite Eq. (2–22) as follows:

$$\frac{1}{s} + \frac{1}{s'} = \frac{1}{f}.\qquad\qquad(2\text{–}24)$$

For $s < R/2$, (2–22) yields $s' < 0$. In this case the image is virtual, i.e., the reflected wave is convex.

In deriving Eq. (2–22), we have assumed that $s < R$. However, the principle of reversibility and the symmetry of (2–22) with respect to s and s' ensures the validity of this equation for all values of s. Indeed, each point of the line FO has a conjugate point on the straight line segment extending from O to infinity, and vice versa.

Equation (2–22) is also valid in the case of *virtual objects*, i.e., when the spherical wave incident upon the mirror is concave. The length s again represents the distance from A of the center of the incident wave, but it must now be taken with the negative sign.

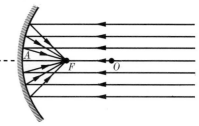

Fig. 2–26. Real focal point of a concave spherical mirror.

It can be shown also that (2–22) is
valid for convex mirrors if the radius
of curvature R is taken to be negative. In this case, a negative value
of s' is obtained for any positive
value of s. Physically, this means
that a convex spherical mirror always forms a virtual image of a real
object. In particular, a convex
mirror has a *negative* focal length;
i.e., its focal point is located behind
the surface of the mirror. This is the
point from which the reflected rays

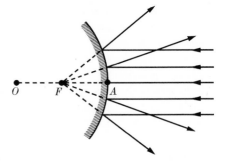

Fig. 2–27. Virtual focal point of a
convex spherical mirror.

diverge when the incident rays are parallel to the axis (Fig. 2–27).

As we have already pointed out, the source S and its image S' are collinear
with the center of curvature O of the mirror (see Figs. 2–24 and 2–25).
As the source moves from S to T on the surface of a sphere centered at O,
the image moves from S' to T' on the surface of a second sphere likewise
centered at O. Thus a two-dimensional object lying on the first sphere
will have as its image a two-dimensional figure lying on the second sphere
(Fig. 2–28). The condition for the production of sharp images stated at
the end of the preceding section requires that the reflecting surface σ, the
object ST, and consequently the image $S'T'$, lie within a double cone of
small aperture with apex at O (Fig. 2–28). For practical purposes we may
regard the object and its image as plane figures, perpendicular to the line
OA. We thus conclude that the image of an object of small dimensions
which lies in a plane perpendicular to OA and close to this line is situated
in another plane, likewise perpendicular to OA. The object and the image
are similar, although, in general, of different dimensions. The ratio of the
linear dimensions of the image to those of the object is called the *lateral
magnification*; we see from Fig. 2–28 that the lateral magnification equals
the ratio of the distances of the image and of the object from O.

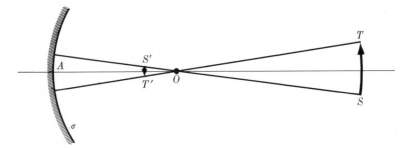

Fig. 2–28. Formation of the image of an extended object by a spherical mirror.

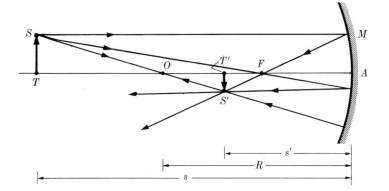

Fɪɢ. 2–29. Graphical construction of the image formed by a spherical mirror.

To conclude this section, we demonstrate in Fig. 2–29 a simple graphical construction that can be used to find the image. Consider a point source at S, a small distance from the line OF which connects the focus F and the center of curvature O. Draw the following three incident rays: (a) SO, passing through the center of curvature of the mirror, (b) SM, parallel to OF, (c) SF, passing through the focal point. Making use of the geometrical properties of the center of curvature and the focal point, we can construct the three corresponding reflected rays, as follows: (a) SO is reflected upon itself, (b) SM is reflected as a ray which passes through the focal point F, (c) SF is reflected as a ray parallel to OF. The image of the point source is the common point of intersection of the three reflected rays. If, instead of a point source, we have an extended source such as ST, perpendicular to OA, we can repeat this process for the other points of the source and obtain the extended image $S'T'$, likewise perpendicular to OA. For the situation shown in Fig. 2–29, we see that the image is real and inverted, and has a lateral magnification of less than 1.

2–9 Aberrations of spherical mirrors. The results of the preceding section apply only to the case where the dimensions of the mirror are small compared with its radius of curvature, and consequently with its focal length. For spherical mirrors which are circular in outline, we define the *relative aperture* to be the ratio of the diameter of the circle to the focal length of the mirror; we can then reword the condition above to state that a spherical mirror will produce a sharp image of a point source only if it has a small relative aperture. In addition, the source must lie near the line QO connecting the center Q of the mirror with the center of curvature O (Fig. 2–30). In this section we shall describe briefly some of the aberrations which are observed when these conditions are not fulfilled.

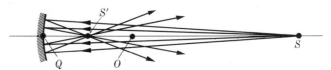

FIG. 2–30. Source on the axis of a spherical mirror of small aperture.

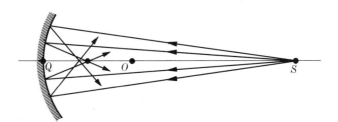

FIG. 2–31. Source on the axis of a spherical mirror of large aperture.

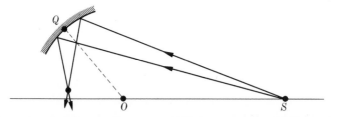

FIG. 2–32. Source off the axis of a spherical mirror of small aperture.

If the mirror has a large relative aperture, the caustic will no longer reduce to a single point; instead, a spot of diffuse illumination with a bright point at its center will appear on a screen through the cusp of the caustic. This unwanted effect is called *spherical aberration*. If the source lies on the line QO (Fig. 2–31), the illuminated disk is circular. If the source does not lie on this line, the disk has an elongated shape, and the effect is called *coma*. In spite of the fact that a spherical mirror of large aperture does not form sharp images, the images will appear sharp (although distorted) to an observer looking into such a mirror. The reason is that the pupil of the eye limits the light received from each point of the source to a narrow pencil, so that only a small fraction of the total surface of the mirror is actually used to form the image of any given point.

If the mirror has a small relative aperture, but the source is located far from the line QO (Fig. 2–32), an aberration called *astigmatism* is observed. As we have already seen, on a screen at the proper location (through the point C in Fig. 2–22), the mirror will image a point source as a short straight segment perpendicular to the plane containing the source and the line QO. It can be shown that as the screen is moved away from the mirror, the image changes from a line segment to a small circle, and then to another line segment perpendicular to the first.

2–10 Image formation by refraction at plane and spherical surfaces. We stated in Section 1–9 that a plane wave incident upon a plane surface of separation between two media gives rise to a plane refracted wave. However, the refraction of a spherical wave at a plane surface does not produce a spherical wave; we can perceive underwater objects distinctly only because the portion of the refracted wave which enters the pupil of the eye is such a small fraction of the total wave front that it is indistinguishable from a portion of a sphere. In the case of spherical boundary surfaces, a plane or spherical wave in the first medium does not, in general, produce a plane or spherical wave in the second medium.* The refracted wave may be concave or convex, depending on the position of the source, the curvature of the boundary surface, and the indices of refraction of the two media. A concave refracted wave will give rise to a caustic similar to that produced by a spherical mirror of large aperture.

Suppose, however, that the incident wave is suitably limited, so that all incident and refracted rays form small angles with the line connecting the source with the center of curvature of the refracting surface. We then find that the refracted wave is practically a sphere, and we can take the image of the source to be at the center of this sphere. The image can be real (Fig. 2–33) or virtual (Fig. 2–34). To determine its position, we proceed in much the same way as for the case of reflection. Consider, at a given instant, the refracted wave front Σ' and the surface Σ on which the

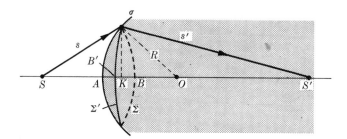

Fig. 2–33. Formation of a real image by refraction at a spherical surface.

---

*It can be shown that for every spherical surface separating two media of given indices of refraction, there are only two points, called *aplanatic points*, such that a spherical wave centered at one of the points is changed by refraction into a spherical wave centered at the other point (see Problem 2–23). In the limiting case of a plane boundary surface, the two aplanatic points are at infinity.

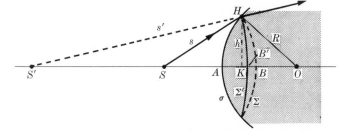

FIG. 2–34. Formation of a virtual image by refraction at a spherical surface.

incident wave front would lie if the refracting surface did not exist and the medium were homogeneous throughout.

The surface Σ is spherical, with its center at S; Σ' can also be considered as a spherical surface, and its center S' represents the position of the image. The two surfaces Σ and Σ' intersect along a circle of radius $h = \overline{HK}$ lying on the refracting surface σ. Let A, B, and B' be the intersections of σ, Σ, and Σ' with the straight line connecting the source at S with the center of curvature O of the refracting surface σ. The following equations then hold:

$$\frac{\overline{AB}}{\overline{AB'}} = \frac{n_2}{n_1}, \tag{2–25}$$

$$\overline{BK} \cdot (2\overline{SB} - \overline{BK}) = h^2,$$
$$\overline{AK} \cdot (2\overline{OA} - \overline{AK}) = h^2,$$
$$\overline{B'K} \cdot (2\overline{S'B'} - \overline{B'K}) = h^2.$$

If $\overline{BK}$, $\overline{AK}$, and $\overline{B'K}$ are small compared with $\overline{SB}$, $\overline{OA}$, and $\overline{S'B'}$, respectively, the last three equations become

$$2\overline{SB} \cdot \overline{BK} = h^2,$$
$$2\overline{OA} \cdot \overline{AK} = h^2, \tag{2–26}$$
$$2\overline{S'B'} \cdot \overline{B'K} = h^2.$$

We see from Figs. 2–33 and 2–34 that

$$\overline{AB} = \overline{AK} + \overline{BK}.$$

Moreover, if the refracted wave is concave (Fig. 2–33), we have

$$\overline{AB'} = \overline{AK} - \overline{B'K},$$

whereas if the refracted wave is convex (Fig. 2–34), we have

$$\overline{AB'} = \overline{AK} + \overline{B'K}.$$

In either case, the following equations hold:

$$\overline{AB} = \frac{h^2}{2}\left(\frac{1}{R} + \frac{1}{s}\right), \qquad \overline{AB'} = \frac{h^2}{2}\left(\frac{1}{R} - \frac{1}{s'}\right),$$

where $R = \overline{OA}$ is the radius of curvature of the refracting surface, $s = \overline{SB}$ is the radius of the incident wave, and $s' = \overline{S'B'}$ is the radius of the refracted wave, considered as positive if the wave is concave and negative if it is convex. Making use of Eq. (2–25), we then obtain

$$n_1 \frac{h^2}{2}\left(\frac{1}{R} + \frac{1}{s}\right) = n_2 \frac{h^2}{2}\left(\frac{1}{R} - \frac{1}{s'}\right),$$

or

$$\frac{n_1}{s} + \frac{n_2}{s'} = \frac{n_2 - n_1}{R}. \qquad (2\text{–}27)$$

Since the distances of B and B' from the point A of the refracting surface are very small compared with s and s', we may consider s and s' to be the distances of the source and of the image from the refracting surface σ.

Equation (2–27) enables us to find the position of the image for any position of the source; the image is real when s' is positive, and virtual when s' is negative. This equation applies also to the case of an incident wave which is concave, i.e., when the source is virtual. In this case the distance s must be taken to be negative.

In deriving Eq. (2–27), we have implicitly assumed that the refracting surface σ is convex toward the source S. The equation is also valid for a concave refracting surface if the radius of curvature R is considered to be negative.

A plane wave incident from the first medium in a direction parallel to the line OA is changed by refraction into a spherical wave with center at a point F_2 on this line. F_2 is called the *second focal point* corresponding to the given direction. If the refracted wave is concave, so that it converges toward F_2 (Fig. 2–35a), the focal point is *real*; if the refracted wave is convex (Fig. 2–35b), the focal point is *virtual*. Similarly, a plane wave incident from the second medium in a direction parallel to the line AO becomes, after refraction, a spherical wave with its center at a point F_1 on this line. F_1 is called the *first focal point*. The distances f_1 and f_2 of F_1 and F_2 from the refracting surface are called the *first* and *second focal*

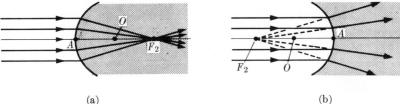

(a)   (b)

FIG. 2–35. (a) Real and (b) virtual focal point of a spherical refracting surface.

lengths, respectively. If we put $s = \infty$ and $s' = f_2$ in Eq. (2–27), we obtain the following expression for the second focal length:

$$f_2 = \frac{n_2}{n_2 - n_1} R. \tag{2–28}$$

Similarly, the expression for the first focal length is

$$f_1 = \frac{n_1}{n_2 - n_1} R. \tag{2–29}$$

Therefore $f_1/f_2 = n_1/n_2$. Note that f_1 and f_2 always have the same sign, so that either both focal points are real, or both are virtual. In the former case the refracting surface is called *convergent,* in the latter case *divergent.* With the help of (2–28) and (2–29) we may rewrite (2–27) as follows:

$$\frac{f_1}{s} + \frac{f_2}{s'} = 1. \tag{2–30}$$

If $R = \infty$, that is, if the boundary is a plane surface, (2–27) yields

$$\frac{s'}{s} = -\frac{n_2}{n_1}. \tag{2–31}$$

For example, since the index of refraction of water relative to air is about $\frac{4}{3}$, we conclude from Eq. (2–31) that an observer looking perpendicularly through a water surface will see an immersed object at a depth equal to about $\frac{3}{4}$ the actual depth. The minus sign on the right side of (2–31) means that in the case here considered the image of a real object is always virtual, i.e., that refraction through a plane surface cannot change a divergent wave into a convergent wave.

Returning to the general case of a spherical refracting surface, we see from Figs. 2–33 and 2–34 that the source at S, the image at S', and the center of curvature O of the refracting surface are collinear. If the point source describes a figure ST on the surface of a sphere with its center at O, the image will describe a figure $S'T'$ on another spherical surface concentric with the first (Fig. 2–36). As in the case of the spherical mirror dis-

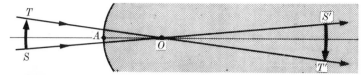

FIG. 2–36. Formation of the image of an extended object by a spherical refracting surface.

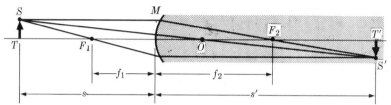

FIG. 2–37. Graphical construction of the image formed by a spherical refracting surface.

cussed in Section 2–8, the image is everywhere sharp only if ST, $S'T'$, and the refracting surface σ lie within a double cone of small aperture with apex at O. Hence we may regard ST and $S'T'$ as plane figures perpendicular to any straight line such as AO which connects a point A of the refracting surface with the center of curvature O. We also recognize that the object and its image are geometrically similar even though, in general, they are of different dimensions, and we find that the lateral magnification equals the ratio of the distances from O of the image and the object.

As in the case of a reflecting surface, we can determine the position of the image formed by a refracting surface by means of a simple geometric construction, once the positions of the focal points are known. Let F_1 and F_2 be the focal points corresponding to a given direction, and consider a point source at S in the first medium, near the straight line passing through F_1, F_2, and O (Fig. 2–37). From the properties of F_1, F_2, and O, it follows that (a) *the ray SO directed toward the center of curvature of the refracting surface traverses this surface without deflection*, (b) *the ray SM parallel to F_1F_2 is refracted into a ray passing through F_2*, (c) *the ray SF_1 passing through F_1 is refracted into a ray parallel to F_1F_2*. The intersection of any two of the three refracted rays determines the position of the image.

2–11 Some general properties of optical systems. Let us now consider an optical system composed of a sequence of media of different indices of refraction separated by spherical surfaces. We shall assume that the centers of curvature of these surfaces all lie on the same straight line, called the *axis* of the system, and we shall further assume that the beam of light is limited by suitable diaphragms so that the system is traversed only by *paraxial rays* (i.e., rays that lie close to the axis and nearly parallel to it).

Then, for all practical purposes, an incident spherical wave remains spherical as it passes through the successive refracting surfaces, and it emerges from the system as another spherical wave whose center is the (real or virtual) image of the source produced by the optical system.

The position of the image may be determined by the following procedure. Given the position of the source in the first medium, we find the position of the image produced by the first refracting surface, using the method of Section 2–10. We then treat this image as if it were a source placed in the second medium, and construct the corresponding image produced by the second refracting surface. We repeat this process with each refracting surface in turn. Note that some of the secondary "sources" may be virtual; i.e., the wave front may be *concave* at some of the refracting surfaces. As already pointed out, Eq. (2–27) still applies in this case, provided that the distance s of the source from the refracting surface is taken with the negative sign.

In practice, it is not necessary to use the cumbersome procedure outlined above whenever we want to determine the image of a point source. Indeed, if we consider only paraxial rays, the optical properties of the system are completely determined by the position of four points along the axis, called the two *focal points* and the two *principal points*.

The two focal points are defined as follows. Consider a plane wave incident from the first medium in the direction of the optic axis. The wave will emerge from the system as a spherical wave, whose center is the *second focal point* F_2 of the optical system. This point may be alternatively defined as the real or virtual image of a point source situated in the first medium at an infinite distance along the optic axis. Similarly, we define as the *first focal point* F_1 the real or virtual image of a point source situated in the last medium at an infinite distance along the axis. The planes through F_1 and F_2 perpendicular to the axis are called *focal planes*.

The two principal points are defined as follows (Fig. 2–38). Consider an arbitrary straight line BB' parallel to the axis. A ray originating in the first medium and incident on the optical system in a direction parallel to BB' emerges from the system as a ray coplanar with BB' and passing through the second focal point F_2. Let Q_2 be the intersection of this ray (or of its continuation) with the line BB'. Similarly, a ray originating in the second medium and incident on the system along the line $B'B$ emerges as a ray passing through the first focal point F_1. Let Q_1 be the intersection of this ray (or of its continuation) with the line $B'B$. Through Q_1 and Q_2 construct the planes perpendicular to the axis; let P_1 and P_2 be their intersections with the axis. The two planes are called the *principal planes*, and the points P_1 and P_2 the *principal points*. The distance $f_1 = \overline{F_1 P_1}$ from the first focal point to the first principal point is called the *first focal length*, and the distance $f_2 = \overline{F_2 P_2}$ from the second focal point to the second principal point is the *second focal length*.

We can easily prove that the points Q_1 and Q_2 are mutually conjugate. Consider a bundle of rays incident from the left upon the optical system, all passing through the point Q_1. The rays will form a convergent beam if the point Q_1 lies to the right of the first refracting surface, as

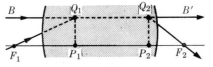

Fig. 2–38. The two focal points (F_1, F_2) and the two principal points (P_1, P_2) of an optical system.

shown in Fig. 2–38, or a divergent beam if Q_1 lies to the left of the first refracting surface; in either case they will emerge from the system as rays passing through a single point, which is the (real or virtual) image of Q_1. To find the position of this image, it is sufficient to find the point of intersection of any two emergent rays. We know that the incident ray BQ_1 emerges from the system along the line Q_2F_2 and that the incident ray F_1Q_1 emerges along the line Q_2B'. These two emergent rays intersect at Q_2; hence Q_2 is the image of Q_1, that is, Q_1 and Q_2 are optically conjugate points. In general, a point lying in the first principal plane has an image lying in the second principal plane; the point and its image are coplanar with the axis and equidistant from it.

Suppose now that the focal points and the principal points of an optical system are known; we wish to show that the optical properties of the system are completely determined. Let S be the location of a point source (Fig. 2–39). From S draw two straight lines: one which is parallel to the axis and intersects the first principal plane at Q_1 and the second principal plane at Q_2, and another which passes through F_1 and intersects the first principal plane at R_1. From R_1 draw a straight line parallel to the axis; let R_2 be its intersection with the second principal plane. From Q_2 draw a straight line through F_2. The image of the source at S is located at the intersection S' of the two straight lines Q_2F_2 and R_1R_2, which are obviously coplanar. To recognize the validity of this statement, we need only remember that (a) to any incident ray passing through F_1 and R_1 there corresponds an emergent ray parallel to the axis and passing through R_2 (the image of R_1), and (b) to any incident ray parallel to the axis and passing through Q_1 there corresponds an emergent ray passing through F_2 and through Q_2 (the image of Q_1).

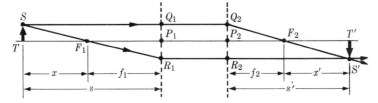

Fig. 2–39. Construction of the image formed by an optical system.

Let us denote by s and s' the distances of S and S' from the first and second principal planes, respectively. From Fig. 2–39 we see that

$$\frac{f_1}{s} = \frac{\overline{P_1 R_1}}{\overline{Q_1 R_1}}, \qquad \frac{f_2}{s'} = \frac{\overline{Q_2 P_2}}{\overline{Q_2 R_2}},$$

and, since $\overline{P_1 R_1} + \overline{Q_2 P_2} = \overline{Q_1 R_1} = \overline{Q_2 R_2}$, we obtain

$$\frac{f_1}{s} + \frac{f_2}{s} = 1. \tag{2–32}$$

If we let x and x' be the distances of S and S' from the first and the second focal planes, respectively, we have

$$s = f_1 + x, \qquad s' = f_2 + x'.$$

Substitution of these expressions for s and s' in Eq. (2–32) yields, after a few simple algebraic transformations,

$$xx' = f_1 f_2. \tag{2–33}$$

This equation is often referred to as *Newton's formula* for the conjugate points.

Equations (2–32) and (2–33) apply also to optical systems containing both reflecting and refracting surfaces; some of these surfaces may be planes perpendicular to the axis.

Single reflecting surfaces (Section 2–8) and single refracting surfaces (Section 2–10) are special cases of the general optical system considered here. In these cases, the two principal planes become coincident, with the plane tangent to the reflecting or refracting surface. Hence the definitions we have previously given for the focal length of a spherical reflecting surface and for the two focal lengths of a spherical refracting surface agree with the more general definition of f_1 and f_2 given in the present section. Note that Eq. (2–32) is formally identical to (2–30), and that it becomes equivalent to (2–24) if we put $f_1 = f_2 = f$. Equation (2–33) applies unchanged to the case of a single refracting surface, and becomes

$$xx' = f^2$$

for the case of a single reflecting surface.

In discussing the properties of an optical system, it is very important to consider the effect of the *diaphragms* that limit the beam of light passing through the system. Even if no external stops are placed in the path of the beam, each refracting or reflecting surface, because of its finite dimensions, acts like a diaphragm.   The presence of diaphragms has two distinct effects. The first is to limit the solid angle subtended at the source by the bundle of rays passing through the system. The diaphragm that controls this solid angle determines what fraction of the light emitted by the source can be transmitted by the system, and thus controls the brightness of the image; it is called the *aperture stop*. The second effect is to limit the field of view, i.e., the dimensions of an object of which the optical system can provide a complete image. The diaphragm that controls the field of view is called the *field stop*. Illustrative examples of the operation of stops will be found in Section 2–15.

2–12 Lenses. A piece of glass or other transparent material bounded by two spherical surfaces (or one plane and one spherical surface) forms an optical system called a *simple lens*.   When the distance between the boundary surfaces is small compared with their radii of curvature, we call the lens *thin*; if this is not true, we call the lens *thick*.

The theory of thin lenses in air is particularly easy to formulate. Let n be the index of refraction of the lens material; the index of refraction of air may be taken as unity. We denote by R_1 and R_2 (Fig. 2–40) the radii of curvature of the two boundary surfaces of the lens, regarded as positive or negative depending upon whether the surfaces are convex or concave toward the direction of arrival of the light wave. Suppose that there is a point source at S, on the axis of the lens (i.e., on the straight line connecting O_1 and O_2, the centers of curvature of the two surfaces). Since the lens is thin, we may consider S to be at the same distance s from both faces, and call s the "distance from the lens." Refraction at the first spherical surface produces an image of the source at the point S'', whose distance s'' from the lens is given by the following special case of Eq. (2–27):

$$\frac{1}{s} + \frac{n}{s''} = \frac{n-1}{R_1}.$$ \hfill (2–34)

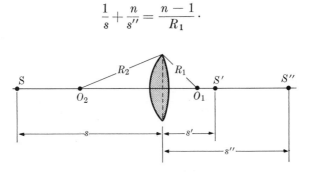

FIG. 2–40. Image formation by a thin lens.

We now treat this first image as if it were a secondary source located at a distance $-s''$ from the surface (note that this source is virtual if the first image is real, and real if the first image is virtual), and consider the image of this source formed by the second spherical surface. This image lies at a distance s' from the lens given by the equation

$$-\frac{n}{s''} + \frac{1}{s'} = \frac{1-n}{R_2}.$$ (2-35)

Combining Eqs. (2-34) and (2-35), we obtain

$$\frac{1}{s} + \frac{1}{s'} = (n-1)\left(\frac{1}{R_1} - \frac{1}{R_2}\right).$$ (2-36)

To determine the focal lengths f_1 and f_2, we let either s or s' go to infinity and solve for the other, obtaining

$$\frac{1}{f_1} = \frac{1}{f_2} = (n-1)\left(\frac{1}{R_1} - \frac{1}{R_2}\right).$$ (2-37)

Thus the two focal points are at the same distance from the lens. If we denote this distance by f, we can rewrite (2-36) as follows:

$$\frac{1}{s} + \frac{1}{s'} = \frac{1}{f}.$$ (2-38)

The quantity $1/f$ is called the *dioptric power* of the lens; if the focal length is expressed in meters, the dioptric power is expressed in *diopters*.

Figure 2-41 illustrates the geometric construction of the image of a point source at S, lying near the axis of a thin lens. The ray SP, parallel to the axis and intersecting the plane of the lens at P, is refracted as the ray PF_2, passing through the second focal point. The ray SF_1, passing through the first focal point and intersecting the plane of the lens at P', is

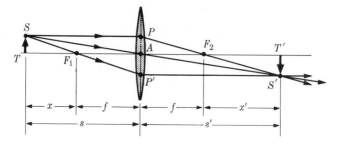

Fig. 2-41. Construction of the image formed by a thin lens.

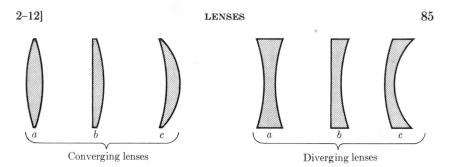

Fig. 2–42. Various kinds of lenses. Converging: (a) double convex, (b) plano-convex, (c) converging meniscus. Diverging: (a) double concave, (b) plano-concave, (c) diverging meniscus.

refracted as a ray passing through P' and parallel to the axis. The two refracted rays intersect at S', the location of the image; it can easily be proved that the straight line SS' passes through the center A of the lens. If we now consider an extended source ST perpendicular to the axis, and its image $S'T'$, likewise perpendicular to the axis, we see that *the lateral magnification equals the ratio of the distances of the image and the object from the lens.* Note that for a thin lens, the two principal planes coincide with the plane of the lens.

Lenses are *converging* or *diverging* depending on whether the focal length is positive or negative; Fig. 2–42 shows the profiles of various converging and diverging lenses. From Eq. (2–38), we see that a diverging lens always gives a virtual image of a real source; a converging lens, however, gives a real or virtual image depending on whether the object is at a distance from the lens greater or smaller than the focal length. For $s = 2f$, Eq. (2–38) yields $s' = 2f = s$. Therefore an object located at a distance from a converging lens equal to twice the focal length has a real image located at a distance also equal to twice the focal length. In this case the image and the object are equal in size. As the object moves from $s = 2f$ to $s = f$, the image moves from $s' = 2f$ to infinity, and becomes progressively larger. As the object moves from $s = 2f$ to $s = \infty$, the image moves from $s' = 2f$ to $s' = f$ and becomes progressively smaller, until it reduces to a point.

The relative aperture of a lens is defined as the diameter divided by the focal length. The theory of thin lenses outlined above is valid only for the case of lenses of small relative aperture, with sources near the axis. If the relative aperture is large, or the source does not lie near the axis, a simple lens will exhibit the same aberrations that affect spherical mirrors (spherical aberration, coma, astigmatism). In addition, unlike mirrors, lenses suffer from *chromatic aberration* (see Section 2–14). Such aberrations can be corrected to a considerable extent, although not completely, by the use of *compound lenses*, i.e., systems of lenses placed one after the other along the path of the light. However, even after the aberrations mentioned above have been corrected, other unwanted effects often remain. Sometimes the image of a plane object lies on a curved surface (*curvature of field*). Sometimes, although the image of a plane object perpendicular to the axis lies in a plane perpendicular to the axis, the object and its image are not geometrically similar figures; for example, the image of a straight line may be a curved line (*distortion*). The detailed study of aberrations and of the various methods used for their correction lies beyond the scope of this book.

2–13 The prism. Another simple and well-known optical instrument is the *prism*. A parallel beam of rays traversing a prism undergoes two deflections, one at the face of entrance, one at the face of exit; since the refraction of a plane wave at a plane surface gives rise to a plane wave, the rays are again parallel when they emerge.

Let δ be the angle of deviation (i.e., the angle between the incident and the emergent beams); if we assume the prism to be immersed in air, this angle depends on the index of refraction n of the prism material, on the angle α between the two refracting surfaces, and on the angle of incidence, φ. To compute δ, we refer to Fig. 2–43, from which we see that

$$\delta = (\varphi - \varphi') + (\varphi_1 - \varphi_1'). \tag{2–39}$$

Consider the triangle $A I I_1$, and note the angular relations

$$\angle A I I_1 = \frac{\pi}{2} - \varphi', \qquad \angle A I_1 I = \frac{\pi}{2} - \varphi_1', \qquad \angle I A I_1 = \alpha,$$

from which it follows that

$$\left(\frac{\pi}{2} - \varphi'\right) + \left(\frac{\pi}{2} - \varphi_1'\right) + \alpha = \pi,$$

or

$$\varphi' + \varphi_1' = \alpha. \tag{2–40}$$

Equation (2–40), together with (2–39), gives the relation

$$\delta = \varphi + \varphi_1 - \alpha; \tag{2–41}$$

Eqs. (2–40) and (2–41), together with the relations

$$\frac{\sin \varphi}{\sin \varphi'} = n, \qquad \frac{\sin \varphi_1}{\sin \varphi_1'} = n, \quad (2\text{–}42)$$

determine δ as a function of φ. We shall not write the explicit solution

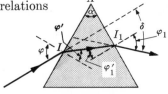

Fig. 2–43. The prism.

for the general case. We note, however, that when φ φ_1, and α are suffi-ciently small, Eqs. (2–42) become

$$\varphi = n\varphi', \qquad \varphi_1 = n\varphi_1'. \tag{2–43}$$

Elimination of φ' and φ_1' between these equations and Eq. (2–40) yields

$$\varphi + \varphi_1 = n\alpha, \tag{2–44}$$

and from (2–41) we then obtain

$$\delta = (n - 1)\alpha. \tag{2–45}$$

Thus in the special case under consideration the deviation is independent of the angle of incidence.

In the general case, we find that as the angle of incidence is gradually decreased from 90°, the angle of deviation decreases and then increases again after passing through a minimum. The minimum deviation occurs when the beam of light traverses the prism in a direction perpendicular to the plane bisecting the angle α formed by the two refracting surfaces; the angle of incidence is then equal to the angle of emergence. In this case Eqs. (2–40) and (2–41) become

$$\varphi' = \varphi_1' = \frac{\alpha}{2}, \qquad \varphi = \varphi_1 = \frac{\delta + \alpha}{2},$$

from which it follows that

$$\frac{\sin \left[\tfrac{1}{2}(\delta + \alpha)\right]}{\sin (\alpha/2)} = n. \tag{2–46}$$

This equation suggests a simple and accurate method for the experimental determination of the index of refraction of a transparent substance.

2–14 Dispersion. As was mentioned in Section 1–1, the index of refraction of a given substance is slightly different for light of different colors, being largest for blue light, smallest for red light, and of intermediate value for yellow light. This effect, called *dispersion*, is responsible for the colored spectrum observed when a beam of white light passes through a prism.*

---

*We shall see later (Section 3–6) that the different colors of light correspond to different wavelengths of the sinusoidal light waves emitted by a source. Hence a dispersive medium is one in which the index of refraction (and therefore the velocity of propagation), is frequency-dependent; for a mechanical analogy, see Section 1–3(d) and Appendix 2(d).

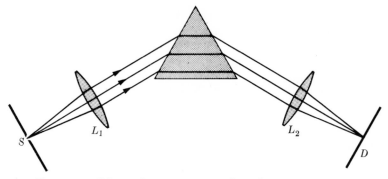

FIG. 2–44. Schematic arrangement of a prism spectroscope.

The instrument used to observe light spectra is called a *spectroscope*; its essential parts are shown in Fig. 2–44. S is an illuminated slit, parallel to the edge of the prism and lying in the first focal plane of the converging lens L_1; L_2 is a second converging lens; and D is a white screen placed in the second focal plane of L_2. If the incident light is monochromatic, this optical system will produce a real image of the slit S on the screen; if the light contains more than one color, a corresponding number of separate images will appear. In the case of white light, a continuous band is observed, made up of colors ranging from red, at the end nearest to the position of the undeviated beam, to blue, at the end farthest from this position. This band is actually a series of images of the slit, each of a different color and hence deviated through a different angle.

Consider a prism with a small enough refracting angle so that Eq. (2–45) holds. We conclude from this equation that the *width* of the spectrum is proportional to the differences of the indices of refraction for red and for blue light, while the mean *deflection* depends on the mean value of the index of refraction n, and, in fact, is proportional to $n - 1$. Table 2–1 lists the quantity $n - 1$ for two different kinds of glass (flint and crown) for each of three different colors, corresponding to three spectral lines known as the Fraunhofer C-line (red), the Fraunhofer D-line (yellow), and the Fraunhofer F-line (blue).

TABLE 2–1

VALUES OF $n - 1$ FOR THREE DIFFERENT SPECTRAL LINES

	C	D	F
Flint	0.644	0.650	0.665
Crown	0.517	0.520	0.527

We see that the mean value of $n - 1$ is about 20% greater for flint than for crown; however, the difference between the values of n corresponding to the blue and to the red lines is about twice as great for flint as for crown. Thus a prism of flint produces a spectrum about twice as wide as the spectrum produced by a prism of crown of the same shape, even though the mean deflection of the flint prism is only about 20% greater than that of the crown prism. This fact is used in the construction of *achromatic prisms*; i.e., prisms which deflect a ray of white light without separating it into rays of different colors. A prism of crown of refracting angle α followed by a prism of flint of refracting angle equal to about $\alpha/2$ will form an achromatic prism if the two prisms are arranged so as to deflect the incident beam in opposite directions, since the dispersion of the flint prism will offset the dispersion of the crown prism, while only part of the deflection produced by the flint prism will be canceled by the opposite deflection of the crown. (Strictly speaking, by a proper choice of the two refracting angles we can obtain *identical* deflections for two arbitrarily chosen spectral lines, e.g., the C- and F-lines, but only *approximately* equal deflections for rays of other colors.)

A similar method is used to correct *chromatic aberration* of lenses. The focal length of a simple lens is inversely proportional to $n - 1$ (see Eq. 2–37) and is therefore different for different colors; it follows that the lens will form a series of separate images of a nonmonochromatic source, one for each color. Consider, however, the system formed by a convergent crown lens and a divergent flint lens, the dioptric power of the second lens being one-half that of the first. The system will be convergent; its focal length will be practically the same for all colors, and equal to somewhat more than twice the mean focal length of the crown lens alone.

Dispersion accounts for the rainbow that appears in the sky when the clouds break after a rainstorm and the sun illuminates the multitude of droplets suspended in the air. The theory of this phenomenon is very complicated, and we can give here only a short qualitative account of its results. Consider a beam of parallel light rays striking a spherical droplet of water (Fig. 2–45). Part of the beam enters the droplet, and emerges after having undergone one or more internal

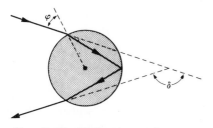

FIG. 2–45. Refraction and internal reflection of a light ray by a water droplet.

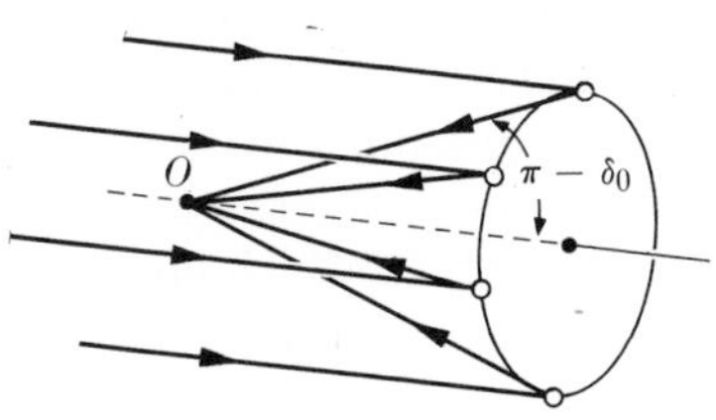

FIG. 2–46. Formation of a rainbow.

reflections; let us concentrate our attention on the rays that suffer only one reflection. The angle of deflection δ, i.e., the angle between the incident and the emergent rays, depends on the angle of incidence φ; the theory shows that for a certain value φ_0 of the angle of incidence, δ has a maximum value δ_0 which depends on the index of refraction and is thus different for different colors. The parallel rays of light strike different parts of the droplet's surface at different angles, so that the emergent rays spread out in different directions; however, there will be a maximum concentration of light in the directions corresponding to the maximum angle of deflection, δ_0. This statement may be justified as follows. To two rays incident at slightly different angles φ and $\varphi + \Delta\varphi$, there correspond two rays emerging at slightly different angles δ and $\delta + \Delta\delta$. $\Delta\delta$ and $\Delta\varphi$ are infinitesimal quantities of the same order except at $\varphi = \varphi_0$, where δ is a maximum, so that its derivative with respect to φ vanishes. At $\varphi = \varphi_0$, $\Delta\delta$ is an infinitesimal quantity of higher order than $\Delta\varphi$, which means that the ratio $\Delta\delta/\Delta\varphi$ tends to zero with $\Delta\varphi$; consequently, two rays incident at appreciably different angles on the drop will undergo practically the same deflection.

Let us now investigate how the light refracted by the droplets will appear to an observer located at some point O. Consider a circular cone having its apex at O and its axis in the direction of the sun's rays (Fig. 2–46); let the half-angle of this cone be $\pi - \delta_0$, where δ_0 is the angle of maximum deflection for rays of a given color, say red. Then red light from the sun will be strongly refracted in the direction of the observer only by drops lying on the surface of this cone; consequently the observer will see in the sky a red circular arc, which has its center in the direction opposite to the sun, and which subtends an angle equal to $\pi - \delta_0$. Similar arcs, of different colors, will appear at slightly different angles. Computations show that $\delta_0 = 138°$ for red light and $140°$ for violet light; hence the average angle subtended by the rainbow is $41°$, and its angular width is $2°$. The colors are in spectral sequence, from the violet on the inside to the red on the outside.

We have considered so far only rays that have undergone a single internal reflection in the water drops. Rays that have undergone two internal reflections give rise to a much fainter arc, concentric with the main arc but of greater radius, which exhibits the opposite sequence of colors.

2–15 Optical instruments and the eye. To a large extent, the science of geometrical optics concerns itself with the design of optical instruments and the study of their operation; this includes a detailed discussion of the various aberrations of mirrors and lenses, and of the methods used to minimize such unwanted features. In this section we shall discuss briefly such aspects of these important subjects as are needed for a clear understanding of experiments in which optical instruments are used.

(a) *The eye.* In many ways, the eye is the most remarkable of all optical instruments. A cross section of the human eye is shown schematically in Fig. 2–47. The eye is protected on the outside by a hard, opaque membrane, roughly spherical in shape; the part of this membrane at the front of the eye, called the *cornea*, is transparent, and has a somewhat smaller radius of

curvature than the rest of the eye-
ball. Behind the cornea lies a diaphragm called the *iris*, which is the
aperture stop (see Section 2–11) of
the eye: the *pupil*, a hole in the
center of the iris, automatically contracts or dilates as the illumination
increases or decreases. Immediately
behind the iris is the *crystalline lens*,
which consists of an elastic, jelly-like

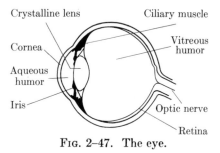

FIG. 2–47. The eye.

substance having an index of refraction that increases gradually from the
outer to the inner portions, and is on the average somewhat greater than
that of water. The curvature of the two faces of this lens is controlled by
the *ciliary muscle*, attached to it by ligaments. The space between the
cornea and the crystalline lens is filled with a clear liquid called the *aqueous
humor;* the space behind the crystalline lens is filled with a clear, soft, jelly-
like substance called the *vitreous humor*. Both these substances have about
the same index of refraction as water.

The cornea, the aqueous humor, the crystalline lens, and the vitreous
humor form an optical system which produces real images of external
objects on the *retina*, a film covering most of the inner surface of the eye.
The retina is composed of the terminal parts of the optic nerve, and the
images produced on the retina are transmitted by this nerve to the brain.
(However, only a small region of the retina is capable of producing sharp
visual sensations.)

In the relaxed normal eye, the second focal point of the optical system
lies on the retina, so that the eye is focused on objects at infinity. The
distinct perception of nearby objects is made possible by a contraction of
the ciliary muscle, which increases the curvature and therefore the dioptric
power of the crystalline lens; this process is called *accommodation*. The
nearest position of an object whose sharp image can be formed on the
retina is called the *near point* of the eye; because of a progressive loss of
elasticity by the crystalline lens (a condition known as *presbyopia*), the
distance of the near point increases gradually with age, from about 7 cm
at 10 years to about 200 cm at 60 years. In a young adult with normal
eyesight, d_0 is about 25 cm.

Two common defects of vision are *myopia* (nearsightedness) and *hyperopia* (farsightedness). The myopic eye is longer than a normal eye, so that
in the relaxed condition the image of an object at infinite distance is formed
in front of the retina; the hyperopic eye is shorter, so that the image of an
object at infinite distance is formed behind the retina. Myopia can be
corrected with a divergent lens, hyperopia with a convergent lens.

(b) *The photographic camera.* Among the optical instruments, the one

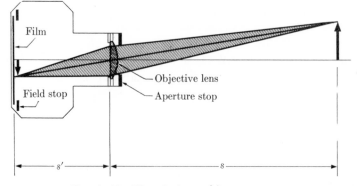

FIG. 2–48. The photographic camera.

whose operation most closely resembles that of the eye is the photographic camera. The essential optical part of the camera is a converging lens, called the *objective*, which forms a real image of external objects on the sensitive film. The field of view is determined by a rectangular diaphragm placed directly in front of the film; this diaphragm is the *field stop*, as defined in Section 2–11. The *aperture stop* is a diaphragm of variable aperture placed immediately before or immediately behind the objective, or sometimes, when the objective is a compound lens, between the components.

The amount of light entering the lens from a given source is proportional to the luminance* of the source and to the solid angle subtended by the aperture stop at the source. If D is the diameter of the aperture stop, and if the source is near the axis of the lens and at a distance $s \gg D$ from it, this solid angle is equal to $\pi D^2/4s^2$. The illuminance of the image is determined by the amount of light *per unit area* incident upon it. For a given luminance of the source, the illuminance of the image is thus inversely proportional to its area, i.e., inversely proportional to the square of the lateral magnification. Since the magnification is equal to s'/s (see Section 2–12), we conclude that the illuminance of the image is proportional to

$$\frac{D^2}{s^2} \cdot \frac{s^2}{s'^2} = \frac{D^2}{s'^2}.$$

For distant objects, s' is practically equal to the focal length; the maximum value of D is the diameter of the objective lens. Hence the illuminance of the image obtained with the widest opening of the aperture stop is proportional to the square of the diameter of the objective lens divided by the

---

*The *luminance* of a source is the number of lumens emitted per steradian by a unit area of the source; the *illuminance* of a surface is the number of lumens per unit area incident upon the surface.

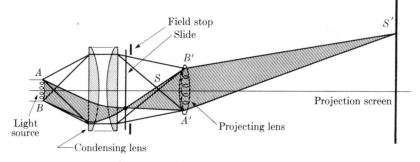

FIG. 2–49. The projection lantern.

square of the focal length. The ratio D/f is the relative aperture of the lens, as defined in Section 2–12; its inverse is known as the f/number. Thus, for example, an f/3 objective is one whose focal length equals three times the diameter. The illuminance of the image determines the speed of the camera, that is, the minimum length of exposure necessary to take a picture for a given luminance of the object; hence the speed of a camera increases with decreasing f/number.

(c) *The projection lantern.* The projection lantern (Fig. 2–49) is similar in principle to the photographic camera, in that it employs a converging lens (the *projecting lens*) to produce a real image of an illuminated object. In this case, however, the object (the lantern slide) lies close to the lens, and the magnified image is projected on a distant screen. An essential part of the projection lantern is the *condensing lens,* a converging lens (or a converging system of lenses) of large dimensions placed immediately in front of the slide. The condensing lens is arranged to form an image $A'B'$ of the light source AB upon the projecting lens. If this image covers the whole area of the projecting lens, the rays passing through an arbitrary point of the slide form a cone that includes the projecting lens. Under these conditions, the *aperture stop* of the optical system coincides with the mounting of the projecting lens, and full use is made of the dimensions of this lens. It is clear that without a condensing lens only a small portion around the center of the slide could be projected upon the screen, and the projected image would be very weak and of nonuniform brightness. The field stop of the projection lantern is provided by the mounting of the slide.

(d) *The microscope.* The size of the retinal image of an object is proportional to the visual angle, i.e., the angle subtended by the object at the eye. An object cannot be perceived distinctly if its distance from the eye is less than the distance d_0 of the near point; it follows that the maximum visual angle of an object of linear dimension y, when viewed by the unaided eye, is y/d_0 (y is here assumed to be small compared with d_0). *Microscopes* are optical devices designed to increase the visual angle and hence enlarge the

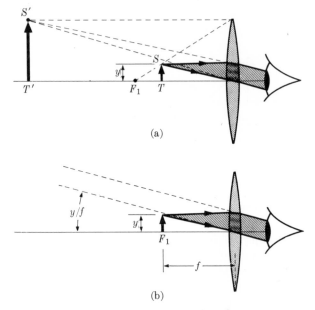

(a)

(b)

FIG. 2–50. The magnifying glass.

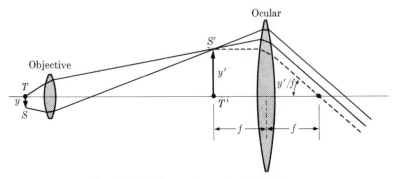

FIG. 2–51. The compound microscope.

retinal image of small objects. The simplest kind of microscope is a converging lens placed before the eye (Fig. 2–50). If the object ST lies between the lens and its first focal point, the lens produces an enlarged virtual image $S'T'$ further removed from the eye than the object itself. Since the normal eye, when relaxed, is focused on infinity, it is convenient to place the object to be viewed in the first focal plane of the lens. The visual angle is then y/f, where f is the focal distance of the lens. This angle is d_0/f times greater than the maximum visual angle at which the unaided eye can perceive the same object. The ratio d_0/f is called the *angular magnification*.

Since aberrations become increasingly serious as the focal length de-

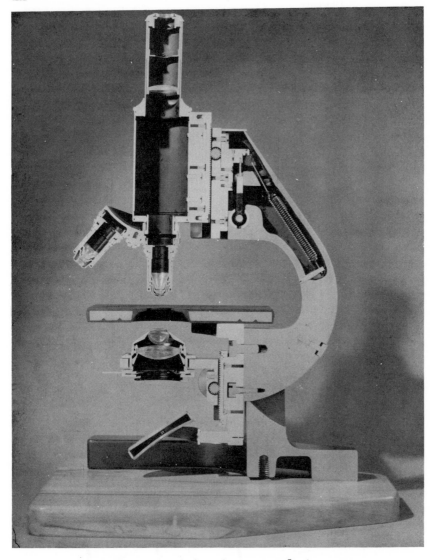

FIG. 2–52. Sectional view of a compound microscope.

creases, it is not practical to use as magnifiers simple lenses with focal lengths less than about 5 cm, which give an angular magnification of about 5. When greater magnification is desired, it is necessary to use a system of lenses designed to minimize aberrations, but even so, it is difficult to obtain magnifications larger than about 20. Much greater magnifications can be obtained, however, with a *compound microscope* (Fig. 2–51), which consists essentially of two corrected compound lenses, the *objective*

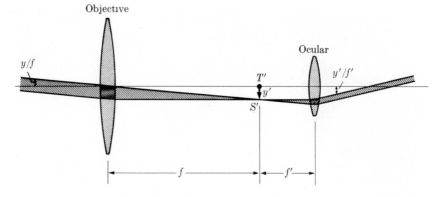

FIG. 2–53. The astronomical telescope.

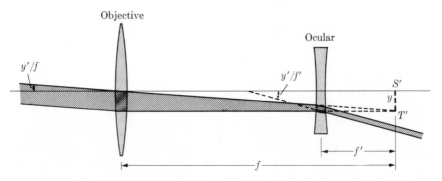

FIG. 2–54. The Galilean telescope.

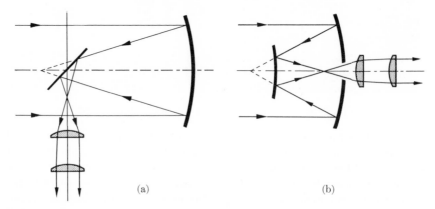

FIG. 2–55. The reflecting telescope: (a) Newtonian mounting, (b) Cassegrainian mounting.

lens and the *ocular*. The objective lens, a converging lens of very small focal length, forms an enlarged image of the object in the focal plane of the ocular; the ocular is used to view this image. The over-all angular magnification is the product of the lateral magnification of the objective lens and the angular magnification of the ocular. A mirror and a condensing lens are used to illuminate the object to be viewed by the microscope; here, as in the case of the projection lantern, the condensing lens serves the purpose of utilizing the full opening of the objective lens. A sectional view of a microscope and its mounting is shown in Fig. 2–52.

(e) *The telescope.* The telescope is an instrument used to observe distant objects. Like the compound microscope, it consists of an objective lens which forms a real image of the object, and an ocular to view this image. However, the objective lens of a telescope, unlike that of a microscope, has a large focal length. When the telescope is trained on a very distant object, the second focus of the objective lens lies in the first focal plane of the ocular; the angular magnification of the telescope is then equal to the ratio of the focal length of the objective lens to that of the ocular.

Figure 2–53 is a schematic drawing of the optical system of the *astronomical telescope*. Here both the objective and the ocular are converging lenses, so that the telescope forms inverted images. The mounting of the objective lens serves as the aperture stop; the field stop is usually a diaphragm placed in the common focal plane of the two lenses.

Figure 2–54 illustrates the *Galilean telescope*, which is named after its inventor. Here the objective is a converging lens and the ocular is a diverging lens, so that the telescope forms erect images. However, this advantage is counterbalanced by the fact that its field of view is smaller than that of the astronomical telescope described above, and it is less sharply defined, since it is not possible to place a field stop in the plane of the image formed by the objective lens.

Other types of telescope form erect images but do not have the disadvantages of the Galilean telescope; their description will be omitted here. However, it should be mentioned that many of the telescopes used for astronomical observations have a concave (parabolic) mirror, rather than a lens, as the objective. These telescopes are called *reflecting telescopes*. Two different devices, illustrated in Figs. 2–55(a) and (b), are used to observe the image. In the *Newtonian* mounting, the rays reflected by the concave mirror fall upon a small plane mirror mounted on the axis of the telescope at an angle of 45°. The image is viewed through the ocular, which is mounted with its axis perpendicular to the axis of the telescope. In the *Cassegrainian* mounting, the rays reflected by the concave parabolic mirror fall on a small convex hyperbolic mirror whose axis coincides with the axis of the telescope. This mirror reflects the rays back through a hole at the center of the parabolic mirror and into the ocular, which is placed behind it.

2-1. The index of refraction of air is $n = 1 + 0.00029 \, (\rho/\rho_0)$, where ρ is the actual density of air and ρ_0 the density at normal pressure ($p_0 = 76$ cm Hg) and 15°C temperature (absolute temperature $T_0 = 288°$). Let θ be the true zenith angle of a star and $\theta - \Delta\theta$ the apparent zenith angle with respect to an observer looking at the star through the atmosphere. (a) Write the equation giving $\Delta\theta$ as a function of θ and of atmospheric pressure p and absolute temperature T. (b) Compute $\Delta\theta$ at sea level for a star with $\theta = 45°$, assuming a temperature $T = T_0$.

2-2. A man stands on a horizontal road, his eyes at a height of $5'6''$ from the pavement. At this height, the air temperature is 15°C. Mirage makes the pavement appear wet at a distance of 600 ft. Compute the temperature of the air in contact with the pavement.

2-3. The trajectory of a ray in a nonhomogeneous medium is represented by $x = A \sin(y/B)$. Compute the index of refraction n in the space between the planes $x = A$ and $x = -A$, assuming that n depends only on x and has the value n_0 at $x = 0$.

2-4. The index of refraction of a certain medium is given by $n = h + kx$. Compute the trajectory of the ray passing through the origin of the coordinate axes and forming at this point an angle φ_0 with the x-axis. Plot the trajectory of the ray, assuming $h = 1$, $k = 1$, $\varphi_0 = 45°$.

2-5. Let s and s' be the distances of the object and the image, respectively, from the surface of a *concave* spherical mirror of radius of curvature R. Plot s'/R against s/R for values of s be-tween $-2R$ and $+2R$. Discuss the significance of the signs of s and s'.

2-6. Let s and s' be the distances of the object and the image, respectively, from the surface of a *convex* spherical mirror of radius of curvature R. Plot s'/R against s/R for values of s between $-2R$ and $+2R$. Discuss the significance of the signs of s and s'.

2-7. The diameter of the moon is 2160 mi and its distance from the earth is 240,000 mi. Find the diameter of the image of the moon formed by a spherical concave telescope mirror of focal length 10 ft.

2-8. Determine the position and the dimensions of the image of the sun in a steel ball bearing $\frac{1}{4}$ in. in diameter. Assume the sun to be behind the observer. (The diameter of the sun is 864,000 mi and the distance of the sun from the earth is 92,900,000 mi.)

2-9. Prove that if the quantities $u = s - R$ and $u' = s' - R$ are used to define the positions of the object and of the image, respectively, with respect to a spherical mirror, the equation for the mirror becomes

$$\frac{1}{u} + \frac{1}{u'} = -\frac{2}{R}.$$

(This form of the equation for a mirror is useful in problems in which one of the given quantities is the magnification.)

2-10. A concave spherical mirror has a radius of curvature of 80 cm. Determine the positions of an object whose image is (a) real and magnified by a factor of four, (b) virtual and magnified by a factor of four.

2-11. Two concave spherical mirrors M_1 and M_2 face each other, at a distance of 2 m. The radius of curvature of M_1 is 0.5 m and that of M_2 is 2 m. A point source lies on the line connecting the centers of curvature of the two mirrors, a distance of 3/11 m from M_1. Compute the positions of the images formed by the rays that have undergone (a) one reflection at M_1, (b) one reflection at M_1 and one reflection at M_2, (c) one reflection at M_1, one reflection at M_2, and another reflection at M_1.

2–12. Solve parts (a) and (b) of problem 2–11 by the graphical method.

2–13. To a person looking perpendicularly through the water of a pond the bottom appears to be at a depth of 4 ft. What is the actual depth of the pond?

·**2–14.** A straight stick is immersed in water at an angle of 45°. Compute the angle θ that the portions of the stick above and below water appear to make with each other to a person looking down from above (Fig. 2–56).

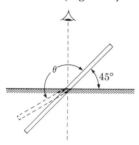

FIGURE 2–56.

2–15. One of the ends of a long cylindrical glass rod is ground and polished to a convex spherical surface whose radius of curvature is R, and whose center of curvature lies on the axis of the cylinder. Let S and S' be two points of the axis conjugate to each other with respect to the spherical surface, and let s and s' be their distances from the vertex. Plot s'/R against s/R for values of s between $2R$ and $-2R$. The index of refraction of the glass is 1.5. Discuss the meaning of the signs of s and s'.

2–16. Repeat Problem 2–15 for a rod terminated by a concave spherical surface.

2–17. A glass sphere 2 cm in diameter contains a small air bubble at a distance of 0.5 cm from the center. Find the position and magnification of the image of the bubble, as seen by a person looking from one or the other of the two opposite directions along the line connecting the center of the sphere with the bubble. The index of refraction of the glass is 1.5.

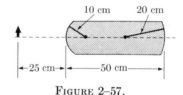

FIGURE 2–57.

2–18. A cylindrical glass rod of index of refraction 1.5 is terminated by two convex spherical surfaces, with radii of curvature of 10 and 20 cm, respectively (Fig. 2–57). The length of the rod between vertices is 50 cm. An arrow 1 mm long lies in front of the first spherical surface, at right angles to the axis of the cylinder and a distance of 25 cm from the vertex. Compute (a) the position and the length of the image of the arrow formed by the first surface, and (b) the position and the length of the image of the arrow formed by both surfaces. Specify whether the images are real or virtual.

2–19. Determine the focal points of the two spherical end surfaces of the glass rod described in Problem 2–18, and solve this problem graphically.

2–20. A solid glass sphere of radius R and index of refraction 1.5 is silvered over one hemisphere. A point source S lies on the line through the center of the sphere and the pole of the unsilvered hemisphere, a distance $2R$ from this pole. Find the position of the final image formed by the refracting and reflecting surfaces.

2–21. Compute the focal lengths of the following thin lenses:

(a) plano-convex, radius of curvature 100 cm,

(b) biconvex, radii of curvature 100 cm and 200 cm,

(c) plano-concave, radius of curvature 250 cm,

(d) meniscus, radii of curvature: convex face 100 cm, concave face 200 cm,

(e) meniscus, radii of curvature: convex face 300 cm, concave face 100 cm.

Assume a value of 1.5 for the index of refraction. Make sketches showing the section of each lens, and specify whether the lens is converging or diverging.

2–22. The focal length of a thin converging lens is 1.5 m. An object 2 mm high is placed in front of the lens, first at a distance of 0.5 m, then at a distance of 1 m, and finally at a distance of 3 m. Compute the positions and the sizes of the three images. Specify whether the images are real or virtual.

2–23. Solve Problem 2–22 for a diverging lens.

2–24. Prove that two thin lenses of focal lengths f_1 and f_2 placed in contact with each other are equivalent to a single lens of focal length

$$f = f_1 f_2 / (f_1 + f_2).$$

2–25. Compute the angle of minimum deviation for a glass prism whose refracting surfaces form an angle of 60°. The index of refraction of the **glass** is 1.6.

2–26. A prism of crown glass and a prism of flint glass are arranged in such a way as to deviate a light beam in opposite directions. The refracting angle of the crown prism is 10° and that of the flint prism is such that the total deviations of the light beam for the C and F spectral lines (see Table 2–1) are equal. Compute (a) the refracting angle of the flint prism, (b) the total deviation for the C- and F-lines, (c) the difference between the deviations for the C- and D-lines.

2–27. The refracting angle of the flint prism in the previous problem is chosen in such a way as to cancel the deviation produced by the crown prism for the D-line. Compute the total deviations produced by the two prisms for the C- and F-lines.

FIGURE 2–58.

2–28. Two lenses, one of flint and the other of crown glass, are arranged as shown in Fig. 2–58 to form an *achromatic doublet*. Which lens is of flint and which of crown? Assume that the radius of curvature of the left surface of the converging lens is 1 m. Compute the radius of curvature of the spherical surface separating the two lenses, using the requirement that the doublet should have the same focal length for the C- and F-lines.

According to Fermat's principle, all rays connecting two conjugate points have the same optical length. Conversely, we say that two points are conjugate to each other if there is an infinite number of trajectories of equal optical lengths connecting the two points. We have discussed in the text optical systems (such as spherical mirrors and spherical refracting surfaces) which form images only in an approximate manner. Conjugate points with respect to these systems may be defined as follows. Consider the trajectory of the ray connecting two points P and Q, and consider another trajectory which is everywhere at a distance smaller than or equal to δ from the former. In general (according to Fermat's principle), the difference between the optical lengths of the two trajectories is of the order of δ². If, however, P and Q are conjugate points, the difference between the optical lengths is proportional to a power of δ higher than the second. The following problems illustrate these conclusions.

2-29. Consider a concave mirror in the shape of an ellipsoid of revolution around the axis passing through the two foci (see Fig. 2–19 in the text). Prove that a point source placed at one of the foci has its real image at the other focus. Give this proof using (a) Fermat's principle, (b) Huygens' construction. (Remember that the sum of the distances of an arbitrary point of an ellipse from the two foci is a constant.)

2-30. Consider a convex mirror in the shape of a hyperboloid of revolution around the axis passing through the two foci (see Fig. 2–20 in the text). Prove that a point source located at the outer focus has its virtual image at the inner focus. Give this proof using (a) Fermat's principle, (b) Huygens' construction. (Remember that the difference of the distances of an arbitrary point of a hyperbola from the two foci is a constant.)

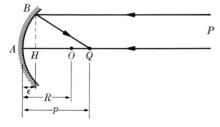

FIGURE 2–59.

2-31. Consider a concave spherical mirror of radius of curvature R and center of curvature O. Let P be a point at infinite distance on the line OA (Fig.

2–59), and Q another point on this line a distance p from the mirror. The ray from P incident upon the mirror along the line OA is reflected upon itself and thus passes through Q. Consider another trajectory such as PBQ connecting P with Q after touching the mirror. Let Δl be the length of this trajectory (PBQ) minus the length of the actual trajectory of the ray connecting P with Q (PAQ). Let BH be the perpendicular to OA through B, and let $h = \overline{BH}$, $\epsilon = \overline{AH}$.

(a) Prove that Δl satisfies the equation:

$$(\Delta l)^2 + \epsilon^2 + 2\,\Delta l(p + \epsilon) + 2\epsilon(2p - R) = 0.$$

(b) Using this equation, show that the actual trajectory of the ray from P to Q has a minimum or a maximum length compared with neighboring trajectories, depending on whether $p < R/2$ or $p > R/2$.

(c) What happens when $p = R/2$?

2-32. Refer to Problem 2–31. Assume $R = 100$ cm. Among the trajectories, such as PBQ, connecting P with Q after touching the mirror, consider those which satisfy the condition $\Delta l < 10^{-5}$ cm. These trajectories form a bundle of cross-sectional area $\Sigma = \pi h^2$, where $h^2 = \epsilon(2R - \epsilon)$. Plot Σ as a function of p for $R/4 < p < R$. Show that the curve has a sharp maximum at $p = R/2$, that is, when Q is at the focal point of the mirror. Interpret this result.

2-33. Consider a glass sphere of radius R and index of refraction n, cut by a plane through a point S at a distance x from the center O and perpendicular to OS (Fig. 2-60). Show that if $x = R/n$, all rays entering the glass sphere from a point source at S will emerge from the sphere along lines diverging from a point S', collinear with O and S at a distance $x' = nR$ from O; this means that S and S' are the *aplanatic* points relative to the spherical surface. (*Hint:* Consider a sphere Σ of arbitrary radius r centered at S'. If S' is the virtual image of S, it follows from Fermat's principle that the optical length l between S and Σ of an arbitrary ray, such as SAB, is a constant. Express this optical length in terms of r, R, x, x', φ. From the requirement that the

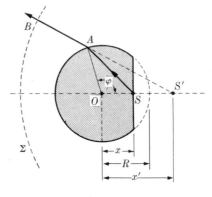

FIGURE 2-60.

derivative with respect to φ should vanish for all values of φ, we obtain two equations, from which x and x' can be determined.

CHAPTER 3

INTERFERENCE

3–1 General considerations. Everyone has noticed the changing colors of a soap bubble, or of a thin film of oil floating on water. These are perhaps the most common manifestations of *interference*, a phenomenon that is observed when two or more beams of light from a common source arrive, along different paths, at the same region of space. In each of these two cases, the interfering beams are those reflected at the two surfaces of a thin film—a film of soapy water in air, or a film of oil between air and water.

The corpuscular model of light does not afford any simple interpretation of interference phenomena. The wave model, however, suggests a most natural interpretation. Indeed, the phenomena observed when two light beams are superimposed are closely analogous to those associated with the superposition of two surface waves, such as are produced by two pebbles falling into a pool of water. A careful observer will notice that in certain regions, where the crest of one wave arrives simultaneously with the trough of the other, the effects of the two waves almost cancel, while in other regions, where a crest meets a crest or a trough meets a trough, the superposition of the two waves produces a more violent disturbance than do the individual waves. Similarly, in the region where two *coherent* (see Section 3–7) monochromatic light beams overlap, there are places where the light intensity is practically zero, and others where it is particularly strong. The situation is more complicated if white light is used. As we have already mentioned, white light is a superposition of light of different colors; each color gives a separate set of maxima and minima, and these combine to give the color effects mentioned above.

In order to interpret interference phenomena, it is necessary to specify the wave model of light more precisely than we have done so far. In Chapter 1 we found that we could account adequately for the phenomena of geometrical optics by assuming that light waves consist of a succession of very short pulses, without making any assumptions as to the exact shape of these pulses. However, knowledge of the shape of light waves, which geometrical optics ignores, is essential for the interpretation of interference phenomena; indeed, it is through the observation of these phenomena that the form of the function $E(x, t)$ describing the optical disturbance can be experimentally determined.

Our analysis of interference phenomena will be based upon the *super-*

position principle already discussed in Section 1–5, which can be stated as follows: *The instantaneous optical disturbance at a point where two or more light waves cross is the sum of the optical disturbances that would be produced by each of the waves separately.* This statement implies that the propagation of a light wave is not affected by the presence of other light waves in the same medium; the observation that two light beams whose paths cross in a region of space continue unperturbed beyond this region is an experimental test of the superposition principle. In the electromagnetic theory of light the rigorous validity of the superposition principle for light waves is guaranteed by the linear character of Maxwell's equations (see Sections 7–2 and 7–3).

For the time being we shall treat E as a scalar quantity, although we shall later learn that the optical disturbance is actually a vector quantity. However, we shall also see (Section 6–3) that this fact does not invalidate the conclusions reached in the present chapter.

One important matter should be emphasized at this point. Unlike the displacement in a surface wave or the pressure change in a sound wave, optical disturbances cannot be observed directly, largely because, as we shall see, E varies with time at an exceedingly rapid rate. Therefore, in order to attach a definite physical significance to the optical disturbance, we must relate this quantity to the *light intensity I*, which measures the observable effects of light.

Light has many different effects: it makes a visual impression on the retina of the eye, it generates an electric current in a photocell, it produces a latent image on a photographic emulsion, it develops heat when it falls upon an absorbing surface. Correspondingly, light intensity could be defined in many different ways. In what follows we shall define it in terms of the response of a light detector, such as a bolometer or a thermocouple, sensitive to the heating effects of light; these effects are proportional to the amount of energy per unit time absorbed by the detector. Other effects (e.g., the photoelectric current or the blackening of a photosensitive emulsion) will be functions of the intensity as defined above, but not necessarily proportional to it.

Two remarks are here in order. (1) The detector must be one that does not appreciably disturb the propagation of the light waves. Only in this case can we speak of the light intensity as a property of the light waves themselves, without explicit reference to the particular detector used to measure this intensity. To postulate the existence of light detectors whose presence has a negligible influence on the propagation of the light waves is consistent with the general philosophy of classical physics; indeed, in classical physics it is always assumed that the influence of the observer on the observed object can be made arbitrarily small. (2) Our definition of intensity leaves a constant factor undetermined. This is not objectionable because, for the time being at least, we shall be concerned only with *relative* values of the intensity.

We must now determine the relationship between the light intensity I and the optical disturbance E. For this purpose, let us consider the special case of a single traveling wave. In our discussion of mechanical waves, we found that the instantaneous value of the energy flux per unit area is proportional to the square of the disturbance or, more precisely, to the square of the velocity u of the particles of the medium [Sections 1–3(c), 1–4(a)]. We shall make use of the mechanical analogy once more, and assume that the energy flux per unit area of a traveling light wave is proportional to the square of the optical disturbance; this assumption will be fully justified by the electromagnetic theory of light (see Section 7–5).

On the other hand, a traveling wave incident upon the absorbing surface of a test body delivers to the body an amount of energy per unit time equal to the energy flux through the surface of the body. The observable heating effects are proportional to the *average* rate of energy absorption, the averaging time being determined by the type of instrument used to measure these effects. Therefore, in a traveling wave, the light intensity is proportional to the *average* energy flux per unit time, hence to the *mean square value* of the optical disturbance, and we conclude that I and E are related by

$$I = \text{const. } (E^2)_{\text{av}}. \tag{3–1}$$

We have obtained this result by considering the special case of isolated traveling waves. However, by the very definition of optical disturbance, a given optical disturbance must always produce the same observable effects, irrespective of whether the disturbance is caused by a single wave or by the superposition of several waves. We are thus justified in assuming that Eq. (3–1) expresses the general relationship between the light intensity and the optical disturbance.

From the foregoing it follows that in the special case of single traveling waves, the intensity and the average energy flux per unit area are proportional to each other, and could be made numerically equal by an appropriate choice of units. However, in regions of space where two or more light waves traveling in different directions overlap, the light intensity is not proportional to the energy flux per unit area. Indeed, the net energy flux may be zero at a point where the optical disturbance is different from zero, and where, therefore, a light detector will give a definite response. As a mechanical example, the reader may recall the stationary waves produced by two sinusoidal waves of equal frequency and amplitude, traveling in opposite directions along a string. Here the energy flux through an arbitrary point of the string is zero. The superposition of the two waves, however, produces a resultant disturbance whose amplitude is different from zero everywhere except at the nodes. It is thus important to keep the concepts of light intensity and energy flux clearly separate.

3–2 Sinusoidal waves. In optics, as in many other fields of physics, *sinusoidal waves* (i.e., waves in which the optical disturbance at any given point is a sinusoidal function of time) play a particularly important role. A plane sinusoidal wave traveling with velocity v in the positive x-direction is represented by an equation of the general form

$$E = A \cos\left[\omega\left(t - \frac{x}{v}\right) + \varphi\right] ; \tag{3-2}$$

if the wave is traveling in the negative direction, the expression $t - x/v$ is replaced by $t + x/v$. The quantities A, ω, and φ are arbitrary constants which depend on the source of the optical disturbance.

A is the *amplitude* of the wave; it represents the maximum absolute value of the optical disturbance.

ω is the *angular frequency*. For an increment of time equal to $2\pi/\omega$, the argument of the cosine increases by 2π and the cosine function passes through a full period. The period T is thus related to the angular frequency ω by the equation

$$T = \frac{2\pi}{\omega}. \tag{3-3}$$

The quantity

$$\nu = \frac{1}{T} = \frac{\omega}{2\pi} \tag{3-4}$$

is called the *frequency* of the wave; it represents the number of oscillations per unit time.

The quantity $-\omega x/v + \varphi$, whose value obviously depends on the chosen origin of time, is called the *phase* of the wave at x.

At any given instant, E is a sinusoidal function of x. The distance λ between two successive maxima or minima (Fig. 3–1) is called the *wavelength*, and satisfies the equation

$$\frac{\omega\lambda}{v} = 2\pi ,$$

which yields for λ the two equivalent expressions

$$\lambda = vT; \qquad \lambda = \frac{v}{\nu}. \tag{3-5}$$

Equation (3–2) may be rewritten so as to make the period and the wavelength appear explicitly:

$$E = A \cos\left[2\pi\left(\frac{t}{T} - \frac{x}{\lambda}\right) + \varphi\right].$$

(3–6)

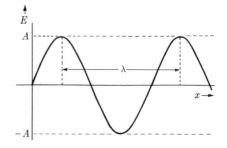

FIG. 3-1. Sinusoidal wave.

Note that, according to the definition, a plane sinusoidal wave extends from minus infinity to plus infinity both in time and in space. Actually, of course, a light wave always has a finite extension, but the results that we shall obtain by considering infinite waves will apply with good approximation to wave trains whose total length is very large compared with the wavelength. We shall return to this point later.

As explained in the preceding section, the intensity I of the light wave is proportional to the mean square value of the optical disturbance E. The averaging time t_0, which was previously left unspecified, will now be assumed to be long compared with the period of the wave. Making use of the trigonometric relation $\cos^2\alpha = \frac{1}{2}(1 + \cos 2\alpha)$, we obtain from Eq. (3–6)

$$(E^2)_{av} = \frac{A^2}{t_0}\int_t^{t+t_0}\cos^2\left[2\pi\left(\frac{t'}{T} - \frac{x}{\lambda}\right) + \varphi\right]dt'$$

$$= \frac{A^2}{2} + \frac{A^2 T}{8\pi t_0}$$

$$\times\left\{\sin\left[4\pi\left(\frac{t}{T} + \frac{t_0}{T} - \frac{x}{\lambda}\right) + 2\varphi\right] - \sin\left[4\pi\left(\frac{t}{T} - \frac{x}{\lambda}\right) + 2\varphi\right]\right\}.$$

We see that $(E^2)_{av}$, for a given value of T, is a function of the averaging time t_0. The expression for $(E^2)_{av}$ contains a constant term, $A^2/2$, and a fluctuating term whose absolute magnitude is smaller than $(A^2/4\pi)(T/t_0)$; the second term becomes negligible when $t_0 \gg T$, and we then obtain

$$(E^2)_{av} = \frac{A^2}{2}.$$

(3–7)

We thus conclude that the intensity I is proportional to the square of the amplitude A, so that we can write

$$I = KA^2, \qquad (3\text{--}8)$$

where K is a constant.

We have tacitly assumed so far that the medium in which the waves travel is transparent, i.e., that it absorbs no appreciable fraction of the energy carried by the wave. In this case, the amplitude A and the intensity I of a plane wave such as that represented by Eq. (3–2) are constant along the direction of propagation. However, if the wave is not plane, its intensity will, in general, change along the direction of propagation even if the medium is perfectly transparent. For example, in the spherical wave originating from a point source the intensity is inversely proportional to r^2 and the amplitude is inversely proportional to r [see Section 1–4(b)]; thus a spherical sinusoidal wave in a perfectly transparent medium is represented by an equation of the form

$$E = \frac{B}{r} \cos \left[2\pi \left(\frac{t}{T} - \frac{r}{\lambda} \right) + \varphi \right], \qquad (3\text{--}9)$$

where B is a constant.

3–3 Propagation of sinusoidal waves. Since a sinusoidal wave may be regarded as a succession of positive and negative pulses, we might expect that the propagation of sinusoidal waves obeys the laws of geometrical optics, provided the dimensions of the obstacles encountered along their paths are large compared with the wavelength. In Section 4–3 we shall verify that this conclusion is correct. For the time being we shall accept its validity, and we shall also assume that the actual experimental conditions are such as to warrant the use of geometrical optics. We can then use the Huygens construction to study the propagation of each individual wave.

Note that the Huygens construction enables us to determine not only the regions of space that can be reached by a particular light wave, but also the relative phase of the wave at each point of space. Indeed, suppose that the sinusoidal wave has a constant phase φ at all points of a given surface Σ_0; for example, if the wave originates from a point in a homogeneous region of the medium, a sphere centered at the source and contained in the homogeneous region is such a surface. The equation of the optical disturbance at the surface Σ_0 has the form

$$E = A(x, y, z) \cos \left(2\pi \frac{t}{T} + \varphi \right), \qquad (3\text{--}10)$$

where we have written the amplitude A as a function of the space coordinates x, y, z to indicate that, in general, A varies from point to point on the surface Σ_0. Now consider Σ_0 to be a wave front at a given instant of time and, by means of Huygens' principle, construct the wave front Σ at some later time. By the very definition of wave front, the time required for any ray to travel from Σ_0 to Σ is a constant. Therefore Σ too is a surface of constant phase, and we conclude that *the surfaces previously defined as successive positions of the wave front are now to be interpreted as surfaces of constant phase.*

If l is the optical distance from Σ_0 to Σ, the disturbance at Σ lags the disturbance at Σ_0 by the constant time interval l/c and therefore the optical disturbance at Σ is given by

$$E = A(x, y, z) \cos\left[2\pi\left(\frac{t}{T} - \frac{l}{cT}\right) + \varphi\right], \qquad (3\text{--}11)$$

or, if we define

$$\lambda_0 = cT$$

as the wavelength *in vacuum*, the optical disturbance is given by

$$E = A(x, y, z) \cos\left[2\pi\left(\frac{t}{T} - \frac{l}{\lambda_0}\right) + \varphi\right]. \qquad (3\text{--}12)$$

3–4 Amplitude and phase relations in reflection and refraction. We know that a light wave incident upon the boundary surface between two different media splits into a reflected wave and a refracted wave. The Huygens construction determines the directions of propagation of these waves, but it does not furnish any information about their amplitudes and phases; for this information we must turn to the electromagnetic theory of light, which we shall discuss in a later chapter. We learn from this theory that when light passes from one transparent substance to another the transmitted wave is always in phase with the incident wave at the boundary surface, while the reflected wave has a phase either equal or opposite to that of the incident wave, depending on whether the velocity of propagation in the second medium is greater or smaller than that in the first (this statement is valid under the assumption that the angle of incidence does not exceed a certain value; see Sections 8–5 and 8–6). The reader will recall that we reached similar conclusions in our discussion of the reflection and transmission of waves at the point of junction between two strings of different mass per unit length [see Section 1–3(e)]. The electromagnetic theory of light predicts also that reflection at the boundary between a transparent medium and a metal produces, in general, a phase change different from zero or π (see Section 8–11).

Some important results concerning the relative amplitudes and phases of the incident, reflected, and refracted rays can be derived from general principles, without reference to any specific model or theory. We shall present here an argument based on the *reversibility principle*, of which the principle of optical reversibility mentioned in Section 2–2 is a special case.

It is well known that if the velocity of every point of a moving mechanical system is reversed in direction at a given instant, the system will run backwards through the states it has just traversed; this statement holds only if the system is not subject to forces of a frictional character which cause part of the mechanical energy to change into heat. With a similar limitation, this reversibility principle can be supposed to apply to all physical phenomena; we may formulate it in mathematical language by saying that if a physical phenomenon does not involve the dissipation of energy as heat, the equations describing it remain valid if we change the sign of the time.

To apply the reversibility principle to our problem, we consider a light ray MO (Fig. 3–2), originating in medium 1 and splitting into a reflected ray ON and a refracted ray OP upon reaching the boundary surface between medium 1 and medium 2. Let v_1 and v_2 be the velocities of propagation in the two media, and let x_m, x_n, x_p be the distances from O measured along the incident, reflected, and refracted rays, respectively. We represent the incident ray (which travels in the direction of decreasing x_m) by the equation

$$E_i = A \cos\left[\omega\left(t + \frac{x_m}{v_1}\right)\right].$$

For the sake of simplicity, we disregard the possibility of phase changes different from zero or π at surfaces of reflection or refraction. Then the reflected and refracted rays can be represented by equations of the type

$$E_r = \rho A \cos\left[\omega\left(t - \frac{x_n}{v_1}\right)\right],$$

$$E_t = \tau A \cos\left[\omega\left(t - \frac{x_p}{v_2}\right)\right].$$

Here ρ is the ratio of the reflected to the incident amplitude at the boundary from 1 to 2; it is positive if there is no phase change, and negative if the phase is inverted. Similarly, τ is the ratio of the transmitted to the incident amplitude, with the same convention regarding the sign.

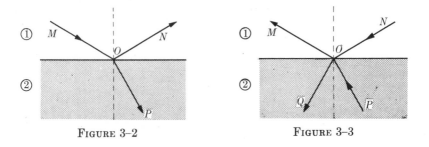

FIGURE 3–2　　　　　　　　　　　　　　FIGURE 3–3

We now reverse the directions of the reflected and refracted rays. The reversed reflected ray NO (Fig. 3–3) is represented by

$$E_r' = \rho A \cos\left[\omega\left(-t - \frac{x_n}{v_1}\right)\right] = \rho A \cos\left[\omega\left(t + \frac{x_n}{v_1}\right)\right],$$

and gives rise to a reflected ray traveling in the direction OM, represented by

$$\rho^2 A \cos\left[\omega\left(t - \frac{x_m}{v_1}\right)\right],$$

and a refracted ray traveling in the direction OQ, represented by

$$\rho \tau A \cos\left[\omega\left(t - \frac{x_q}{v_2}\right)\right],$$

where x_q is the distance from O along OQ. Similarly, the reversed refracted ray PO is represented by

$$E_t' = \tau A \cos\left[\omega\left(t + \frac{x_p}{v_2}\right)\right].$$

It gives rise to a refracted ray in the direction OM, represented by

$$\tau \tau' A \cos\left[\omega\left(t - \frac{x_m}{v_1}\right)\right],$$

and a reflected ray in the direction OQ, represented by

$$\tau \rho' A \cos\left[\omega\left(t - \frac{x_q}{v_2}\right)\right].$$

In the above expressions, ρ' and τ' are the ratios of the reflected and transmitted amplitudes to the incident amplitude at the boundary from 2 to 1.

The two rays traveling in the direction OM must reproduce the reversed incident ray, whereas the two rays traveling in the direction OQ must cancel. These two conditions furnish the following equations:

$$\rho^2 A \cos\left[\omega\left(t - \frac{x_m}{v_1}\right)\right] + \tau\tau' A \cos\left[\omega\left(t - \frac{x_m}{v_1}\right)\right] = A \cos\left[\omega\left(t - \frac{x_m}{v_1}\right)\right],$$

$$\rho\tau A \cos\left[\omega\left(t - \frac{x_q}{v_2}\right)\right] + \tau\rho' A \cos\left[\omega\left(t - \frac{x_q}{v_2}\right)\right] = 0,$$

which yield

$$\rho^2 + \tau\tau' = 1, \tag{3-13}$$

$$\rho = -\rho'. \tag{3-14}$$

The last equation shows that ρ and ρ' are equal in magnitude and opposite in sign. This means that if there is no phase change in the reflection from 1 to 2, there is phase change in the reflection from 2 to 1, and vice versa; moreover, the ratio of the reflected to the incident amplitude has the same absolute value in both cases.

Note that the quantity $\rho^2 = (\rho')^2$ represents the ratio of the reflected to the incident intensity. This quantity is known as *reflectance*.

In several optical experiments *half-silvered mirrors* are used; these are glass plates covered with a light silver deposit that increases the reflectance and yet allows part of the light to go through. It should be pointed out explicitly that the results obtained above do not apply to the reflection and transmission of light at a half-silvered surface because light absorption by the metallic film removes the conditions for the validity of the reversibility principle.

3–5 Addition of sinusoidal functions. Since the theory of the interference of sinusoidal waves is based upon the rules for the addition of sinusoidal functions, we shall review these rules briefly before continuing our study. It is well known that the sum of two or more sinusoidal functions of a given frequency is a sinusoidal function of the same frequency, whose amplitude and phase bear definite relations to the amplitudes and phases of the component functions. In mathematical language,

$$A_1 \cos(\omega t + \alpha_1) + A_2 \cos(\omega t + \alpha_2) + \cdots = A \cos(\omega t + \alpha). \quad (3\text{–}15)$$

We can prove this statement and determine the amplitude A and the phase α of the resultant function by any one of three methods, which we shall now describe.

(a) *Direct method.* Equation (3–15) may be rewritten as

$$(A_1 \cos\alpha_1 + A_2 \cos\alpha_2 + \cdots) \cos\omega t - (A_1 \sin\alpha_1 + A_2 \sin\alpha_2 + \cdots) \sin\omega t$$

$$= A \cos\alpha \cos\omega t - A \sin\alpha \sin\omega t,$$

which can be satisfied for all values of the time t only if the coefficients of $\cos\omega t$ on both sides of the equation are identical, and if the same is true of the coefficients of $\sin\omega t$. This condition gives us the two equations

$$A_1 \cos\alpha_1 + A_2 \cos\alpha_2 + \cdots = A \cos\alpha,$$

$$(3\text{–}16)$$

$$A_1 \sin\alpha_1 + A_2 \sin\alpha_2 + \cdots = A \sin\alpha,$$

which can be solved for the two unknown quantities A and α.

(b) *Vector representation.* Consider a vector of length A_1, rotating with angular velocity ω. Let α_1 be the angle that this vector makes with a fixed

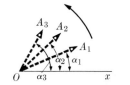

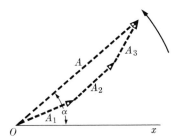

FIG. 3–4. Representation of sinusoidal functions by rotating vectors.

FIG. 3–5. Vector method for the addition of sinusoidal functions.

axis Ox at the time zero; then at time t the projection of the rotating vector on the axis Ox has the expression $A_1 \cos(\omega t + \alpha_1)$. We can use this rotating vector to represent the sinusoidal function $A_1 \cos(\omega t + \alpha_1)$, and the other sinusoidal functions, $A_2 \cos(\omega t + \alpha_2)$, ..., can be represented in a similar way (Fig. 3–4). The vector sum of these vectors is a vector of constant magnitude A, which rotates with the same angular velocity ω as the component vectors (Fig. 3–5). Its projection on the axis Ox represents the sum of the sinusoidal functions $A_1 \cos(\omega t + \alpha_1)$, $A_2 \cos(\omega t + \alpha_2)$, ..., as we immediately recognize if we remember that the projection of a vector on a fixed axis equals the algebraic sum of the projections of its components. We thus conclude that the vector representing the sum of two or more sinusoidal functions results from vector addition of the vectors representing the individual functions.

(c) *Representation by complex functions.* The sinusoidal function $A_1 \cos(\omega t + \alpha_1)$ is the real part of the complex function $A_1 e^{i(\omega t + \alpha_1)}$ [see Appendix 1(b)]. Since the real part of a sum of complex numbers equals the sum of the real parts of its terms, the values of A and α that satisfy the equation

$$A_1 e^{i(\omega t + \alpha_1)} + A_2 e^{i(\omega t + \alpha_2)} + \cdots = A e^{i(\omega t + \alpha)} \tag{3–17}$$

also satisfy Eq. (3–15). Thus instead of adding the sinusoidal functions $A_1 \cos(\omega t + \alpha_1)$, $A_2 \cos(\omega t + \alpha_2)$, ..., we can add the corresponding exponential functions $A_1 e^{i(\omega t + \alpha_1)}$, $A_2 e^{i(\omega t + \alpha_2)}$, ..., and then take the real part of the sum. Dividing through by the common factor $e^{i\omega t}$, we can write (3–17) as

$$A_1 e^{i\alpha_1} + A_2 e^{i\alpha_2} + \cdots = A e^{i\alpha}, \tag{3–18}$$

where the time no longer appears. From this we see that the resultant amplitude and phase are given respectively by the absolute value and by the argument of the complex number representing the sum $A_1 e^{i\alpha_1} + A_2 e^{i\alpha_2} \cdots$.

To actually compute A, we may use the well-known theorem that the square of the absolute value of a complex number equals the product of the number itself and its *complex conjugate number*. Indeed, by substituting $-i$ for i in Eq. (3–18) we obtain

$$A_1 e^{-i\alpha_1} + A_2 e^{-i\alpha_2} + \cdots = A e^{-i\alpha}, \qquad (3\text{–}19)$$

and (3–18) and (3–19) then yield

$$(A_1 e^{i\alpha_1} + A_2 e^{i\alpha_2} + \cdots) \cdot (A_1 e^{-i\alpha_1} + A_2 e^{-i\alpha_2} + \cdots)$$
$$= (A e^{i\alpha})(A e^{-i\alpha}) = A^2. \qquad (3\text{–}20)$$

There is, of course, a close connection between the two methods of representation of sinusoidal functions described under (b) and (c). In fact, it is well known that complex numbers can be represented graphically by points in the so-called complex plane [see Appendix 1(b)].

As an application of the rules of addition, we compute the sum of two sinusoidal functions, $A_1 \cos(\omega t + \alpha_1)$ and $A_2 \cos(\omega t + \alpha_2)$, by means of the vector method. For this purpose we construct two vectors of magnitudes A_1 and A_2, forming the angles α_1 and α_2, respectively, with the fixed axis OX (Fig. 3–6); the angle between the two vectors is then $\alpha_2 - \alpha_1$. The magnitude A of the vector sum satisfies the equation

$$A^2 = A_1^2 + A_2^2 + 2A_1 A_2 \cos(\alpha_2 - \alpha_1) . \qquad (3\text{–}21)$$

We see from this equation that the amplitude of A is a maximum when the phase difference $\alpha_2 - \alpha_1$ is zero or an even multiple of π, that is, when the two oscillations are *in phase*. In this case, A is the sum of A_1 and A_2. The resultant amplitude is a minimum when $\alpha_2 - \alpha_1$ is π or an odd multiple of π, that is, when the two oscillations have *opposite phase*. In this case, the resultant amplitude A is the difference between A_1 and A_2. In the general case, the resultant phase α satisfies the equations

$A \cos \alpha = A_1 \cos \alpha_1 + A_2 \cos \alpha_2,$

$A \sin \alpha = A_1 \sin \alpha_1 + A_2 \sin \alpha_2,$

$$(3\text{–}22)$$

which follow immediately from inspection of Fig. 3–6, and are identical to Eqs. (3–16). These equations

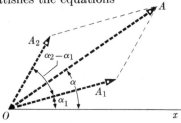

FIG. 3–6. Addition of two sinusoidal functions.

yield

$$\tan \alpha = \frac{A_1 \sin \alpha_1 + A_2 \sin \alpha_2}{A_1 \cos \alpha_1 + A_2 \cos \alpha_2}. \tag{3-23}$$

3–6 Interference of two spherical waves. Consider a homogeneous medium in which there are two point sources of sinusoidal spherical waves, S_1 and S_2 (Fig. 3–7), with the same period T. Let E_1 and E_2 be the optical disturbances arriving from the two sources at a point P; these can be written as

$$E_1 = A_1 \cos \left[2\pi \left(\frac{t}{T} - \frac{r_1}{\lambda} \right) + \varphi_1 \right],$$
$$E_2 = A_2 \cos \left[2\pi \left(\frac{t}{T} - \frac{r_2}{\lambda} \right) + \varphi_2 \right], \tag{3-24}$$

where r_1 and r_2 are the distances of S_1 and S_2 from P, and the amplitudes A_1 and A_2 depend on the strengths of the sources and on the distances r_1 and r_2. From the theorems of the preceding section, we conclude that the resultant optical disturbance at P is a sinusoidal function of period T and amplitude A given by

$$A^2 = A_1^2 + A_2^2 + 2A_1A_2 \cos \left[\frac{2\pi}{\lambda} (r_2 - r_1) - (\varphi_2 - \varphi_1) \right]. \tag{3-25}$$

Making use of the definition of intensity (Eq. 3–8), we obtain for the distribution of light intensity in the region of space surrounding the sources:

$$I = I_1 + I_2 + 2\sqrt{I_1 I_2} \cos \left[\frac{2\pi}{\lambda} (r_2 - r_1) - (\varphi_2 - \varphi_1) \right], \tag{3-26}$$

where I_1 and I_2 are the intensities observed when one or the other source is present alone, and I is the intensity observed when both sources are

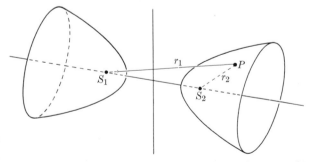

FIG. 3–7. Interference of spherical waves from two coherent point sources.

present simultaneously. We see that the resultant intensity I is greater or smaller than the sum of the two separate intensities, $I_1 + I_2$, depending on whether the third term on the right side of (3–26) is positive or negative; this term represents the effect of interference.   Intensity maxima are found at points where the two waves are in phase; i.e., where the two optical disturbances are simultaneously positive and simultaneously negative. Intensity minima are found at points where the two waves have opposite phase; i.e., where the maximum positive value of one optical disturbance occurs simultaneously with the maximum negative value of the other. Thus interference phenomena have a considerable effect on the local distribution of light intensity in the space surrounding the sources. They do not, however, change the space average of the intensity, which remains equal to the space average of $I_1 + I_2$, as is required by the principle of conservation of energy; we see immediately that this is true when we note that the average value over space of the interference term in Eq. (3–26) is zero.

In many instances, the distance between the two point sources is a very small fraction of the distance of either source from the point of observation, and the interference phenomena are observed in a region of space whose dimensions are also small compared with r_1 and r_2; I_1 and I_2 may then be regarded as independent of position. If, in addition, the two sources have equal strength, so that we can write $I_1 = I_2$, Eq. (3–26) becomes

$$I = 2I_1 \left\{ 1 + \cos\left[\frac{2\pi}{\lambda} (r_2 - r_1) - (\varphi_2 - \varphi_1) \right] \right\}. \qquad (3\text{–}27)$$

In this case, the intensity is zero at the minima and $4I_1$, or twice the sum of the separate intensities, at the maxima. Note that if we let I_0 represent the intensity at the maxima (so that $I_0 = 4I_1$), we can rewrite (3–27) as

$$I = I_0 \cos^2 \left[\frac{\pi}{\lambda} (r_2 - r_1) - \frac{\varphi_2 - \varphi_1}{2} \right]. \qquad (3\text{–}28)$$

The points of minimum and maximum intensity satisfy the equations

Intensity minima: $\dfrac{r_2 - r_1}{\lambda} - \dfrac{\varphi_2 - \varphi_1}{2\pi} = k + \dfrac{1}{2},$ (3–29)

Intensity maxima: $\dfrac{r_2 - r_1}{\lambda} - \dfrac{\varphi_2 - \varphi_1}{2\pi} = k,$ (3–30)

where k is zero or an integer (positive or negative). The surfaces defined by (3–29) and (3–30) are hyperboloids of revolution with their foci at the two point sources (Fig. 3–7).

If a diffusing screen lies in the path of the interfering waves, a series of bands, alternately light and dark, will appear on it. These are called *interference fringes;* the lines of minimum and maximum illumination are the intersections with the screen of the hyperboloids described by Eqs. (3–29) and (3–30). If the plane of the screen is perpendicular to the line connecting the two sources S_1, S_2, the interference fringes are circular, while if the plane of the screen is parallel to S_1S_2, they are hyperbolic. However, if the interference phenomena are observed near the plane $r_1 = r_2$, and if the dimensions of the screen are small compared with its distance from the sources, the fringes are practically straight, and are perpendicular to the line S_1S_2. Their positions can be determined by the elementary procedure illustrated in Fig. 3–8, where σ represents the plane of observation, perpendicular to the plane of the drawing. Let us assume, for the sake of simplicity, that the two sources are in phase, so that $\varphi_1 = \varphi_2$. Then at the point P_0, equidistant from S_1 and S_2, the two waves are in phase, and the resultant intensity is a maximum. Consider now a point P, a distance y from P_0. Let H be the foot of the perpendicular through S_1 to the straight line S_2P (Fig. 3–8). Since $\overline{S_1H}$ is very small compared with $\overline{S_1P}$, the triangle PS_1H is very nearly isosceles, and we can write, to good approximation,

$$r_2 - r_1 = \overline{S_2P} - \overline{S_1P} = \overline{S_2H}.$$

Let $h = \overline{S_1S_2}$ be the distance between the two sources, O the midpoint of the segment S_1S_2, $D = \overline{OP_0}$ the distance of the sources from the screen, and ϑ the angle POP_0. This angle is assumed to be very small, so that we may write

$$y = \overline{P_0P} = D\vartheta.$$

The angle ϑ is very nearly equal to the angle between S_2P and the perpendicular to S_1S_2, which is equal to the angle S_2S_1H. We thus obtain

$$r_2 - r_1 = \overline{S_2H} = h\vartheta.$$

From the last two equations, it follows that

$$y = \frac{D(r_2 - r_1)}{h} . \qquad (3\text{--}31)$$

Since interference maxima occur when $r_2 - r_1$ is an integral multiple of λ, and minima when $r_2 - r_1$ is an odd multiple of $\lambda/2$, Eq. (3–31)

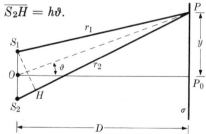

FIG. 3–8. Computation of the phase difference between waves from two point sources.

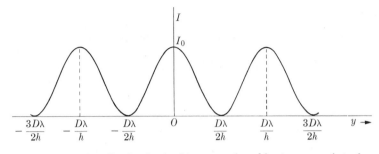

FIG. 3-9. Intensity distribution in the fringes produced by two-wave interference.

yields the following values of y at the centers of the fringes:

Bright fringes: $y = 0, \quad \lambda\dfrac{D}{h}, \quad 2\lambda\dfrac{D}{h}, \quad \cdots, \quad k\lambda\dfrac{D}{h}, \quad \cdots,$

$$(3\text{-}32)$$

Dark fringes: $y = \dfrac{\lambda}{2}\dfrac{D}{h}, \quad \dfrac{3\lambda}{2}\dfrac{D}{h}, \quad \cdots, \quad (k+\tfrac{1}{2})\lambda\dfrac{D}{h}, \quad \cdots.$

Thus bright and dark fringes follow each other at equal distances, the spacing between two neighboring bright or dark fringes being $\lambda D/h$. We see that this spacing is proportional to the wavelength λ, so that if λ is very small, it will be necessary to use sources very close to each other in order to produce interference fringes of sufficient width to be easily observed.

Between the maxima and the minima the intensity varies in a gradual fashion, as shown by the curve in Fig. 3-9, which applies to two sources with the same intensity and phase. The equation of this curve follows immediately from Eqs. (3-28) and (3-31); it is

$$I = I_0 \cos^2\left(\frac{\pi h y}{D\lambda}\right). \qquad (3\text{-}33)$$

3-7 Fresnel double mirror, Fresnel biprism, Lloyd's mirror. As was mentioned in Section 3-1, the observation of interference effects may be used as a means of investigating the form of light waves experimentally, since for any position of the sources the character of the interference pattern bears a definite relation to the function which describes the time dependence of the optical disturbance. For example, in the interference fringes discussed at the end of the preceding section, the spacing is proportional to the period of the wave, and the distribution of light intensity between the maxima and the minima is a consequence of the sinusoidal character of the function describing the time dependence of the optical disturbance.

Before discussing the results of interference experiments, we must state explicitly that it is impossible to observe interference effects between light waves emitted by independent sources. We can easily understand why this is so, if we take into consideration the fact that any light source used in optical experiments, such as an incandescent wire or a gas discharge tube, consists of a large number of microscopic, uncorrelated sources, each of which is active for certain short periods of time, and quiescent the rest of the time. Assume, for the sake of argument, that during their active periods all microscopic sources emit trains of sinusoidal waves of the same wavelength. The resultant optical disturbance produced by the source as a whole may then be represented by a sinusoidal function of time, whose phase and amplitude change whenever one of the microscopic sources goes on or off. Consequently, the optical disturbances produced by two such microscopic sources, however similar they may be, will have a phase difference $\varphi_2 - \varphi_1$ that varies rapidly and irregularly with time; we say that the two sources are *incoherent*. The positions of the interference fringes will change as the phase difference changes; at a given instant, a maximum of intensity will occur at a point where a minimum was present a short time before, and vice versa. Since neither the eye nor other optical devices can resolve such very rapid fluctuations of intensity, the observable result will be uniform illumination of the screen.

It is clear from the foregoing that in order to observe interference phenomena, it is necessary to use *coherent* light sources, i.e., sources whose phase difference remains constant in time. It is possible to create such sources either by using a source S and its optical image S', or by using two different images S_1 and S_2 of the same source. In this manner, we observe interference between light beams which originated at the same source and meet again in a given region of space after having followed different paths.

Figure 3–10 illustrates schematically the principle of one well-known method, the *Fresnel double-mirror experiment*, by which interference phenomena can be observed.

A beam of light coming from a point source S (which may be, for example, a small hole in an opaque screen strongly illuminated with yellow light from a sodium arc*) is reflected by two mirrors whose planes form a very small angle. The reflected beams appear to originate from the two virtual mirror images S_1 and S_2 of S. In the region of space where the two beams overlap, interference phenomena occur, and a series of equally spaced bright and dark fringes, such as those described at the end of the preceding

---

*A sodium arc can be obtained from an ordinary DC carbon arc lamp by drilling a hole in the end of the positive carbon and filling it with common salt.

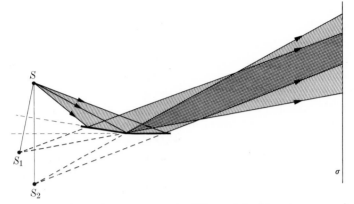

FIG. 3–10. Schematic arrangement of Fresnel double-mirror experiment.

section, appears on a diffusing screen σ parallel to the intersection of the mirrors. Moreover, careful measurements show that the variation of intensity across the interference band follows the law derived from the assumption that the interfering waves are sinusoidal in character (Eq. 3–28); thus we conclude that the light emitted by the sodium arc consists of waves which are nearly sinusoidal.

We obtain similar results using other light sources, such as certain gas discharge tubes or ordinary carbon arcs with appropriate light filters. Whenever the observed interference pattern has the characteristic appearance predicted for the case of sinusoidal waves, we find that the light which produces it has a definite color. We also find that the width of the interference fringes changes as the color changes; for example, the fringes observed with red light are almost twice as wide as those observed with blue light. These results lead us to associate sinusoidal waves of different wavelengths with light of different pure colors. The eye, of course, is a rather crude instrument, incapable of distinguishing between wave forms that differ only slightly; hence we shall adopt a physical rather than a physiological definition of color, and when we refer to a *monochromatic* wave, or wave of a single color, we shall mean a perfectly sinusoidal light wave. Of course, since a perfectly sinusoidal wave of infinite length does not exist in nature, the concept of perfectly monochromatic light is also an abstraction. We shall return to this point later.

Fresnel mirrors give easily observable interference fringes only when the two mirrors form a very small angle, so that the two virtual sources S_1 and S_2 are very close to each other; this indicates that light waves have a very small length. By measuring the angle between the mirrors, we can determine the distance h between the two sources in a given experiment, and from this quantity, the known distance of the screen, and the observed spacing of the interference fringes, we can compute the wavelength of the light used in the experiment [see Eqs. (3–32)]. Table 3–1 gives the wavelengths corresponding to different colors, expressed in angstroms [1 angstrom (1 A) $= 10^{-8}$ cm $= 10^{-10}$ m]. The values listed have only an approximate meaning, of course, because a color described generically as "red" or "blue" corresponds to a fairly wide range of wavelengths.

In Chapter 5 we shall describe experiments for the determination of the velocity of light. Anticipating the results obtained there, we state here that the velocity of light in vacuum or in air is approximately 3×10^{10} cm/sec. From the relation $\lambda = cT$ and from the known wavelength, we can then compute the period T of light waves; this also appears in Table 3–1. We see that the period is an extremely short interval on any ordinary time scale.

TABLE 3–1

Color	Red	Yellow	Green	Blue	Violet
(A)	6500	5800	5000	4500	4000
T (10^{-15} sec)	2.2	1.9	1.7	1.5	1.3

Consider two rays that arrive from the source at the same point P in space after being reflected by two different mirrors. Since the two rays are in phase when they leave the source, it is clear that their phase difference at P is $2\pi(r_2 - r_1)/\lambda$, where r_1 and r_2 represent the distances actually traveled by the two rays between S and P. It follows from the laws of reflection that r_1 and r_2 also represent the distances of the two virtual sources S_1 and S_2, respectively, from P. Points that are equidistant from S_1 and S_2 (that is, points such that $r_1 = r_2$) are reached simultaneously by rays that have left the source S at the same instant. At these points the intensity has a maximum called the *interference maximum of order zero*. Similarly, the interference maxima of order one, two, . . . , k, are defined as those occurring at points such that $r_2 - r_1 = \lambda, 2\lambda, \ldots, k\lambda$. Two rays arriving simultaneously at the interference maximum of order k have left S at times such that one is delayed k periods with respect to the other.

The following detail is worth mentioning. If the point source S moves in a direction parallel to the intersection of the mirrors, the interference fringes, which are also parallel to this direction, slide along themselves. For moderate displacements of the source, no appreciable change occurs in the interference pattern observed on the screen. Consequently, we can use a line source instead of a point source of light in the experiment here discussed, which makes it possible to increase the intensity of illumination.

Figure 3–11 shows how the Fresnel double-mirror experiment can

Slit   Double mirror   Ocular

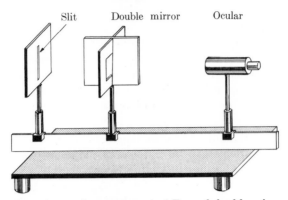

FIG. 3–11. Experimental arrangement of Fresnel double-mirror experiment.

FIG. 3–12. Photograph of the interference fringes produced by Fresnel's double mirror.

actually be performed. Figure 3–12 is a photograph of the interference fringes obtained with this experiment.

Let us now consider what happens if we perform the double-mirror experiment with white light instead of monochromatic light. White light, as we have already mentioned, results from the superposition of light of many different colors, i.e., many different wavelengths. Each wavelength gives rise to a separate system of fringes. The interference maximum of order zero is common to all wavelengths, for it occurs at points equidistant from S_1 and S_2; therefore the line satisfying the equation $r_2 = r_1$ appears on the screen as a bright white fringe. This fringe is bordered on both sides by bands of various colors, caused by the superposition of the interference fringes corresponding to the different wavelengths. For example, the place where the violet light produces the interference maximum of the first order lies not far from the place where red light interferes destructively. Weakening of the long wavelengths and strengthening of the short ones results in the appearance of a bluish hue (further discussion of interference with white light will appear in Section 3–14).

Interference phenomena similar to those produced by Fresnel mirrors can be observed by means of other experimental arrangements, such as the *Fresnel biprism* and *Lloyd's mirror*. The Fresnel biprism, which is schematically illustrated in Fig. 3–13, produces two coherent virtual images of a point source or a line source located in its plane of symmetry. With

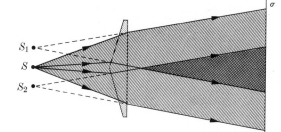

FIG. 3–13. Fresnel biprism.

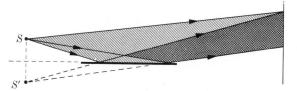

FIG. 3–14. Lloyd's mirror.

Lloyd's mirror (Fig. 3–14), we obtain interference between light waves coming from a point source and from its specular image in a plane mirror.

3–8 Interference in thin films. Reflection of light from the two surfaces of a thin transparent film produces interference phenomena that are particularly easy to observe. To interpret these phenomena, we refer to Fig. 3–15. Monochromatic light from the point source S falls on a thin film and is reflected to the converging lens L, which forms an image of the film on the screen σ. Consider the ray SPA reflected at the point P of the upper surface of the film, and the ray $SCEPB$ that passes through the same point P after having been reflected at the point E of the lower surface. The lens L brings the two rays together again at P', the image of P. As we saw in Section 2–5, the optical path lengths of the two rays between P and P' are equal; therefore the two rays arrive at P' with the same phase difference that they had at P. To compute this phase difference, we note that the optical path lengths of the two rays from S to P are $l_1 = n_0\,\overline{SP}$ and $l_2 = n_0\,\overline{SC} + n(\overline{CE} + \overline{EP})$, where n is the index of refraction of the film and n_0 that of the medium in which the film is immersed ($n_0 = 1$ if this medium is air). Therefore

$$l_2 - l_1 = -n_0(\overline{SP} - \overline{SC}) + n(\overline{CE} + \overline{EP}).$$

Let d be the thickness of the film, and φ and φ' the angles of incidence and refraction of the ray SC. Making use of Snell's law ($n_0 \sin \varphi = n \sin \varphi'$)

and considering that, since the film is very thin, $\overline{PC}$ is very small compared with $\overline{SC}$, we obtain, to a good approximation,

$$n_0 \left(\overline{SP} - \overline{SC} \right) = n_0 \, \overline{PC} \sin \varphi$$

$$= 2d \, n_0 \tan \varphi' \sin \varphi$$

$$= 2n \, d \, \frac{\sin^2 \varphi'}{\cos \varphi'} \, ,$$

$$n \left(\overline{CE} + \overline{EP} \right) = \frac{2d \, n}{\cos \varphi'} \, ,$$

and therefore

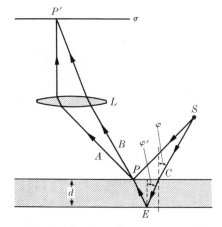

FIG. 3–15.   Interference in a thin film, observed by reflection.

$$l_2 - l_1 = 2d \, n \left(-\frac{\sin^2 \varphi'}{\cos \varphi'} + \frac{1}{\cos \varphi'} \right) = 2d \, n \cos \varphi'. \qquad (3\text{–}34)$$

The phase difference corresponding to this difference in optical path length (see Section 3–3) is $2\pi(l_2 - l_1)/\lambda_0$, where λ_0 is the wavelength in vacuum. There is, however, an additional phase difference π due to the fact that the ray SPA is reflected at the upper surface of the film, where the index of refraction changes from n_0 to n, while the ray $SCEPB$ is reflected at the lower surface, where the index of refraction changes from n to n_0 (See Section 3–4). Thus the two reflected rays meet at P and then again at P' with a phase difference α given by

$$\alpha = 2\pi \frac{l_2 - l_1}{\lambda_0} - \pi, \qquad \text{or} \qquad \alpha = 2\pi \left(\frac{2nd \cos \varphi'}{\lambda_0} - \frac{1}{2} \right). \quad (3\text{–}35)$$

In particular, if the lens is so located as to collect rays that are reflected by the film in a nearly perpendicular direction, $\cos \varphi'$ is very close to unity, and (3–35) reduces to

$$\alpha = 2\pi \left(\frac{2nd}{\lambda_0} - \frac{1}{2} \right). \qquad (3\text{–}36)$$

Interference of the two rays at P' will produce a maximum of intensity if α is an integral multiple of 2π; that is, if the condition

$$\frac{2nd}{\lambda_0} = k + \frac{1}{2} \, , \qquad k = 0, 1, 2, \ldots, \qquad (3\text{–}37)$$

is satisfied. The interference will produce a minimum of intensity if α is an odd multiple of π, that is, if

$$\frac{2nd}{\lambda_0} = k, \qquad k = 0, 1, 2, \ldots \tag{3-38}$$

If we let $\lambda = \lambda_0/n$ be the wavelength in the film, we can rewrite (3–37) and (3–38) as

$$\text{Interference maxima:} \qquad d = (2k + 1)\frac{\lambda}{4}, \tag{3-39}$$

$$\text{Interference minima:} \qquad d = k\frac{\lambda}{2}. \tag{3-40}$$

Hence we conclude that interference maxima occur when the thickness d of the film is an odd multiple of $\lambda/4$, and minima occur when d is an even multiple of $\lambda/4$. If the film does not have the same thickness everywhere, the image of the film formed by the lens on the screen will show a different brightness from place to place.

It should be pointed out that it is possible to observe interference phenomena in thin films without the use of a lens, by looking at the film directly. In this case, the optical system of the eye forms a real image of the film on the retina. On a film of variable thickness illuminated by a monochromatic light source, a system of dark and bright interference fringes will be seen; the lines where the thickness of the film satisfies Eq. (3–39) will stand out as lines of maximum brightness, and those where the thickness of the film satisfies (3–40) will stand out as dark lines. In general, lines of equal thickness will appear as lines of equal brightness.

With a point source such as we have considered so far, interference fringes are seen on only that portion of the film which reflects the light rays from the source into the lens (or the pupil of the eye). This portion becomes smaller as the diameter of the lens decreases; on the other hand, if the diameter of the lens is sufficiently small compared with the distance of the lens from the film, we can use a broad light source, and thus observe interference fringes on the whole film. The reason for this is that with a small lens diameter, the angle of reflection φ' is practically the same for all rays reflected at a given point of the film into the lens, and so, for all pairs of rays that can enter the lens (Fig. 3–15), $\cos\varphi'$ and d are constant and the phase difference α (Eq. 3–35) also has a constant value. The pupil of the eye, in particular, is small enough so that the condition described above is always satisfied when we look at the film directly.

The case of nearly perpendicular incidence is particularly interesting. Here the interference fringes remain sharp even if the lens has a fairly large diameter, because $\cos\varphi'$ changes very slowly in the neighborhood of $\varphi' = 0$. For the actual observation of the fringes, the experimental arrangement shown in Fig. 3–16 may be used: light from a source placed on one side of the film is partially reflected onto the film by a half-silvered

glass plate whose plane forms an angle of 45° with the plane of the film,
and a fraction of the light reflected by
the film passes through the plate to
reach the lens or the observer's eye.

It may be useful to look at the
phenomena analyzed above from a
slightly different point of view. Rays
coming from a given point of an extended source and undergoing reflection at the two faces of a thin film
produce a given system of interference fringes on an arbitrary observation plane. In general, the interference patterns corresponding to dif-

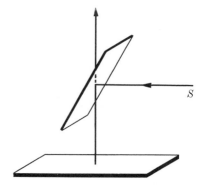

Fig. 3–16. Observation of interference fringes in a thin film, for light at
perpendicular incidence.

ferent points of the source do not overlap. At each point of the observation
plane, rays originating from certain points of the source will interfere constructively, while rays originating from certain other points of the source
will interfere destructively, and the resultant effect will be a nearly uniform
illumination. However, if the source is not too extended, and if the rays
from the source strike the film in directions not too far from the perpendicular, there is one plane of observation, namely, the plane of the film
itself, on which the various systems of interference fringes are almost
exactly coincident. This will not happen on any other plane except the
plane on which a converging lens may form a real image of the film. To
describe this situation, we say that the interference fringes produced by a
film of variable thickness illuminated by a broad source are *localized in the
plane of the film*.

We note that the above results apply both to films whose index of
refraction is greater than that of the surrounding medium (e.g., a thin
plate of glass, or a film of soapy water in air) and to films whose index of
refraction is smaller than that of the surrounding medium (e.g., a thin air
space between two glass plates). In the latter case, inversion of phase
does not occur in the reflection of light at the surface of entrance into the
film, but it does occur at the second surface. The situation is different if
the film lies between two media of which one has a larger and the other a
smaller index of refraction than the film. In this case either there is
inversion of phase at both surfaces, or there is no inversion at either surface,
and consequently Eq. (3–39) becomes the condition for interference
minima and (3–40) that for interference maxima. In all cases, of course,
n represents the index of refraction of the film, and λ the wavelength in
the film.

Figure 3–17 illustrates a historical experiment on interference in thin

films. A plano-convex lens of great
focal length lies with its curved face
on a plane glass plate. The air space
between the lens and the plate is the
equivalent of a film of variable thickness, which produces the interference fringes described previously. If
light from a broad source falls upon
the film at nearly right angles to its
surfaces, the fringes are circular,
with a common center at the point of
contact between the lens and the
plate (Fig. 3–18). The interference
fringes observed with this arrangement were described in detail by

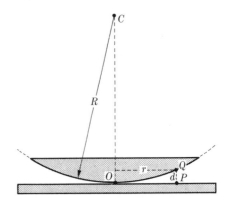

FIG. 3–17. Schematic arrangement
for the observation of Newton's rings.

Newton, and are known as Newton's rings; they were probably the first
interference phenomena to be studied quantitatively.

Let R be the radius of curvature of the lens, and $d = \overline{PQ}$ be the thickness of the air film at a distance $r = \overline{OP}$ from the point of contact. From
the sagitta theorem [see Appendix 1(d)], we obtain

$$(2R - d)d = r^2,$$

or, since $d \ll R$,

$$r^2 = 2Rd. \qquad (3\text{--}41)$$

This equation, together with (3–39)
and (3–40), yields for the radii of the
circles of maximum and minimum
intensity:

Interference maxima:

$$r^2 = \frac{2k+1}{2}\,R\lambda,$$

$$\qquad (3\text{--}42)$$

Interference minima:

$$r^2 = kR\lambda.$$

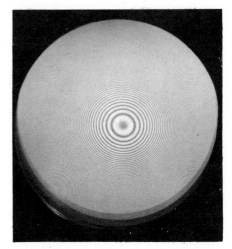

In particular, the point of contact
($r = 0$) appears dark by reflection.

FIG. 3–18. Photograph of Newton's
rings.

This is natural, of course, because a film of zero thickness is equivalent to no film at all.

If the plane glass plate and the lens are slowly moved apart, the radius of the circle formed by the points where the thickness of the air film has a given fixed value will gradually decrease. Therefore the interference rings will gradually collapse toward the center, while new rings will appear at the periphery. Every time the separation between the lens and the plate changes by a quarter of a wavelength, a bright interference fringe will take the place of a dark one, and vice versa. In particular, the common center of the rings, which is dark when the lens is in direct contact with the plate, becomes alternately bright and dark, the maximum of intensity at this point being observed when the minimum distance of the lens from the plate is $\lambda/4$, $3\lambda/4$ or, in general, an odd multiple of $\lambda/4$. The effect described above may be used as a sensitive and precise method for measuring very small displacements, of the order of the wavelength of light.

For the reasons explained before, the experimental arrangement used for the observation of Newton's rings produces fringes localized in the plane of the air film if the source is broad, and nonlocalized interference phenomena if the source has very small dimensions. The latter phenomena can be analyzed quantitatively in the present case. The plane and spherical surfaces that limit the air film form two virtual specular images S_1 and S_2 of a point source S (Fig. 3–19), and the reflected spherical waves centered at S_1 and S_2 overlap, producing the interference effects described in Section 3–6. The surfaces of maximum and minimum intensity are hyperboloids of revolution around the line $S_1 S_2$. Suppose that the source lies on the straight line passing through the center of curvature of the spherical surface and through its point of contact with the plane surface; then on any plane perpendicular to this line there will appear a system of circular interference fringes. These are identical to Newton's rings if the plane of observation coincides with the plane of the film.

This discussion of interference in thin films illustrates the general rule that localized sources give rise to nonlocalized interference effects, whereas nonlocalized sources can produce only localized interference effects.

Interference phenomena in thin films can be observed not only by reflection but also by transmission. In the latter case, interference takes place between the light beam that traverses the film directly and the one that emerges from the film after two internal reflections (Fig. 3–20). The second beam undergoes no change of phase at reflection if the index of refraction of the film is greater than that of the surrounding medium, whereas it reverses its phase twice if the index of refraction of the film is smaller than that of the medium; since a change of phase of 2π is equivalent to no change, the result is the same in either case. We can easily see that Eq. (3–39) now becomes the condition for the interference minima,

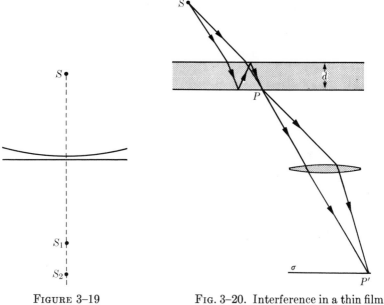

FIGURE 3–19   FIG. 3–20. Interference in a thin film
                          observed by transmission.

and (3–40) the condition for the maxima; therefore, the interference fringes observed by transmission are complementary to those observed by reflection. Note, however, that the interference fringes observed by transmission are much fainter than those observed by reflection. This is so because the reflected light wave has a much smaller amplitude than the directly transmitted light wave, so that the two waves do not even approximately cancel each other at the interference minima. In the case discussed previously, on the other hand, the two waves reflected by the opposite faces of the film have nearly the same intensity.

For a more rigorous and complete discussion of interference phenomena in thin films, it would be necessary also to consider the waves that have undergone multiple reflections within the film (see next section). However, unless the surfaces of the film are made highly reflecting by a light metallic deposit, the intensity decreases rapidly with the increasing number of reflections, so that the contribution of multiply reflected waves is negligible.

In the previous discussion we have assumed that the light source is monochromatic. With a source of white light, the interference in thin films will produce fringes of different colors instead of fringes of different brightness. This effect, analogous to that discussed in Section 3–8, explains, for example, the bright colors of soap bubbles.

3–9 Interference fringes observed with plane-parallel plates.   Interference by many waves.   In the preceding section we have considered the interference effects that appear in the plane of a film of variable thickness. We now wish to investigate a related but somewhat different class of interference phenomena.   Instead of a film of variable thickness, we use a film or a plate with rigorously plane and parallel surfaces, and instead of looking directly at the film, we receive the reflected or transmitted rays on a telescope focused at infinity.   In this manner we can observe interference between parallel rays that arise from a single ray by reflection at the surfaces of the plate and are brought together again in the focal plane of the objective lens of the telescope (Fig. 3–21).

As in the previous case, we use a broad source, so that the plate is illuminated by rays coming from various directions.   The phase difference between interfering rays is a function of the angle at which the rays are reflected or transmitted by the plate, and rays entering the telescope at a given angle to its axis are focused by the objective lens at points of a circle lying in its focal plane. Thus, if the axis of the telescope is perpendicular to the plate, the interference fringes have a circular shape. These interference fringes are said to be *localized at infinity*.

If the surfaces of the plate are uncoated, we could, as before, disregard rays that have undergone more than two internal reflections and study the interference effects as if they were due to the superposition of only two waves. However, we choose to treat the problem in a more general way, taking into account multiple internal reflections, so that the validity of the results will not be restricted to the case where the reflectivity of the surfaces of the plate is small.   Each ray incident upon the plate (such as SR_0 in Fig. 3–22) gives rise to an infinite number of parallel transmitted rays $(T_1T_1', T_2T_2', T_3T_3',$ etc.): the first has gone directly through the plate, the second has undergone two internal reflections, the third four, etc. Similarly, the incident ray gives rise to an infinite number of parallel reflected rays $(R_0R_0', R_1R_1', R_2R_2',$ etc.): the first has been reflected at the upper surface of the plate, the second has undergone one internal reflection, the third three, etc.

Let us consider first the transmitted rays, which are brought together at a point P in the focal plane of the objective lens of the telescope. Two neighboring rays (e.g., T_1T_1' and T_2T_2') arrive at P with the same

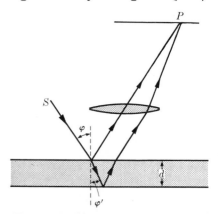

FIG. 3–21. Observation of the interference fringes localized at infinity.

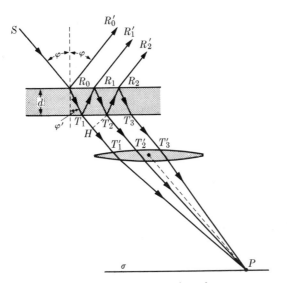

FIG. 3–22. Multiple-wave interference.

phase difference that they have at the points H and T_2, where H is the foot of the perpendicular to $T_1 T_1'$ through T_2. If l_1 and l_2 are optical distances from the source to the points H and T_2, we find that

$$l_2 - l_1 = 2n \, \overline{R_0 T_1} - n_0 \, \overline{T_1 H},$$

where n is the index of refraction of the plate, and n_0 that of the surrounding medium. If we let d be the thickness of the plate, φ the angle of incidence, and φ' the angle of refraction, we obtain from the above equation

$$l_2 - l_1 = 2n \, \frac{d}{\cos \varphi'} - n_0 \, 2d \tan \varphi' \sin \varphi,$$

or

$$l_2 - l_1 = 2d \, n \cos \varphi'. \tag{3–43}$$

This equation gives the difference in optical path between two neighboring transmitted rays, from the source to the point of convergence. Note that Eq. (3–43) happens to be identical to Eq. (3–34); however (3–43) holds rigorously, while (3–34) is valid only for the case of a small film thickness.

If the surfaces of the plate are uncoated, the internal reflections occur without change of phase when $n > n_0$ and with a phase change of π when $n < n_0$. The phase change due to a double internal reflection is zero in the first case and 2π in the second. In both cases the phase difference between neighboring rays is due exclusively to the difference in their optical paths, and is therefore given by

$$\alpha = 2\pi \frac{l_2 - l_1}{\lambda_0},$$

or

$$\alpha = 2\pi \frac{2d \cos \varphi'}{\lambda}, \tag{3-44}$$

where λ_0 is the wavelength in the surrounding medium and $\lambda = n_0\lambda_0/n$ is the wavelength in the plate. If the surfaces of the plate are lightly silvered, the internal reflections may produce a phase change different from zero or π, and the phase difference between neighboring rays may differ by a constant quantity from the value given above.

When the angle of incidence is such that α is zero or an integral multiple of 2π, all transmitted rays are in phase, so that in the vector diagram (Fig. 3–23) the rotating vectors representing the various rays are parallel. Their lengths form an infinite geometric series, because each internal reflection reduces the amplitude by a constant factor; the terms of the series decrease slowly in magnitude if the reflectance of the surfaces of the plate is high, and rapidly if it is low (Fig. 3–23b). The sum of these vectors (found by drawing them so that the head of the mth vector coincides with the tail of the $(m + 1)$th) is a vector of finite length, representing the resultant amplitude.

Consider now a slightly different angle of incidence, such that the phase difference between neighboring rays differs by a small amount $\Delta\alpha$ from an integral multiple of 2π. In the case of high reflectance (Fig. 3–24a), the straight segment formed by the representative vectors changes into a broken line, approaching the shape of a spiral. This line consists of an infinite number of segments of slowly decreasing length, each at an angle $\Delta\alpha$ to the preceding one. The vector connecting the tail end of the first vector with the asymptotic point of the "spiral" represents the resultant optical disturbance. Its length decreases rapidly at first with increasing $\Delta\alpha$. Then, as $\Delta\alpha$ continues to increase, the "spiral" winds in an increasing number of turns, but the length of the resultant vector always remains very small compared with the stretched-out length of the "spiral" until

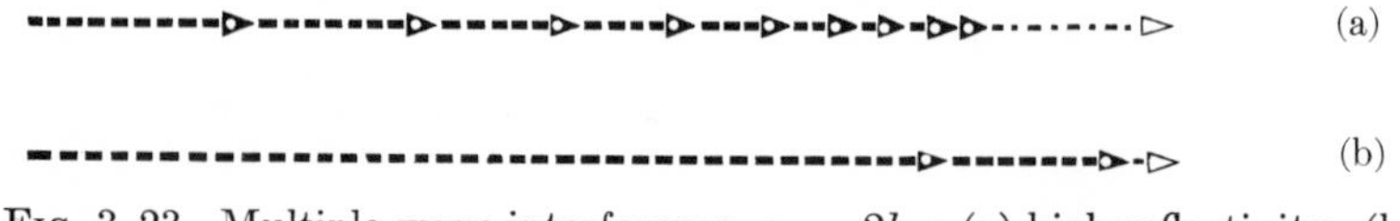

Fig. 3–23. Multiple-wave interference, $\alpha = 2k\pi$; (a) high reflectivity, (b) low reflectivity.

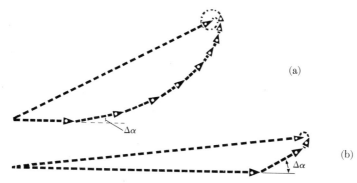

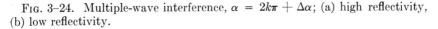

FIG. 3–24. Multiple-wave interference, $\alpha = 2k\pi + \Delta\alpha$; (a) high reflectivity, (b) low reflectivity.

$\Delta\alpha$ approaches 2π. When $\Delta\alpha$ equals 2π the rays are again all in phase and the resultant amplitude again acquires its maximum value.

We see that the light intensity will always be small, except when the phase difference between neighboring rays is close to an integral multiple of 2π. It follows that the interference fringes observed by transmission through a plane parallel plate with highly reflecting surfaces consist of *narrow bright lines on a dark background*.

If, on the other hand, the reflectance is low (Fig. 3–24b), the resultant optical disturbance is practically equal to the vector sum of the vectors representing the two first transmitted rays (T_1T_1', T_2T_2'). Its amplitude changes slowly with increasing $\Delta\alpha$ and never approaches zero. Thus the interference fringes are broad and faint.

In either case the position of the maxima is determined by the equation

$$\alpha = 2k\pi,$$

or, from Eq. (3–44),

$$d \cos \varphi' = \frac{k}{2} \lambda. \tag{3–45}$$

Making use of Snell's law, we can write the above equation in terms of the angle of incidence φ and the wavelength λ_0 in the surrounding medium, as

$$d \sqrt{n^2 - n_0^2 \sin^2 \varphi} = \frac{k}{2} n_0\lambda_0. \tag{3–46}$$

To make our discussion quantitative, let us suppose that the thickness of the plate is such as to make the maximum of order k_0 appear at the center, i.e., at the point corresponding to $\varphi = 0$, $\varphi' = 0$. This condition yields

$$d = \frac{k_0}{2}\,\lambda.$$

The maximum of order k then corresponds to the angle φ_k' given by

$$\cos \varphi_k' = \frac{k}{k_0}.$$

If φ_k' is small, so that we can take $\cos \varphi_k' = 1 - (\varphi_k')^2/2$, we obtain

$$\varphi_k' = \sqrt{\frac{2}{k_0}}\,\sqrt{k_0 - k} = \sqrt{\frac{\lambda}{d}}\,\sqrt{k_0 - k}. \qquad (3\text{--}47)$$

The corresponding angle of incidence (and of emergence) is

$$\varphi_k = \frac{n}{n_0}\,\varphi_k' = \frac{n\lambda_0}{dn_0}\,\sqrt{k_0 - k}. \qquad (3\text{--}48)$$

Thus, for example, the first bright ring (i.e., the ring corresponding to the interference maximum of order $k = k_0 - 1$) is formed by rays emerging from the plate at an angle equal to $\sqrt{(n\lambda_0)/(dn_0)}$ with respect to the normal.

We see that the width of the fringes decreases as the thickness of the plates increases. Only if $\sqrt{\lambda/d}$ is a small fraction of a radian will several rings be visible through the telescope; therefore, in order to observe the interference fringes here described, we must use plates of thickness large compared with the wavelength.* The reader will remember that, on the contrary, interference fringes of equal thickness are observed with films of thickness comparable to the wavelength.

We have assumed so far that α is given by Eq. (3–44). As we have already pointed out, if there is a metallic deposit at the surfaces of the plates, α differs from the value given by (3–44) by an essentially constant additive term. The presence of this term does not significantly alter the results.

If we investigate the interference fringes produced by the reflected rays, we find that when the surfaces of the plate have high reflectance, these fringes appear as dark rings on a bright background, while when the reflectance is low, the intensity maxima are broad. If the surfaces of the plate are uncoated, the interference pattern observed by reflection is exactly complementary to the interference pattern observed by trans-

---

*There is, however, an upper limit to the thickness, as we shall see in Section 3–14.

mission, as is required by the conservation of energy. This is no longer true when the surfaces of the plate are covered by a thin metallic film, which, while increasing the reflectance, also partially absorbs the light rays.

*3–10 Mathematical treatment of multiple-wave interference. In order to develop a more complete and rigorous theory of the interference phenomena observed with plane-parallel plates, it is convenient to use the complex representation of sinusoidal functions discussed in Section 3–5(c). Let us first assume, for the sake of simplicity, that there is no metallic deposit on the surface of the plates, so that no phase changes different from zero or π occur at reflection or refraction. We shall denote by τ the ratio of the transmitted to the incident amplitude when the wave passes from the plate to the surrounding medium, and by τ' this ratio when the wave passes from the surrounding medium to the plate. Let ρ and ρ' be the corresponding ratios of the reflected to the incident amplitudes (see Section 3–4), and let A be the amplitude of the incident ray. The first transmitted ray, $T_1 T_1'$ (Fig. 3–22), has been refracted once at the face of entrance into the plate and again at the face of exit. The second transmitted ray, $T_2 T_2'$, has undergone the same two refractions and, in addition, two internal reflections; and so on for the other rays. Thus, apart from a common phase factor which depends upon the location of the telescope, the optical disturbances of the various transmitted rays at the point of interference are represented by

$$E_{t1} = \tau\tau'Ae^{i\omega t},$$

$$E_{t2} = \tau\tau'\rho^2 Ae^{i(\omega t - \alpha)},$$

$$\vdots$$

$$E_{tm} = \tau\tau'\rho^{2(m-1)}Ae^{i[\omega t - (m-1)\alpha]} = \tau\tau'Ae^{i\omega t}(\rho^2 e^{-i\alpha})^{m-1},$$

$$\vdots$$

where α is again the phase difference between neighboring rays. The resultant optical disturbance is

$$E_t = E_{t1} + E_{t2} + \cdots + E_{tm} + \cdots = \tau\tau'Ae^{i\omega t} \sum_{m=1}^{\infty} (\rho^2 e^{-i\alpha})^{m-1}.$$

The infinite sum [see Appendix 1(c)] has the value

$$\sum_{1}^{\infty} (\rho^2 e^{-i\alpha})^{m-1} = \frac{1}{1 - \rho^2 e^{-i\alpha}} \; ; \qquad (3-49)$$

and therefore E_t is given by

$$E_t = \frac{\tau\tau'}{1 - \rho^2 e^{-i\alpha}} A e^{i\omega t}. \qquad (3\text{-}50)$$

To find the corresponding intensity I_t, we recall the relation between intensity and amplitude of a sinusoidal wave (Eq. 3-8) and the theorem stating that the square of the absolute value of a complex number equals the product of the number and its complex conjugate [see Appendix 1(b)]. From Eq. (3-49) it then follows that

$$I_t = \frac{K(\tau\tau')^2 A^2}{(1 - \rho^2 e^{-i\alpha})(1 - \rho^2 e^{i\alpha})} = \frac{K(\tau\tau')^2 A^2}{1 + \rho^4 - \rho^2(e^{i\alpha} + e^{-i\alpha})} .$$

If we let I be the intensity of the incident ray,

$$I = KA^2,$$

and if we take into account Eq. (A1-16) of the Appendix, we obtain

$$I_t = \frac{(\tau\tau')^2}{1 + \rho^4 - 2\rho^2 \cos\alpha} I. \qquad (3\text{-}51)$$

The reflected intensity can be computed by a similar procedure. The optical disturbances produced at the point of interference of the various reflected rays are represented by

$$E_{r0} = \rho' A e^{i\omega t},$$

$$E_{r1} = \tau\tau' \rho A e^{i(\omega t - \alpha)},$$

$$E_{r2} = \tau\tau' \rho^3 A e^{i(\omega t - 2\alpha)},$$

$$\vdots$$

$$E_{rm} = \tau\tau' \rho^{2m-1} A e^{i(\omega t - m\alpha)},$$

$$\vdots$$

The resultant disturbance is

$$E_r = E_{r0} + E_{r1} + E_{r2} + \cdots + E_{rm} + \cdots$$

$$= A e^{i\omega t} \left[\rho' + \tau\tau' \rho e^{-i\alpha} \sum_{1}^{\infty} \left(\rho^2 e^{-i\alpha} \right)^{m-1} \right],$$

or

$$E_r = \left[\rho' + \frac{\tau\tau'\,\rho e^{-i\alpha}}{1 - \rho^2 e^{-i\alpha}} \right] A e^{i\omega t}. \tag{3-52}$$

In the case under discussion, the relations between ρ, ρ', τ, and τ' developed in Section 3–4 [Eqs. (3–13) and (3–14)] apply. We can use these equations to eliminate ρ' and $\tau\tau'$. The equations for the transmitted and reflected disturbances [Eqs. (3–50) and (3–52)] then become

$$E_t = \frac{1 - \rho^2}{1 - \rho^2 e^{-i\alpha}} A e^{i\omega t}, \tag{3-53}$$

$$E_r = \frac{\rho(e^{-i\alpha} - 1)}{1 - \rho^2 e^{-i\alpha}} A e^{i\omega t}. \tag{3-54}$$

The equation for the transmitted intensity (Eq. 3–51) may be written as

$$I_t = \frac{(1 - \rho^2)^2}{1 + \rho^4 - 2\rho^2 \cos\alpha} I. \tag{3-55}$$

From Eq. (3–54) it follows that the reflected intensity is

$$I_r = K \frac{\rho^2 (e^{-i\alpha} - 1)(e^{i\alpha} - 1)}{(1 - \rho^2 e^{-i\alpha})(1 - \rho^2 e^{i\alpha})} A^2,$$

or

$$I_r = \frac{2\rho^2 (1 - \cos\alpha)}{1 + \rho^4 - 2\rho^2 \cos\alpha} I. \tag{3-56}$$

Equations (3–55) and (3–56) contain the complete solution of our problem. Remembering that $\cos\alpha = 1 - 2\sin^2(\alpha/2)$, the reader can easily check that these equations are equivalent to

$$I_t = \frac{(1 - \rho^2)^2}{(1 - \rho^2)^2 + 4\rho^2 \sin^2(\alpha/2)} I, \tag{3-57}$$

$$I_r = \frac{4\rho^2 \sin^2(\alpha/2)}{(1 - \rho^2)^2 + 4\rho^2 \sin^2(\alpha/2)} I. \tag{3-58}$$

Note that
$$I_t + I_r = I;$$

that is, the sum of the transmitted and reflected intensities is equal to the intensity of the incident ray for all values of α. As already pointed out, this result, which also follows directly from the law of conservation of energy, shows that the interference fringes observed by transmission and by reflection are complementary.

Let us first consider the transmitted beam. When α is an integral multiple of 2π, intensity maxima appear, with the value

$$(I_t)_{\max} = I.$$

When α is an odd multiple of π, intensity minima appear, with the value

$$(I_t)_{\min} = \left(\frac{1 - \rho^2}{1 + \rho^2}\right)^2 I;$$

note that this value is a decreasing function of ρ. If $\rho \ll 1$, we may write the expression for the transmitted intensity as follows, neglecting terms proportional to ρ^4:

$$I_t = \left[1 - \frac{4\rho^2}{(1 - \rho^2)^2} \sin^2 \frac{\alpha}{2}\right] I. \tag{3-59}$$

This equation shows that the intensity varies gradually from the maxima to the minima, and that the relative value of the total change is small. To discuss the case in which ρ is close to 1, we note that when $2 \sin (\alpha/2) \gg (1 - \rho)/\rho$, then I_t is very small compared with I (Eq. 3-57). Thus, if $(1 - \rho)/\rho \ll 1$, I_t will be much smaller than I except when $\sin (\alpha/2)$ is close to zero, i.e., except when α has a value close to an integral multiple of 2π. This means that the interference maxima appear as narrow bright rings on a dark background, in agreement with our previous conclusions.

Let us next consider the reflected beam. In this case, intensity maxima appear when α is an odd multiple of π; the intensity of the maxima is

$$(I_r)_{\max} = \frac{4\rho^2}{(1 + \rho^2)^2} I.$$

Intensity minima appear when α is an integral multiple of 2π. At the minima the intensity vanishes:

$$(I_r)_{\min} = 0.$$

If $\rho \ll 1$, the expression for the reflected intensity becomes approximately

$$I_r = \frac{4\rho^2 \sin^2 (\alpha/2)}{(1 - \rho^2)^2} I. \qquad (3\text{-}60)$$

To discuss the case in which ρ is close to 1, we note that when $2 \sin (\alpha/2) \gg (1 - \rho)/\rho$, Eq. (3-58) yields approximately $I_r = I$. Thus if $(1 - \rho)/\rho \ll 1$, then I_r is practically equal to I, except when $\sin (\alpha/2)$ is close to zero, i.e., except when α is close to an integral multiple of 2π. Thus, as stated previously, the interference pattern consists of narrow dark rings on a bright background.

The results obtained here are illustrated in Figs. 3-25 and 3-26, which give I_t/I and I_r/I as functions of α for $\rho^2 = 0.04$ (small reflectance) and $\rho^2 = 0.8$ (large reflectance).

We have assumed so far that the surfaces of the plate are uncoated. However, to obtain high reflectance it is generally necessary to use half-silvered surfaces, and the presence of the thin metallic film introduces certain phase changes at reflection and refraction, as we have already

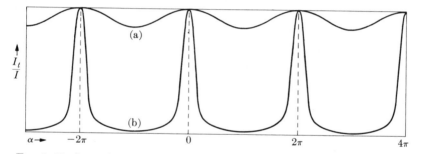

FIG. 3-25. Intensity distribution in the interference fringes observed by transmission, using a plane-parallel plate; (a) $\rho^2 = 0.04$, (b) $\rho^2 = 0.8$.

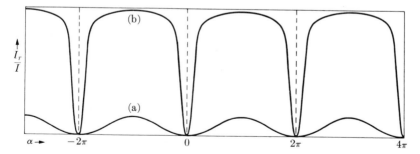

FIG. 3-26. Intensity distribution in the interference fringes observed by reflection, using a plane-parallel plate; (a) $\rho^2 = 0.04$, (b) $\rho^2 = 0.8$ (effect of metal coating on the plate surfaces neglected).

pointed out. Let us first investigate the effect of these phase changes on the appearance of the interference fringes observed by transmission.

Each transmitted ray has undergone two refractions, one upon entering and one upon leaving the plate. Since the observed interference effects depend only on the *relative* phase differences between the interfering rays, we need not concern ourselves with possible phase changes at refraction. On the other hand, each ray has undergone two more internal reflections than the preceding one. If each internal reflection is accompanied by a phase change φ, the phase difference α between two neighboring rays is given by

$$\alpha = 2\pi \frac{2\,d\cos\varphi'}{\lambda} + 2\,\varphi \qquad (3\text{-}61)$$

rather than by Eq. (3-44). With this new definition of α, Eq. (3-51) is still valid; however, the quantities τ, τ', and ρ appearing there are no longer related by Eqs. (3-13).

The phase change φ is, in general, a function of the angle of incidence. However, in the experiments under discussion here, the angles of incidence are always small and therefore φ may be regarded as a constant. Thus we conclude that the interference fringes observed by transmission through a plane-parallel plate with half-silvered surfaces consist of narrow bright rings on a dark background. The spacing of the rings is practically the same as that which we would compute if we neglected the phase changes at reflection due to the metallic deposit; however, their position is shifted, and the intensity at the maxima is less than the incident intensity I because of the absorption in the metallic film [formally, because $\tau\tau'/(1-\rho^2)$ is no longer unity].

The situation regarding the interference pattern observed by reflection is somewhat more complicated. It will suffice for our purposes to state that in this case also, the results obtained by neglecting the phase changes due to the metallic deposit remain valid, in the sense that the interference fringes consist of narrow dark rings on a bright background. However, the positions of the minima in the reflected interference pattern do not coincide with those of the maxima in the transmitted interference pattern, so that the two patterns are no longer complementary.

3-11 The Fabry-Perot interferometer and the Lummer-Gehrke plate. A well-known instrument which makes use of the fringes produced by the interference of many waves is the *Fabry-Perot interferometer*, shown schematically in Fig. 3-27. Two plane glass plates, separated by a distance d, are held rigorously parallel to each other. Light from a broad source is reflected back and forth between the plates, which have lightly silvered surfaces, so that some of the light escapes at each reflection. The rays

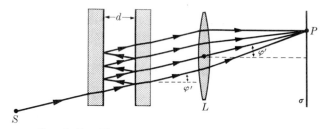

FIG. 3–27. The Fabry-Perot interferometer.

which emerge in the direction opposite to that of the source fall upon a converging lens L, and produce, in its focal plane, the interference fringes described in the preceding sections (Fig. 3–28).

This interferometer has important spectroscopic applications. Since the bright rings are very narrow, a light source which emits two different wavelengths will give rise to two clearly separated sets of rings, even if the wavelengths are nearly equal. Observe that if the plates were not silvered, the interference maxima and minima would be broad, and the interference rings given by the two wavelengths would blend into a single system which could not be distinguished from that obtained with monochromatic light.

To analyze the operation of the Fabry-Perot interferometer quantitatively, we begin by noting that here the material between the two reflecting surfaces is air, so that (apart from a constant representing a possible phase change due to reflection at the metallic film) the phase difference between two neighboring rays traveling within the air space at an angle φ' to the perpendicular is

$$\alpha = 4\pi \, d \, \frac{\cos \varphi'}{\lambda_0} \, ,$$

where λ_0 is the wavelength in air (or vacuum). Let φ'_k be the value of φ' corresponding to the maximum of order k; this angle satisfies the equation

$$4\pi \, d \, \frac{\cos \varphi'_k}{\lambda_0} = 2\pi k,$$

which yields

$$\cos \varphi'_k = \frac{k\lambda_0}{2d} \, . \qquad (3\text{--}62)$$

FIG. 3–28. Fringes produced by a Fabry-Perot interferometer.

We see from Fig. 3–27 that if the axis of the lens is perpendicular to the plates, φ'_k also represents the half-angle subtended at the center of the lens by the bright interference ring of order k. To a different wavelength, $\lambda_0 + \Delta\lambda$, there corresponds a different value $\varphi'_k + \Delta\varphi'$ of this angle, which we can obtain by substituting $\varphi'_k + \Delta\varphi'$ for φ'_k and $\lambda_0 + \Delta\lambda$ for λ_0 in Eq. (3–62). If we assume that $\Delta\varphi' \ll \varphi'_k$, so that we can use the approximation $\cos(\varphi'_k + \Delta\varphi') = \cos\varphi'_k - \sin\varphi'_k \, \Delta\varphi'$, we obtain (in absolute value)

$$\sin\varphi'_k \cdot \Delta\varphi' = (k/2d)\,\Delta\lambda. \qquad (3\text{–}63)$$

In the notation of Section 3–9, the number $k_0 = 2d/\lambda_0$ represents the order of interference at the center of the rings. So long as φ'_k is sufficiently small, we may write

$$\sin\varphi'_k = \varphi'_k = \sqrt{\frac{2}{k_0}}\sqrt{k_0 - k}$$

[see Eq. (3–47)], and (3–63) yields

$$\Delta\varphi' = \frac{k}{k_0}\sqrt{\frac{k_0}{2(k_0 - k)}}\,\frac{\Delta\lambda}{\lambda_0}. \qquad (3\text{–}64)$$

Suppose, for example, that the separation of the plates is $d = 2$ cm, and that the wavelength is $\lambda_0 = 5000$ A. The order of interference at the center of the rings is then $k_0 = 8 \times 10^4$. The radius of the first bright ring $(k = k_0 - 1)$ subtends at the center of the lens an angle $\varphi'_{k_0 - 1} = 1/200$, so that the relation between $\Delta\varphi'$ and $\Delta\lambda$ is

$$\frac{\Delta\varphi'}{\varphi'_{k_0 - 1}} = 4 \times 10^4\,\frac{\Delta\lambda}{\lambda_0}.$$

Thus a change of wavelength of only 1.25×10^{-2} A produces a change of 10% in the radius of the ring.

The above example shows that the Fabry-Perot interferometer, arranged as shown in Fig. 3–27, can be used as a powerful spectroscope to reveal the presence of slightly different wavelengths in a nearly monochromatic light beam. Suppose, however, that the light beam is not nearly monochromatic; i.e., that it contains wavelengths sufficiently different from one another so that the distances between the various rings of a given order corresponding to the various wavelengths are not small compared with the distances between rings of different orders. Then the interference pattern becomes confused and difficult to interpret, unless some other device is used to achieve a preliminary separation of wavelengths. For this purpose the interferometer is often combined with a prism spectroscope

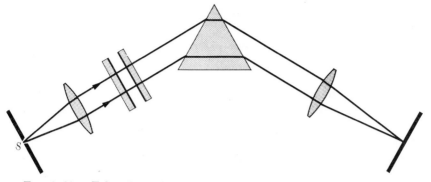

FIG. 3–29.   Fabry-Perot interferometer used in conjunction with a prism spectroscope.

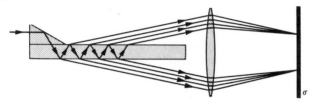

FIG. 3–30.   The Lummer-Gehrke plate.

(see Section 2–14), as shown in Fig. 3–29. The illuminated slit of the spectroscope is now used for a source. Suppose that the light to be analyzed contains a certain number of nearly monochromatic components; then the lenses and the prism form a corresponding number of separate images of the slit on the observation screen. Within each image appears the interference pattern produced by the Fabry-Perot interferometer. This pattern is just a section of the system of rings that would be produced by the interferometer with an extended light source. An examination of the interference patterns reveals the fine structure of the nearly monochromatic components of the incident light.

Another device making use of multiple reflections to produce sharp interference fringes is the *Lummer-Gehrke plate,* which consists of an accurately plane-parallel plate of quartz or glass with a prism cemented near one end, as shown in Fig. 3–30. The plate is usually from 10 to 20 cm long, from 1 to 2 cm wide, and several mm thick. A light ray entering the plate through the prism undergoes multiple reflections which occur at angles near the limiting angle for total reflection. Under these conditions, as we shall see in a later chapter, only a small fraction of the light emerges at each reflection. Hence, for each incident ray, a large number of parallel rays emerge from both sides of the plate; neighboring rays have nearly the same amplitude and a constant phase difference. The two groups of emerging rays fall upon a converging lens, in whose focal plane they produce two sets of interference fringes. As in the case of the Fabry-Perot interferometer, multiple-wave interference causes the fringes to appear as thin bright lines on a dark background.

3-12 The Michelson interferometer. One of the most important instruments making use of interference phenomena is the *Michelson interferometer*, shown schematically in Fig. 3-31. This consists essentially of two plane mirrors M and M', and two plane-parallel glass plates N and N'. The mirrors are perpendicular to each other, and their positions can be accurately adjusted by means of screws; in addition, M' can be moved back and forth by means of a carefully machined screw. A broad source of light is located at S. The plate N, which is half-silvered on the surface facing M, splits each ray coming from S into two perpendicular rays, one going toward M and the other toward M'. The first ray is reflected by M' back to N; part of it traverses the half-silvered surface and continues in the direction NO. Between N and M lies the clear glass plate N', which is otherwise identical to N. This is parallel to N, and is included in the system to make the optical path lengths of the two rays equal when M and M' are equidistant from the half-silvered surface of N.

The interference pattern seen by an observer at O is very similar to that produced by two reflecting surfaces, as discussed in detail in Sections 3-8, 3-9, and 3-10. The two reflecting surfaces in this case are the mirror M' and the specular image of the mirror M made by the half-silvered surface of the plate N. If M and M' are exactly at right angles, and if the half-silvered surface of N forms angles of exactly 45° with M and M', the mirror M' and the image of the mirror M are parallel to each other. The interference pattern, which can be observed by means of a telescope focused at infinity, then consists of the circular fringes described in Sections 3-9 and 3-10. If M and M' are not exactly perpendicular, so that the mirror M' and the image of the mirror M form a small angle, the interference pattern is a system of straight interference fringes localized in the plane of the mirror M'. These are lines of constant thickness of the wedge-shaped air film enclosed between M' and the image of M (see Section 3-8).

In either case, if the mirror M' is slowly displaced by means of the screw, the interference pattern changes gradually. For example, looking at the circular fringes localized at infinity, we will see that the center becomes alternately bright

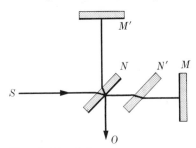

FIG. 3-31. Schematic arrangement of Michelson's interferometer.

and dark. To go from a maximum to a minimum of intensity, we must change the optical path length of the ray reflected by the movable mirror by half a wavelength. Therefore, if the wavelength is known, we can accurately measure small displacements by counting the number of times that the center of the interference pattern changes from dark to bright and vice versa.

The Michelson interferometer differs from many other interferential devices in one important respect. The two light beams that are eventually brought together to produce the interference pattern travel part of the way along widely separate paths. This fact makes possible many applications; for example, we can let the beams pass through different substances and thus determine small differences in the indices of refraction of these substances.

The measurement of lengths in terms of the wavelength of monochromatic light is another important application of the Michelson interferometer. By means of this interferometer, the length of the standard meter in Paris has been compared with the wavelength of the red line of the cadmium spectrum. Thus our fundamental unit of length can now be defined as a known multiple of the presumably invariable wavelength of a given monochromatic spectral line. (For the actual measurement, nine intermediate standards were used, each about twice as long as the next. The shortest standard was compared directly with the cadmium wavelength; the various standards were then compared with one another and with the standard meter.)

3-13 The Mach-Zender interferometer. Another interference device with important practical applications is the *Mach-Zender interferometer*, shown schematically in Fig. 3-32. The incident light beam is split by the half-silvered glass plate N into two beams traveling at right angles to each other. The mirrors M and M' reflect both beams toward a second half-silvered plate N'. In the direction $N'O$, the beam which is reflected by M and then partially reflected by N' overlaps the beam which is reflected by M' and then partially transmitted by N'; the superposition of these two coherent beams gives rise to interference effects similar to those produced by the Michelson interferometer. As in the latter, the two beams that eventually interfere with each other travel along widely separated paths. Small changes in the index of refraction of the medium along the path of one of the beams produce easily detectable changes in the appearance of the interference fringes.

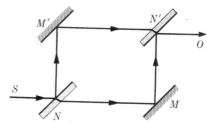

FIG. 3-32. The Mach-Zender interferometer.

3-14 Length of wave trains and monochromaticity. We have already mentioned that interference fringes can be observed with a white ·light source only if the difference l in the optical path lengths of the interfering rays is not much greater than the mean wavelength of the light. The reason is easily understood, since the point where the rays meet is an interference maximum for all wavelengths λ satisfying the equation $k\lambda = l$,* and an interference minimum for all those satisfying the equation $(k + \frac{1}{2})\lambda/2 = l$. Therefore, if λ and $\lambda + \Delta\lambda$ are two neighboring wavelengths, each giving an interference maximum at the same point, we can write

$$(k + 1)\lambda = k(\lambda + \Delta\lambda) = l,$$

from which we obtain

$$\frac{\lambda}{\Delta\lambda} = k = \frac{l}{\lambda} - 1. \qquad (3\text{--}65)$$

If l is a small multiple of λ, $\Delta\lambda$ is a large fraction of λ, which means that the interference enhances some wide regions of the spectrum and nearly suppresses others, so that the light at the interference point will appear distinctly colored. If, on the other hand, $l/\lambda \gg 1$, then $\Delta\lambda \ll \lambda$, and in each small region of the spectrum we will find wavelengths that are alternately strengthened and weakened by interference. The result will be a practically white illumination.

If the light source is nearly monochromatic, however, it is possible to observe interference even when the optical path lengths of the interfering rays differ considerably. Assume, for example, that the wavelengths in the incident beam are uniformly distributed between two narrowly spaced limits λ_1 and λ_2. The wavelength λ_1 will produce the interference maximum of order k at points where the difference in optical path length is $l_1 = k\lambda_1$, the wavelength λ_2 will produce the maximum of the same order at points where the difference in path length is $l_2 = k\lambda_2$, and the maxima of order k corresponding to the intermediate wavelengths will appear at intermediate positions. Since $l_2 - l_1 = k(\lambda_2 - \lambda_1)$, the width of the region containing the interference maxima of order k increases with k. Hence the interference fringes will become less and less distinct as the difference in the optical path lengths of the interfering rays increases. The interference fringes will practically disappear when the width of the region containing the interference maxima of order k for the various wavelengths becomes equal to the distance between the lines representing the interference maxima of order k and $k + 1$ for a given wavelength. The highest observable order of interference is thus determined by the condition that the interference maximum of order k for the wavelength λ_2

---

*We neglect here possible phase changes at reflection.

coincides with the maximum of order $k + 1$ for the wavelength λ_1, that is, by the condition that

$$k\lambda_2 = (k + 1)\lambda_1.$$

This is equivalent to

$$k = \frac{\lambda_1}{\lambda_2 - \lambda_1}, \tag{3-66}$$

which shows that the maximum observable order of interference is inversely proportional to the spread in wavelengths.

The Michelson interferometer described in the preceding section lends itself very well to a study of the change in the appearance of the interference fringes as the difference in optical path lengths increases. It turns out that the highest observable order of interference varies greatly from source to source; indeed, when the electric discharge in a rarefied gas is used as a light source, it is found that interference fringes are sometimes still visible when the optical lengths of the rays reflected by the two mirrors differ by a sizable fraction of a meter. In all cases, however, the fringes become progressively more diffuse as the difference in optical path length increases, and eventually they disappear. This observation may be interpreted to mean that no light source is perfectly monochromatic; however, the gradual disappearance of the fringes can also be explained from a different point of view. It is natural to assume that any light source consists of many uncorrelated microscopic sources, each of which is active during only short periods of time (see Section 3-7). Let k be the number of waves in the train of waves emitted by one such source during each period of activity, and let λ be the wavelength; the length of the train is then $k\lambda$. Now consider what happens when such a wave train is sent through a Michelson interferometer. The train is split into two parts, which come together again at O after having been reflected at M and M', respectively. One of the resulting trains will lag the other by a distance l, equal to the

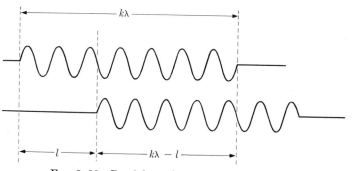

Fig. 3–33. Partial overlap of two wave trains.

difference in optical path length between the rays reflected at the two mirrors. Since each train has a length $k\lambda$, the two trains will overlap over a length $k\lambda - l$ (Fig. 3–33). In the region where they overlap, they will reenforce or weaken each other, depending on their phase differences, but no interference effects can occur outside the overlap region. As we increase the difference in optical path length by displacing the movable mirror, the length over which the two trains overlap obviously decreases, and therefore the interference phenomena become less pronounced. Interference will cease altogether when l becomes greater than the length of the wave trains, because then the tail end of the train reflected by one of the mirrors will have gone by before the front end of the train reflected by the other mirror arrives.

3–15 Physical implications of Fourier's theorem. We have presented above two apparently different interpretations of the fact that with any given light source the interference fringes disappear when the difference in optical path length of the interfering rays exceeds a certain value. One is that the light is not perfectly monochromatic; the other is that the source, instead of emitting a continuous sinusoidal wave, emits individual trains of finite length. We wish to emphasize here that these two points of view are entirely equivalent, as can be proved by making use of a general mathematical theorem known as *Fourier's theorem*. This theorem states that any function satisfying certain not very restrictive conditions may be regarded as the sum of a finite or infinite number of sinusoidal functions (in the case of nonperiodic functions, the sum becomes an integral).

For our purposes, we are particularly interested in certain quasi-sinusoidal functions of time that can be represented as products of a sinusoidal function and a much more slowly varying function. If we do not insist on mathematical rigor, we may describe such functions as *sinusoidal functions of variable amplitude*. A wave train of finite length falls within this category. According to Fourier's theorem, any sinusoidal function of variable amplitude results from the superposition of a finite or infinite number of truly sinusoidal functions whose frequencies lie within a certain range. We shall illustrate this conclusion by the following examples.

Consider first a source emitting two sinusoidal waves of infinite length which have slightly different angular frequencies ω_1 and ω_2. Sup-

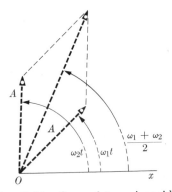

Fig. 3–34. Sum of two sinusoidal functions of different frequencies.

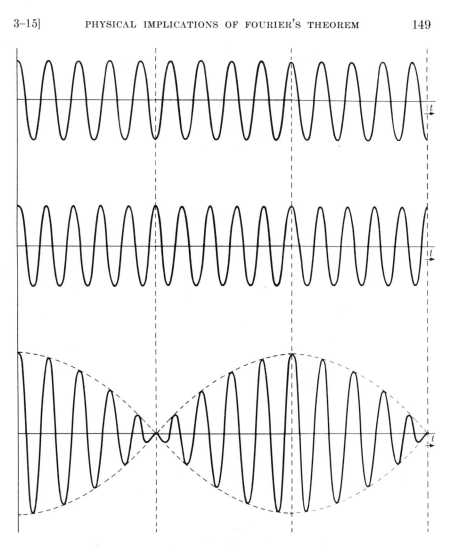

FIG. 3–35. Superposition of two sinusoidal waves of different frequencies.

pose, for the sake of simplicity, that both waves have the same amplitude A. The two corresponding optical disturbances are represented by two vectors of length A, which we assume to be parallel to each other at the time zero. The first rotates with angular velocity ω_1, the other with angular velocity ω_2. The resultant vector (Fig. 3–34) rotates with an angular velocity $(\omega_1 + \omega_2)/2$; its length varies with time and, at the time t, is given by

$$A \sqrt{2[1 + \cos{(\omega_2 - \omega_1)t]}} = 2A \cos\left(\frac{\omega_2 - \omega_1}{2} t\right).$$

Thus the resultant optical disturbance is

$$E = 2A \cos\left(\frac{\omega_2 - \omega_1}{2}t\right)\cos\left(\frac{\omega_2 + \omega_1}{2}t\right), \qquad (3\text{-}67)$$

which, of course, could also have been obtained by direct addition of the functions representing the two optical disturbances. We see that the light emitted by the source may be regarded either as resulting from the superposition of two perfectly sinusoidal waves of angular frequencies ω_1 and ω_2 or as a single quasi-sinusoidal wave, of frequency $(\omega_1 + \omega_2)/2$ whose amplitude varies periodically with time (Fig. 3–35).

Consider next a light source emitting n sinusoidal waves, equally spaced in angular frequency from ω_1 to ω_2, and all of the same amplitude A. The corresponding optical disturbances are represented by n vectors of the same length, which we assume to be parallel to each other at the time zero. These vectors rotate with slightly different angular velocities. Their sum is a vector of gradually varying length, which rotates with some angular velocity intermediate between ω_1 and ω_2. Thus again the superposition of a number of perfectly sinusoidal waves is shown to be equivalent to a quasi-sinusoidal wave of gradually varying amplitude.

At a given time t, the n rotating vectors are equally spaced (Fig. 3–36a), the angle between two neighboring vectors being $(\omega_2 - \omega_1)t/(n - 1)$. The resultant vector first becomes zero at the time t_1, when the component vectors are symmetrically distributed, so that each vector forms an angle $2\pi/n$ with its neighbor (Fig. 3–36b). Thus t_1 satisfies the equation

$$(\omega_2 - \omega_1)t_1 = 2\pi\,\frac{n - 1}{n}. \qquad (3\text{-}68)$$

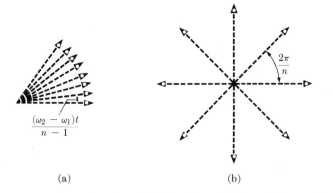

(a)   (b)

FIG. 3–36. Sum of n sinusoidal functions of different frequencies.

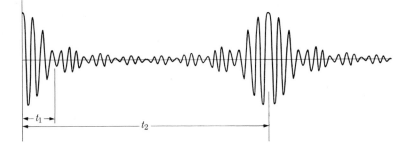

FIG. 3–37. Superposition of n waves of different frequencies.

As t increases further, the amplitude of the resultant vector goes through a sequence of maxima and minima, but it always remains small compared with the initial value of A until the angle between two neighboring vectors becomes 2π, when all waves are again in phase. The time t_2 at which this happens satisfies the equation

$$(\omega_2 - \omega_1)t_2 = 2\pi(n - 1),$$ (3–69)

which, together with (3–68), yields

$$\frac{t_2}{t_1} = n.$$ (3–70)

We thus see that the resultant optical disturbance has a large amplitude during relatively short periods of time which are separated by periods of relative quiescence (Fig. 3–37). The duration of each group of oscillations is defined as

$$\Delta t = 2t_1 = \frac{4\pi}{\omega_2 - \omega_1} \frac{n - 1}{n}.$$

If $n \gg 1$, Δt is essentially independent of n and has the value

$$\Delta t = \frac{2}{\Delta \nu},$$ (3–71)

where we have written $\Delta \nu = (\omega_2 - \omega_1)/2\pi$ for the frequency interval of the waves.

The separation $t_2 - t_1$ between successive groups of oscillations increases with increasing n, as shown by Eq. (3–70). Thus, at the limit for $n = \infty$, there will remain only one group. In other words, it is possible to construct a single wave train of finite duration Δt by superposing an infinite number of sinusoidal waves in a frequency interval $\Delta \nu$ such that Δt and $\Delta \nu$

are related by Eq. (3–71). This equation expresses only a relation between orders of magnitude. Actually, it is possible to construct wave trains of arbitrary profiles by properly choosing the distribution of amplitude among the component sinusoidal waves. However, in all cases it remains true that the product of the duration of the wave train and the mean spread in frequency of the component waves is of the order of unity:

$$\Delta t \cdot \Delta \nu \approx 1. \tag{3–72}$$

Let $\Delta \lambda$ be the spread in wavelength corresponding to the spread $\Delta \nu$ in frequency, and assume that $\Delta \nu$ and $\Delta \lambda$ are small compared with the mean frequency ν and the mean wavelength λ. Then the relation $\lambda = v/\nu$ (Eq. 3–5) yields, upon differentiation,

$$\Delta \lambda = -\frac{v}{\nu^2} \Delta \nu,$$

or, in absolute value,

$$\frac{|\Delta \lambda|}{\lambda} = \frac{|\Delta \nu|}{\nu}.$$

From this equation and from (3–72) it then follows that

$$\frac{\lambda}{|\Delta \lambda|} \approx \nu \, \Delta t.$$

Since $\nu \, \Delta t$ equals the number k of waves in the wave train, the above equation is equivalent to Eq. (3–66) and we thus obtain a quantitative justification of our previous conclusions concerning the physical equivalence between a wave train of finite length and the superposition of infinite waves of different frequencies.

An interferometric device like the Fabry-Perot interferometer, which gives very narrow bright interference lines in monochromatic light, may be looked upon as an instrument that automatically analyzes an incident light beam into its Fourier components.

It is interesting to examine how this happens physically. Figure 3–38 shows the optical disturbances corresponding to the various wave trains arising from multiple reflections of a single train incident upon the plates of the interferometer, that are brought together at a point in the focal plane of the lens in Fig. 3–27. Each train contains the same number m of waves, and is represented by a rotating vector which appears suddenly at a certain instant of time, performs m complete revolutions, and then disappears again. The resultant optical disturbance at any instant of time is represented by the vector sum of the rotating vectors present at that instant, as shown in Fig. 3–39.

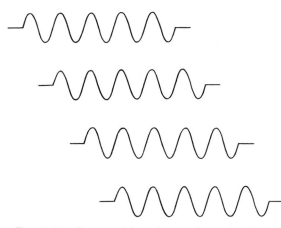

FIG. 3–38. Superposition of several wave trains.

The number of component vectors always remains the same. However, at regular intervals δt, a new vector is added at the front end of the broken line, and one disappears at the back end. If δt is an integral multiple of the period T of the waves, so that all the oscillations are in phase, the component vectors are parallel to one another. Their resultant remains constant in amplitude (disregarding the small progressive attenuation of the multiply reflected wave trains), and rotates with the same angular velocity ω as does each of the component vectors. We thus conclude that the optical disturbance at the center of a bright interference fringe is represented by a sinusoidal function of the same frequency as the incident wave train, which, however, does not terminate abruptly after m oscillations but lasts for a very long time (this time, of course, is determined by the reflectance of the interferometer plates).

Suppose now that we move to a slightly different point of the interference pattern, such that δt exceeds by a small amount an integral multiple of T. In the broken line of Fig. 3–39, each segment will form a small angle $\delta \alpha$ with the preceding segment. The broken line as a whole rotates with angular velocity ω. At time intervals δt, however, one segment disappears at the beginning and one appears at the end, which produces a discontinuous change $\delta \alpha$ in the angular position of the resultant vector. Thus the resultant vector rotates with an average angular velocity $\omega + \delta \alpha / \delta t$, slightly greater than the angular velocity ω of each component vector. We conclude that the optical disturbance at a point off the center of the bright interference fringe has a frequency slightly different from the main frequency of the incident wave train; in fact, it represents the component of frequency $\omega + \delta \alpha / \delta t$ in the Fourier analysis of the incident quasi-monochromatic wave train.

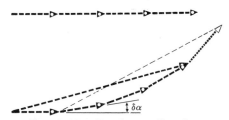

FIG. 3–39. Resultant disturbance from the superposition of several wave trains.

3–16 Superposition of waves from incoherent sources. We have repeatedly mentioned that a macroscopic source of monochromatic light is composed of a large number of uncorrelated microscopic sources emitting nearly sinusoidal waves of the same frequency. The relative phases of these waves at any particular point are distributed at random; that is, every phase difference between zero and 2π occurs with equal likelihood. We wish to discuss here in more detail the character of the resultant wave.

Let N be the number of microscopic sources and

$$E_j = A_j e^{i(\omega t + \alpha_j)}$$

the optical disturbance received from the jth source. Let

$$E = A e^{i(\omega t + \alpha)}$$

be the resultant optical disturbance. Then we can write

$$A e^{i\alpha} = \sum_{j=1}^{N} A_j e^{i\alpha_j}. \tag{3–73}$$

Taking the complex conjugate of this equation and renaming the summation index k, we obtain

$$A e^{-i\alpha} = \sum_{k=1}^{N} A_k e^{-i\alpha_k}. \tag{3–74}$$

Multiplication of Eqs. (3–73) and (3–74) yields

$$A^2 = \left(\sum_{j=1}^{N} A_j e^{i\alpha_j} \right)\left(\sum_{k=1}^{N} A_k e^{-i\alpha_k} \right).$$

The product of the two summations contains N terms of the form $A_j^2 e^{i\alpha_j} e^{-i\alpha_j} = A_j^2$. The other terms are of the form $A_j A_k e^{i(\alpha_j - \alpha_k)}$, with $\alpha_j \neq \alpha_k$, and can be combined two by two to form expressions of the type

$$A_j A_k e^{i(\alpha_j - \alpha_k)} + A_k A_j e^{i(\alpha_k - \alpha_j)} = A_j A_k [e^{i(\alpha_j - \alpha_k)} + e^{-i(\alpha_j - \alpha_k)}]$$

$$= 2 A_j A_k \cos(\alpha_j - \alpha_k)$$

[see Eq. (A1–16) in the Appendix]. These terms can be either positive or negative, depending on the value of the phase difference $\alpha_j - \alpha_k$. Moreover, since the phases are distributed at random, and since the number of microscopic sources is very large, positive and negative terms will appear in almost equal numbers, and will nearly cancel. Therefore we obtain, to excellent approximation,

$$A^2 = \sum_{j=1}^{N} A_j^2 .$$

Since the intensity is proportional to the square of the amplitude, the above equation yields

$$I = \sum_{j=1}^{N} I_j ,$$

where the I_j's represent the intensities of the individual waves, and I the resultant intensity. We thus conclude that the superposition of incoherent light waves produces an intensity equal to the sum of the intensities of the various waves.

3–1. Compute the amplitude A and the phase α of the sinusoidal function represented by the sum $A_1 \cos(\omega t + \alpha_1) + A_2 \cos(\omega t + \alpha_2)$, using the direct method discussed in Section 3–5 (a).

3–2. Solve Problem 3–1 using the complex notation.

3–3. Compute the sum:

$A_1 \cos(\omega t + \alpha_1)$
$+ A_1 \cos(\omega t - \alpha_1) + A_2 \cos(\omega t),$

using the vector representation of sinusoidal functions.

3–4. Solve the preceding problem, using the complex notation.

3–5. Compute the amplitude A and the phase α of the sinusoidal function:

$A_1 [\cos \omega t + \cos(\omega t + \alpha_1)$
$+ \cos(\omega t + 2\alpha_1) + \cos(\omega t + 3\alpha_1)],$

using vector representation.

3–6. Compute the amplitude and the phase of the sinusoidal function:

$E(t) = A [\cos \omega t + \cos(\omega t + \alpha)$
$+ \cos(\omega t + 2\alpha) + \cdots + \cos(\omega t + n\alpha)].$

Use the complex notation and recall Eq. (A1–22) in the Appendix.

3–7. A pair of Fresnel mirrors produces two images of a point source of monochromatic light separated by a distance of 0.2 mm. Compute the width Δx of the interference fringes observed at a distance of 50 cm from these images, assuming the wavelength to be either 6500 A or 4500 A.

3–8. Interference fringes are observed by means of Fresnel mirrors, the light source being a narrow slit illuminated by the yellow light of a sodium arc. The separation between specular images of the slit is 1 mm, and the plane of observation is 1 m from these

images. The sodium light contains two wavelengths of 5890 A and 5896 A, respectively. (a) Compute the separation between the maxima of the order k corresponding to the two wavelengths. (b) Compute the order of interference for which this separation is 5% of the distance between consecutive maxima.

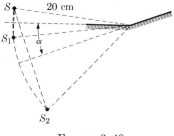

FIGURE 3–40

3–9. In a Fresnel double-mirror experiment the light source is a slit S illuminated by monochromatic light of wavelength 4000 A and placed 20 cm from the intersection of the mirrors (Fig. 3–40). The interference fringes observed at a distance of 1 m have a width of 1 mm between maxima. Compute the angle α between the planes of the mirrors. (*Hint:* Note that the source and its two specular images are equidistant from the intersection of the mirrors.)

3–10. A Fresnel biprism of crown glass with refracting angles equal to 1° is used to produce interference fringes. The observation screen is placed 60 cm and the light source 15 cm from the prism. Compute the width of the fringes observed with red light of wavelength 6562 A (Fraunhofer C-line), and with blue light of wavelength 4861 A (Fraunhofer F-line). The pertinent indices of refraction are listed in Table A4–3, p. 485.

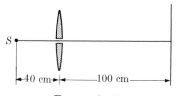

FIGURE 3–41

3–11. *Billet's split lens.* A converging lens of 20 cm focal length is cut in two by means of a plane passing through its optic axis. A source S of monochromatic light lies in this plane 40 cm from the lens (Fig. 3–41). As the two half-lenses are gradually moved apart, the image of the slit splits into two images, acting as coherent sources. Determine the width of the interference fringes observed on a screen at a distance of 100 cm when the lenses are 0.5 mm apart. Assume $\lambda = 5000$ A.

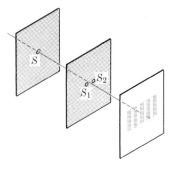

FIGURE 3–42

3–12. *Young's experiment.* The first interference experiment with light waves originating from two coherent point sources was performed by Young with the arrangement shown in Fig. 3–42. The primary source was a strongly illuminated pinhole S in an opaque screen. Some distance away, two pinholes S_1 and S_2 on a second opaque screen acted as centers of coherent diffracted waves (see Chapter 4). Suppose that Young's experiment is performed with monochromatic light of wavelength 5000 A, and that the interference fringes observed on a screen 1 m from the pinholes have a width of 0.5 mm between maxima. Compute the distance between the pinholes.

3–13. White light falls perpendicularly upon a film of soapy water whose thickness is 5×10^{-5} cm and whose index of refraction is 1.33. (a) Which wavelengths in the visible range will be reflected most strongly? (b) Which wavelengths will not be reflected?

3–14. Spectral analysis of white light reflected at nearly perpendicular incidence by a soap bubble shows, in the visible region, a single maximum and a single minimum of intensity. Compute the thickness of the bubble for the two following cases: (a) the maximum occurs at $\lambda = 6000$ A and the minimum in the violet region of the spectrum, and (b) the maximum occurs at $\lambda = 6000$ A and the minimum in the blue-green region of the spectrum. The index of refraction is 1.33.

3–15. A parallel beam of light of intensity I and wavelength λ is incident perpendicularly on a film of thickness d and index of refraction n immersed in air. Compute the intensity I_r of the reflected beam in terms of λ, n, d, and of the reflectance ρ^2. Show that for $d \ll \lambda$, I_r is proportional to d^2. (Assume small reflectance and consider only the first two reflected rays.)

3–16. Solve Problem 3–15, considering all reflected rays.

3–17. *Nonreflecting films.* We can decrease the fraction of light reflected by a glass surface (correspondingly increasing the fraction of transmitted light) by evaporating on the glass a thin film of transparent material (the so-called "coated lenses" are prepared in this manner). The index of refraction n' of the film must be intermediate between those of the air and of the glass. Suppose that $n' = 1.3$. What is the thickness of film that will minimize reflection at nearly perpendicular incidence for a wide band of wavelengths centered at the middle of the visible spectrum ($\lambda \sim 5000$ A)?

3–18. Newton's rings are observed with a plano-convex lens resting on a plane glass surface (see Fig. 3–17 in the text). The radius of curvature of the lens is 10 m. (a) Find the radii of the dark interference rings of the various orders observed by reflection under nearly perpendicular incidence, using light of wavelength 4800 A. (b) How many rings are seen if the lens is 4 cm in diameter?

3–19. Solve Problem 3–18, assuming that the space between the lens and the plane surface is filled with water ($n = 1.33$).

3–20. Refer to the experiment with Newton's rings described in Problem 3–18. Assume that the lens is slowly moved away from the plane glass surface until the separation d_0 between this surface and the spherical surface of the lens is 0.1 mm. (a) Do the radii of the rings increase or decrease? (b) How many times does the intensity at the center of the interference rings go through a maximum if the incident light is monochromatic and has a wavelength $\lambda = 5000$ A?

3–21. A Newton's rings experiment is performed with light consisting of the superposition of two waves of the same intensity and of slightly different wavelengths λ_1 and λ_2. It is found that as the distance d_0 between the lens and the plane glass surface is gradually in-

creased, the sharpness of the interference fringes changes periodically and the fringes disappear altogether for certain values of d_0. Investigate this effect quantitatively by deriving an expression for the intensity I as a function of d_0, R, r, λ, and $\Delta\lambda$, where R is the radius of curvature of the spherical surface, r the radial distance from the center of the rings, and the quantities λ and $\Delta\lambda$ are defined by

$$2/\lambda = (1/\lambda_1) + (1/\lambda_2),$$
$$\Delta\lambda/\lambda^2 = (1/\lambda_1) - (1/\lambda_2).$$

Assume that when the lens and the plane glass surface are in contact, the maximum thickness of the air film is small compared with the length $\lambda^2/\Delta\lambda$.

3–22. A Newton's rings experiment is performed with light consisting of the superposition of three waves of the same intensity and of slightly different wavelengths λ_1, λ_2, λ_3, such that

$$1/\lambda_1 = (1/\lambda_2) + (\Delta\lambda/\lambda_2^2)$$
and
$$1/\lambda_3 = (1/\lambda_2) - (\Delta\lambda/\lambda_2^2).$$

How does the sharpness of the interference fringes change as the distance d_0 between the lens and the plane glass surface is gradually increased?

d_1 ⬚ d_2

FIGURE 3–43

3–23. A square piece of cellophane film with index of refraction n, has a wedge-shaped section, so that its thickness at two opposite sides is d_1 and d_2 (Fig. 3–43). (a) Describe the interference fringes observed on the film by reflection, if monochromatic light of wavelength λ from a broad source is incident upon the film at nearly right angles. (b) Take $n = 1.5$ and assume that with $\lambda = 6000$ A the number of fringes appearing on the film is 10. What is then the difference $d_2 - d_1$?

3–24. A plate with rigorously parallel surfaces made of glass having an index of refraction $n = 1.53$, is illuminated by a broad source of wavelength $\lambda = 6000$ A. The reflected rays enter a telescope focused at infinity, whose axis is perpendicular to the plate surfaces. The objective lens of the telescope has a focal length of 30 cm. A diaphragm of 1 cm diameter, placed in the focal plane of the objective lens, limits the field of view. What is the thickness of the plate if 10 interference rings appear in the field of view?

3–25. A parallel beam of white light is incident at an angle θ upon a plane transparent film of index of refraction n and thickness d. Let ρ^2 be the reflectance of the film surfaces. Let $I_0(\lambda)$ represent the spectral energy distribution in the incident beam [that is, $I_0(\lambda) \, d\lambda$ is the intensity in the wavelength interval between λ and $\lambda + d\lambda$]. Determine the spectral energy distribution in the reflected beam, $I(\lambda)$, assuming $\rho^2 \ll 1$, so that only the two first reflected waves need be considered.

3–26. In the previous problem, assume $n = 1.6$, $d = 2 \times 10^{-3}$ mm, $\theta = 45°$, and $I_0(\lambda) = $ const. Compute the wavelengths in the visible spectrum for which the reflected intensity is a minimum or a maximum.

3–27. The reflecting surfaces of a Fabry-Perot interferometer are 2.5 cm apart. The interference fringes are observed with a telescope focused at infinity, whose axis is perpendicular to the plates of the interferometer.

(a) Compute the maximum order of interference, k_0, observed with monochromatic light of wavelength 5000 A.

(b) Compute the angles subtended at the center of the objective lens of the

telescope by the interference rings of order $k_0 - 1$, $k_0 - 2$, and $k_0 - 3$.

(c) Assume next that the incident light contains two wavelengths, $\lambda = 5000$ A and $\lambda = 5000.01$ A, and compute the angular separation of the maxima of order $k_0 - 1$ corresponding to the two wavelengths.

3–28. Suppose that the separation between the reflecting surfaces of a Fabry-Perot interferometer is gradually increased. (a) Do the radii of the interference rings increase or decrease? (b) Suppose that, as the separation of the plates is increased from 2.0 to 2.1 cm, the intensity at the center of the interference pattern goes through a minimum 4000 times. What is the wavelength of the light?

3–29. Refer to Problem 3–27 and assume a reflectance $\rho^2 = 0.8$. Compute the width of the interference maximum of order $k_0 - 1$, defined as the angular separation $\Delta\varphi$ between the two circles on either side of the maximum, where the intensity is one-half that at the maximum.

3–30. *Interference filters.* Monochromatic light filters may be prepared by the following procedure. On a plane glass plate are deposited successively by evaporation in vacuum (1) a semitransparent metallic film, (2) a thin layer of quartz or other transparent substance, (3) a second semitransparent metallic film. Another glass plate over the composite coating ensures mechanical protection. Assume that the transparent layer between the two metallic films has an index of refraction of 1.5. Compute several possible values for the thickness of this layer in a filter designed to select monochromatic light of wavelength 4861 A. For each value, determine whether other wavelengths in the visible range are transmitted by the filter.

3–31. The metallic films of an interference filter have a reflectance $\rho^2 = 0.85$. Assume that transmission is a maximum at the wavelength λ, and determine the wavelengths $\lambda_1 > \lambda$ and $\lambda_2 < \lambda$ for which the transmission is one-half the maximum value.

3–32. A Michelson interferometer is adjusted for the observation of the circular fringes localized at infinity. The objective lens of the telescope has a focal length of 40 cm; a diaphragm with a hole 1.6 cm in diameter in its focal plane serves as a field stop. The two mirrors M and M' (Fig. 3-31) are at distances of 30 and 32 cm, respectively, from the half-silvered mirror N. How many interference maxima are seen with a light source of 5700 A?

3–33. Two identical tubes 20 cm in length, closed by glass plates with parallel surfaces, are placed in the two arms of a Michelson interferometer. The interferometer is adjusted for the observation of the circular interference fringes localized at infinity. A monochromatic light source of wavelength 6000 A is used. The tubes are initially filled with air at standard temperature and pressure, whose index of refraction n_1 is $1 + 2.9 \times 10^{-4}$. Describe quantitatively the changes that occur in the interference pattern as one of the tubes is gradually evacuated.

3–34. (a) What is the maximum order of interference that can be observed with a light source whose spectrum extends continuously from $\lambda = 5000$ A to $\lambda = 5500$ A? (b) Assume that this light source is used in conjunction with a Michelson interferometer and estimate the maximum difference between the lengths of the two arms for which distinct interference effects can be observed. (c) Under these conditions, can we conveniently observe the circular interference fringes localized at infinity, or should we adjust the interferometer for the observation of the interference fringes of equal thickness?

3–35. Using vector representation, show that the sum of the three sinusoidal functions $A \cos \omega t$, $A \cos (\omega + \Delta\omega)t$, $A \cos (\omega - \Delta\omega)t$, equals the function $E(t) = A(1 + 2 \cos \Delta\omega t) \cos \omega t$. Plot the quantity $A(1 + 2 \cos \Delta\omega t)$ as a function of t for $0 < t < 2\pi/\Delta\omega$, and make a sketch of the function $E(t)$ in the same time interval, assuming $\omega = 200 \Delta\omega$.

3–36. Using the complex representation of sinusoidal functions, show that

$$E(t) = A [\cos \omega t + \cos (\omega + \Delta\omega)t + \cdots + \cos (\omega + n \Delta\omega)t]$$

is equivalent to

$$E(t) = A \left[\frac{\sin \left(\frac{n+1}{2} \Delta\omega t \right)}{\sin \left(\frac{\Delta\omega}{2} t \right)} \right] \times \cos \left(\omega + \frac{n \Delta\omega}{2} \right) t.$$

If $n \Delta\omega \ll \omega$, the bracketed term varies much more slowly than the cosine function; hence $E(t)$ may be regarded as a sinusoidal function of slowly varying amplitude. For which values of t does this amplitude vanish?

CHAPTER 4

DIFFRACTION

4–1 The principle of Huygens-Fresnel. We have already pointed out that the law of rectilinear propagation of light is not rigorously correct. To some extent, light bends around opaque obstacles, so that shadows always have slightly blurred boundaries, even in the limiting case of an ideal point source.

These departures from the law of rectilinear propagation are known as *diffraction phenomena*. They are not very conspicuous because the dimensions of the obstacles that light encounters along its path are usually large compared with the wavelength. However, they are part of our common experience. Diffraction phenomena are responsible for the intensely luminous border that outlines the profile of a mountain a few seconds before the sun rises behind it. The light streaks that we perceive when we look at a strong and concentrated light source with half-shut eyes are due to diffraction. The colored spectra, arranged in the pattern of a cross, that we see when we look at a distant electric light bulb through a piece of thin, closely woven material are again diffraction phenomena.

We can explain diffraction phenomena by making use of the general concepts embodied in Huygens' principle. However, it will no longer suffice to work out the consequences of Huygens' principle for the limiting case of infinitely short pulses. It will be necessary, instead, to take the actual form of the optical disturbance into account, and consider in detail how the secondary waves interfere with one another at various points of space. The results are simplest in the case of sinusoidal waves. We shall therefore begin by developing the theory of diffraction for monochromatic light and then treat nonmonochromatic light as a superposition of sinusoidal waves of different wavelengths.

For the special case of sinusoidal waves, Huygens' principle may be stated as follows:

Consider an arbitrary surface σ surrounding a source of monochromatic light. *The various points of σ behave as virtual secondary sources of sinusoidal waves, and the optical disturbance beyond the surface σ results from the interference of these waves.*

This formulation of Huygens' principle was first given by Fresnel and is known as the principle of Huygens-Fresnel. The frequency of the secondary sources is, of course, identical with that of the primary wave, and their phase relations are determined by the relative phases of the primary wave at the points where the secondary sources are located. If, in particular, the auxiliary surface σ is a wave surface, then the secondary sources are all in phase with one another.

To compute the resultant disturbance, we can use the methods for the addition of sinusoidal functions developed in the preceding chapter. In the present application, however, we shall be faced with the problem of dealing with an infinite number of interfering waves, each having an infinitesimal intensity, while in the study of interference phenomena we had to consider only a finite number of interfering waves of finite intensity or, at most, a discrete series of such waves.

4–2 Free propagation of a spherical wave. The vibration curve. As a first application of the principle of Huygens-Fresnel, we shall analyze the propagation of a spherical sinusoidal wave in a transparent homogeneous medium free of any obstacles. This will enable us to verify that the conclusions reached in Section 1–6 for the case of a single short pulse of radiation also apply to sinusoidal waves of short wavelength.

Consider a point source at S, a spherical surface σ of radius a centered at S, and a point P at a distance $a + r_0$ from S (Fig. 4–1). We assume a and r_0 to be large compared with the wavelength λ. To compute the resultant at P of the secondary wavelets originating from the surface σ we subdivide this surface into a number of infinitesimal circular zones with their centers on the line SP. We choose the zones in such a way that the distances r and $r + \Delta r$ of two successive boundaries from the point P differ by a constant amount Δr, where Δr is small compared with the wavelength λ. Hence the disturbances arriving at P from the various points of a given zone are essentially in phase. The total contribution of the infinitesimal zone is thus a disturbance whose amplitude is proportional to the area $\Delta\sigma$ of the zone and inversely proportional to the distance r of the zone from P. This amplitude also depends on the angle θ through the obliquity factor

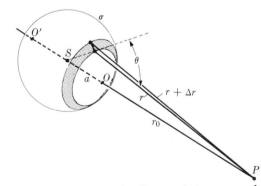

Fig. 4–1. Infinitesimal zone at the distance between r and $r + \Delta r$ from P.

$q(\theta)$, which varies from unity in the forward direction to zero in the backward direction.

In Section 1–6 (Eq. 1–27), we found the following expression for $\Delta\sigma$:

$$\Delta\sigma = \frac{2\pi ar}{a + r_0}\, \Delta r, \tag{4-1}$$

from which we obtain

$$\frac{\Delta\sigma}{r}\, q(\theta) = \frac{2\pi a}{a + r_0}\, \Delta r\, q(\theta). \tag{4-2}$$

All the quantities that appear on the right side of Eq. (4–2) are constant, except for θ. Thus, apart from the obliquity factor, the contributions of the various infinitesimal zones have equal amplitudes. The obliquity factor causes the amplitude to decrease gradually from a maximum to zero as one proceeds from the point O of the spherical surface closest to P to the diametrically opposite point O'.

We can now use the vector representation of sinusoidal functions to find the resultant of the disturbances arising from the various infinitesimal zones. We note for this purpose that the average distance from P increases by a constant amount Δr as we go from one infinitesimal zone to the next. Thus, the disturbances arising from two neighboring zones arrive at P with a phase difference

$$\Delta\alpha = 2\pi\, \Delta r/\lambda, \tag{4-3}$$

and are therefore represented by two vectors of almost identical length, forming an infinitesimal angle $\Delta\alpha$ with each other.

To add the contributions of the various infinitesimal zones, we plot the corresponding infinitesimal vectors one after the other, and obtain a broken line of the kind shown in Fig. 4–2. If it were not for the obliquity factor, all the segments forming the broken line would have the same length. Since all the angles between contiguous segments are identical, the broken line would close upon itself, forming a polygon with a number of sides equal to $2\pi/\Delta\alpha = \lambda/\Delta r$ (we regard this number as an integer for the purpose of our argument). In other words, the segment representing the contribution of the infinitesimal zone for which $r = r_0 + \lambda$ would exactly overlap the segment representing the contribution of the central zone. Because of the

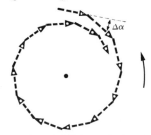

Fig. 4-2. Addition of the disturbances from the various infinitesimal zones.

obliquity factor, the lengths of the segments decrease gradually, and therefore the broken line does not exactly close. However, it very nearly closes, because, since $\lambda \ll r_0$, the obliquity factor changes by a very small amount as r increases from r_0 to $r_0 + \lambda$.

To obtain a rigorous solution of our problem, we must now go to the limit for $\Delta r = 0$. As Δr decreases, both the length of each segment and the angle between adjoining segments in Fig. 4–2 decrease proportionately. Ultimately the broken line becomes a curve in the shape of a spiral, as shown in Fig. 4–3. This curve may be termed the *vibration curve* relative to the subdivision of the wave surface σ into circular elementary zones.

The concept of the vibration curve is very useful in the study of diffraction phenomena. Indeed, the construction of the appropriate vibration curve provides a graphical method for adding an infinite number of sinusoidal functions of infinitesimally small amplitude, just as the ordinary vector addition provides a graphical method for adding a finite number of sinusoidal functions of finite amplitude. It is thus important to clearly understand the properties and the significance of the vibration curve.

In our example, we see that each point B of the vibration curve corresponds to a given circle on the wave surface σ characterized by a given constant value of the distance r from P. In particular, the beginning of the spiral, A, corresponds to the center O of the wave surface, i.e., to the point for which $r = r_0$.

Since the length of an infinitesimal element of the curve represents the amplitude of the disturbance arising from the corresponding infinitesimal zone of the wave surface σ, the *length* s of the spiral arc between two points B_1 and B_2 represents the *arithmetic sum* of the amplitudes of the disturbances arising from that portion of the wave surface that lies between the circles of radii r_1 and r_2 corresponding to the points B_1 and B_2 (Fig.

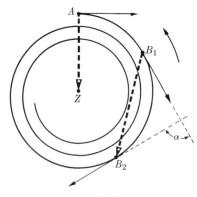

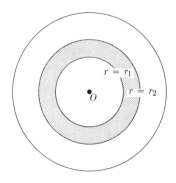

Fig. 4–3. The vibration curve relative to the subdivision of the wave surface into circular zones.

Fig. 4–4. View of the wave surface from P_1, showing the circles at the distances r_1 and r_2.

4-4). The *chord* B_1B_2, on the other hand, represents the *resultant* of these disturbances.

The angle between the tangents to the curve at the points B_1 and B_2 represents the *phase difference* α between the disturbances arriving at P from the points of the circles at the distances r_2 and r_1, respectively, from P:

$$\alpha = 2\pi \frac{r_2 - r_1}{\lambda}. \tag{4-4}$$

If, in particular, $r_2 - r_1 = \lambda$, then $\alpha = 2\pi$; that is, the arc B_1B_2 corresponds to a full turn of the spiral.

The radius of curvature ρ of the spiral at the point B is, by definition,

$$\rho = \left| \frac{\Delta s}{\Delta \alpha} \right|, \tag{4-5}$$

where Δs is the length of an infinitesimal arc BB' and $\Delta \alpha$ is the angle between the tangents to the spiral at B and B', respectively. As already pointed out, Δs represents the amplitude of the disturbance arising from the infinitesimal zone corresponding to the arc BB', and is thus proportional to $[(2\pi a)/(a + r_0)]q(\theta)\,\Delta r$ (Eq. 4-2). Since $\Delta \alpha$ is given by Eq. (4-3), we find that ρ is proportional to

$$\frac{2\pi a}{a + r_0} q(\theta) \frac{\Delta r}{2\pi(\Delta r/\lambda)} = \frac{a\lambda}{a + r_0} q(\theta). \tag{4-6}$$

Thus the radius of curvature is constant, apart from the obliquity factor $q(\theta)$. This factor decreases by an exceedingly small amount as r increases by λ, i.e., as one goes over a full turn of the spiral, which means that each turn of the spiral is *very nearly* a circle.

To summarize: The vibration curve appropriate to our problem is a very tightly wound spiral. Since the obliquity factor $q(\theta)$ goes to zero as θ approaches π, the radius of curvature vanishes after a sufficiently large number of turns, and the spiral ends at a point Z. This point is the common center of all the quasi-circular turns of the spiral; it corresponds to the point O' of the wave surface that is farthest from O (Fig. 4-1). The resultant disturbance at P due to the complete wave is therefore represented by the vector AZ. The length of this vector equals the radius of curvature of the spiral near A (i.e., at $\theta = 0$), and is thus inversely proportional to $a + r_0$ (Eq. 4-6). We thus find, correctly, that the amplitude of the resultant wave varies as the inverse distance from the source.

To actually compute the disturbance at P, we assume that on the spherical surface σ the disturbance E is given by

$$E(a, t) = f(t) = A \sin \omega t. \tag{4-7}$$

According to the results obtained in Section 1–6 (Eq. 1–34), the secondary wave arriving at P from an element of surface $\Delta\sigma$ is represented by the equation

$$\Delta E_s = \frac{1}{2\pi v} \dot{f}\left(t - \frac{r}{v}\right) \frac{\Delta\sigma}{r} q(\theta),$$

where v is the velocity of propagation. Remembering Eq. (4–2) and considering that

$$\dot{f}\left(t - \frac{r}{v}\right) = A\omega \cos\omega\left(t - \frac{r}{v}\right) = A\omega \sin\left[\omega\left(t - \frac{r}{v}\right) + \frac{\pi}{2}\right],$$

we obtain

$$\Delta E_s = \frac{A\omega}{2\pi v} \frac{2\pi a}{a + r_0} \Delta r \; q(\theta) \sin\left[\omega\left(t - \frac{r}{v}\right) + \frac{\pi}{2}\right]$$

or, since $\omega/2\pi v = 1/\lambda$,

$$\Delta E_s = 2\pi A \frac{a}{a + r_0} \frac{\Delta r}{\lambda} q(\theta) \sin\left[\omega\left(t - \frac{r}{v}\right) + \frac{\pi}{2}\right]. \qquad (4\text{–}8)$$

We see, incidentally, that *the secondary waves are emitted with a phase difference of $\pi/2$ with respect to the incident wave.*

For the central zone, i.e., for the zone around the point O, $\theta = 0$, $q(\theta) = 1$, $r = r_0$, and Eq. (4–8) becomes

$$\Delta E_s = 2\pi A \frac{a}{a + r_0} \frac{\Delta r}{\lambda} \sin\left[\omega\left(t - \frac{r_0}{v}\right) + \frac{\pi}{2}\right]. \qquad (4\text{–}9)$$

The amplitude of this sinusoidal function is

$$\Delta A_s = \frac{2\pi A a}{a + r_0} \frac{\Delta r}{\lambda}. \qquad (4\text{–}10)$$

According to our previous conclusions, the amplitude $\overrightarrow{AZ}$ of the resultant disturbance equals the radius of curvature of the vibration spiral near the point A. From the expressions for the radius of curvature (Eq. 4–5), for $\Delta\alpha$ (Eq. 4–3), and for ΔA_s (Eq. 4–10), we thus obtain

$$\overline{AZ} = \frac{\Delta A_s}{\Delta\alpha} = \frac{Aa}{a + r_0}. \qquad (4\text{–}11)$$

Considering further that the vector AZ forms an angle $-\pi/2$ with the tangent to the spiral at A (Fig. 4–3), we recognize that the resultant disturbance lags the disturbance arising from the central zone [represented by Eq. (4–9)] by a phase angle $\pi/2$. Thus the resultant disturbance has the expression

$$E(a + r_0, t) = \frac{Aa}{a + r_0} \sin \omega \left(t - \frac{r_0}{v} \right) \tag{4–12}$$

This is the correct expression for the optical disturbance in the spherical wave that diverges from S and which, on the spherical surface σ of radius a, is represented by Eq. (4–7).

4–3 Fresnel zones. On the spherical surface σ, centered at the point source S, let us draw a series of circles defined by the following equations:

$$r = r_1 = r_0 + \lambda/2,$$

$$r = r_2 = r_0 + \lambda,$$

$$r = r_3 = r_0 + \frac{3}{2}\lambda, \tag{4–13}$$

$$\vdots$$

$$r = r_n = r_0 + \frac{n}{2}\lambda.$$

These circles subdivide the wave surface in a series of zones, called *Fresnel zones* (Fig. 4–5). Needless to say, the Fresnel zones defined here should not be confused with the infinitesimal zones considered in the preceding section.

In the vibration spiral discussed previously, the half-turn from A to A_1 corresponds to the first Fresnel zone, the half-turn from A_1 to A_2 corresponds to the second Fresnel zone, etc. (Fig. 4–6). Thus the contribution

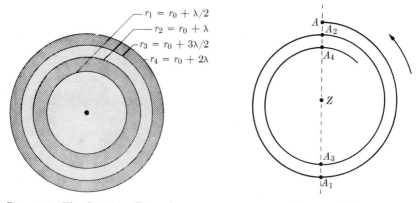

FIG. 4–5. The first four Fresnel zones.   FIGURE 4–6

of the first Fresnel zone to the optical disturbance at P is represented by the vector AA_1, that of the second Fresenel zone by the vector A_1A_2, etc., and we see that the contributions of two neighboring Fresnel zones have opposite phases. It is also evident that the amplitudes of the disturbances originating from the various Fresnel zones form a very slowly decreasing series.

As a special case, let us compute the radii of the Fresnel zones under the assumption that the source is at a very large distance, so that the incident wave may be regarded as plane. Let O be the foot of the perpendicular to the wave surface through P, r_0 the distance of P from O, r the distance of a point on the wave surface from P, and R the distance of the same point from O (Fig. 4–7).

The lengths r, r_0, and R are related by the equation

$$r^2 = r_0^2 + R^2. \tag{4–14}$$

From this equation, we can find the outer radii of the successive Fresnel zones $(R_1, R_2, \ldots, R_n)$ by replacing r with $r_1 = r_0 + \lambda/2$, $r_2 = r_1 + \lambda/2$, $\ldots, r_n = r_{n-1} + \lambda/2$. Since $\lambda \ll r_0$, the equation

$$r_n^2 = \left(r_{n-1} + \frac{\lambda}{2} \right)^2,$$

to excellent approximation, yields

$$r_n^2 = r_{n-1}^2 + \lambda r_{n-1}. \tag{4–15}$$

We thus obtain

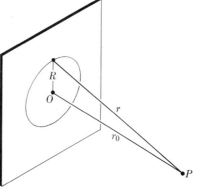

FIG. 4–7. Computation of the radii of the Fresnel zones.

$$R_1^2 = r_1^2 - r_0^2 = \lambda r_0,$$

$$R_2^2 = r_2^2 - r_0^2 = (r_2^2 - r_1^2) + (r_1^2 - r_0^2) = \lambda(r_0 + r_1), \tag{4–16}$$

$$\vdots$$

$$R_n^2 = \lambda(r_0 + r_1 + \cdots + r_{n-1}).$$

For sufficiently small values of n, the $r_1, r_2, \ldots, r_{n-1}$ do not differ appreciably from r_0, and we can write

$$R_n^2 = n\lambda r_0. \tag{4–17}$$

Thus the outer radii of the first few Fresnel zones are proportional to the square roots of the successive integers.

For large values of n, the difference $\delta_n = R_n - R_{n-1}$ becomes small compared with R_n, so that we may write, to good approximation,

$$R_n^2 = (R_{n-1} + \delta_n)^2 = R_{n-1}^2 + 2\delta_n R_{n-1}.$$

or

$$\delta_n = \frac{R_n^2 - R_{n-1}^2}{2 R_{n-1}}.$$

This equation, together with (4–16), yields the following expression for the width of the nth Fresnel zones $(n \gg 1)$:

$$\delta_n = \frac{\lambda}{2} \frac{r_{n-1}}{R_{n-1}}. \tag{4–18}$$

As we shall see, consideration of Fresnel zones is very useful in the semi-quantitative discussion of various diffraction phenomena.

*4–4 Further discussion of the principle of Huygens-Fresnel. As already pointed out, the principle of Huygens-Fresnel is just a special case of the general Huygens' principle, enunciated in Section 1–6. However, the method of computation followed in the actual applications of the principle of Huygens-Fresnel (Sections 4–2, 4–3) appears to differ considerably from the procedure used in the general case.

The present method is based on the rules for the addition of sinusoidal functions. We consider each point of the auxiliary surface σ as a steady source of secondary waves. To find the resultant disturbance at a point P beyond the surface σ, we construct the appropriate vibration spiral. We must think of the whole vibration spiral as rotating with the angular velocity ω, so that, at the time t, the tangent to the spiral at A forms an angle $\omega(t - r_0/v)$ with a fixed axis ZR (Fig. 4–8). The resultant disturbance at the time t is then represented by the instantaneous projection on the axis ZR of the vector AZ connecting the two endpoints of the spiral.

On the other hand, according to the point of view adopted in the discussion of the general case (Section 1–6), the sinusoidal disturbance at the surface σ, $E = A \sin \omega t$, is re-

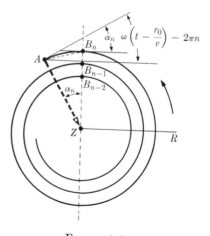

FIGURE 4–8

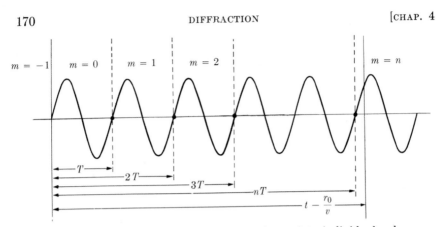

FIG. 4–9. Resolution of a sinusoidal disturbance into individual pulses.

garded as a succession of individual pulses. Each pulse includes a complete oscillation, so that, if T is the period, the pulse number m lasts from $t = mT$ to $T = (m + 1)T$ (Fig. 4–9), where m, of course, varies from $-\infty$ to $+\infty$.

To each pulse there corresponds a separate "active region" on the surface σ. At the time t the active region corresponding to the pulse number m lies between the circles at the distances $r_m = v\,(t - mT)$ and $r_{m+1} = v\,[t - (m + 1)T]$ from the point of observation P (where $r_m > r_{m+1}$; see Fig. 4–10). Note that the boundaries of the various "active regions" are not fixed, but change with time.

Let n be the largest number of complete periods included in the time interval $t - r_0/v$. Then the active region corresponding to the pulse number n is a disk centered at O and bounded by the circle at a distance from P equal to

$$r_n = v(t - nT)$$

(Fig. 4–10). The phase difference between the disturbances arriving at P from the points of this circle and from the point O, respectively, is

$$\alpha_n = 2\pi \frac{r_n - r_0}{\lambda} = \omega \left(t - nT - \frac{r_0}{v} \right)$$

$$= \omega \left(t - \frac{r_0}{v} \right) - 2\pi n.$$

Let B_n be the point of the vibration spiral corresponding to $r = r_n$ (Fig. 4–8). Then α_n represents the angle between the tangents at the points B_n and A of the vibration spiral. This angle differs by an integral multiple of 2π from the angle $\omega(t - r_0/v)$ formed by the tangent at A with the ZR axis. Hence we conclude that the tangent to the vibration spiral at B_n is parallel to the ZR axis, and that consequently the segment B_nZ is practically perpendicular to ZR.

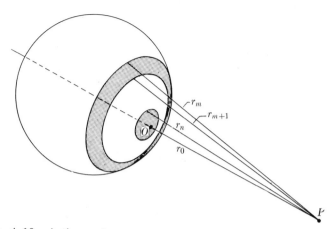

FIG. 4–10. Active regions corresponding to the pulse number m and to the pulse number n.

Let B_{n-1}, B_{n-2}, etc. be the successive intersections of the segment B_nZ with the vibration spiral. The contributions to the resultant disturbance of pulses characterized by the numbers $n - 1$, $n - 2$, etc. are represented by the projections on the ZR axis of the vectors B_nB_{n-1}, $B_{n-1}B_{n-2}$, etc. Since these vectors are perpendicular to ZR, the contributions of the corresponding pulses are zero. There remains only the contribution of the pulse number n, and this is represented by the projection of the vector AB_n on the axis ZR. Hence we can take the view that the disturbance observed at P at the time t is due entirely to the pulse number n, whose active region includes the pole O. The contributions of all other pulses are zero.

It is clear that the two methods of computation lead to the same result, for obviously the instantaneous projections of the vectors AZ and AB_n on the ZR axis are identical (Fig. 4–8).

4–5 The approximation of geometrical optics. In Section 1–7 we argued that since very short pulses of radiation travel along straight lines, and since a sinusoidal wave is essentially a succession of positive and negative pulses, the law of rectilinear propagation must also apply to sinusoidal waves of sufficiently short wavelength. We now wish to give a more rigorous proof of this important result.

For this purpose we consider an opaque screen partially obstructing the propagation of a spherical wave originating from S, and two points P and P', the first outside, the second inside the region of geometrical shadow (Fig. 4–11). For the sake of simplicity, we may assume that the screen surface is part of a spherical surface σ centered at S, and we take this as our auxiliary surface. Figure 4–11 shows the pole O of the sphere relative to P

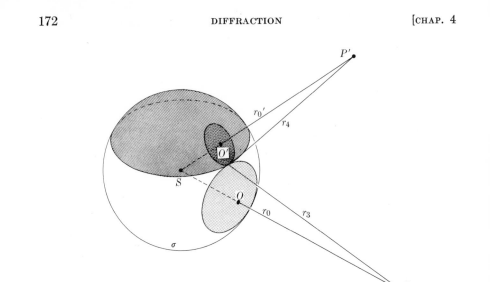

FIG. 4–11. An opaque obstacle partially obstructing the propagation of a spherical wave.

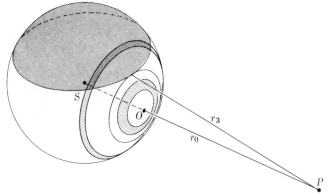

FIG. 4–12. Two elementary zones on the spherical wave surface as seen from P (Fig. 4–11).

and the circle on σ centered at O and tangent to the edge of the screen. Let r_3 be the distance of this circle from P. Figure 4–13 shows the vibration curve needed for the computation of the intensity at P. The curve is constructed by the identical procedure used in the preceding section, i.e., by subdividing the surface σ into infinitesimal zones, each at a distance between r and $r + \Delta r$ from P, and then adding the infinitesimal vectors that represent the contributions of the various elementary zones. Let A be the initial point of the vibration curve (corresponding to O) and B the point corresponding to the circle tangent to the screen (for which $r = r_3$). So long as r

is smaller than r_3, the elementary zone is completely exposed (Fig. 4–12). It follows that from A to B the vibration curve is identical to that corresponding to the unobstructed wave. As r increases beyond r_3, however, an increasingly greater portion of the elementary zone is blotted out by the screen. The length of the arc element of the vibration curve corresponding to a given value of Δr, and therefore of $\Delta\alpha = 2\pi\,\Delta r/\lambda$, is now smaller than

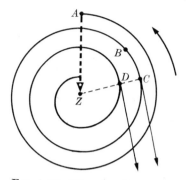

Fig. 4–13. The vibration curve relative to point P in Fig. 4–11.

it was in the absence of the screen. Thus, beyond the point B, the vibration curve begins to spiral inward more rapidly than does the vibration spiral of the unobstructed wave.

Let us examine this behavior in more detail. Consider on the surface σ the two circles defined by $r = r_C$ and $r = r_D$ such that $r_D = r_C + \lambda$ (Fig. 4–14). At the two corresponding points C and D of the vibration curve, the tangents form an angle of 2π; in other words, the arc CD represents a full turn of the spiral. The radius of curvature of the spiral is smaller at D than at C both because of the obliquity factor and because the opaque screen blots out a larger fraction of the circle $r = r_D$ than of the circle $r = r_C$. In the case of the unobstructed wave, on the other hand, the decrease of the radius of curvature from C to D is due to the obliquity factor alone.

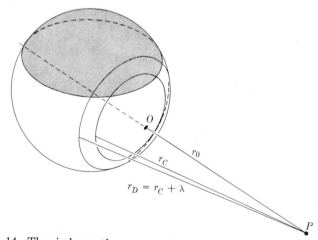

Fig. 4–14. The circles on the wave surface corresponding to points C and D of the vibration curve (Fig. 4–13).

As the wavelength decreases, however, the distance between the circles $r = r_C$ and $r = r_C + \lambda$ decreases also. If the wavelength is sufficiently small, the fractions of the two circles that lie behind the screen become almost equal. Since the obliquity factor, too, is nearly the same at the two circles, it follows that the radius of curvature decreases by only a very small amount as one goes from C to D. In other words, each turn of the vibration spiral will still closely resemble a circle, as it did in the case of the unobstructed wave. Hence the vibration spiral will gradually collapse toward the point Z, which is the common center of its various quasi-circular turns. The resultant disturbance, represented by the vector AZ, is thus practically the same as in the absence of the screen.

We conclude that *at the limit for infinitely small wavelengths, the light has full intensity at all points outside the geometrical shadow.*

We next consider the point P' inside the geometrical shadow (Fig 4–11). Figure 4–15 shows the pole O' of the wave surface σ relative to P' and the circle centered at O' and tangent to the edge of the screen. Let r_4 be the distance of this circle from P'. We consider, as before, an elementary zone on the wave surface, at a distance between r and $r + \Delta r$ from P'. For $r < r_4$ the elementary zone is completely obscured by the screen. It begins to emerge from the screen at $r = r_4$, and its exposed area increases gradually as r increases. The vibration curve (Fig. 4–16) begins with zero radius of curvature at the point B corresponding to r_4, and spirals gradually outward as the radius of curvature increases. Eventually, however, the obliquity factor will cause the vibration curve to spiral inward again. As the wavelength decreases, the spiral becomes more and more tightly wound, each turn becoming more and more similar to a circle. If the wavelength is

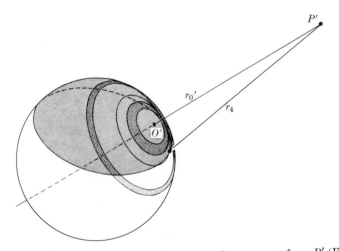

Fig. 4–15. Two elementary zones on the wave surface, as seen from P' (Fig. 4–11).

sufficiently small, the initial point B and the endpoint Z of the spiral become coincident with the common center of the various quasi-circular turns.   The resultant disturbance, represented by the vector BZ, is then zero.

We thus conclude that *at the limit for infinitely small wavelengths, the light intensity vanishes at all points inside the geometrical shadow.*

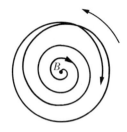

Fig. 4–16. The vibration curve relative to point P' in Fig. 4–11.

4–6 Diffraction by a circular aperture.   Let us consider a plane opaque screen with a circular aperture of radius R, and a point source of monochromatic light S, placed on the axis of the aperture (Fig. 4–17). We wish to compute the optical disturbance at a point P, which also lies on the axis of the aperture, on the opposite side of the screen.

We again apply the principle of Huygens-Fresnel, taking as auxiliary surface the spherical wave surface σ centered at S that touches the edge of the aperture.   We construct the vibration spiral, as explained in Section 4–2.   If AB is the arc of the spiral that corresponds to the unobstructed portion of the wave surface (Fig. 4–18), the chord AB represents the optical disturbance at P.

Suppose now that the diameter of the circular aperture, initially very small, is gradually increased.   The point B moves along the spiral, away from A, and the length of the vector AB goes through a series of maxima and minima.   The first maximum occurs when B coincides with the point A_1 of the spiral that is farthest from A, i.e., when the aperture uncovers the

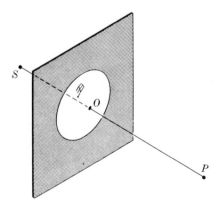

Fig. 4–17.   Diffraction by a circular aperture.

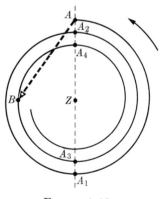

FIGURE 4–18

first Fresnel zone (Section 4–3). The amplitude of the optical disturbance is then almost exactly *twice* the amplitude of the optical disturbance produced by the complete wave, represented by the vector AZ. Thus the intensity of the illumination at P is *four times* that observed in the absence of the screen.

The subsequent minimum occurs when B coincides with the point A_2, i.e., when the first two Fresnel zones appear through the aperture. Since the spiral is very tightly wound, the intensity is practically zero under these conditions. Further maxima occur when the aperture uncovers 3, 5, or, in general, an odd number of Fresnel zones; further minima occur when the aperture uncovers an even number of Fresnel zones.

We may also ask how the intensity changes when the point of observation P moves along the axis of a circular aperture of fixed dimensions. Since the radii of the Fresnel zones depend on the position of P, we again find that the intensity goes through a series of maxima and minima, occurring respectively when the aperture includes an odd or an even number of Fresnel zones.

As a special case, assume that the source is very far away, so that the incident wave may be regarded as a plane wave. The first of Eqs. (4-16) then shows that the radius R_1 of the first Fresnel zone increases indefinitely as the distance r_0 of P from the screen goes to infinity. Thus if the point of observation is sufficiently far away, the radius of the aperture is certainly smaller than that of the first Fresnel zone. As the distance r_0 gradually decreases, i.e., as P approaches the aperture, the radius R_1 decreases correspondingly; hence an increasingly large fraction of the first Fresnel zone appears through the aperture. The intensity therefore increases and reaches a maximum when $R_1 = R$, that is, when

$$r_0 = R^2/\lambda. \qquad (4\text{-}19)$$

If, for example, $R = 0.5$ mm (5×10^{-4} m) and $\lambda = 5000$ A (5×10^{-7} m), Eq. (4-19) gives $r_0 = 0.5$ m.

As r_0 decreases further the intensity decreases and becomes practically zero when $R = R_2$, that is, when

$$r_0 = R^2/2\lambda.$$

As P moves closer and closer to the aperture, maxima and minima follow each other at decreasing distances. In order to determine these distances, we note that if we define

$$l = r - r_0,$$

we can rewrite Eq. (4-14) as follows:

$$(l + r_0)^2 = r_0^2 + R^2. \tag{4-20}$$

Differentiation of (4-20) with $R = $ const. yields the following relation between Δl, an infinitesimal change of l, and Δr_0, the corresponding infinitesimal change of r_0:

$$2(l + r_0)(\Delta l + \Delta r_0) = 2r_0\,\Delta r_0,$$

or

$$\Delta r_0 = -\frac{l + r_0}{l}\,\Delta l = -\frac{r}{r - r_0}\,\Delta l. \tag{4-21}$$

We now recall that the intensity is a maximum when $l = r - r_0$ is an odd multiple of $\lambda/2$, and a minimum when l is an even multiple of $\lambda/2$. Thus a change from one maximum to the subsequent minimum occurs when l changes by $\lambda/2$. With $\Delta l = \lambda/2$, Eq. (4-21) yields

$$|\Delta r_0| = \frac{r}{r - r_0}\,\frac{\lambda}{2}. \tag{4-22}$$

When the distance r_0 of P from the aperture is not very large compared with the radius R of the aperture, $r - r_0$ becomes comparable to r. Equation (4-22) then shows that the distances between successive maxima and minima approach the magnitude of the wavelength. Under these conditions, of course, the maxima and minima can no longer be practically observed.

From our previous discussion it follows that when the distances of the source and of the point of observation from the aperture are large compared with the square of the radius of the aperture divided by λ, only a small fraction of a Fresnel zone appears through the aperture. The diffraction phenomena observed in these circumstances are called *Fraunhofer diffraction phenomena;* we shall investigate these later in some detail. When, however, the distance from the aperture of either the point of observation or the source is R^2/λ or smaller, then the aperture uncovers one or more Fresnel zones. The diffraction phenomena observed under these conditions are called *Fresnel diffraction phenomena.*

The theory of Fresnel diffraction phenomena involves greater mathematical difficulties than that of Fraunhofer diffraction phenomena. Here we wish only to inquire in a qualitative way into the distribution of intensity to be expected in a plane perpendicular to the axis of the circular aperture, maintaining the assumption of a plane incident wave.

Let P' be a point at a distance y from the axis of the circular aperture (Fig. 4-19). On the plane wave surface we construct the Fresnel zones relative to the point P'. The boundaries of these zones are circles whose common center O' is a distance y from the center O of the aperture (Fig. 4-20).

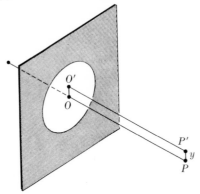

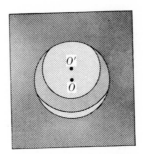

FIG. 4–19. The disturbance at a point P' off the axis of a circular aperture.

FIG. 4–20. The Fresnel zones with respect to the point P' in Fig. 4–19.

Thus only portions of the various Fresnel zones appear through the aperture. We can estimate the amplitude of the optical disturbance at P' by considering that the contribution of a given Fresnel zone is, in absolute value, closely proportional to the exposed portion of its area, and that contributions of neighboring Fresnel zones have opposite sign. Suppose, for example, that the plane of observation is a distance $R^2/2\lambda$ from the aperture. Then, as we have pointed out before, we can see the first two Fresnel zones from the point P where the plane of observation intersects the axis. The contributions of these two zones have opposite sign, say positive for the first zone and negative for the second. Since they have practically the same magnitude, the intensity at P is zero. As we move away from the axis, the second (negative) Fresnel zone is partially obscured, while the third (positive) Fresnel zone begins to appear. Thus the positive contribution increases, while the negative contribution decreases (Fig. 4–20). There is no longer cancellation, light appears, and as the distance y from the axis gradually increases, the light intensity will go through a sequence of maxima and minima, corresponding to the gradual appearance and disappearance of successive "positive" and "negative" Fresnel zones. Because of the symmetry of the arrangement, the lines of equal intensity will be circles with center on the axis. Thus the diffraction pattern observed on the plane through P will consist of a series of bright and dark rings. (Fig. 4–21).

It is interesting to discuss in more detail what happens when the radius R of the aperture is not very small compared with the distance of the plane of observation, r_0. In this case, as shown by Eq. (4–18), the width of the peripheral Fresnel zones is not much greater than the wavelength. For example, with $R = 1$ cm, $r_0 = 10$ cm, $\lambda = 5000$ A $= 5 \times 10^{-5}$ cm, Eq. (4–18) yields a value $\delta_n = 2.5 \times 10^{-4}$ cm for the width of the last Fresnel zone as seen from the point P. With respect to a point P', at a distance of only $1/10$ mm from the axis, the last 40 Fresnel zones are partially exposed.

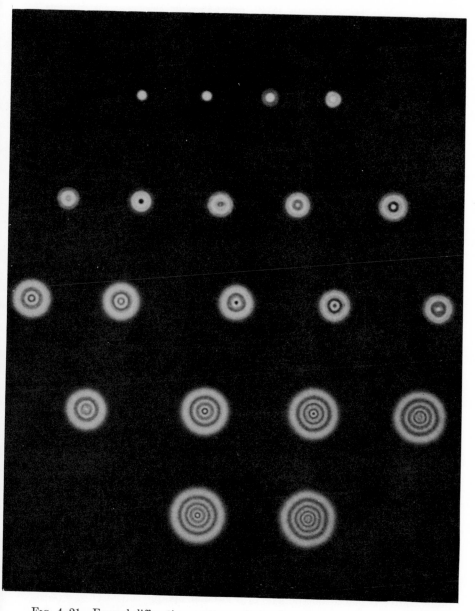

FIG. 4–21. Fresnel diffraction patterns of circular apertures of decreasing radii.

If we now construct the vibration curve relative to P', we obtain a result analogous to that described in Section 4–5 (Fig. 4–13). The first several turns of the vibration curve are identical to those of the vibration curve relative to the unobstructed wave. Starting from the point that corresponds to the circle centered at O' and tangent to the aperture, the curve begins to spiral inward more rapidly than in the absence of the screen. The radius of curvature decreases to zero in a certain number of turns which, in

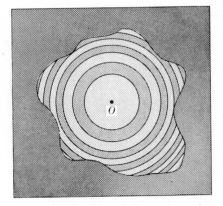

FIG. 4–22. Fresnel zones appearing through an irregular aperture.

the example considered above, is $40/2 = 20$. This number is sufficiently large to bring the endpoint of the vibration curve very near the center Z of the quasi-circular first turns. The intensity at P' is thus practically the same as it would be in the absence of a screen.

From our previous discussion we had concluded that when R/r_0 is not a very small number, the maxima and minima of intensity along the axis of the aperture follow each other at exceedingly small distances. We now find that such maxima and minima no longer occur if we move back and forth along a line parallel to the axis, but at a very small distance from it.

We have assumed so far that the aperture is exactly circular. If the edge of the aperture has some slight irregularities, the peripheral Fresnel zones relative to a point of the axis will be partly exposed and partly obscured, as illustrated in Fig. 4–22. The effect of these irregularities will be similar to the effect of the eccentricity discussed previously. Thus even on the axis the intensity will be practically the same as in the absence of the screen.

We therefore conclude that the illumination observed near the axis of an aperture whose dimensions are comparable to the distance from the point of observation is practically identical with that produced by the unobstructed wave, in agreement with the prediction of geometrical optics.

4–7 Diffraction by a circular opaque screen. Consider now the case of a point source S placed on the axis of a circular opaque screen (Fig. 4–23). We first inquire into the distribution of intensity along the axis on the opposite side of the screen from the source. For this purpose we again construct the vibration spiral relative to a point P on the axis (Fig. 4–24). Let Z be the center of the spiral and B the point of the spiral corresponding to the edge of the opaque screen. The exposed portion of the wave surface cor-

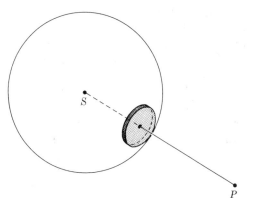

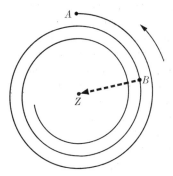

FIG. 4–23. Diffraction by a circular opaque disk.

FIGURE 4–24

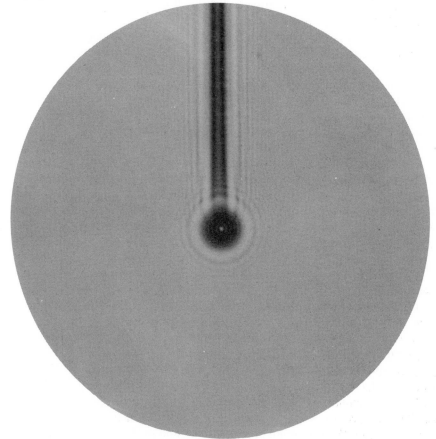

FIG. 4–25. Diffraction by a ball bearing.

responds to the portion of the vibration spiral extending from B to Z. Thus the optical disturbance at P is represented by the vector BZ. As the radius of the opaque disk increases gradually, the point B moves along the spiral toward Z, and the intensity decreases very slowly, without going through maxima and minima as it does in the case of a circular aperture. Also, no maxima or minima are observed as the point P moves along the axis.

We can investigate qualitatively the distribution of intensity in a plane perpendicular to the axis by considering the contributions of the various Fresnel zones, as we have done in the case of a circular aperture. We again find that the diffraction pattern consists of a series of concentric rings alternately bright and dark. At the center, however, the intensity is always a *maximum* (Fig. 4–25).

Again we may discuss what happens when the radius R of the disk is not very small compared with the distance r_0 of the point of observation. Suppose that the point of observation is slightly off the axis, or that the disk is not perfectly circular in shape (so that several Fresnel zones are partially exposed and partially obstructed). With an argument analogous to that developed in Section 4–5, we find that the vibration curve begins with zero curvature, and spirals first outward and then inward again. If the radius of the opaque screen is sufficiently large, both the expanding and the shrinking portions of the spiral are tightly wound and the spiral ends at very nearly the same point where it begins (Fig. 4–16). The light intensity is thus practically zero, in agreement with the prediction of geometrical optics.

4–8 Zone plates. A zone plate is a screen made of alternately transparent and opaque zones equal in dimensions to the Fresnel zones, and hence covering all even (or odd) zones. At the point of observation the exposed zones produce optical disturbances of the same phase. The resultant optical disturbance is therefore much greater than that observed in the absence of a screen, which, as we have seen, has an amplitude of half that produced by the central zone alone.

A zone plate is easily prepared by drawing a series of concentric circles of appropriate dimensions on white paper, painting alternate zones black, and then photographing the pattern thus obtained from a suitable distance (Fig. 4–26).

To compute the dimensions of the zones, we refer to Fig. 4–27, where S represents the source, P the point of observation, σ the plane of the zone plate (perpendicular to SP), and O the intersection of SP with σ. Let r_0 and r_0' be the distances of O from S and P, respectively. We assume that both these distances are large compared with the wavelength λ. As our auxiliary surface we now take the plane σ of the zone plate. We must, of course, consider that this is not a wave surface, and so the virtual secondary sources are not in phase. We denote by R the distance of an arbitrary point

Q of this plane from O, and by r and r' the distances of Q from S and P, respectively. If we define

$$l = r - r_0, \qquad l' = r' - r_0',$$

we have

$$(r_0 + l)^2 - r_0^2 = R^2,$$

$$(r_0' + l')^2 - r_0'^2 = R^2.$$

If we assume that R is small compared with r_0 and r_0', l and l' are also small compared with r_0 and r_0' and the above equations, to a good approximation, yield

$$l = \frac{R^2}{2r_0}, \qquad l' = \frac{R^2}{2r_0'}. \qquad (4\text{–}23)$$

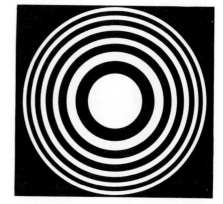

FIG. 4–26. Zone plate.

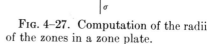

FIG. 4–27. Computation of the radii of the zones in a zone plate.

The difference l between the distances of Q and O from S introduces a phase delay $2\pi l/\lambda$ between the virtual secondary sources located at Q and O, respectively. The difference l' between the distances of Q and O from P introduces an additional phase delay $2\pi l'/\lambda$ between the secondary waves traveling from Q to P and from O to P, respectively. Hence the total phase difference between the two secondary waves at P is $2\pi(l + l')/\lambda$.

The outer boundary of the first Fresnel zone is a circle of radius R_1 defined by the conditions that the secondary waves originating from points of this circle arrive at P with a phase opposite to that of the secondary wave originating from the center O of the circle. The radius R_1 is thus determined by the equation

$$l + l' = \frac{\lambda}{2},$$

which, together with (4–23), yields

$$R_1^2 \left(\frac{1}{2r_0} + \frac{1}{2r_0'} \right) = \frac{\lambda}{2}. \qquad (4\text{–}24)$$

Similarly, the outer boundary of the second Fresnel zone has a radius R_2 determined by the equation

$$R_2^2\left(\frac{1}{2r_0} + \frac{1}{2r_0'}\right) = \lambda.$$ (4–25)

In general, we obtain

$$R_n^2\left(\frac{1}{2r_0} + \frac{1}{2r_0'}\right) = n\frac{\lambda}{2}.$$ (4–26)

Thus the boundaries of the successive zones are circles whose radii increase as the square roots of the integers, a result already obtained in Section 4-3 for the special case of a plane incident wave.

The actual widths of the individual zones depend on the positions of the source and the point of observation, i.e., on the values of r_0 and r_0'. However, there are infinite pairs of values for r_0 and r_0' that correspond to zones of the same dimensions; indeed, they comprise all pairs satisfying the equation

$$\frac{1}{r_0} + \frac{1}{r_0'} = \frac{\lambda}{R_1^2}$$ (4–27)

(see Eq. 4–24). The values of r_0 and r_0' that satisfy (4–27) define two points that we may call *conjugate* with respect to a given zone plate. The zone plate concentrates a large fraction of the light coming from one of its conjugate points upon the second, much as a lens does. In fact, (4–27) becomes identical to the equation of a thin lens (Eq. 2–38) if we put $r_0 = s$, $r_0' = s'$, and

$$f = \frac{R_1^2}{\lambda}.$$ (4–28)

4–9 The Cornu spiral. In the study of the Fresnel diffraction phenomena considered so far we have made use of the vibration curve described in Section 4–2, which refers to a subdivision of the wave surface into infinitesimal circular zones. For a certain class of diffraction phenomena it is more convenient, however, to subdivide the wave surface into infinitesimal rectilinear strips.

We consider a plane wave surface (Fig. 4–28) and a system of cartesian coordinates with the y- and z-axes in the plane of the wave, the origin at O, and the x-axis through the point of observation P. Let x_0 be the distance of P from the wave surface. We wish first to compute the disturbance produced at P by the secondary waves originating from points of an infinitesimal strip parallel to the z-axis, extending from y to $y + \Delta y$. These waves

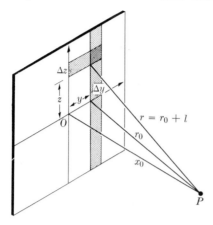

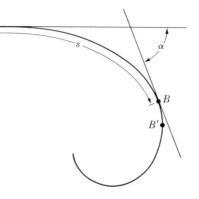

FIG. 4–28. Subdivision of a plane wave surface into infinitesimal strips.   FIG. 4–29. Construction of Cornu's spiral.

arrive at P with different phases, and we can again find their resultant by constructing the appropriate vibration curve.

To investigate the shape of this curve, we consider an element of the strip extending from z to $z + \Delta z$, and the corresponding element BB' of the vibration curve (Fig. 4–29). Let us assume first that y and z are small compared with x_0. Then, in computing the amplitude of the disturbance produced at P by the element $\Delta y\, \Delta z$, we can neglect the obliquity factor and also consider the distance of the element from P as essentially independent of y and z. The amplitude of the disturbance and the length of the representative arc BB' are thus proportional to the area $\Delta y\, \Delta z$ of the element.

It follows that the length s of the arc AB corresponding to the portion of the strip that extends from the y-axis to a distance z above the y-axis is proportional to the area $z\, \Delta y$ of this portion. On the other hand, the disturbance originating from the point of coordinates y,z lags that originating from the point of coordinates $y,0$ by a phase angle α given by

$$\alpha = 2\pi \frac{r - r_0}{\lambda}, \qquad (4\text{–}29)$$

where r and r_0 are the distances of the two points from P (see Fig. 4–28); α represents also the angle formed by the tangents to the vibration curve at the points B and A, respectively (Fig. 4–29). If we put

$$l = r - r_0,$$

we have

$$(r_0 + l)^2 = r_0^2 + z^2.$$

According to our assumption ($z \ll x_0$, $y \ll x_0$), l is very small compared with r_0 and therefore the above equation, to sufficiently good approximation, yields

$$r - r_0 = l = \frac{z^2}{2r_0},$$

which, together with (4–29), gives

$$\alpha = \frac{\pi z^2}{r_0 \lambda}. \qquad (4\text{--}30)$$

Thus α is proportional to z^2. Since z is proportional to the arc length s of the vibration curve, α is proportional to s^2 and we can write

$$\alpha = Ks^2, \qquad (4\text{--}31)$$

where K is a constant. Recalling that the radius of curvature ρ of the vibration curve is defined by the equation

$$\frac{1}{\rho} = \left| \frac{d\alpha}{ds} \right|$$

(see Eq. 4–5), we obtain from Eq. (4–31)

$$\frac{1}{\rho} = 2Ks. \qquad (4\text{--}32)$$

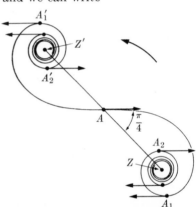

Fig. 4–30. The Cornu spiral (schematic).

The curve defined by Eq. (4–31) or (4–32) is known as *Cornu's spiral*. The shape of this curve is shown schematically in Fig. 4–30, while an accurate plot of the same curve appears in Fig. 4–31. The midpoint A, where the radius of curvature is infinite, corresponds to the intersection of the strip with the y-axis ($z = 0$, $s = 0$). The lower part of the curve (from A to Z) corresponds to the portion of the strip for which $z > 0$; the upper part of the curve (from A to Z') corresponds to the portion of the strip for which $z < 0$. The points A_1 and A_1', where the tangents to the curve are anti-parallel to the tangent at A, i.e., for which $\alpha = \pi$, correspond to points of the strip for which $r - r_0 = \lambda/2$. The points A_2, A_2', for which $\alpha = 2\pi$, correspond to points of the strip for which $r - r_0 = \lambda$, etc.

Notice the difference between the shape of the Cornu spiral and that of the vibration curve corresponding to a subdivision of the wave surface into circular zones (Fig. 4–3). This difference is due to the fact that in the latter the radius of curvature decreases very slowly as we proceed along the curve,

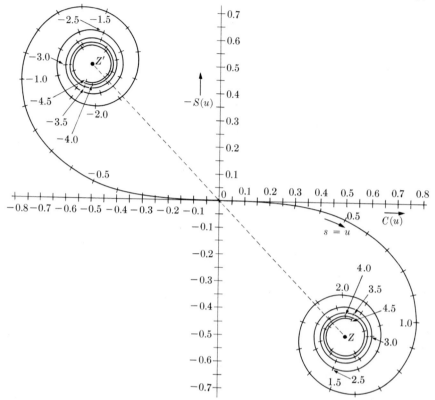

FIG. 4–31. The Cornu spiral (accurate plot). The curve is a graph of $-S(u)$ against $C(u)$ (see Section 4–10). The figures along the curve indicate the values of the parameter u, which is proportional to the arc length from the midpoint of the spiral.

the decrease being due exclusively to the obliquity factor. In the Cornu spiral, on the other hand, the radius of curvature decreases rapidly, for according to Eq. (4–32), it is inversely proportional to the arc length. Because of the rapid decrease of the radius of curvature, the two branches of the Cornu spiral rapidly approach the asymptotic points Z, Z'. The spiral is symmetric with respect to the point A, hence the line $Z'Z$ passes through A. By working out the mathematical equation of the Cornu spiral, we find that this line forms an angle $\pi/4$ with the tangent to the spiral at A (see next section).

If the strip extends a sufficiently large distance from the y-axis, both in the positive and in the negative z-directions, the vector representing the resultant disturbance becomes practically equal to the vector $Z'Z$, and is thus independent of the exact length of the strip. The amplitude of the resultant disturbance is proportional, of course, to the width Δy of the strip. Its phase

differs by $\pi/4$ from the phase of the
disturbance arriving at P from the
intersection of the strip with the
y-axis.

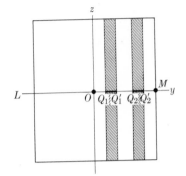

We now consider a rectangular
portion of the wave surface intersecting the yz-plane along the segment LM of the y-axis (Fig. 4–32)
and subdivide this surface into infinitesimal strips parallel to the z-axis.
We assume that the portion of the
wave surface under consideration extends sufficiently far in the directions
of the positive and negative z-axis so

Fig. 4–32. Two infinitesimal strips
on the plane wave surface.

that the disturbance arising from an individual strip may be represented by
the asymptotic chord $Z'Z$ of the corresponding Cornu spiral. Then, as we
have just proved, the disturbance arriving at P from a given strip has an
amplitude proportional to the width Δy of the strip. Moreover, the contributions of two different strips intersecting the y-axis along the segments
Q_1Q_1' and Q_2Q_2', respectively, have a phase difference equal to the phase
difference of the disturbances produced at P by the secondary waves
originating from these two segments.

The mathematical problem of computing the resultant disturbance
originating from the infinitesimal strips that form the rectangular wave
portion is thus formally identical to the problem already discussed of computing the resultant disturbance originating from the various elements that
form one infinitesimal strip. The Cornu spiral, whose properties we have
discussed in detail, provides the solution to both problems.

A remark is here necessary. In our discussion we have disregarded the
obliquity factor as well as the dependence of the amplitude of the secondary
waves on the distance from the point of observation of the element of surface from which it originates. If we were to take these factors into account,
we would obtain a vibration curve in which the radius of curvature decreases somewhat more rapidly than in the Cornu spiral as we move away
from the center point A. However, if P is sufficiently far from the wave
surface (more precisely, if $x_0 \gg \lambda$), the vibration curve begins to deviate
appreciably from the Cornu spiral only after a large number of turns, when
the spiral has practically reached its limiting point, Z or Z'. Thus the simplifying assumptions that we have made do not introduce any essential
limitation.

It may be mentioned that the Cornu spiral may be used to study diffraction phenomena produced by cylindrical waves as well as by plane waves.
We do not wish, however, to discuss this point in detail.

*4–10 The Fresnel integrals. The problem discussed in the preceding section may be treated analytically as follows. Let

$$E = f(t) = A \sin \omega t \tag{4–33}$$

represent the optical disturbance on the plane of a rectangular aperture, perpendicular to the direction of propagation of a plane wave (Fig. 4–33). If r is the distance of the element of area $dy\,dz$ from the point of observation P, the disturbance produced at P by the secondary wave originating from this element is given by

$$dE_s = \frac{1}{2\pi vr} \dot{f}\left(t - \frac{r}{v}\right) q(\theta)\,dy\,dz = \frac{A}{r\lambda} \cos \omega \left(t - \frac{r}{v}\right) q(\theta)\,dy\,dz$$

(see Eq. 1–34a). If the dimensions of the aperture are small compared with x_0, we can take the obliquity factor $q(\theta)$ as unity and replace r with x_0 in the denominator (not, however, in the argument of the cosine function). By writing $r = x_0 + l'$, we obtain the equation

$$(x_0 + l')^2 = x_0^2 + y^2 + z^2,$$

which, if $(l')^2$ can be neglected, yields

$$l' = \frac{y^2 + z^2}{2x_0},$$

and therefore

$$r = x_0 + \frac{y^2 + z^2}{2x_0}.$$

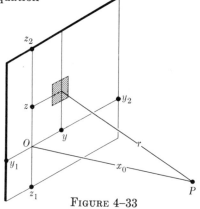

FIGURE 4–33

By using this expression for r in the cosine function, and by changing to the complex representation, we obtain

$$dE_s = \frac{A}{x_0\lambda}\, e^{i\omega(t - x_0/v)} e^{-i\pi(y^2 + z^2)/(x_0\lambda)}\,dy\,dz.$$

Note that the approximations made in the derivation of the above formula are permissible if the quantities y/x_0, z/x_0, and $(l')^2/(x_0\lambda)$ are very small compared with unity. The condition $(l')^2/(x_0\lambda) \ll 1$ implies that $y^4/(x_0^3\lambda) \ll 1$ and that $z^4/(x_0^3\lambda) \ll 1$.

Let us assume that the aperture extends from $y = y_1$ to $y = y_2$ and from $z = z_1$ to $z = z_2$ (if P is in the region of light according to geometrical optics,

y_1, z_1 are negative, and y_2, z_2 are positive quantities). The resultant disturbance at P is then

$$E_P = \frac{A}{x_0\lambda} e^{i\omega(t - x_0/v)} \int_{y_1}^{y_2} e^{-i\pi y^2/(x_0\lambda)} \, dy \int_{z_1}^{z_2} e^{-i\pi z^2/(x_0\lambda)} \, dz. \tag{4-34}$$

Let us define the integrals

$$C(u) = \int_0^u \cos \frac{\pi(u')^2}{2} \, du',$$

$$\tag{4-35}$$

$$S(u) = \int_0^u \sin \frac{\pi(u')^2}{2} \, du'.$$

With the change of variable

$$u' = \frac{\sqrt{2}\, y}{\sqrt{x_0\lambda}} \tag{4-36}$$

the first integral in (4-34) becomes

$$\int_{y_1}^{y_2} e^{-i\pi y^2/(x_0\lambda)} \, dy = \sqrt{\frac{x_0\lambda}{2}} \int_{u_1}^{u_2} e^{-i\pi(u')^2/2} \, du'$$

$$= \sqrt{\frac{x_0\lambda}{2}} \left(\int_{u_1}^{u_2} \cos \frac{\pi(u')^2}{2} \, du' - i \int_{u_1}^{u_2} \sin \frac{\pi(u')^2}{2} \, du' \right)$$

$$= \sqrt{\frac{x_0\lambda}{2}} \left\{ [C(u_2) - C(u_1)] - i[S(u_2) - S(u_1)] \right\},$$

where we have put

$$u_1 = \frac{\sqrt{2}\, y_1}{\sqrt{x_0\lambda}}, \qquad u_2 = \frac{\sqrt{2}\, y_2}{\sqrt{x_0\lambda}}. \tag{4-37}$$

Similarly, we obtain

$$\int_{z_1}^{z_2} e^{-i\pi z^2/(x_0\lambda)} \, dz = \sqrt{\frac{x_0\lambda}{2}} \left\{ [C(u_4) - C(u_3)] - i[S(u_4) - S(u_3)] \right\},$$

where

$$u_3 = \frac{\sqrt{2}\, z_1}{\sqrt{x_0\lambda}}, \qquad u_4 = \frac{\sqrt{2}\, z_2}{\sqrt{x_0\lambda}}, \tag{4-38}$$

and the expression for E_P becomes

$$E_P = \frac{A}{2} e^{i\omega(t - x_0/v)} \{[C(u_2) - C(u_1)] - i[S(u_2) - S(u_1)]\}$$
$$\times \{[C(u_4) - C(u_3)] - i[S(u_4) - S(u_3)]\}. \tag{4–39}$$

The corresponding expression for the resultant intensity is

$$I_P = \frac{I}{4} \{[C(u_2) - C(u_1)]^2 + [S(u_2) - S(u_1)]^2\}$$
$$\times \{[C(u_4) - C(u_3)]^2 + [S(u_4) - S(u_3)]^2\}, \tag{4–40}$$

where I is the intensity of the incident wave.

The functions $C(u)$ and $S(u)$ are called the *Fresnel integrals*. Their numerical values are given in Table 4–1. Note that $C(-u) = -C(u)$ and $S(-u) = -S(u)$. Note also that as u increases indefinitely both C and S tend to the limiting value of $\frac{1}{2}$. Hence if the aperture is sufficiently long in the direction parallel to the z-axis so that $u_3 = \sqrt{2}\, z_1/\sqrt{x_0\lambda} \ll -1$, $u_4 = \sqrt{2}\, z_2/\sqrt{x_0\lambda} \gg 1$, Eqs. (4–39) and (4–40) become*

$$E_P = \frac{A}{\sqrt{2}} e^{i[\omega(t - x_0/v) - \pi/4]} \{[C(u_2) - C(u_1)] - i[S(u_2) - S(u_1)]\}, \tag{4–41}$$

$$I_P = \frac{I}{2} \{[C(u_2) - C(u_1)]^2 + [S(u_2) - S(u_1)]^2\}. \tag{4–42}$$

If also $u_1 = \sqrt{2}\, y_1/\sqrt{x_0\lambda} \ll -1$ and $u_2 = \sqrt{2}\, y_2/\sqrt{x_0\lambda} \gg 1$, the expression for E_P becomes

$$E_P = A e^{i[\omega(t - x_0/v) - \pi/2]}$$

or

$$E_P = A \sin \omega \left(t - \frac{x_0}{v} \right), \tag{4–43}$$

and the expression for I_P becomes

$$I_P = I. \tag{4–44}$$

---

*We recall that $1 - i = \sqrt{2}\, e^{-(\pi/4)i}$.

Table 4–1

Table of Fresnel Integrals

u	$C(u)$	$S(u)$	u	$C(u)$	$S(u)$	u	$C(u)$	$S(u)$
0.0	0	0	3.0	0.6057	0.4963	6.0	0.4995	0.4469
0.1	0.0999	0.0005	3.1	0.5616	0.5818	6.1	0.5495	0.5165
0.2	0.1999	0.0042	3.2	0.4663	0.5933	6.2	0.4676	0.5398
0.3	0.2994	0.0141	3.3	0.4057	0.5193	6.3	0.4760	0.4555
0.4	0.3975	0.0334	3.4	0.4385	0.4297	6.4	0.5496	0.4965
0.5	0.4923	0.0647	3.5	0.5326	0.4153	6.5	0.4816	0.5454
0.6	0.5811	0.1105	3.6	0.5880	0.4923	6.6	0.4690	0.4631
0.7	0.6597	0.1721	3.7	0.5419	0.5750	6.7	0.5467	0.4915
0.8	0.7230	0.2493	3.8	0.4481	0.5656	6.8	0.4831	0.5436
0.9	0.7648	0.3398	3.9	0.4223	0.4752	6.9	0.4732	0.4624
1.0	0.7799	0.4383	4.0	0.4984	0.4205	7.0	0.5455	0.4997
1.1	0.7638	0.5365	4.1	0.5737	0.4758	7.1	0.4733	0.5360
1.2	0.7154	0.6234	4.2	0.5417	0.5632	7.2	0.4887	0.4572
1.3	0.6386	0.6863	4.3	0.4494	0.5540	7.3	0.5393	0.5199
1.4	0.5431	0.7135	4.4	0.4383	0.4623	7.4	0.4601	0.5161
1.5	0.4453	0.6975	4.5	0.5258	0.4342	7.5	0.5160	0.4607
1.6	0.3655	0.6389	4.6	0.5672	0.5162	7.6	0.5156	0.5389
1.7	0.3238	0.5492	4.7	0.4914	0.5669	7.7	0.4628	0.4820
1.8	0.3337	0.4509	4.8	0.4338	0.4968	7.8	0.5395	0.4896
1.9	0.3945	0.3734	4.9	0.5002	0.4351	7.9	0.4760	0.5323
2.0	0.4883	0.3434	5.0	0.5636	0.4992	8.0	0.4998	0.4602
2.1	0.5814	0.3743	5.1	0.4987	0.5624	8.1	0.5228	0.5320
2.2	0.6362	0.4556	5.2	0.4389	0.4969	8.2	0.4638	0.4859
2.3	0.6268	0.5531	5.3	0.5078	0.4404	8.3	0.5378	0.4932
2.4	0.5550	0.6197	5.4	0.5573	0.5140	8.4	0.4709	0.5243
2.5	0.4574	0.6192	5.5	0.4784	0.5537	8.5	0.5142	0.4653
2.6	0.3889	0.5500	5.6	0.4517	0.4700			
2.7	0.3926	0.4529	5.7	0.5385	0.4595			
2.8	0.4675	0.3915	5.8	0.5298	0.5461			
2.9	0.5624	0.4102	5.9	0.4484	0.5163			

Equations (4–43) and (4–44) describe, of course, the free propagation of the incident wave.

In order to compare the above results with those obtained in the preceding section, we note that the
complex quantity $C(u) - iS(u)$ is
represented, in the complex plane,
by a point of abscissa equal to $C(u)$
and ordinate equal to $-S(u)$ (Fig.
4–34). As u changes, the point describes a curve. Since Eq. (4–41)
can be written

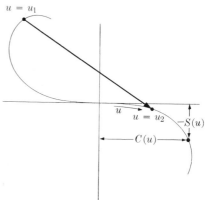

Fig. 4–34.   Plot of the function
$C(u) - iS(u)$ in the complex plane.

$$E_P = \frac{A}{\sqrt{2}} e^{i[\omega(t - x_0/v) - \pi/4]} \{[C(u_2) - iS(u_2)] - [C(u_1) - iS(u_1)]\},$$

we see that, apart from a constant factor, the disturbance at P is represented by the vector in the complex plane connecting the point of the
curve corresponding to $u = u_1$ with the point corresponding to $u = u_2$. It
is easy to show that the curve in Fig. 4–34 is identical to the Cornu spiral.
Indeed, the length of the arc corresponding to an infinitesimal change du of
the parameter u is

$$ds = \sqrt{dC^2 + dS^2} = \sqrt{\cos^2 \frac{\pi u^2}{2} + \sin^2 \frac{\pi u^2}{2}}\, du = du,$$

or, if we take $s = 0$ at the origin $(u = 0)$,

$$s = u. \tag{4–45}$$

In agreement with the definition given in the preceding section, we denote by $-\alpha$ the angle formed with the real axis by the tangent to the curve
(pointing in the direction of increasing s). Then we have

$$\tan \alpha = \frac{dS}{dC} = \tan \frac{\pi u^2}{2}$$

or

$$\alpha = \frac{\pi u^2}{2}. \tag{4–46}$$

Equations (4–45) and (4–46) show that α is proportional to s^2, in agreement with the equation that defines the Cornu spiral (Eq. 4–31). Since C

and S become equal to $\pm\frac{1}{2}$ at the limit for $u = \pm\infty$, we conclude that the line connecting the two asymptotic points of the Cornu spiral passes through the origin and forms an angle of 45° with the C-axis, as already mentioned.

4–11 Fresnel diffraction by a straight edge. As a first application of the methods described in the preceding sections, we consider the diffraction phenomena observed near the boundary of the geometric shadow cast by the straight edge of a plane opaque screen. The incident wave is assumed to be plane and parallel to the plane of the screen. Figure 4–35 represents a section perpendicular to this plane, where L is the edge of the screen and Σ is the plane where the diffraction phenomena are observed. From a point P_0 of Σ at the limit of the geometrical shadow we see just half of the wave surface, extending from L downward to infinity. Thus the optical disturbance at P_0 is represented by the vector $Z'A$ connecting the asymptotic point Z' of the Cornu spiral with its midpoint A (Fig. 4–36). The length of this vector is half the length of the vector $Z'Z$, representing the effect of the complete wave surface. Thus the *intensity* of light at the boundary of the geometrical shadow is *one-fourth* the intensity that we would observe in the absence of the screen.

As we move from P_0 into the region of the geometrical shadow, an increasingly greater portion of the wave becomes obscured. The point B of the Cornu spiral corresponding to the edge L of the screen moves along the upper branch of the spiral toward Z', and the length of the vector $Z'B$, representing the optical disturbance, decreases gradually and uniformly toward zero.

As we move from P_0 away from the region of shadow, the point B of the Cornu spiral corresponding to the edge of the screen moves along the lower branch of the spiral, toward Z. The length of the vector $Z'B$ goes through a

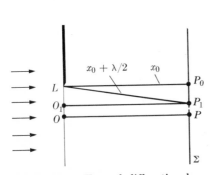

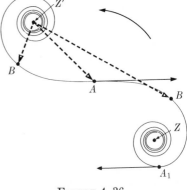

FIG. 4–35. Fresnel diffraction by a straight edge.

FIGURE 4–36

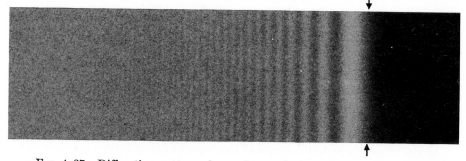

Fig. 4–37. Diffraction pattern observed near the boundary of the geometric shadow cast by the straight edge of an opaque screen (the arrows indicate the boundary).

succession of maxima and minima and eventually tends asymptotically to the length of the segment $Z'Z$. Needless to say, the optical disturbance will be the same at all points of a line parallel to the edge of the screen and therefore perpendicular to the plane of the drawing. Thus in the region where, according to geometrical optics, we should observe full illumination, we will find instead a series of diffraction fringes of varying brightness. The contrast between the bright and dark fringes becomes less pronounced as the distance from the boundary of the geometric shadow increases, until eventually the illumination becomes practically uniform, and equal to that observed without the screen (Fig 4–37).

To determine the actual width of the fringes, we must establish a relation between the position of a point on the observation plane, and the position on the Cornu spiral of the point B corresponding to the edge L of the diffracting screen. For this purpose, consider a point P_1 (Fig. 4–35) such that

$$\overline{P_1L} - \overline{P_0L} = \frac{\lambda}{2}.$$

If O_1 is the foot of the perpendicular to the wave surface through P_1, we have also

$$\overline{P_1L} - \overline{P_1O_1} = \frac{\lambda}{2}.$$

Thus the secondary waves arriving at P_1 from O_1 and L respectively have a phase difference of π. The point O_1 corresponds to the point A of the Cornu spiral. The point L corresponds, therefore, to that point A_1 where the tangent is antiparallel to the tangent at A (see Fig. 4–36). The actual distance of P_1 from the edge of the geometrical shadow P_0 is determined by the equation

$$\overline{P_0P_1}^2 = \overline{LP_1}^2 - \overline{LP_0}^2 = \left(x_0 + \frac{\lambda}{2}\right)^2 - x_0^2,$$

or, since $\lambda/2 \ll x_0$,

$$\overline{P_0P_1}^2 = x_0\lambda. \tag{4-47}$$

It is now easy to determine the position of the point B on the Cornu spiral corresponding to an arbitrary position of the point P of observation. Indeed, we have found that the arc of the spiral between A and B has a length proportional to the length of the segment $\overline{LO} = \overline{P_0P}$, where O is the foot of the perpendicular to the wave front through P (Fig. 4-35). Therefore

$$\frac{s}{s_1} = \frac{\overline{P_0P}}{\overline{P_0P_1}},$$

where s is the length of the arc AB (Fig. 4-36), s_1 is the length of the arc AA_1, and $\overline{P_0P_1}$ is given by Eq. (4-47). This equation determines s and therefore the position of the point B for every position of P. To facilitate the actual computations, the Cornu spiral in Fig. 4-31 is subdivided into small arcs of equal lengths. The unit is chosen so as to make $s_1 = \sqrt{2}$, which gives

$$s = \frac{\sqrt{2}}{\sqrt{x_0\lambda}} \overline{P_0P}.$$

For the experiment described, one can use a point source of light, if it is located sufficiently far from the screen, or an intensely illuminated slit parallel to the diffracting edge. Because the various points of a slit give rise to identical and coincident systems of fringes, the use of a linear instead of a point source does not affect the sharpness of the diffraction pattern. The fringes can be observed on a white diffusing screen, or directly, by means of an eyepiece.

If white light is used in place of monochromatic light, the diffraction pattern will consist of variously colored fringes instead of alternately bright and dark fringes.

4-12 Fresnel diffraction by a slit. Consider now an opaque screen with a long narrow slit illuminated by a plane wave parallel to the screen. We observe the diffraction pattern on a plane Σ, parallel to the screen (Fig. 4-38). The optical disturbance at a point P of the surface Σ is represented by the vector CB (Fig. 4-39), where B and C are the points of the Cornu spiral relative to P corresponding to the edges L and M of the slit. If P is equidistant from L and M (i.e., if P coincides with P_0 in Fig. 4-38), B and C are two

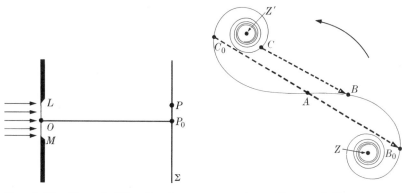

FIG. 4–38. Fresnel diffraction by a slit.

FIGURE 4–39

FIG. 4–40. Fresnel diffraction by two slits of different widths.

points symmetrically located with respect to the midpoint A of the spiral (such as B_0 and C_0 in Fig. 4–39). As P moves away from P_0, e.g., in the upward direction, B and C slide along the Cornu spiral, and approach the asymptotic point Z'. The length of the spiral arc between C and B remains constant because this arc corresponds to a strip of the wave surface of constant width. However, the length of the chord CB, which represents the amplitude of the disturbance, changes periodically. Thus on the observation plane there will appear a series of alternately bright and dark diffraction fringes (Fig. 4–40).

4–13 Shadow of a wire. Consider a wire, or any other straight, narrow, opaque obstacle, placed along the path of a plane wave (Fig. 4–41). The optical disturbance at a point P is the vector sum of the two vectors BZ and $Z'C$, where B and C are the two points of the Cornu spiral relative to P that correspond to the edges L and M of the obstacle (Fig. 4–42).

If the observation point is at P_0, the center of the geometrical shadow, B and C are two points symmetrically located with respect to the midpoint A of the spiral, such as the points B_0 and C_0 in Fig. 4–42. The vectors B_0Z and $Z'C_0$ are equal and parallel. As the point of observation P moves gradually away from P_0, the points B and C slide along the spiral in the same direction. The vector sum of the vectors BZ and $Z'C$, representing the optical disturbance at P, at first decreases in magnitude, and then goes

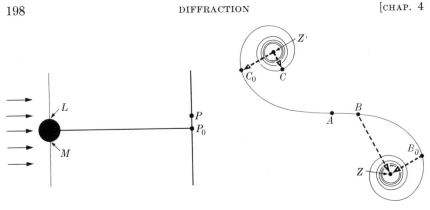

FIG. 4–41. Diffraction by a wire.   FIGURE 4–42

through a succession of maxima and minima. Thus on a plane perpendicular to the direction of propagation of the wave, there will appear a diffraction pattern consisting of a series of alternately bright and dark fringes (Fig. 4–43). At the center of the geometric shadow the intensity is always a maximum.

4–14 Fraunhofer diffraction by a slit: elementary treatment. We now turn our attention to diffraction phenomena observed at very large distances from the diffracting screen, with a light source that also lies at a very large distance from this screen. Recall from Section 4–6 that these are known as Fraunhofer diffraction phenomena; their theory is considerably simpler from a mathematical point of view than that of the Fresnel diffraction phenomena considered so far. Instead of a very distant light source, we can more conveniently use a point source at the focal point of a converging lens (collimator) which changes the spherical wave diverging from the source into a plane wave. Instead of observing the diffraction pattern on a plane at a very large distance from the diffracting screen, we can collect the diffracted light by means of a second converging lens, and observe the fringes in the focal plane of this lens.

As a first example, we shall investigate in an elementary way the Fraunhofer diffraction by a long, narrow slit. Figure 4–44 shows a section of the experimental arrangement with the plane passing through the point source S, perpendicular to the edges of the slit. In the figure L_1 is the collimator and L_2 is the second lens; M and N are the traces of the edges of the slit, P_0 is the second focal point of L_2, and Σ is the trace of the observation plane, coincident with the second focal plane of L_2.

Since the slit is assumed to be very long, diffraction in the direction parallel to the slit is negligible and the diffracted rays emerge from the slit in directions perpendicular to its edges. The lens L_2 causes these rays to

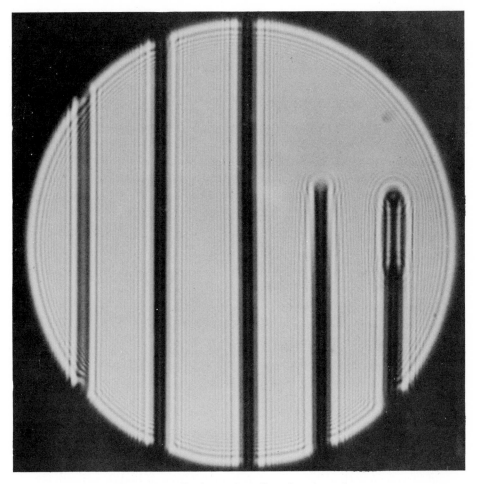

FIG. 4–43. Shadows of needles of various sizes.

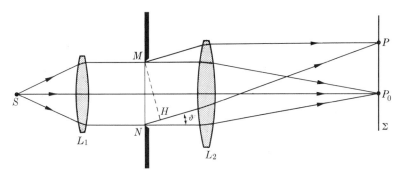

FIG. 4–44. Fraunhofer diffraction by a slit.

converge on a line passing through P_0 and contained in the plane of the drawing. The problem is to determine the distribution of intensity along this line.

For this purpose, we first recall that if a parallel bundle of rays falls on a converging lens, the optical paths of all rays between any plane intersecting the parallel bundle perpendicularly and the point P where the rays converge after traversing the lens are equal (see Section 2–5). The relative phases of the rays at the point P of convergence are thus the same as at the plane just considered.

The various points of the slit behave like secondary sources of the same frequency and phase. Therefore the rays emitted in the direction perpendicular to the plane of the slit arrive at the focal point P_0 of the lens L_2 in phase with one another, and P_0 is a point of maximum intensity.

Consider next the rays emitted at an angle ϑ with respect to the perpendicular to the plane of the slit, and the two rays of this bundle originating from the points M and N at the edges of the slit (Fig. 4–44). Let H be the foot of the perpendicular drawn from M to the ray through N, and let a be the width of the slit ($a = \overline{MN}$), so that

$$\overline{NH} = a \sin \vartheta. \qquad (4\text{--}48)$$

Let us first assume that $\overline{NH} = \lambda$, that is, that $\sin \vartheta = \lambda/a$. Let Q be the midpoint of the segment MN, and let T be the intersection with MH of the ray originating from Q and belonging to the parallel beam under consideration (Fig. 4–45a). We then have

$$\overline{QT} = \frac{1}{2} \overline{NH} = \frac{\lambda}{2},$$

and we conclude that the two rays reaching P from M and Q, respectively, have opposite phases and cancel each other. The same is true of any pair of rays coming from points of the segment MN separated by a distance of half the width of the slit. It now becomes clear that if we subdivide the slit into infinitesimal strips of equal width parallel to its edges, we can pair these strips so that their effects at P cancel, and consequently the light intensity at P is zero.

Consider now the case $\overline{NH} = 3\lambda/2$, that is, $\sin \vartheta = 3\lambda/2a$. We can now divide the segment MN into three equal parts MQ, QR, and RN, as shown in Fig. 4–45(b). We conclude, as before, that the disturbances arising from MQ and QR interfere destructively at P, and that therefore the optical disturbance observed at P is that originating from RN alone. At P there will be a certain amount of illumination and, as it turns out, the intensity at this point is nearly a maximum with respect to that observed at neighboring

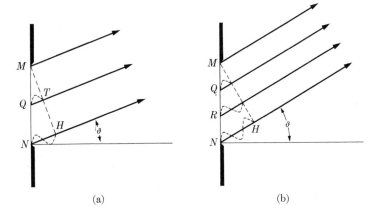

(a)   (b)

Fig. 4–45. The diffracted intensity (a) is zero for $\overline{NH} = \lambda$, and (b) has a secondary maximum for $\overline{NH} = 3\lambda/2$.

points. Such a secondary maximum, however, is much weaker than the primary maximum observed at P_0, both because only one-third of the slit is effective, and because the disturbances arising from the various points of the active portion are not exactly in phase.

By a similar argument, we find that the intensity is again zero when $\sin \vartheta = 2\lambda/a$, is again nearly a maximum when $\sin \vartheta = 5\lambda/2a$ (in which case one-fifth of the slit is effective), etc.

We thus conclude that the intensity of the line appearing on the focal plane of the lens L_2 has an absolute maximum at the center P_0 ($\vartheta = 0$), and the diffraction pattern is symmetrical with respect to the point P_0. The intensity is zero for values of ϑ given by the following equations:

$$\sin \vartheta = \pm \frac{\lambda}{a}, \qquad \sin \vartheta = \pm 2\frac{\lambda}{a} \cdots, \qquad \sin \vartheta = \pm n\frac{\lambda}{a} \cdots, \quad (4\text{–}49)$$

where n is an integer. Secondary maxima occur about halfway between adjoining minima, and the intensity at the secondary maxima decreases rapidly with increasing n.

Since ϑ is usually a small angle, we can, to good approximation, write $\sin \vartheta = \vartheta$. If f is the focal length of the lens L_2, and Z the distance of a point P from P_0, the intensity minima occur at the following values of Z:

$$Z = \pm f\frac{\lambda}{a}, \qquad Z = \pm 2f\frac{\lambda}{a} \cdots, \qquad Z = \pm nf\frac{\lambda}{a} \cdots, \quad (4\text{–}50)$$

and we see that the width of the principal maximum, i.e., the distance between the minima at $Z = f\lambda/a$ and at $Z = -f\lambda/a$, is twice the width of the

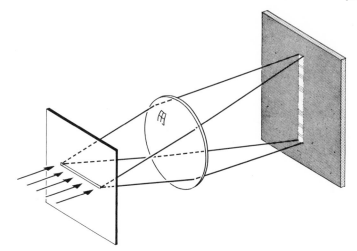

Fɪɢ. 4–46. Fraunhofer diffraction pattern of a long, narrow slit.

secondary maxima. The widths of the principal and of the secondary maxima are inversely proportional to the width a of the slit.

Note that, in the case of a point source, the *Fresnel* diffraction pattern of a slit (discussed in Section 4–12) is a band, whereas the *Fraunhofer* diffraction pattern discussed here is a line perpendicular to the slit (see Fig. 4–46). This line may be regarded as a spread-out image of the point source; the spread decreases as the width of the slit increases. For a sufficiently large width the diffraction line reduces practically to a point, the ordinary image of the source. Instead of a point source, however, we can use a linear light source parallel to the slit and placed in the focal plane of the collimator. The Fraunhofer diffraction pattern then appears in the form of a band, and the length of the fringes equals the length of the geometrical image of the line source given by the combination of the two lenses L_1 and L_2.

In the discussion above we have assumed that the light source is monochromatic. If, instead, the source emits white light, the diffraction line or the diffraction band will exhibit a succession of different colors.

4–15 Fraunhofer diffraction by a rectangular aperture: rigorous treatment. In place of the infinitely long slit discussed in the previous section, we now consider a rectangular aperture of sides a and b. We again use a point source S of monochromatic light, placed at the focal point of a lens L_1 which provides a plane wave incident perpendicularly upon the plane of the slit. We wish to rigorously compute the two-dimensional diffraction pattern observed in the focal plane Σ of the second lens L_2.

Let us define a cartesian system of coordinates with the origin at the center O of the rectangular aperture, and with the y- and z-axes parallel to

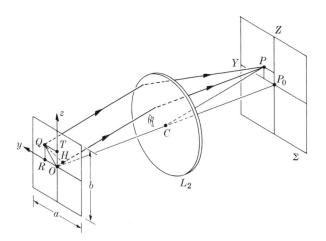

FIG. 4–47. Fraunhofer diffraction by a rectangular aperture.

the sides of this aperture. Consider, in the plane of the aperture, an element of area $dy\,dz$ around the point Q of coordinates $y = \overline{OR}$, $z = \overline{OT}$ (Fig. 4–47). Consider also two parallel rays through O and Q, respectively, and let H be the foot of the perpendicular from Q to the ray through O. Let us call γ_y and γ_z the cosines of the angles formed with the y- and z-axes, respectively, by the rays under consideration, that is,

$$\gamma_y = \cos\,(\angle ROH), \qquad \gamma_z = \cos\,(\angle TOH). \tag{4–51}$$

The segment OH is the projection of the vector OQ on the ray through O. The vector OQ is the vector sum of the vectors OR and OT. Thus $\overline{OH}$ is the sum of the projections of these two vectors on the ray through O. Taking the definitions of γ_y and γ_z (Eqs. 4–51) and considering that $\overline{OR} = y$, $\overline{OT} = z$, we obtain

$$\overline{OH} = \gamma_y y + \gamma_z z.$$

The two parallel rays through O and Q are brought together by the lens L_2 at a point P of its second focal plane. The optical paths from Q to P and from H to P are equal. Hence the two rays arrive at P with a phase difference equal to

$$2\pi\,\frac{\overline{OH}}{\lambda} = 2\pi\,\frac{\gamma_y y + \gamma_z z}{\lambda}\,.$$

Let $Ae^{i(\omega t - \varphi)}\,dy\,dz$ represent the optical disturbance produced at P by the secondary waves originating from the element of area $dy\ dz$ *around the point* O. The disturbance produced by the secondary waves originating from the element of area $dy\ dz$ *around the point* Q is then given by

$$dE_s = Ae^{i(\omega t-\varphi)}\,e^{2\pi i(\gamma_y y+\gamma_z z)/\lambda}\,dy\,dz. \tag{4–52}$$

In deriving the above equation we have neglected the obliquity factor, which is permissible since we are considering only directions nearly perpendicular to the plane of the aperture.

To compute the total optical disturbance at P there remains only integration of the expression (4–52) over the area of the aperture that extends from $-a/2$ to $+a/2$ in the y-direction, and from $-b/2$ to $+b/2$ in the z-direction. We obtain

$$E_P = Ae^{i(\omega t-\varphi)}\int_{-a/2}^{+a/2}\int_{-b/2}^{+b/2}e^{2\pi i(\gamma_y y+\gamma_z z)/\lambda}\,dy\,dz$$

$$= Ae^{i(\omega t-\varphi)}\left(\int_{-a/2}^{+a/2}e^{2\pi i(\gamma_y y/\lambda)}\,dy\right)\left(\int_{-b/2}^{+b/2}e^{2\pi i(\gamma_z z/\lambda)}\,dz\right).$$

If we let

$$\alpha = \frac{\pi\gamma_y a}{\lambda}, \qquad \beta = \frac{\pi\gamma_z b}{\lambda} \tag{4–53}$$

and make use of Eq. (A1–17) from the Appendix, we obtain

$$\int_{-a/2}^{+a/2}e^{2\pi i(\gamma_y y/\lambda)}\,dy = a\frac{e^{i\alpha}-e^{-i\alpha}}{2i\alpha} = a\frac{\sin\alpha}{\alpha},$$

$$\int_{-b/2}^{+b/2}e^{2\pi i(\gamma_z z/\lambda)}\,dz = b\frac{e^{i\beta}-e^{-i\beta}}{2i\beta} = b\frac{\sin\beta}{\beta}.$$

The expression for E_P then becomes

$$E_P = Aab\frac{\sin\alpha}{\alpha}\frac{\sin\beta}{\beta}e^{i(\omega t-\varphi)}. \tag{4–54}$$

In the direction perpendicular to the aperture, $\gamma_y = 0$, $\gamma_z = 0$ and therefore $\alpha = 0$, $\beta = 0$. Remembering that for small values of α and β we can approximate $\sin\alpha$ by α and $\sin\beta$ by β, we find that, at the limits for $\alpha = 0$

and $\beta = 0$, $(\sin \alpha)/\alpha$ and $(\sin \beta)/\beta$ become equal to unity. Thus, at the point P_0 where the rays emerging perpendicularly from the aperture meet, the optical disturbance is

$$E_0 = Aabe^{i(\omega t - \varphi)}. \qquad (4\text{--}55)$$

Since the light intensity is proportional to the square of the amplitude of the optical disturbance, the intensity I_P at an arbitrary point P of the plane of observation is given by the following expression in terms of the intensity I_0 at the point P_0 and of the parameters α and β defined by Eqs. (4–53):

$$I_P = I_0 \frac{\sin^2 \alpha}{\alpha^2} \frac{\sin^2 \beta}{\beta^2}. \qquad (4\text{--}56)$$

This equation represents the solution to our problem.

To determine, on the observation plane Σ, the position of the point P that corresponds to given values of the parameters α and β, consider a system of cartesian coordinates with origin at P_0 and axes Y and Z parallel to the y- and z-axes in the plane of the diffracting aperture (Fig. 4–47). Note that the rays passing through the center C of the lens L_2 do not undergo angular deflection. Thus the point P is the intersection with the plane Σ of the line through C, parallel to the direction characterized by the parameters α and β, and this line forms, with the Y- and Z-axes, angles whose cosines are γ_y and γ_z, respectively. Since the Y-coordinate of the point P is the projection of the segment CP on the Y-axis, and the Z-coordinate of P is the projection of CP on the Z-axis, we obtain

$$Y = \overline{CP} \cdot \gamma_y, \qquad Z = \overline{CP} \cdot \gamma_z. \qquad (4\text{--}57)$$

If we consider only directions that form small angles with the line of OP_0, which is perpendicular to the diffracting aperture and to the observation plane, $\overline{CP}$ is almost identical with the focal length f of the lens L_2. Equations 4–57 then become

$$Y = f\gamma_y, \qquad Z = f\gamma_z, \qquad (4\text{--}58)$$

and we thus arrive (remembering Eqs. 4–53) at the following relations between the parameters α, β and the coordinates Y and Z of the corresponding point on the observation plane:

$$\alpha = \pi \frac{aY}{f\lambda}, \qquad \beta = \pi \frac{bZ}{f\lambda}. \qquad (4\text{--}59)$$

With these expressions for α and β, Eq. (4–56) then gives the intensity as a function of the coordinates Y and Z on the observation plane.

We see that the expression for the intensity contains the products of two factors of exactly the same form, one depending only on α (and therefore on Y), the other depending only on β (and therefore on Z). Let us investigate the character of these factors.

The maxima and minima of the function

$$D(\alpha) = \frac{\sin^2 \alpha}{\alpha^2} \qquad (4\text{–}60)$$

are determined by the equation

$$\frac{dD}{d\alpha} = 0$$

or

$$\frac{\sin \alpha}{\alpha} \, \frac{\alpha \cos \alpha - \sin \alpha}{\alpha^2} = 0. \qquad (4\text{–}61)$$

Remembering that

$$\sin \alpha = \alpha - \alpha^3/3! + \cdots \qquad \text{and} \qquad \cos \alpha = 1 - \alpha^2/2 + \cdots,$$

we can easily verify that $\alpha = 0$ is a solution of (4–61). It is obvious that this solution corresponds to the absolute maximum of the function $D(\alpha)$. Indeed, as already pointed out, $D(\alpha) = 1$ for $\alpha = 0$, while for $\alpha \neq 0$, $\sin \alpha < \alpha$ and therefore $D(\alpha) < 1$.

Equation (4–61) is also satisfied by all values of α that satisfy the equation $\sin \alpha = 0$, that is, by

$$\alpha = \pm\pi, \qquad \alpha = \pm 2\pi, \cdots, \qquad \alpha = \pm n\pi, \qquad (4\text{–}62)$$

where n is any integer different from zero. For these values of α, $D(\alpha) = 0$. Since $D(\alpha)$ is never negative, Eqs. (4–62) define the positions of the minima.

Finally, Eq. (4–61) is satisfied by all values of α that satisfy the equation $\alpha \cos \alpha = \sin \alpha$, or

$$\tan \alpha = \alpha. \qquad (4\text{–}63)$$

We can find the solutions of this transcendental equation by a graphical method, as shown in Fig. 4–48, where the curve representing the function $f_1(\alpha) = \tan \alpha$ and the straight line representing the function $f_2(\alpha) = \alpha$ are plotted. The intersections of the curve with the straight line define the values of α that satisfy (4–63). These values correspond to the maxima of the function $D(\alpha)$; we see that they lie *about* halfway between the values of α corresponding to the minima, being close to $3\pi/2$, $5\pi/2$, etc.

Figure 4-49 is a graph of the function $D(\alpha) = (\sin^2 \alpha)/\alpha^2$ plotted against α. We recognize that the secondary maxima are much lower than the principal maximum, and that they decrease rapidly in magnitude as α increases.

It is now possible to describe in detail the appearance of the diffraction pattern on the observation plane Σ. The intensity has an absolute maximum at the center P_0, that is, at $Y = 0, Z = 0$. The intensity is zero along the straight lines defined by the equations

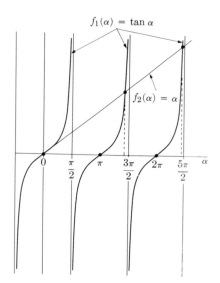

Fig. 4-48. Graphical solution of the equation $\tan \alpha = \alpha$.

$$\alpha = \pm n\pi, \qquad \beta = \pm n\pi, \qquad (4\text{-}64)$$

or (Eq. 4-59):

$$Y = \pm n\frac{f\lambda}{a}, \qquad Z = \pm n\frac{f\lambda}{b}. \qquad (4\text{-}65)$$

These lines form a rectangular network (Fig 4-50). Most of the light is concentrated in the central rectangle, whose sides are $2f\lambda/a$, $2f\lambda/b$, and are thus *inversely proportional to the sides of the aperture*. Along any line parallel to the Y- or Z-axis, the intensity varies in the manner shown by the graph of Fig. 4-49.

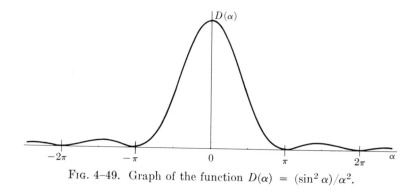

Fig. 4-49. Graph of the function $D(\alpha) = (\sin^2 \alpha)/\alpha^2$.

FIG. 4-50. Fraunhofer diffraction of a rectangular aperture whose height is twice its width.

If $a \ll b$, that is, if the rectangular aperture reduces to a long, narrow slit parallel to the Z-axis, the intensity on the plane of observation drops rapidly to zero on both sides of the line $Z = 0$. Thus the diffraction pattern reduces to a line coincident with the Y-axis. On this axis, $\beta = 0$, $(\sin \beta)/\beta = 1$, and Eqs. (4-54) and (4-56) reduce to the following:

$$E = C \frac{\sin \alpha}{\alpha} e^{i(\omega t - \varphi)}, \qquad (4\text{-}66)$$

$$I = I_0 \frac{\sin^2 \alpha}{\alpha^2}, \qquad (4\text{-}67)$$

where $C = Aab$ is a constant. These equations give the exact solution of the problem of the Fraunhofer diffraction by a single slit discussed in the previous section from a more elementary point of view. Note that in this case $\gamma_y = \sin \vartheta$, and therefore

$$\alpha = \pi a \sin \vartheta / \lambda. \qquad (4\text{-}68)$$

Hence the condition for the minima:

$$\alpha = \pm n\pi,$$

reduces to the condition previously found (Eqs. 4-49):

$$a \sin \vartheta = \pm n\lambda.$$

4-16 Fraunhofer diffraction by a circular aperture. Limit of resolution of optical instruments. The theory of Fraunhofer diffraction by a circular aperture requires more elaborate mathematical computations than that of Fraunhofer diffraction by a rectangular aperture. From these computa-

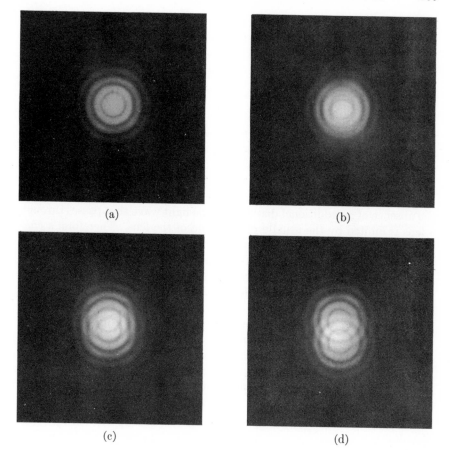

(a)   (b)

(c)   (d)

Fig. 4–51. Enlargements from photographs of typical diffraction patterns produced by a lens: (a) for a single distant point object, (b) for two distant point objects whose diffraction patterns are separated by a distance equal to one-half the radius of the central disk, (c) the same, with the separation equal to the radius of the disk, (d) the same, with the separation equal to twice the radius of the disk. (Hardy and Perrin, *Principles of Optics*, McGraw-Hill Book Company, Inc., 1932. Photographs by A. C. Hall.)

tions, which we shall not attempt here, it is found that the Fraunhofer diffraction pattern of a circular aperture consists of a bright circular disk surrounded by a series of dark and bright rings of rapidly decreasing intensity (Fig. 4–51a). As viewed from the center of the aperture, the radius R of the first dark ring subtends an angle ϑ given by

$$\sin \vartheta = 1.22 \frac{\lambda}{a},$$

(4–69)

where a is the diameter of the circular aperture and λ is the wavelength. Since most of the light falls within this ring, the radius R is often referred to as the radius of the diffraction disk. If ϑ is a small angle, the actual value of R is

$$R = 1.22\, f\, \frac{\lambda}{a}, \tag{4-70}$$

where f is the focal length of the lens. (For comparison, recall that a square aperture of side a produces a diffraction pattern with a central bright region surrounded by a dark line in the shape of a square of half side $f\lambda/a$.)

Diffraction by a circular aperture is an effect of great practical importance in connection with the properties of optical instruments. Even in the absence of an additional diaphragm, the light wave that passes through a lens is limited by the usually circular rim of the lens. Therefore, a converging lens will never produce a point image of a distant point source, no matter how carefully we correct for aberrations. Indeed, under the most favorable conditions, the image will be a disk of radius R, given by Eq. (4-70), where now a must be understood as the diameter of the lens.

Note that this result applies not only to the case of a point source at infinite distance, but also to the case of a point source at a finite distance, i.e., to the case in which the incident wave is spherical rather than plane. In both cases the wave emerging from the lens is a portion of a spherical wave, and the diffraction pattern observed near the point of convergence of this spherical wave is obviously independent of whether the wave originates from a plane or from a spherical wave incident upon the lens. Thus, in general, the image of a point source formed by a lens of diameter a is a disk of radius

$$R = 1.22\, s'\, \frac{\lambda}{a}, \tag{4-71}$$

where s' is the distance of the image from the lens.

A similar result is obtained for the case of images formed by concave spherical mirrors, such as those used in the construction of telescopes.

It is the finite dimension of the diffraction disk representing the image of a point source that sets a limit to the *resolving power* of an optical instrument. If the angular distance between two point sources is large compared with the angle ϑ given by (4-69), the two corresponding diffraction patterns are clearly separated. If this angular distance is small compared with ϑ, the two diffraction patterns merge into one that cannot be distinguished from that corresponding to a single source (Fig. 4-51). A practical (though somewhat arbitrary) criterion established by Rayleigh stipulates that two point sources can be resolved if the centers of the two diffraction disks are at a distance greater than the radius of the disks. Thus Eq. (4-69) defines the minimum angular distance of two point sources that can be separated by a lens or a mirror of diameter a. The angle ϑ may thus be called the *minimum angle of resolution* of the lens or the mirror.

It is in part for the purpose of improving the resolution that the objective lenses and mirrors of telescopes have large diameters. Another important reason, of course, is that if we increase the area over which light is collected, the images of stars become more intense and therefore it becomes possible to photograph faint stars.

4-17 Fraunhofer diffraction by a double slit. As another example, consider the case of an opaque screen with two narrow slits parallel to each other. We assume that the two slits have the same width a, and that their centers O_1, O_2 (Fig. 4-52) are a distance h apart. As in the previous examples, the light source S is in the focal plane of the lens L_1, which acts as a collimator and provides a beam of parallel rays falling perpendicularly upon the double slit. The diffraction pattern is observed in the second focal plane Σ of the lens L_2. Each slit separately produces the diffraction pattern described in Sections 4-14 and 4-15. Note that, despite the different positions of the slits, the two diffraction patterns on the plane of observation Σ are coincident. Indeed, both diffraction patterns have their centers at P_0, the point of convergence of the rays that emerge perpendicularly from the slits.

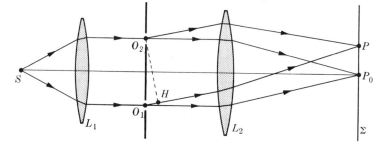

FIG. 4-52. Fraunhofer diffraction by a double slit.

To determine the optical disturbance that results from the overlap of the two diffraction patterns, we must consider the interference effects between the disturbances arriving at a given point P of the observation plane from the two slits.

The optical disturbances E_1 and E_2 produced at P by the two slits separately are represented by the following equations (see Eq. 4-66):

$$E_1 = C \frac{\sin \alpha}{\alpha} e^{i(\omega t - \varphi_1)},$$

$$E_2 = C \frac{\sin \alpha}{\alpha} e^{i(\omega t - \varphi_2)}. \tag{4-72}$$

Equation (4–68) relates the parameter α to the angle of emergence ϑ of the rays that converge at P after passing through the lens L_2. The angles $-\varphi_1$ and $-\varphi_2$ represent the relative phases at P of the parallel rays originating from the midpoints of the two apertures O_1 and O_2, respectively, and forming the angle ϑ with the normal to the screen. Let H be the foot of the perpendicular through O_2 to the ray passing through O_1 (Fig. 4–52). The phase difference of the two rays at P is then

$$\frac{2\pi \overline{O_1 H}}{\lambda} = \frac{2\pi h \sin \theta}{\lambda} .$$

If we define

$$\delta = \frac{\pi h \sin \theta}{\lambda} , \qquad (4\text{–}73)$$

we can write

$$\varphi_2 = \varphi_1 - 2\delta,$$

and we obtain the following expression for the resultant disturbance at P:

$$E_P = E_1 + E_2 = C \frac{\sin \alpha}{\alpha} [e^{i(\omega t - \varphi_1)} + e^{i(\omega t - \varphi_1 + 2\delta)}]$$

$$= C \frac{\sin \alpha}{\alpha} (1 + e^{2i\delta}) e^{i(\omega t - \varphi_1)}$$

or, since $1 + e^{2i\delta} = e^{i\delta}(e^{i\delta} + e^{-i\delta}) = 2e^{i\delta} \cos\delta$ (see Eq. A1–17),

$$E_P = 2C \frac{\sin \alpha}{\alpha} \cos \delta \, e^{i(\omega t - \varphi_1 + \delta)} . \qquad (4\text{–}74)$$

This equation represents a sinusoidal function of time, of amplitude $2C(\sin \alpha/\alpha) \cos \delta$. For $\vartheta = 0$, $\alpha = 0$, $\delta = 0$ and the amplitude acquires its maximum value, $2C$. Considering that the intensity is proportional to the square of the amplitude, we obtain

$$I = I_0 \frac{\sin^2 \alpha}{\alpha^2} \cos^2 \delta, \qquad (4\text{–}75)$$

which gives the intensity observed at an arbitrary point P in terms of the intensity I_0 at P_0 and of the parameters α and δ which depend on the position of P.

The term $(\sin^2 \alpha)/\alpha^2$ (diffraction term) is the same as that which enters into the expression for the intensity distribution in the diffraction pattern of a single slit. The term $\cos^2 \delta$ (interference term) is identical with the term that enters into the expression for the distribution of intensity resulting from the interference of two waves (Eq. 3–28). Thus (4–75) may be interpreted as the expression for the intensity resulting from the interference of two diffracted waves whose intensities are equal to $(I_0/4) \times (\sin^2 \alpha)/\alpha^2$, and whose phase difference is 2δ.

In Fig. 4–53, the diffraction term, the interference term, and their product (which represents the ratio I/I_0) are plotted against $\sin \vartheta$. In preparing these graphs we have taken $h = 4a$.

As in the case for the single slit, the pattern that appears on the focal plane Σ of the lens L_2 is a line of variable intensity or a system of bright and dark fringes, depending on whether the light source S is a point or a line parallel to the slits (Fig. 4–54). The intensity is zero at the points where $\cos \delta = 0$, that is, for the following values of $\sin \vartheta$:

$$\sin \vartheta = \pm \frac{1}{2} \frac{\lambda}{h},$$

$$\sin \vartheta = \pm \frac{3}{2} \frac{\lambda}{h}, \qquad (4\text{–}76)$$

$$\vdots$$

$$\sin \vartheta = \pm \frac{2k+1}{2} \frac{\lambda}{h},$$

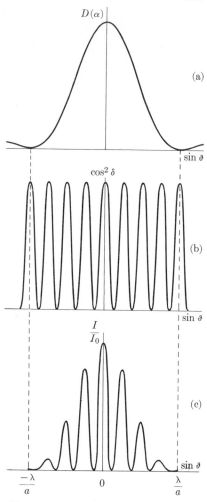

Fig. 4–53. Intensity distribution in the Fraunhofer diffraction pattern of a double slit: (a) the diffraction term $D(\alpha) = (\sin^2 \alpha)/\alpha^2$, (b) the interference term, $\cos^2 \delta$, (c) the product $D(\alpha) \cos^2 \delta$ $[h = 4a]$.

where k is an integer.

If the width a of the slits is small compared with the distance h between their centers, the width of the central maximum of the diffraction term is large compared with the distance between successive zeros of the interference term. In this case, for sufficiently small values of $\sin \vartheta$, the diffraction term is essentially a constant and the distribution of intensity is con-

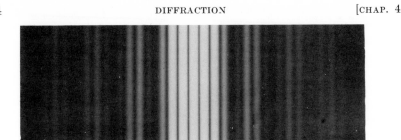

Fig. 4-54. Fraunhofer diffraction pattern of a double slit.

trolled by the interference term. Then the fringes observed near the central fringe ($\vartheta = 0$) have practically equal intensities. The maxima of intensity will appear at the following values of $\sin \vartheta$:

$$\sin \vartheta = 0, \qquad \sin \vartheta = \pm \frac{\lambda}{h}, \qquad \cdots, \qquad \sin \vartheta = \pm k \frac{\lambda}{h}. \qquad (4\text{-}77)$$

The integer k here represents the order of interference, i.e., the difference between the optical paths of the two rays arriving at P from the centers of the slits, expressed in wavelengths. Note that the interference maximum of order zero appears at the same position (corresponding to $\sin \vartheta = 0$) for all wavelengths. The positions of the successive maxima, however, depend on the wavelength.

4–18 The diffraction grating. The diffraction grating is an optical instrument with important spectroscopic applications. One form of this instrument consists of an opaque screen with a large number of parallel and equidistant slits of equal widths. The light source is usually an intensely illuminated slit parallel to the slits of the grating, placed in the focal plane of a lens L_1. The diffraction pattern is observed in the focal plane of a lens L_2 placed in front of the grating (Fig. 4–55). As in the case of the double slit, intensity maxima appear at points corresponding to the following values of $\sin \vartheta$:

$$\sin \vartheta = 0, \quad \sin \vartheta = \pm \frac{\lambda}{h}, \quad \sin \vartheta = \pm 2 \frac{\lambda}{h}, \quad \cdots, \quad \sin \vartheta = \pm k \frac{\lambda}{h}, \quad (4\text{-}78)$$

where h represents the distance between the centers of neighboring slits. This is easily understandable, for Eqs. (4–78) signify that the optical paths of two rays reaching the point of convergence from the centers of two neighboring slits are equal or differ by an integral multiple of a wavelength. Thus Eqs. (4–78) determine the positions where the disturbances arising from all the various slits arrive with the same phase.

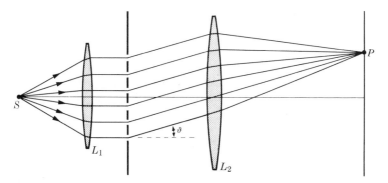

Fig. 4–55. The diffraction grating.

In the case of the double slit, there is only one minimum between the maxima corresponding to consecutive values of k in (4–78). We shall presently show, however, that in the case of the grating, there is, between these maxima, a large number of minima separated by a correspondingly large number of maxima of much smaller intensity. The latter are *secondary maxima*, and the maxima defined by (4–78) are *principal maxima*.

It is easy to see that if N is the number of slits, the intensity is zero when ϑ satisfies the equation

$$\sin \vartheta = \pm \frac{\lambda}{Nh}. \tag{4–79}$$

Indeed, for this value of ϑ, the difference between the optical paths of two rays from adjoining slits is $h \sin \vartheta = \pm\lambda/N$, and hence their phase difference at the interference point is $2\pi/N$. The disturbances arising from the N different slits are thus represented by N vectors of equal length, each forming an angle of $2\pi/N$ with its neighbor. When plotted one after another, these vectors form a closed regular polygon of N sides. The resultant vector, representing the resultant disturbance, is therefore zero.

Equation (4–79) determines the position of the first minimum next to the maximum of order zero. In general, we find that minima occur at all the following values of $\sin \vartheta$:

$$\sin \vartheta = \pm \frac{\lambda}{Nh}, \quad \sin \vartheta = \pm \frac{2\lambda}{Nh}, \quad \cdots, \quad \sin \vartheta = \pm \frac{m\lambda}{Nh}, \tag{4–80}$$

where m is an integer which is neither zero nor a multiple of N. Thus, between the principal maxima of order zero and the principal maxima of order one, as well as between any other pair of contiguous principal maxima, there are $N - 1$ equally spaced minima separated by $N - 2$ secondary maxima.

In order to actually compute the intensity at the point P corresponding to the angle ϑ (Fig. 4–55), we again define the parameter $\delta = \pi h \sin \vartheta / \lambda$ as in the previous section (Eq. 4–73) and remark that $2n\delta$ represents the phase difference between the optical disturbances arriving at the interference point from slit 1 and slit $n + 1$, respectively. We can represent the disturbance arising from the first slit by an equation of the following type (see Eq. 4–66):

$$E_1 = C \frac{\sin \alpha}{\alpha} e^{i(\omega t - \varphi)}.$$

The disturbance arising from slit $n + 1$ is then given by

$$E_{n+1} = C \frac{\sin \alpha}{\alpha} e^{i(\omega t - \varphi + 2n\delta)},$$

or

$$E_{n+1} = C \frac{\sin \alpha}{\alpha} e^{i(\omega t - \varphi)} e^{2in\delta}. \tag{4–81}$$

The disturbance at P resulting from the interference of the N diffracted beams is

$$E_P = E_1 + E_2 + \cdots + E_N,$$

or

$$E_P = C \frac{\sin \alpha}{\alpha} e^{i(\omega t - \varphi)} \sum_0^{N-1} e^{2in\delta}. \tag{4–82}$$

From Eq. (A1–22), we obtain

$$\sum_0^{N-1} e^{2in\delta} = \frac{1 - e^{2iN\delta}}{1 - e^{2i\delta}} = \frac{e^{iN\delta}}{e^{i\delta}} \frac{e^{iN\delta} - e^{-iN\delta}}{e^{i\delta} - e^{-i\delta}}$$

$$= e^{i(N-1)\delta} \frac{\sin (N\delta)}{\sin \delta}.$$

The expression for E_P then becomes

$$E_P = C \frac{\sin \alpha}{\alpha} \frac{\sin (N\delta)}{\sin \delta} e^{i[\omega t - \varphi + (N-1)\delta]}, \tag{4–83}$$

which represents a sinusoidal function of time, of amplitude

$$C \frac{\sin \alpha}{\alpha} \frac{\sin (N\delta)}{\sin \delta}.$$

Considering that

$$\frac{\sin \alpha}{\alpha} = 1, \qquad \text{for } \alpha = 0,$$

and that

$$\left| \frac{\sin (N\delta)}{\sin \delta} \right| = N, \qquad \text{for } \delta = 0 \text{ or, in general, for } \delta = \pm k\pi, \qquad (4\text{--}84)$$

we find that the amplitude at the maximum of order zero, i.e., at the point corresponding to $\vartheta = 0$, is NC. We now obtain the following expression for the intensity I_P at the point P corresponding to the angle ϑ:

$$I_P = \frac{I_0}{N^2} \frac{\sin^2 \alpha}{\alpha^2} \frac{\sin^2 (N\delta)}{\sin^2 \delta}, \qquad (4\text{--}85)$$

where I_0 is the intensity at the maximum of order zero, i.e., at the point corresponding to $\vartheta = 0$.

Here again, as in the case of the double slit, the expression for I_P contains a diffraction term $(\sin^2 \alpha / \alpha^2)$ and an interference term $[\sin^2 (N\delta)/\sin^2 \delta]$. These two terms and their product (representing the quantity $I_P N^2 / I_0$) are shown in Fig. 4–56 as functions of $\sin \vartheta$, for the case where $N = 10$ and $h = 2a$.

In agreement with the results of the previous discussion, Eq. (4–85) shows that the principal maxima occur when δ is an integral multiple of π, that is, when ϑ satisfies one of Eqs. (4–78). Recalling (4–84), we recognize that the intensity at the principal maxima is given by

$$I_P = I_0 \frac{\sin^2 \alpha}{\alpha^2}. \qquad (4\text{--}86)$$

Also in agreement with the previous discussion, we find that the intensity is zero when $N\delta$ is an integral multiple of π but δ is not, i.e., when ϑ satisfies one of Eqs. (4–80). The secondary maxima occur *approximately* halfway between the minima, i.e., approximately for the following values of $\sin \vartheta$:

$$\sin \vartheta = \pm \frac{3}{2} \frac{\lambda}{Nh}, \quad \sin \vartheta = \pm \frac{5}{2} \frac{\lambda}{Nh}, \cdots \qquad (4\text{--}87)$$

For these values of ϑ, $|\sin N\delta| = 1$ and (4–85) yields

$$I_P = \frac{I_0}{N^2} \frac{\sin^2 \alpha}{\alpha^2} \frac{1}{\sin^2 \delta}. \qquad (4\text{--}88)$$

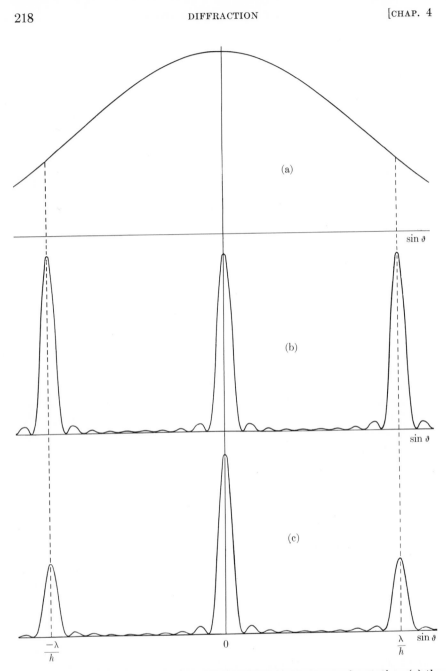

(a)

$\sin \vartheta$

(b)

$\sin \vartheta$

(c)

$\dfrac{-\lambda}{h}$ 0 $\dfrac{\lambda}{h}$ $\sin \vartheta$

FIG. 4–56. Intensity distribution in the diffraction pattern of a grating: (a) the diffraction term, (b) the interference term, (c) the product of the two terms.

In particular, at the secondary maxima adjacent to the principal maximum of order k, δ has the value $k\pi + 3\pi/2N$. Since N is a large number, $3\pi/2N \ll 1$, $|\sin \delta| \approx 3\pi/2N$, and (4–88) becomes

$$I_P = I_0 \frac{\sin^2 \alpha}{\alpha^2}\left(\frac{2}{3\pi}\right)^2 \approx \frac{1}{22} I_0 \frac{\sin^2 \alpha}{\alpha^2}. \tag{4–89}$$

Thus the intensities of these maxima are only $1/22$ that of the principal maximum.

The intensities of the secondary maxima decrease as $\sin \delta$ increases, i.e., as one approaches the region halfway between two principal maxima. In this region, $\sin \delta \approx 1$ and the intensities of the secondary maxima are about $1/N^2$ that of the adjacent principal maxima.

Gratings commonly used in spectroscopy have as many as several hundred thousand slits. For such a large value of N, the principal maxima are very narrow. The secondary maxima adjacent to the principal maxima cannot be seen because of the very small angular separation from the principal maxima, and the other maxima cannot be detected because of their small intensities. When monochromatic light is used, the interference pattern produced by the grating consists of a number of narrow bright lines on a dark background, each line corresponding to a different order of interference.

It is evident that increasing the number of slits from two to N does not change the position of the maxima, but makes them much sharper. We encountered a similar situation when we investigated other examples of interference by many waves in Section 3–9.

It is the sharpness of the interference lines that makes the grating a valuable spectroscopic instrument. In order to analyze the operation of the grating as a spectroscope, let us now assume that the light source, instead of emitting monochromatic waves, emits waves of several different wavelengths. The position of the maxima of order zero is the same for all wavelengths ($\vartheta = 0$). The other maxima, however, appear at different positions for the different wavelengths; thus, for each order of interference except the zeroth, we will find as many lines as there are different wavelengths in the light source. These lines may be regarded as separate monochromatic images of the source, and the lines corresponding to the first, second, etc., order of interference are said to form the spectra of the first, second, etc., order. These spectra bear some resemblance to the spectra produced by prisms (see Section 2–14) but, unlike the prism, the grating deflects light of long wavelengths more strongly than it does light of short wavelengths. Moreover, in the case of the grating the angular position of a line of given order is related by a simple equation to the wavelength and to the distance between the slits. Therefore, the grating affords the possibility of an absolute measurement of the wavelength.

Suppose that the source emits light of two different wavelengths λ and $\lambda + \Delta\lambda$, near to each other. The corresponding maxima of order k appear at angles ϑ and $\vartheta + \Delta\vartheta$ such that

$$\sin\vartheta = k\frac{\lambda}{h}, \qquad \sin(\vartheta + \Delta\vartheta) = k(\lambda + \Delta\lambda)/h$$

(see Eqs. 4–78). If $\Delta\lambda \ll \lambda$, then $\Delta\vartheta \ll \vartheta$, and we can write $\sin(\vartheta + \Delta\vartheta) = \sin\vartheta + \Delta\vartheta\cos\vartheta$. The above two equations then yield

$$\frac{\Delta\vartheta}{\Delta\lambda} = \frac{k}{h\cos\vartheta}. \tag{4–90}$$

The quantity $\Delta\vartheta/\Delta\lambda$ is called the *angular dispersion* of the grating in the kth order. It is proportional to k and inversely proportional to h, the distance between slits.

The width of the spectral lines formed by a grating remains finite, even when the width of the illuminated slit used as a source tends to zero. Therefore, as the difference in wavelength $\Delta\lambda$ decreases indefinitely, the lines corresponding to the two wavelengths considered above will eventually merge into a single line. As a practical criterion, we shall assume that the two lines can be resolved if their separation exceeds the half-width of each line, i.e., the distance between a principal maximum and the adjoining minimum. If ϑ is the angular position of the maximum of order k and $\vartheta + \delta\vartheta$ that of the adjoining minimum, we have

$$\sin\vartheta = k\frac{\lambda}{h}, \qquad \sin(\vartheta + \delta\vartheta) = \left(k + \frac{1}{N}\right)\frac{\lambda}{h}$$

(Eqs. 4–78 and 4–80). Since $\delta\vartheta$ is a very small angle, the two equations above yield

$$\delta\vartheta = \frac{\lambda}{Nh}\frac{1}{\cos\vartheta}. \tag{4–91}$$

By equating the quantity $\Delta\vartheta$ given by (4–90) to the quantity $\delta\vartheta$ given by (4–91), we find

$$\frac{k}{h\cos\vartheta}\Delta\lambda = \frac{\lambda}{Nh}\frac{1}{\cos\vartheta},$$

or

$$\frac{\lambda}{\Delta\lambda} = Nk. \tag{4–92}$$

According to the criterion established above, this equation determines the smallest difference in wavelength $\Delta\lambda$ that a given grating can resolve in the

kth order. The quantity $\lambda/\Delta\lambda$ (i.e., the inverse ratio of the difference in wavelength to the average wavelength of two radiations) is called the *resolving power* of the grating. We see from Eq. (4–92) that the resolving power is the product of the number of slits, N, times the order, k, of the spectrum considered. It is thus practically equal to the difference between the optical paths of the rays arriving at the point of interference from the first and the last slit of the grating, respectively, expressed in wavelengths.

Note that the resolving power (unlike dispersion) is independent of the separation of the slits.

Gratings of the type considered so far are known as *transmission gratings*. A transmission grating can be made by photographing a piece of white paper on which a number of parallel black lines have been drawn. Gratings of higher quality are made of glass plates on which fine grooves have been machine ruled.

Figure 4–57 shows a typical arrangement of transmission gratings. A metal tube, with a slit S at one end and a lens L_1 at the other, acts as a collimator which provides a beam of light, incident perpendicularly upon the grating G. A telescope is mounted in such a way that it can be rotated about an axis passing through the center of the grating and parallel to the slits. The objective lens L_2 of the telescope causes the rays diffracted by the gratings at a given angle ϑ to converge at a point of its focal plane, where they can be photographed or observed by means of the eyepiece L_3. To determine experimentally the angle ϑ corresponding to a given principal maximum, the image of the slit corresponding to this maximum is brought to the center of the field of the telescope. The telescope is then rotated until the image of the slit corresponding to the order zero of interference appears at the same position in the field of view. The angle ϑ equals the angle by which the telescope has been rotated. To make an accurate measurement possible, a cross hair or a glass plate carrying a thin reference line is placed in the focal plane of the telescope.

In addition to the transmission gratings described above, *reflection gratings* are also commonly used in spectroscopy. These are ruled on polished

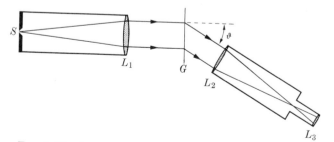

Fig. 4–57. Arrangement for the use of transmission gratings.

metal surfaces by methods similar to those employed in ruling glass surfaces for the preparation of transmission gratings. If the ruled surface is concave, it acts as a concave mirror as well as a grating and thus produces sharp spectral lines without the use of lenses. The avoidance of the use of lenses is an important advantage in the spectroscopy of the ultraviolet because ultraviolet rays are strongly absorbed by common optical glass.

4–19 Two-dimensional gratings. An opaque screen with a number of small apertures placed at the points of intersection of two mutually perpendicular families of parallel and equidistant lines forms a so-called two-dimensional grating. We assume first that the grating is illuminated by a plane monochromatic wave, incident perpendicularly upon it, and that the light diffracted by the various apertures is collected by a converging lens. The apertures operate essentially as synchronous sources. In the focal plane of the lens, the intensity will be a maximum at those points where the rays originating from all the apertures arrive with the same phase. This happens when the optical paths between the grating and the point of convergence differ by integral multiples of the wavelength.

Consider, in the plane of the grating, two orthogonal axes, y and z, parallel to the lines on which the apertures lie. Let h_y and h_z be the spacings between the apertures in the directions of the y- and z-axes, respectively (Fig. 4–58). If the origin is at the center of one of the apertures, the y- and z-coordinates of all other apertures are integral multiples of h_y and h_z, respectively. As in Section 4–15, we characterize a given direction of the diffracted rays by the quantities γ_y and γ_z, representing the cosines of the angles which these rays form with the y- and z-axes. In the directions that satisfy equations of the type

$$h_y \gamma_y = k_y \lambda, \tag{4-93}$$

where k_y is an integer, the disturbances arising from the openings that lie on lines parallel to the y-axis arrive in phase at the point of interference. Similarly, in the directions that satisfy equations of the type

$$h_z \gamma_z = k_z \lambda, \tag{4-94}$$

where k_z is likewise an integer, the disturbances arising from the openings that lie on lines parallel to the z-axis arrive in phase at the point of interference.

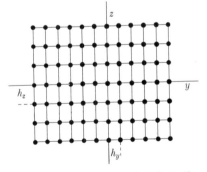

Fig. 4–58. Two-dimensional grating.

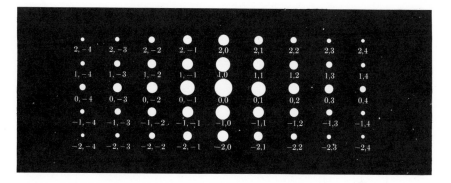

Fig. 4–59. Diffraction pattern of a two-dimensional grating (schematic).

At points corresponding to directions that *simultaneously* satisfy (4–93) and (4–94), the disturbances arising from *all* apertures are in phase, and the interference maxima that appear at such points correspond to the principal maxima produced by the linear gratings. When there are many openings, the light intensity is concentrated in the immediate neighborhood of the points defined by (4–93) and (4–94), for essentially the same reasons that account for the narrow interference maxima of the linear grating. Consequently, a rectangular array of bright dots on a dark background, each a separate image of the point source, will be observed in the focal plane of the lens that collects the diffracted light, as shown in Fig. 4–59. Each dot may be considered as a separate image of the point source. If f is the focal length of the lens, the spacing of the dots in the direction of the y-axis is $f\lambda/h_y$, and the spacing in the direction of the z-axis is $f\lambda/h_z$. In Fig. 4–59 the numbers attached to each dot indicate the values of k_y and k_z, respectively. The dot corresponding to $k_y = k_z = 0$ lies on the axis of the lens, and since the brightness of the dots decreases with increasing values of k_y and k_z, the brightest dots are arranged in the general pattern of a cross, around the lines corresponding to $k_y = 0$ and $k_z = 0$.

When white light is used as a source, instead of monochromatic light, an array of small colored spectra will appear in place of the dots. At the center, however, there will be a white dot, since the position of the maximum corresponding to $k_y = k_z = 0$ is independent of wavelength.

At the beginning of this chapter, we mentioned that the phenomena described above can be observed by looking at a distant light through a piece of thin, closely woven cloth. In this case, the optical system of the eye, adjusted to infinity, takes the place of the lens and the retina takes the place of the observation screen.

We have assumed so far that the incident wave travels in a direction perpendicular to the plane of the grating. If this is not the case, the virtual

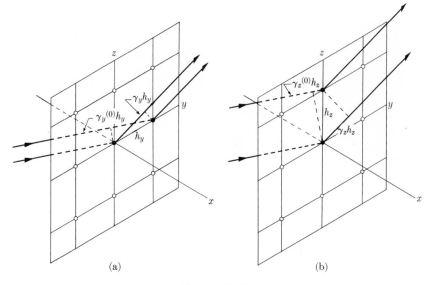

FIGURE 4–60

sources corresponding to the diffracting holes are no longer in phase with one another. As before, we denote by γ_y and γ_z the cosines of the angles that a given parallel beam of diffracted rays forms with the y- and z-axes, respectively. We then define $\gamma_y^{(0)}$ and $\gamma_z^{(0)}$ as the cosines of the angles formed by the incident ray with the same two axes. We find that, between the source and the point of interference, the paths of two rays passing through two neighboring holes along the y-direction differ by $\gamma_y h_y - \gamma_y^{(0)} h_y$ (Fig. 4–60). Therefore the disturbances arising from the openings that lie on lines parallel to the y-axis arrive in phase with one another at the point of interference if the following equation is satisfied:

$$(\gamma_y - \gamma_y^{(0)})h_y = k_y\lambda. \tag{4–95}$$

The corresponding condition relative to the z-direction is

$$(\gamma_z - \gamma_z^{(0)})h_z = k_z\lambda. \tag{4–96}$$

These equations are generalizations of Eqs. (4-93) and (4-94).

4–20 Three-dimensional gratings. X-ray diffraction by crystals. As a further extension of the one-dimensional and two-dimensional gratings discussed in the preceding sections, let us now consider a *three-dimensional grating*. We assume that the diffracting centers form a rectangular lattice whose elements have dimensions h_x, h_y, and h_z in the directions of the x-,

y-, and z-axes, respectively (Fig. 4–61). We denote by $\gamma_x^{(0)}$, $\gamma_y^{(0)}$, and $\gamma_z^{(0)}$ the cosines of the angles formed by the direction of propagation of the incident plane wave with the three coordinate axes, and by γ_x, γ_y, γ_z the cosines defining the direction of a parallel bundle of diffracted rays. An argument similar to that developed in the preceding section shows that the diffracted rays, when brought together by a converging lens, will interfere constructively only when the following conditions are satisfied:

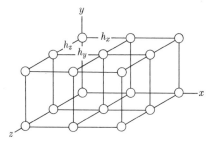

FIG. 4–61. Three-dimensional grating.

$$(\gamma_x - \gamma_x^{(0)})h_x = k_x\lambda,$$

$$(\gamma_y - \gamma_y^{(0)})h_y = k_y\lambda, \qquad (4\text{–}97)$$

$$(\gamma_z - \gamma_z^{(0)})h_z = k_z\lambda,$$

where k_x, k_y, k_z are integers.

If $k_x = k_y = k_z = 0$, these equations yield $\gamma_x = \gamma_x^{(0)}$, $\gamma_y = \gamma_y^{(0)}$, $\gamma_z = \gamma_z^{(0)}$, and there is always constructive interference in the forward direction with respect to the incident beam. However, if at least one of the three numbers k_x, k_y, k_z is different from zero, and if λ as well as the quantities $\gamma_x^{(0)}$, $\gamma_y^{(0)}$, $\gamma_z^{(0)}$ are given, Eqs. (4–97) do not, in general, have a common solution. Indeed, the first of Eqs. (4–97) determines the value of γ_x and thus defines a circular cone with the axis in the x-direction. Similarly, the second equation defines a cone with the axis in the y-direction, and the third defines a cone with the axis in the z-direction. The three equations can be simultaneously satisfied only if the three cones intersect along the same line which, in general, will not be true. We thus conclude that, in general, the three-dimensional grating will not diffract a parallel beam of monochromatic light and will thus behave in this respect like a transparent medium.

However, *for any given value of* λ there are certain preferred directions of incidence for which diffraction occurs, i.e., for which the interference maxima of order different from zero become observable. Conversely, *for any given direction of incidence* there are certain special values of λ for which such interference maxima appear. Indeed, since γ_x, γ_y, and γ_z are the components of a unit vector, the sum of their squares is unity, and Eqs. (4–97) yield

$$\left(\frac{k_x}{h_x}\lambda + \gamma_x^{(0)}\right)^2 + \left(\frac{k_y}{h_y}\lambda + \gamma_y^{(0)}\right)^2 + \left(\frac{k_z}{h_z}\lambda + \gamma_z^{(0)}\right)^2 = 1. \qquad (4\text{–}98)$$

This equation expresses a relation between the wavelength λ and the direction of incidence (characterized by $\gamma_x^{(0)}$, $\gamma_y^{(0)}$, and $\gamma_z^{(0)}$) which must be satisfied if the maximum of order k_x, k_y, k_z is to be observed.

Three-dimensional gratings of the kind discussed here are supplied to us by nature in the form of *crystals*. A crystal is a three-dimensional array of atoms, ions, or molecules forming a regular space lattice. When a light wave impinges upon the crystal, the atoms (or ions, or molecules) become coherent sources of secondary waves. The effect responsible for the secondary emission is more properly described as a scattering process than as a diffraction phenomenon (see Section 8–8), but this does not alter the results that follow from a consideration of the interference of the secondary waves.

In what follows we shall limit our discussion to the case of crystals with rectangular lattices, although many other types of crystal lattices are found in nature. The results, however, will apply, at least qualitatively, to all kinds of crystals.

The distances h_x, h_y, h_z between neighboring atoms in a crystal lattice are of the order of several angstroms, and thus much smaller than the wavelength of visible light. Since the quantities $\gamma_x - \gamma_x^{(0)}$, $\gamma_y - \gamma_y^{(0)}$, $\gamma_z - \gamma_z^{(0)}$ cannot be larger than 2, Eqs. (4–97) have then only one solution, corresponding to $k_x = k_y = k_z = 0$, irrespective of the direction of incidence and of the precise value of λ. Hence crystals do not diffract visible light.

There exist, however, radiations similar to visible light in their physical nature, but of shorter wavelengths (see Section 7–5). Radiations with wavelengths somewhat smaller than twice the distance between neighboring atoms in crystals will give rise to easily observable diffraction phenomena of the kind discussed above. The radiations fall in the so-called x-ray region.

The observation of diffraction by crystals has provided physicists with an invaluable tool both for the investigation of the crystal structure and for x-ray spectroscopy. Here we shall merely mention some typical experiments.

(a) In Fig. 4–62, S represents a point source producing a *continuous spectrum* of x-rays, D is a metal screen with a small hole defining a narrow beam of x-rays, C is a crystal, and Σ is a photographic plate. If the diameter of the hole in the screen D is sufficiently small compared with the distances from S to D and from C to Σ, the rays incident upon the crystal are *nearly* parallel to one another, and so are the diffracted rays that converge upon a given point P of the photographic plate (note that lenses cannot be used in experiments with x-rays, because these rays are not refracted by glass).

Since a crystal behaves as a transparent medium for almost all wavelengths, most of the incident beam traverses the crystal undeflected. For

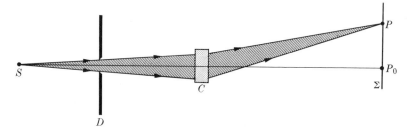

Fig. 4–62. Experimental arrangement for the observation of Laue diffraction.

certain values of λ, however, diffraction occurs. These values are given by Eq. (4–98), where $\gamma_x^{(0)}$, $\gamma_y^{(0)}$, and $\gamma_z^{(0)}$ are fixed numbers indicating the direction of the incident beam relative to the axes of the crystal lattice, and k_x, k_y, k_z are integers, describing the order of interference. For example, the equation

$$\left(\frac{\lambda}{h_x} + \gamma_x^{(0)}\right)^2 + (\gamma_y^{(0)})^2 + (\gamma_z^{(0)})^2 = 1$$

determines the wavelength that produces an interference maximum of order $(1, 0, 0)$. The direction of the scattered rays giving rise to this interference maximum is determined by Eqs. (4–97) which, with $k_x = 1, k_y = 0, k_z = 0$, give

$$\gamma_x = \gamma_x^{(0)} + \lambda/h_x, \qquad \gamma_y = \gamma_y^{(0)}, \qquad \gamma_z = \gamma_z^{(0)}.$$

Hence the diffraction pattern produced on the photographic plate will consist of a number of spots, regularly arranged around the central spot where the undeflected beam strikes the plate. This type of diffraction pattern is known as a *Laue pattern*. (Fig. 4–63).

(b) Consider again the experimental arrangement shown in Fig. 4–62, but assume now that S is a monochromatic source of x-rays. Then, in general, the x-ray beam will pass through the crystal undeflected. However, for any given choice of the integral numbers k_x, k_y, k_z there are

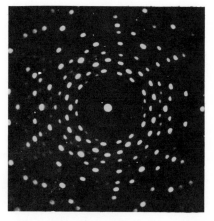

Fig. 4–63. Laue diffraction pattern formed by x-rays traversing a quartz crystal.

certain orientations of the crystal for which Eq. (4–98) is satisfied and for
which, therefore, the crystal will diffract the x-ray beam, producing an interference maximum of order (k_x, k_y, k_z). If, starting from one of these orientations, we rotate the crystal about an axis parallel to the incident beam, we
do not change the direction of the incident beam with respect to the crystal
lattice. Hence the crystal continues to produce an interference maximum of
order (k_x, k_y, k_z), and the point on the photographic plate where this maximum occurs describes a circle (Fig. 4–64).

Suppose now that the single crystal C is replaced by a *crystalline powder*,
consisting of a very large number of small crystals oriented at random. For
each order of interference (k_x, k_y, k_z) the orientations of some of the crystals
will satisfy Eq. (4–98) and the diffraction spots produced by these crystals
on the photographic plates will lie on the circle described above. Figure
4–65 shows the resulting diffraction pattern; note that each line corresponds
to a different order of interference. This type of diffraction pattern is known
as a *powder pattern*.

In the discussion of x-ray diffraction it is often useful to formulate the conditions for the production of the various interference maxima in a somewhat different manner. Let us multiply the three formulas of Eq. (4–97) by three *integers*
m_x, m_y, m_z, and add them term by term. If we define the integer M as follows:

$$m_x k_x + m_y k_y + m_z k_z = M, \qquad (4\text{–}99)$$

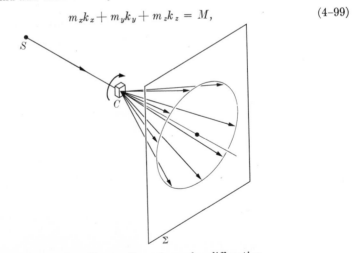

FIG. 4–64. Observation of powder diffraction.

FIG. 4–65. X-ray powder diffraction pattern of copper (courtesy of B. E. War-
ren; the diffraction lines are not circular because the photographic film was
arranged on a cylindrical surface).

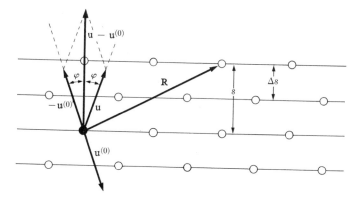

FIG. 4–66. X-ray diffraction from the point of view of crystal planes.

we obtain

$$(\gamma_x - \gamma_x^{(0)})(m_x h_x) + (\gamma_y - \gamma_y^{(0)})(m_y h_y) + (\gamma_z - \gamma_z^{(0)})(m_z h_z) = M\lambda. \quad (4\text{--}100)$$

The three integers m_x, m_y, m_z define a scattering center in the crystal lattice, i.e., the one located at $x = m_x h_x$, $y = m_y h_y$, $z = m_z h_z$. For a given choice of the numbers k_x, k_y, k_z, to each scattering center there corresponds a definite value of M (Eq. 4–99). However, in a crystal of any reasonable size, there is a very large number of scattering centers corresponding to the same value of M. For example, M does not change if, in (4–99), m_x is replaced by $m_x + k_y$ and m_y by $m_y - k_x$, or if m_x is replaced by $m_x + k_y + k_z$, m_y by $m_y - k_x$, and m_z by $m_z - k_x$. From (4–100) we see that all centers corresponding to the same value of M lie on a plane, and that the planes defined by two different values of M are parallel to each other. We conclude that if an x-ray beam incident in the direction $(\gamma_x^{(0)}, \gamma_y^{(0)}, \gamma_z^{(0)})$ produces an interference maximum of order (k_x, k_y, k_z) in the direction $(\gamma_x, \gamma_y, \gamma_z)$, then all scattering centers of the crystal can be arranged into a family of parallel planes, *each containing a very large number of centers* (see example in Fig. 4–66).

We now note that $\gamma_x^{(0)}$, $\gamma_y^{(0)}$, and $\gamma_z^{(0)}$ are the three components of the unit vector $\mathbf{u}^{(0)}$ pointing in the direction of the incident beam, and that γ_x, γ_y, and γ_z are the three components of the unit vector $\mathbf{u}$ pointing in the direction of the diffracted beam. Therefore $(\gamma_x - \gamma_x^{(0)})$, $(\gamma_y - \gamma_y^{(0)})$, and $(\gamma_z - \gamma_z^{(0)})$ are the three components of the vector $\mathbf{u} - \mathbf{u}^{(0)}$ (Fig. 4–66), which forms equal angles with the vectors $\mathbf{u}$ and $-\mathbf{u}^{(0)}$. Let us denote by φ the common value of these angles. The magnitude of the vector $\mathbf{u} - \mathbf{u}^{(0)}$ is then $2 \cos \varphi$.

Now consider the vector $\mathbf{R}$ connecting the origin with the scattering center of coordinates $x = m_x h_x$, $y = m_y h_y$, $z = m_z h_z$. Equation (4–100) can then be written in the form

$$(\mathbf{u} - \mathbf{u}^{(0)}) \cdot \mathbf{R} = M\lambda. \quad (4\text{--}101)$$

and we see that the planes corresponding to a given order of interference (k_x, k_y, k_z) and to different values of M are perpendicular to the vector $\mathbf{u} - \mathbf{u}^{(0)}$.

The distance s from the origin to the plane passing through the point defined by the position vector $\mathbf{R}$ is given by

$$s = \frac{\mathbf{R} \cdot (\mathbf{u} - \mathbf{u}^{(0)})}{|\mathbf{u} - \mathbf{u}^{(0)}|},$$

where $|\mathbf{u} - \mathbf{u}^{(0)}|$ represents the magnitude of the vector $\mathbf{u} - \mathbf{u}^{(0)}$ (Fig. 4–66). Remembering that $|\mathbf{u} - \mathbf{u}^{(0)}| = 2 \cos \varphi$ and taking Eq. (4–101) into account, we obtain

$$s = \frac{M\lambda}{2 \cos \varphi}. \tag{4-102}$$

The set of integral values that M can acquire depends on k_x, k_y, k_z. For example, if $k_x = k_y = k_z = 1$, M can be any integer. If, however, $k_x = k_y = k_z = 2$, M is always an even number. In general, for any given choice of k_x, k_y, k_z, the possible values of M are all integral multiples of a given integer m. Therefore, the separation between neighboring planes is

$$\Delta s = \frac{m\lambda}{2 \cos \varphi}. \tag{4-103}$$

The above results lend themselves to a simple physical interpretation. The various scattering centers of a crystal may be variously arranged into plane, parallel, and equidistant layers, called *crystal planes*. Each crystal plane acts as a partially reflecting surface, and reflection occurs according to the laws of geometrical optics (the incident and reflected rays are coplanar with the perpendicular to the reflecting surface, and the angle of reflection φ equals the angle of incidence). However, in order to produce constructive interference, the rays reflected by the crystal planes of a given family must be in phase with each other. Since the difference in path between two rays reflected at neighboring crystal planes is $2 \Delta s \cos \varphi$, this leads to the condition

$$2 \Delta s \cos \varphi = m\lambda,$$

where m is an integer. This equation is identical to Eq. (4–103).

4–21 Abbe's theory of image formation and phase-contrast microscopy. It was pointed out by Ernst Abbe (1840–1905) that the formation of the image of an illuminated object by a lens may be regarded as the result of a twofold diffraction process: diffraction of the incident light beam by the object, and diffraction of the diffracted beams by the objective lens. This point of view forms the basis of a theory that has many interesting applications. Very important among them is the *phase-contrast microscope*, an instrument capable of revealing minute structures characterized by differences in thickness or in index of refraction, rather than by differences in color or opacity. Cellular structures are often of this kind and therefore the phase-contrast microscope is a useful instrument for biological studies. The following simple examples will illustrate the basic concepts of Abbe's theory and the principle of phase-contrast microscopy.

Three lenses, L, L', L'', are arranged coaxially so that the second focal plane Σ' of L' coincides with the first focal plane of L'' (Fig. 4–67). A point source S of monochromatic light is placed at the first focal point of L. The parallel light beam emerging from L falls perpendicularly on a linear transmission grating whose plane coincides with the first focal plane of L'. In Σ'', the second focal plane of L'' (the image plane), appears a real image of the grating. In the plane Σ' (the diffraction plane) appears the characteristic diffraction pattern described in Section 4–18. If the number of slits is very large, this diffraction pattern reduces to a number of luminous points P_0, P_1, P_2, $\cdots$, P_{-1}, P_{-2}, $\cdots$, each corresponding to a different order of interference, lying on a straight line perpendicular to the slits.

In the spirit of Abbe's theory, we consider the luminous points P_0, P_1, P_2, $\cdots$, P_{-1}, P_{-2}, $\cdots$ as coherent secondary sources, and we consider the optical disturbance in the image plane Σ'' as the resultant of the waves originating from these sources. Each secondary source has a definite amplitude and a definite phase relation to the other sources, and can thus be properly represented by a rotating vector. It is clear that the set of rotating vectors associated with the various interference maxima in the diffraction plane Σ' uniquely determines the appearance of the pattern observed on the image plane Σ''.

Let a represent the width of each slit of the grating, h (Fig. 4–67) the distance between centers of the slits, O the intersection of the axis of the optical system with the plane of the grating, and b the distance from O to the center

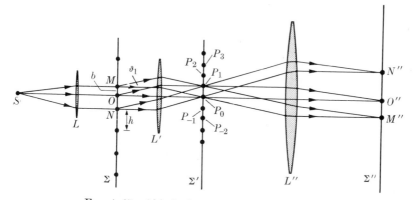

FIG. 4–67. Abbe's theory of image formation.

M of a given slit. Let N be the center of one of the neighboring slits, and let O'', M'', N'' be the images of O, M, N, on Σ''. After traversing L', the two rays passing through M and N, perpendicular to the plane of the grating, meet at the point P_0 of the diffraction plane Σ', where the maximum of order zero occurs. This point lies on the axis of the optical system. Consider next the two parallel rays passing through M and N and forming with the perpendicular to the grating an angle ϑ_1 such that

$$\sin \vartheta_1 = \frac{\lambda}{h}. \tag{4-104}$$

After traversing L', these rays intersect at the point P_1, where the maximum of order $+1$ occurs. In general, the rays emerging from the grating at angle ϑ_k such that

$$\sin \vartheta_k = k \frac{\lambda}{h} \tag{4-105}$$

are brought together by the lens at the point P_k.

As we displace the grating in its plane, i.e., as we change b, the *positions* of the interference maxima, P_0, P_1, $\ldots$, P_k $\ldots$ do not change, nor do the *amplitudes* of the optical disturbances at these points. The *phases* of the disturbances, however, do change, and these phase changes are responsible for the displacement of the image of the grating on the plane Σ''. Let us investigate this point quantitatively.

According to the results obtained in Sections 4–15 and 4–18, the amplitude of the optical disturbance at the interference maximum of order k is proportional to $(\sin \alpha_k)/\alpha_k$, where

$$\alpha_k = \frac{\pi a \sin \vartheta_k}{\lambda}. \tag{4-106}$$

A *positive amplitude* means that the resultant disturbance has *the same phase* as the disturbance arriving from the midpoint of each slit. A *negative amplitude* means that the phase of the resultant disturbance is *opposite* to that of the disturbance arriving from the midpoint of each slit. The quantity $(\sin \alpha)/\alpha$ is plotted in Fig. 4–68 as a function of $(2a \sin \vartheta)/\lambda$, for the special case where $h = 2a$, that is, where the width of a slit equals the width of the opaque strip between slits. Also shown in the figure are the amplitudes of the various interference maxima; here the abscissa represents the order of interference, and we note that in the case under consideration the maxima of even order are missing.

All rays emerging perpendicularly from the grating converge to P_0 in phase with one another. We shall take as zero the phase of the disturbance

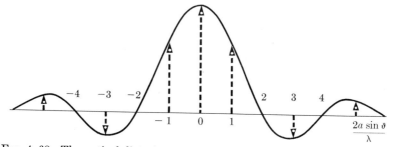

FIG. 4–68. The optical disturbances at the various interference maxima in the diffraction plane (Fig. 4–67).

resulting from their superposition at this point. At P_1 the resultant optical disturbance is in phase with the disturbance originating from M (Fig. 4-67). This, in turn, leads the disturbance arriving at P_1 from O by a phase angle

$$\varphi_1 = 2\pi b (\sin \vartheta_1)/\lambda,$$

or (from Eq. 4-104)

$$\varphi_1 = 2\pi b/h. \tag{4-107}$$

On the other hand, the disturbances arriving at P_1 and P_0 from O are in phase with each other because O is the focal point of L', and the points P_0 and P_1 lie in a plane perpendicular to the axis of this lens. We thus conclude that φ_1 represents the phase of the resultant optical disturbance at P_1, relative to that of the disturbance at P_0. Similarly, the phase of the disturbance at the interference maximum of order $\pm k$ is found to be

$$\varphi_k = \pm 2k\pi b/h$$

if $(\sin \alpha_k)/\alpha_k > 0$, and

$$\varphi_k = \pi \pm 2k\pi b/h$$

if $(\sin \alpha_k)/\alpha_k < 0$.

Figure 4–69 shows the vector diagrams of the disturbances at the various interference maxima for three different positions of the grating, i.e., for three different values of b, namely, $b = 0$, $b = h/4$, and $b = h/2$. Shown also are the images appearing on Σ'' and their positions relative to point O''. We have again assumed $h = 2a$. In this case, increasing b from 0 to $h/2$ is equivalent to interchanging the opaque and transparent portions of the grating. Figure 4–69 shows that, correspondingly, there is a phase reversal at all interference maxima except that of order zero.

Note that in the absence of the grating the diffraction pattern in Σ' reduces to a single point P_0 which is the geometrical image of S, and the cor-

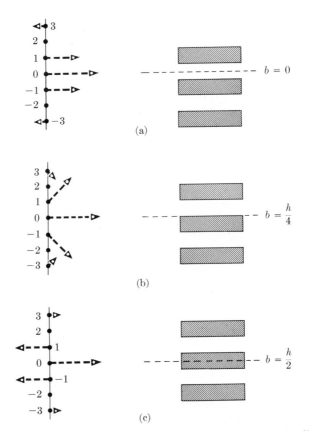

Fig. 4–69. Amplitude and phases of the optical disturbances in the diffraction plane for three different positions of the grating.

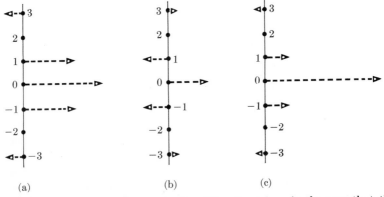

Fig. 4–70. Optical disturbances in the diffraction plane in the case that the strips between slits are partially transparent.

responding vector diagram reduces to a single vector. This same result is obtained by superposing the vector diagrams shown in parts (a) and (c) of Fig. 4–69. It is thus evident that the coherent superposition of the waves transmitted by two "complementary" gratings reproduces the incident wave.

Suppose now that the spaces between the slits of the grating are partially transparent. The resultant diffracted wave may be regarded as the superposition of the wave diffracted by the open slits and the wave diffracted by the partially transparent strips. The vector diagrams corresponding to the two component waves and to the resultant wave are shown in Fig. 4–70. The vector diagram representing the resultant diffraction pattern is similar to that corresponding to an ordinary grating (Fig. 4–70a) except that the disturbance at P_0 now has a greater amplitude relative to the disturbances at the other interference maxima.

The above considerations show that we can modify the appearance of the image on Σ'' by changing the amplitudes or the phases of the disturbances at the various interference maxima on the diffraction plane Σ'. Consider the following examples.

(a) If we cover with an opaque screen all interference maxima except the one at P_0, the diffraction pattern in Σ' is the same as that obtained in the absence of the grating, and the image of the grating in Σ'' disappears.

(b) If the screen covering the interference maxima of order different from zero is not perfectly opaque, the effective diffraction pattern in Σ' is the same as that corresponding to a grating with partially transparent strips between the openings, and we shall see on Σ'' a white-and-gray image of the grating.

(c) We may invert the phase of the disturbance at P_0 by placing on Σ' a glass plate with a region around the center covered by a transparent film of appropriate thickness. Since only the relative phases are significant, introduction of the plate will change a vector diagram such as that shown in Fig. 4–69(a) into a vector diagram such as that shown in Fig. 4–69(c), that is, with the plate, we shall see on Σ'' a *negative image* of the grating.

We now turn our attention to a somewhat different experimental situation. Instead of the transmission grating considered above, consisting of alternate opaque and transparent strips, we place in the focal plane of the lens L' a "transparent grating" consisting of transparent strips all of the same width a but alternately of two different thicknesses d_1 and d_2. Suppose, for example, that the optical axis of the lenses passes through the midpoint of one of the strips of thickness d_1. Then the light that passes through the strips of thickness d_1 forms on Σ' the diffraction pattern shown by the vector diagram in Fig. 4–69(a) and reproduced in Fig. 4–71(a). If d_2 were *equal* to d_1, the light passing through the strips of thickness d_2 would form on Σ' a diffraction pattern represented by a vector diagram identical to

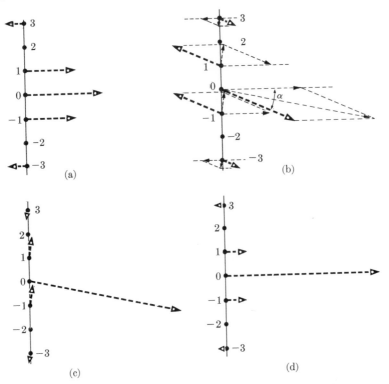

FIG. 4–71. Illustration of the principle of phase-contrast microscopy.

that shown in Fig. 4–69(c). The sum of the two vector diagrams, representing the resultant disturbance, would then reduce to a single vector at P_0, as already pointed out.

Suppose, now, that d_2 is slightly *greater* than d_1. Then the vectors representing the diffraction pattern produced by the light passing through the strips of thickness d_2 are rotated by a certain angle α with respect to those shown in Fig. 4–69(c) (see Fig. 4–71b), and these vectors add to those shown in Fig. 4–71(a) to produce the resultant vector diagram shown in Fig. 4–71(c). If α is sufficiently small, the phase angles closely approximate the following:

$$0 \text{ at } P_0, \quad \pi/2 \text{ at } P_1, \quad -\pi/2 \text{ at } P_3, \quad \pi/2 \text{ at } P_{-1}, \quad -\pi/2 \text{ at } P_{-3}, \text{ etc.}$$

To the diffraction pattern represented by this vector diagram there corresponds on the image plane Σ'' a region of uniform illumination which is obviously the image of the transparent grating. But let us now place on the diffraction plane Σ' a glass plate covered everywhere except near the

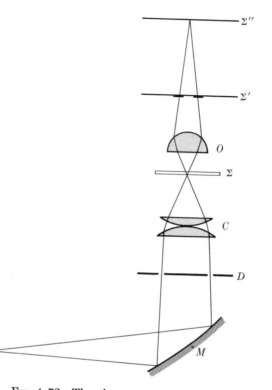

FIG. 4–72. The phase-contrast microscope.

center by a transparent film of such thickness as to produce a phase delay of $\pi/2$ at all interference maxima of order different from zero with respect to the interference maximum of order zero. The diffraction pattern in Σ' is thus represented by the vector diagram shown in Fig. 4–71(d), which differs from that in Fig. 4–71(c) because all vectors except the one at P_0 are rotated clockwise by 90°. The vector diagram in Fig. 4–71(d) is similar to that in Fig. 4–70(c). We thus conclude that on the plane Σ'' there will appear a white-and-gray image of the grating, although the grating itself is perfectly transparent.

This, in essence, is the principle of phase-contrast microscopy. The special optical arrangement on which we have based our discussion was chosen for the purpose of obtaining a particularly simple relationship between the vector diagram representing the diffraction pattern on the diffraction plane, and the structure of the image on the image plane. The essential feature of the method is the use of a plate (called a *phase plate*) in the diffraction plane, i.e., in the plane where the geometrical image of the *light source* appears. This plate must have two different thicknesses in the region covered by the image of the source and in the rest of the plane, so as to introduce a phase difference of $\pi/2$ between the diffracted light beam and the light beam traveling along the path prescribed by geometrical optics. Changing the sign of the phase difference changes the light regions of the image into dark, and vice versa.

Figure 4–72 shows schematically the actual arrangement of a phase-contrast microscope. In front of the condenser lens C of an ordinary microscope is placed an *annular diaphragm* D, consisting of a narrow annular aperture in an opaque screen. This aperture acts effectively as the light source of the previous example. The specimen to be examined lies in the plane Σ. The objective lens O forms a real image of the specimen in the plane Σ''. Moreover, the condenser lens C and the objective lens O form an image of D on the plane Σ', where the phase plate is located. The phase plate usually consists of a glass plate on which an annular layer of transparent material has been deposited by evaporation. The dimensions of the layer are such as to exactly cover the image of D.

4-1. A plane monochromatic light wave of wavelength $\lambda = 5000$ A is incident perpendicularly upon an opaque screen which has a circular aperture 0.4 cm in diameter. (a) Determine the positions of the points of minimum and maximum intensity along the axis of the screen. (b) How far from the screen does the last minimum occur?

4-2. Refer to Problem 4-1. Assume that the incident light is a mixture of two monochromatic light beams of wavelengths $\lambda_1 = 6000$ A and $\lambda_2 = 4000$ A, respectively. Determine the points on the axis where monochromatic light of 6000 A or 4000 A is observed.

4-3. A point source S lies on the axis of an opaque circular disk, 1 m from its center. As seen from a point of the axis 2 m from S, the disk covers the first two Fresnel zones. Assuming a wavelength of 6000 A, compute the radius of the disk.

4-4. A plane monochromatic light wave of wavelength 6400 A is incident perpendicularly upon a zone plate 2 cm in diameter. The maximum of the diffracted light intensity is found to occur 1 m from the plate. (a) Compute the radii of the successive transparent and opaque zones. (b) Compute the total number of transparent zones.

4-5. Refer to Problem 4-4. Determine the position of the point where the zone plate concentrates light of wavelength 6400 A coming from a point source located on the axis, 2 m from the plate.

4-6. A plane monochromatic light wave of wavelength $\lambda = 4000$ A, amplitude A, and intensity I is incident perpendicularly upon an opaque screen which has an aperture in the shape of a circular zone. The inner and outer radii of the zone are 1 mm and 1.41 mm, respectively. (a) Determine the amplitude and the intensity of the optical disturbance at a point P located on the axis of the zone, 2.5 m from the screen. (b) Determine the phase of this disturbance relative to that of the disturbance observed at P in the absence of a screen.

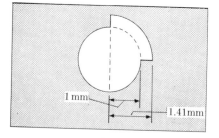

FIGURE 4-73

4-7. A plane monochromatic light wave of wavelength $\lambda = 5000$ A, amplitude A, and intensity I is incident perpendicularly upon an opaque screen which has an aperture of the shape shown in Fig. 4-73. The radius of the inner circle is 1 mm and that of the outer circle is 1.41 mm. (a) Compute the amplitude and the intensity of the optical disturbance at a point P on the axis of the circles, 2 m from the screen. (b) Determine the phase of this disturbance relative to that of the disturbance observed at P without a screen.

4-8. Solve Problem 4-7, interchanging the opaque and transparent portions of the screen. Show that the sum of the disturbances observed with the two "complementary" screens equals the disturbance observed in the absence of a screen.

4-9. A plane monochromatic wave of wavelength λ = 4000 A is incident perpendicularly upon an opaque plane screen bounded by a straight edge. Using Cornu's spiral (Fig. 4-31) determine the positions of the minima and maxima in the diffraction pattern observed on a plane parallel to the screen, at a distance of 2 m.

4-10. Refer to Problem 4-9. Compute (a) the intensities at the first two maxima and the first two minima observed *outside* the region of geometric shadow, and (b) the intensities at the two corresponding points inside the region of geometric shadow (use the graph in Fig. 4-31 or the numerical values of Fresnel integrals listed in Table 4-1).

4-11. A plane monochromatic wave of wavelength λ = 6400 A is incident perpendicularly upon an opaque screen which has a long slit of width a. Making use of Cornu's spiral, compute the intensity in the diffraction pattern observed on a plane 1 m from the slit (a) when a = 0.565 mm and (b) when a = 2.26 mm.

4-12. A straight wire 1 mm in diameter lies along the path of a plane light wave of wavelength λ = 5000 A, perpendicular to the direction of propagation. Plot the distribution of intensity in the diffraction pattern observed on a screen 2 m from the wire. Mark the edges of the geometrical shadow.

4-13. A plane light wave of wavelength λ = 5000 A is incident perpendicularly upon an opaque screen that has five slits of different widths (Fig. 4-74). The optical disturbances produced by the individual slits at a point P_0 on the median plane of the central

FIGURE 4-74

slit are in phase with one another and with the disturbance observed at P_0 in the absence of a screen. P_0 lies 2 m from the plane of the slits. (a) Determine the distances of the edges of the slits from the median plane. (b) Compute the resultant intensity at P_0 in terms of the intensity observed without a screen.

4-14. Refer to Problem 4-11. Assume that a converging lens of 1 m focal length is placed directly behind the slit. Describe the diffraction patterns appearing in the focal plane of the lens and compare with the diffraction patterns obtained without the lens.

4-15. A plane monochromatic wave of wavelength λ is incident perpendicularly upon a converging lens of focal length f. Describe the diffraction pattern observed in the focal plane of the lens when a wire of diameter h is placed in front of the lens.

4-16. The Fraunhofer diffraction pattern of a single slit is observed in the focal plane of a lens of focal length 1 m. The width of the slit is 0.4 mm. The incident light contains two wavelengths, λ_1 and λ_2. It is found that the fourth minimum corresponding to λ_1 and the fifth minimum corresponding to λ_2 occur at the same point, 5 mm from the central maximum. Compute λ_1 and λ_2.

4-17. Show that the vibration curve appropriate to the study of Fraunhofer diffraction by a slit is part of a circle. In particular, if a is the width of the slit and λ the wavelength, the optical disturbance produced by the rays emerging from the slit at an angle θ with respect to the perpendicular to the plane of the slit is represented by the chord of an arc subtending an angle $2\alpha = (2\pi a \sin\theta)/\lambda$. Use this result to derive the expression for the intensity given by Eq. (4–67).

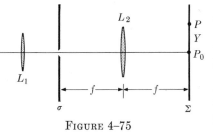

FIGURE 4–75

4–18. In Fig. 4–75, L_1 and L_2 are two converging lenses, S is a point source of monochromatic light located at the first focal point of L_1, σ is an opaque screen with a slit of width $a \gg \lambda$ and length $b \gg a$, and Σ is the plane of observation. σ and Σ are coincident with the first and the second focal planes of L_2. The focal length of L_2 is f. The common axis of L_1 and L_2 passes through the center of the slit and intersects Σ at P_0.
(a) Compute the intensity and the phase of the optical disturbance along the line through P_0 and perpendicular to the slit as functions of the distance Y from P_0. Normalize the results, taking the intensity at P_0 as unity and the phase at P_0 as zero.
(b) Discuss qualitatively the effects of a change in the distance between the slit and the lens L_2.

4–19. Solve Problem 4–18, part (a), assuming that the slit is displaced in the direction perpendicular to its larger

dimension until the line SP_0 passes through the edge of the slit.

4–20. A plane monochromatic wave of wavelength 6000 A is incident perpendicularly upon an opaque screen which has a rectangular aperture of 0.5 mm × 1.0 mm. (a) Describe the diffraction pattern observed in the focal plane of a converging lens of focal length 2 m placed directly behind the aperture. (b) Compute the sides of the rectangle formed by the dark lines surrounding the central maximum.

4–21. A plane monochromatic wave of 6000 A wavelength is incident perpendicularly upon an opaque screen which has a square aperture of 5 mm on a side with an opaque rectangle of 0.5 mm × 10 mm at the center. Compute the intensity distribution in the diffraction pattern observed in the focal plane of a converging lens of 2 m focal length placed directly behind the aperture.

4–22. A plane monochromatic wave of wavelength λ is incident at 30° upon a plane opaque screen which has a long narrow slit of width a (Fig. 4–76). Behind the screen is a converging lens whose axis is perpendicular to the plane of the screen. Describe the diffraction pattern observed in the focal plane Σ of this lens.

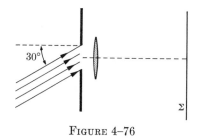

FIGURE 4–76

4–23. Compute the minimum angular separation between two stars that can be barely resolved by a 100-cm telescope when filters selecting red light of wavelength $\lambda = 6500$ A and blue light of $\lambda = 4000$ A are used. Compute the corresponding distances between centers of the images of the stars, assuming a focal length of 10 m for the objective lens of the telescope.

4-24. The headlights of an approaching automobile are 1.30 m apart. Estimate the distance at which the two headlights can be resolved by the naked eye if the resolution of the eye is determined by diffraction alone. Assume a mean wavelength of 5500 A and take the diameter of the pupil of the eye as 5 mm.

4-25. Consider a prism spectroscope such as that described in Section 2–14. The prism is made of glass whose dispersion curve is represented by *Cauchy's equation* $n = A+(B/\lambda^2)$, where $A = 1.47$ and $B = 1.6 \times 10^6$ (angstroms)^2. The refracting angle is 60°. The width of the light beam passing through the prism is 3 cm; the prism is used at nearly minimum deviation, so that Eq. (2–46) applies.

(a) Assuming monochromatic light of wavelength 5890 A, compute the angular distance between the two minima on either side of the diffraction maximum appearing in the focal plane of the telescope.

(b) Assume that the light contains two wavelengths, λ_1 and $\lambda_1 + \Delta\lambda$, in the neighborhood of 5890 A; compute the value of $\Delta\lambda$ for which the central maximum corresponding to λ_1 coincides with one of the minima adjacent to the central maximum corresponding to $\lambda_1 + \Delta\lambda$ (this value of $\Delta\lambda$ may be regarded as the limit of resolution of the spectroscope).

4-26. Refer to Fig. 4–52, describing the experimental arrangement for the observation of the Fraunhofer diffraction by a double slit. Assume that the distance h between the centers of the slits, the width a of each slit, and the wavelength λ of the incident light wave are in the ratios $h/a = 3$, $a/\lambda = 200$. Assume that the lens L_2 has a focal length of 1 m. Plot the amplitude of the optical disturbance along the line through P_0 as a function of the distance Y from P_0, assuming (a) that only the slit centered at O_1 is open, (b) that only the slit centered at O_2 is open, and (c) that both slits are open.

4-27. The Fraunhofer diffraction of a double slit is observed in the focal plane of a lens of focal length 50 cm. The incident monochromatic light has a wavelength of 5000 A. It is found that the distance between the two minima adjacent to the maximum of order zero is 0.5 cm, and that the maxima of the fourth order are missing. Compute the width of the slits and the distance between their centers.

4-28. A plane monochromatic wave of wavelength λ falls perpendicularly upon an opaque screen which has two slits, one of width a and the other of width $2a$. The distance between the centers of the slits is $4a$. Light emerging from the slits falls upon a converging lens of focal length f, and the diffraction pattern is observed in the focal plane of this lens. Compute the intensity distribution along the diffraction line (a) when only the first slit is open, (b) when only the second slit is open, and (c) when both slits are open.

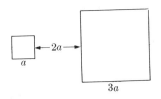

FIGURE 4–77

4–29. A plane monochromatic wave of wavelength λ is incident perpendicularly upon an opaque screen which has two square openings of sides a and $3a$, respectively, arranged as shown in Fig. 4–77. Compute the distribution of intensity in the diffraction pattern observed in the focal plane of a lens placed behind the screen.

4–30. The objective lens of a telescope is covered by an opaque screen with two narrow, parallel slits a distance h apart. Suppose that the telescope is pointed at a double star and that the line connecting the two stars is perpendicular to the slits. Each star will produce in the focal plane of the lens a separate diffraction pattern. For a certain angular separation of the stars, the minima of one diffraction pattern will coincide with the maxima of the other, and the fringes will disappear. Show that this occurs when the angular separation of the two stars is about 0.4 times the conventional limit of resolution of a lens of diameter h.

4–31. *The Michelson stellar interferometer* is shown schematically in Fig. 4–78. An opaque screen with two parallel slits is placed in front of the objective lens of a telescope. The light from a star arrives at one of the slits after reflection at the plane mirrors M_1 and M_1', and at the other slit after reflection at the mirrors M_2 and M_2'. The two slits act as coherent sources of light waves whose interference is observed in the focal plane of the objective lens. Assume that the mirrors are arranged symmetrically with respect to the axis of the telescope, and that a filter selecting monochromatic light of wavelength λ is used. Let h be the separation of the slits, D the separation of the mirrors M_1 and M_2, and f the focal length of the objective lens. Determine the positions of the interference maxima of the various orders relative to the focal point P_0 of the objective lens (a) when the star lies on the axis of the telescope, and (b) when the star lies at a small angle δ to the axis of the telescope, in the direction perpendicular to the slits.

4–32. Suppose that the Michelson stellar interferometer described in Problem 4–31 is pointed at a double star whose two components lie on a line

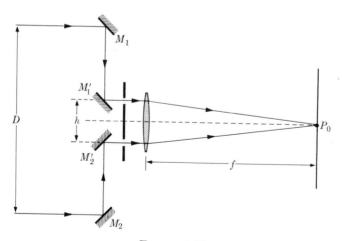

FIGURE 4–78

perpendicular to the slits at an angular distance δ from each other. Suppose that the distance D between the mirrors M_1 and M'_1 is gradually changed. (a) For what values of D will the interference fringes disappear, and for what values of D will they be sharpest? (b) If the maximum value of D is 2.5 m, what is the minimum value of δ for which it will be possible to observe the disappearance of the fringes (assume a mean wavelength of 5700 A)?

4–33. Suppose that the Michelson stellar interferometer described in Problem 4–31 is pointed at a star whose disk subtends an angle δ. How will the appearance of the fringes change as D is gradually increased?

4–34. Compute the intensity distribution in the Fraunhofer diffraction pattern formed by three parallel and equidistant slits with monochromatic light of wavelength λ. The width of each slit is a and the distance between centers of neighboring slits is $3a$.

4–35. Compute the intensity distribution in the Fraunhofer diffraction pattern formed by four parallel and equidistant slits with monochromatic light of wavelength λ. The width of each slit is a and the distance between centers of neighboring slits is $4a$.

4–36. Consider a grating 5 cm in total width, containing 5000 lines. Compute (a) the angles at which the first-order maxima corresponding to the wavelengths $\lambda = 4000$ A and $\lambda = 6000$ A will appear, (b) the angular distance between the minima adjacent to these maxima, and (c) the resolving power of the grating in the first and in the second o der.

4–37. Suppose that the light source used with the grating described in Problem 4–36 is an illuminated slit 1 cm long and placed in the focal plane of a lens of focal length 50 cm. (a) How

narrow should the slit be in order to fully utilize the resolving power afforded by the grating? (b) How accurately should the slit be oriented with respect to the lines of the grating?

4–38. Consider the gratings characterized by the following quantities:

	Total width	Line spacing (h)	Line width (a)
(1)	5 cm	10^{-3} cm	3×10^{-4} cm
(2)	5 cm	10^{-2} cm	5×10^{-4} cm
(3)	2 cm	10^{-2} cm	5×10^{-3} cm

For each of the gratings, compute (a) the resolving power in the first order, (b) the angular dispersion in the first order, and (c) the ratio between the intensities at the maxima of orders 1 and 3.

4–39. Compute the intensity distribution in the diffraction pattern produced by a grating with $3N + 1$ slits in which every third slit (including the first and the last) is covered. Determine the positions of the maxima and their relative intensities in the limit $N = \infty$. Assume that the width of the slits is small compared with their separation, so that the diffraction term may be regarded as a constant.

4–40. A plane monochromatic wave of wavelength λ, traveling in the direction of the x-axis, is incident perpendicularly upon an opaque screen which has a square opening, extending from $y = a$ to $y = -a$ and from $z = a$ to $z = -a$. The opening is covered by a plate whose transparency is constant in the z-direction and which varies sinusoidally in the y-direction, so that the transmitted amplitude is represented by $A(y) = (A_0/2)[1 + \cos(2\pi y/h)]$. Assume $a \gg h \gg \lambda$. The transmitted wave falls upon a converging lens of focal length f whose axis coincides with the x-axis. Compute the intensity distribution along the line parallel to the y-axis and passing through the second focal point of the lens. Show that the intensity has three principal maxima, at the distances $Y = 0$, $Y = f\lambda/h$, and $Y = -f\lambda/h$ from the x-axis.

4–41. A person looking from a distance of 30 m at a point source of yellow light ($\lambda = 5890$ A), through a piece of light, closely woven material, sees a square array of bright points with an apparent separation of 30 cm between points. Compute the number of threads per inch of the material.

4–42. Refer to the experimental arrangement illustrated in Fig. 4–67. Assume that on the plane Σ lies a two-dimensional grating formed by a large number of square holes in an opaque screen. The holes, each of side a, form a square lattice of side $2a$, parallel to the y- and z-axes of a cartesian frame of reference. (a) Describe the figures appearing on the planes Σ' and Σ''. (b) Compute the amplitude and the phase of the optical disturbance at the points of maximum intensity in the plane Σ'.

4–43. Refer to Problem 4–42 and Fig. 4–67. An opaque screen with a narrow rectilinear slit is placed in the plane Σ'. The width of the slit is smaller than the distance between the various interference maxima appearing on the plane Σ'. The slit passes through the point P_0 and is oriented first parallel to the y-axis, then parallel to the z-axis. Describe the appearance of the figures seen on the plane Σ'' for the two orientations of the slit.

CHAPTER 5

THE VELOCITY OF LIGHT

5-1 Astronomical methods for the measurement of the velocity of light.
The velocity of light in empty space, c, is one of the most important natural
constants. It describes a fundamental property of empty space and, according to the theory of relativity, represents an upper limit for the velocity
of any material object or any signal that may occur in nature. Furthermore,
it enters into the well-known relation between mass and energy,

$$\text{energy} = \text{mass} \times c^2.$$

It is thus no wonder that great effort has been put into making increasingly
accurate experimental determinations of its value.

The first experimental proof that light actually travels with finite velocity
was obtained from astronomical observations, which also provided a fairly
accurate determination of the value of this velocity. In this section we shall
describe two astronomical methods of measuring the velocity of light.

The planet Jupiter has several satellites; of these, the one that is nearest
to the planet moves along an orbit that lies approximately in the plane of
the orbit of Jupiter around the sun. Thus, at every revolution, the satellite
enters the cone of shadow of Jupiter and disappears from sight (Fig. 5-1).
This happens, on the average, once every 42 hr 28 min 16 sec. However,
careful observations by the astronomer Roemer in 1676 showed that the
eclipses do not occur at exactly equal intervals of time: the intervals are
somewhat *longer* than their average value when Jupiter and the earth are
moving *away* from each other, and
somewhat *shorter* when they are *approaching* each other. Roemer correctly interpreted this fact as a proof
that light travels with finite speed.
It is clear that if the velocity of light
is not infinitely great, the time interval T between the observations of
two successive eclipses is not, in
general, equal to the period of revolution T_0 of the satellite around
Jupiter. For if the distance between

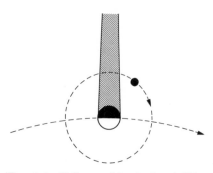

Fig. 5-1. Eclipses of Jupiter's satellite.

Jupiter and the earth has *increased* by an amount Δr during the revolution, T will exceed T_0 by an amount equal to the time necessary for the light to travel the additional distance Δr, so that

$$T - T_0 = \Delta r / c,$$

while if the distance between Jupiter and the earth has *decreased* by Δr during the revolution of the satellite, T will be *smaller* than T_0 by an amount

$$T_0 - T = \Delta r / c$$

To actually determine the velocity of light from these observations, the procedure is as follows. The intervals T between eclipses are recorded, starting at a time when Jupiter and the earth are nearest to each other, and continuing through the time when they are farthest apart to the time when they are again at their closest. The average value of the observed time intervals gives the actual period of revolution T_0. Let r be the distance from Jupiter to the earth at the time of a given eclipse, and $r + \Delta r$ the distance at the time of the next eclipse. Then the difference $T - T_0 = \Delta r / c$ represents the time necessary for light to travel the distance Δr; it is positive if Jupiter and the earth are receding from each other, and negative in the opposite case. Hence the sum of all such differences observed while Jupiter and the earth are receding from each other is the time necessary for the light to travel a distance equal to the difference between the maximum and the minimum separation of the two planets; since the orbits of Jupiter and the earth are approximately coplanar circles, this distance is approximately equal to the diameter of the earth's orbit (Fig. 5-2).

The most accurate value of c that was obtained by this method is

$$c = 301{,}500 \text{ km/sec.}$$

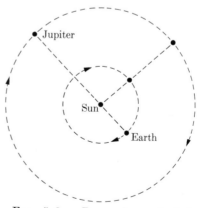

Another astronomical effect that depends on the finite velocity of light, and hence affords a determination of this velocity, is the *aberration* discovered by Bradley at the beginning of the 18th century. This is a displacement in the apparent position of a star due to the motion of the observer. Suppose that we observe a star through a telescope which, of course, participates in the motion of the earth and therefore

FIG. 5-2.   Roemer's method for measuring the velocity of light.

travels through space with a certain
velocity w with respect to the fixed
stars. Assume, for the sake of simplicity, that the telescope moves in a
direction perpendicular to the direction of arrival of the light from the
star. The light that passes through
the objective lens of the telescope is
brought to a focus at a point F on
the focal plane of the lens (Fig. 5–3).
The position of this point *in space*
does not change because of the motion of the telescope; however, while
the light travels the distance D from

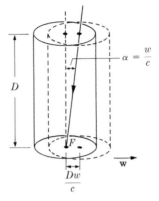

FIG. 5–3. Aberration of light.

the lens to the focal plane the telescope as a whole travels a distance
$\Delta x = Dw/c$. Thus, *with respect to the moving telescope*, the image of the star
undergoes a displacement Dw/c in the direction opposite to that of the motion of the telescope. The same displacement of the image would be observed if the telescope were stationary and the star were at an angular distance α from its actual position, where

$$\alpha = \frac{\Delta x}{D} = \frac{w}{c}.\qquad(5\text{–}1)$$

Thus the effect of the motion of the telescope is to change the apparent
angular position of the star in the sky by an angle α. Note that the apparent
displacement is in the direction of the motion of the earth; it has a maximum
value w/c when the star lies in a direction perpendicular to this motion, and
is zero when the star lies in the direction of the motion of the earth.

The earth participates in the motion of the solar system through space,
and, in addition, revolves around the sun. The direction of the velocity of
revolution changes during the course of the year, and causes the apparent
position of each star in the sky to change correspondingly. Considering that
the trajectory of the earth is approximately a circle, we find, in general, that
the apparent position of a star will describe an ellipse, which reduces to a
straight segment for stars located in the plane of the earth's orbit, and to a
circle for stars at right angles to this plane.* The major semiaxis of the
ellipse subtends an angle equal to w/c, where w is now the velocity of revolu-

---

*Aberration should not be confused with the apparent change in the relative
position of stars due to the change in the position of the observer with respect to
the stars during the course of the year. The latter effect, called *parallax*, decreases
with increasing distance of the star, while aberration is independent of distance.

tion of the earth around the sun (about 30 km/sec). Experimentally, we find a value of 20.479 sec for this angle, and from this we obtain

$$c = 299,700 \text{ km/sec.}$$

5–2 Terrestrial methods for the measurement of the velocity of light. The first successful experiment for measuring the velocity of light from terrestrial sources was carried out by Fizeau in 1849; Fig. 5–4 is a schematic drawing of the method he used.

A lens L_1, through the half-silvered mirror M', forms a real image of a point source S at S_1, and a second lens L_2 changes the light beam diverging from S_1 into a parallel beam. Several miles away, a third lens L_3 collects the parallel beam and brings it to a focus at S_2, on a mirror M. The light reflected by the mirror travels back through L_3 and L_2 and produces another real image of the source at S_1. By means of an eyepiece, the observer views the image of S_1 in the half-silvered mirror M'. At S_1 the light beam is intercepted by a cogwheel, which rotates about an axis parallel to the beam that travels from L_1 to L_2. The cogwheel is so constructed that the width of the cogs is equal to the width of the open spaces between cogs. If the wheel turns slowly, the image of the source will appear intermittently to the observer; as its velocity is increased, the eye will soon cease to perceive the interruptions because of the persistence of the image on the retina. However, as the velocity continues to increase, the image becomes dimmer until, when the velocity of rotation of the wheel is such that a cog replaces an open space during the time necessary for the light to travel from S_1 to S_2 and back to S_1, the image disappears. Then, of course, the light that has passed through an open space on its way to the mirror M is intercepted by the opaque cog on its way back. If the velocity of the wheel is further increased, the image reappears, becoming brightest at twice the speed cor-

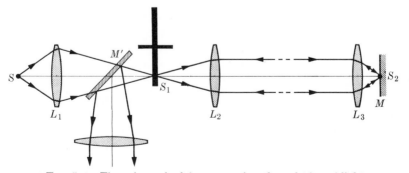

FIG. 5–4. Fizeau's method for measuring the velocity of light.

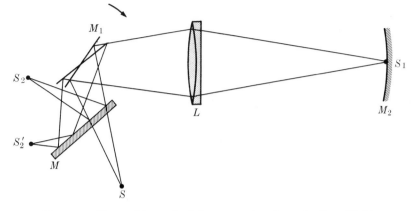

FIG. 5–5. Foucault's method for measuring the velocity of light.

responding to the first eclipse; i.e., at such a speed that an open space replaces the neighboring open space during the transit time of the light from
S_1 to S_2 and back. A second eclipse will occur at three times the speed of
the first eclipse, and so on. By measuring the speed of rotation of the wheel
at which each eclipse occurs, we can determine the transit time of the light
signals between S_1 and S_2, and therefore the velocity of light. The result
obtained by Fizeau was $c = 313,300$ km/sec. Later and more accurate
measurements by the same method gave

$$c = 301,400 \text{ km/sec.}$$

A second method, suggested originally by Arago and applied for the first
time by Fizeau and Foucault in 1850, is illustrated schematically in Fig.
5–5. A plane mirror M_1 and a lens L form a real image of the light source
S at S_1. The mirror is mounted on an axis perpendicular to the plane of the
incident and reflected rays. As the mirror rotates about this axis, S_1 describes a curve. During part of the rotation period, the image is focused
upon a concave mirror M_2, which reflects the light back through the lens L
to the rotating mirror M_1. Partial reflection at the half-silvered glass plate
M causes an image of the source to appear at S_2, where it can be observed
by means of an eyepiece. If the mirror M_1 is stationary or rotates slowly,
S_2 and S are symmetrically located with respect to the half-reflecting surface M. Suppose, however, that the speed of rotation of the mirror M_1 is
such that the mirror rotates through an appreciable angle α while the light
travels from M_1 to M_2 and back. Then the rotating mirror reflects the returning rays in a direction that forms an angle 2α with the rays coming directly from the source S, and the image is correspondingly displaced from
S_2 to S_2'. From this displacement and the known speed of rotation of the
mirror M_1 it is possible to compute the velocity of light.

The above method provides a much more accurate determination of short time intervals than the cogwheel method described previously. It thus affords the possibility of measuring the velocity of light over much shorter distances, which is an important advantage if it is desired to determine the velocity in material substances other than air (see Section 5–6). Alternatively, use of this method over large distances results in a high degree of accuracy. In Foucault's experiment, the distance between the rotating mirror M_1 and the stationary concave mirror M_2 was 20 m, and the velocity of light was found to be

$$c = 298{,}000 \text{ km/sec.}$$

The method of the rotating mirror was greatly improved by several experimenters, particularly by Michelson and his collaborators. In a series of measurements carried out in 1926 over a distance of 22 miles, Michelson obtained the value

$$c = 299{,}796 \pm 4 \text{ km/sec.}$$

In measurements of such high accuracy it is necessary to take into account the index of refraction of air, in order to reduce the observed velocity to the velocity in empty space. The correction is not precise, however, because of uncertainty in the pressure and temperature of the atmosphere. To eliminate this possible source of error, Michelson and his collaborators undertook to measure the velocity of light in an evacuated iron pipe one mile long. The experiment, which was completed in 1931 shortly after Michelson's death, gave the value

$$c = 299{,}774 \text{ km/sec.}$$

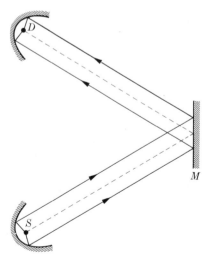

Several high-precision determinations of the velocity of light were carried out after World War II. Figure 5–6 illustrates schematically an experiment performed by Bergstrand in 1950, which is a modification of a previous experiment by Anderson. Here, S represents a light source whose intensity is modulated at a frequency of about 8 Mc per sec by means of a Kerr cell (see Section 6–16); the electronic oscillator which drives the cell also modulates the sensitivity of a light detector D (a photoelectric cell; see Sec-

Fig. 5–6.   Kerr-cell method for measuring the velocity of light.

tion 9–1). The source S is located at the focal point of a concave mirror. The parallel beam of light produced by this mirror is reflected by a distant mirror M toward a second concave mirror, which concentrates the beam upon the detector D. The signal obtained from the detector varies in strength as the distance of the mirror M from the source and from the detector changes, the condition for maximum signal being that the intensity of the modulated light beam at the detector should be greatest at the instants when the sensitivity of the detector is also greatest. An accurate determination of the positions of the mirror for which such "resonances" occur, combined with a knowledge of the oscillator frequency, yields the velocity of light. Two separate measurements by the method here described gave

$$c = (299{,}793 \pm 2) \text{ km/sec},$$

$$c = (299{,}792.7 \pm 0.25) \text{ km/sec}.$$

Very accurate determinations of c have also been made by indirect methods, based upon the assumption that light waves are electromagnetic waves (see Chapter 7); we shall not discuss these measurements here. We wish to mention, however, that from a critical discussion of all the data available in 1955* the best value of the velocity of light in a vacuum appears to be

$$c = (299{,}793.0 \pm 0.3) \text{ km/sec}. \tag{5–2}$$

5–3 The Michelson-Morley experiment. In 1881 Michelson and Morley undertook an experiment whose result had far-reaching consequences in the development of physics. Their purpose was to detect the motion of the earth with respect to the medium in which light waves are propagated. There was, of course, no rigorous argument capable of predicting the frame of reference in which this medium was at rest, but it certainly could not be at rest with respect to the earth, which revolves around the sun at a speed of about 30 km/sec, while the solar system as a whole moves toward the constellation of Hercules at a speed of about 19 km/sec.

The instrument used for this experiment was the Michelson interferometer described in Section 3–12. In this instrument, a half-silvered glass plate M splits the light beam from a source S into two beams that travel at right angles to each other and are brought together again after reflection at two plane mirrors M_1 and M_2 (Fig. 5–7). The interference pattern observed with the telescope depends on the difference between the

---

*See E. R. Cohen, J. W. M. Dumond, T. W. Layton, and J. S. Rollett, *Rev. Mod. Phys.* **27**, 363 (1955).

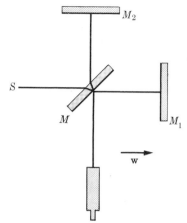

lengths of the optical paths of the
ray that travels from M to M_1 and
back, and the ray that travels from
M to M_2 and back.

Let l be the distance of M_1 and
M_2 from M. Suppose that the earth
is moving in the direction of the ray
that travels from M to M_1, and that
it has a velocity w with respect to the
medium in which light is propagated. Since the light ray has velocity c with respect to the medium, its
velocity with respect to the earth is
$c - w$, and its time of travel from
M to M_1 is $l/(c - w)$. Similarly, on
the return path from M_1 to M, the
ray travels with velocity $c + w$ with respect to the earth, and its time of
travel from M_1 to M is $l/(c + w)$. The total time of travel of the ray from
M to M_1 and back to M is therefore

Fig. 5–7. The Michelson-Morley experiment.

$$T_1 = \frac{l}{c - w} + \frac{l}{c + w} = \frac{2l}{c}\frac{1}{1 - w^2/c^2}. \qquad (5\text{–}3)$$

Now consider the ray traveling between M and M_2. In this case the velocity
$\mathbf{c} - \mathbf{w}$ of the light beam with respect to the earth is perpendicular to the
velocity $\mathbf{w}$ of the earth with respect to the medium. From Fig. 5–8 we
recognize that the magnitude of the relative velocity of the light with respect to the earth is $\sqrt{c^2 - w^2}$, and the time of travel from M to M_2 and
back to M is

$$T_2 = \frac{2l}{\sqrt{c^2 - w^2}} = \frac{2l}{c}\frac{1}{\sqrt{1 - w^2/c^2}}.$$

Since w is very small compared with c, we can develop each of the expressions $1/(1 - w^2/c^2)$ and $1/\sqrt{1 - w^2/c^2}$ in a series, and disregard terms
containing powers of w/c higher than
the second. We obtain

$$\frac{1}{1 - w^2/c^2} = 1 + \frac{w^2}{c^2},$$

$$\frac{1}{\sqrt{1 - w^2/c^2}} = 1 + \frac{1}{2}\frac{w^2}{c^2},$$

Figure 5–8

and therefore

$$T_1 = \frac{2l}{c}\left(1 + \frac{w^2}{c^2}\right),$$

$$T_2 = \frac{2l}{c}\left(1 + \frac{1}{2}\frac{w^2}{c^2}\right).$$

We thus conclude that the ray reflected at M_1 returns to M with a delay

$$T_1 - T_2 = \frac{l}{c}\frac{w^2}{c^2}$$

with respect to the ray reflected at M_2; this corresponds to a difference in optical path of

$$\Delta l = (T_1 - T_2)c = l\frac{w^2}{c^2}. \tag{5–4}$$

If we now rotate the interferometer through 90°, so that the ray traveling from M to M_1 is perpendicular and that traveling from M to M_2 is parallel to the motion of the earth, the situation will be reversed, and the optical path of the ray reflected at M_2 will exceed that of the ray reflected at M_1 by the amount Δl. Thus the rotation of the interferometer changes the optical path of one ray with respect to the other by an amount $2\Delta l$. If the experiment is performed with monochromatic light of wavelength λ, a change of $2\,\Delta l$ in the difference between the optical paths of the two interfering rays causes the interference fringes to shift by a fraction of the width of a fringe, given by

$$\frac{2\Delta l}{\lambda} = 2\frac{w^2}{c^2}\frac{l}{\lambda}. \tag{5–5}$$

This equation shows that the expected shift is proportional to l. In order to increase l without increasing the physical dimensions of the equipment, Michelson and Morley modified the original design of the interferometer and made the light travel back and forth several times in the two perpendicular directions between mirrors. The whole instrument was mounted on a concrete base floating on mercury, so that the instrument could be rotated without the use of forces capable of producing mechanical deformations. Continuous observations were made while the instrument was slowly rotating. Conditions were such that a shift of the interference fringes should have been easily detected if the earth were moving at a velocity of the order of its orbital velocity (30 km/sec) with respect to the medium in which light waves travel. Contrary to expectation, no such effect was observed.

This astonishing result, confirmed by later experiments, was the subject of many speculations, until Einstein in 1905 suggested an interpretation that was at the same time the most simple and most revolutionary. His assumption was that light actually travels with a constant velocity that is independent of direction in all *inertial* frames of reference. (An inertial frame of reference is defined as one in which, when there are no forces, an object moves with constant rectilinear velocity; it is well known that all frames of reference executing uniform rectilinear translations with respect to a given inertial frame of reference are also inertial frames of reference.)

Einstein's assumption is the fundamental postulate of the theory of special relativity. It is obviously in direct contradiction to the results of classical mechanics, and can be accepted only if one is willing to revise drastically the fundamental concepts on which classical mechanics rests. For example, it follows from this assumption that the measure of length and the measure of time become different in different inertial frames of reference. Even the concept of simultaneity between two events occurring at different points of space loses its absolute meaning. Another important consequence of the postulate of relativity is that the velocity of light becomes a limiting velocity, which can be approached but never reached in the motion of material bodies and can never be exceeded in the propagation of any signal.

5–4 The Doppler effect. When a source of sinusoidal waves is in motion with respect to the observer, the frequency of the disturbance perceived by the observer differs from the source frequency. This phenomenon, called the *Doppler effect*, has a simple explanation. Consider a spherical wave emitted by a point source S. At any given instant, there will be a set of spherical surfaces on which the phase of the wave is an integral multiple of 2π; the radii r_n and r_{n+1} of two such consecutive spheres differ by one wavelength, so that we have

$$r_{n+1} - r_n = \lambda.$$

If the source is stationary, the spheres have a common center at the source (Fig. 5–9); however, if the source moves with a constant velocity, w, the spheres are no longer concentric. The disturbances occurring at the time t on the surfaces of radii r_n and r_{n+1} have left the source at the times $t_n = t - r_n/c$ and $t_{n+1} = t - r_{n+1}/c$, respectively; the time interval $t_n - t_{n+1}$ equals the period T of the waves, since $t_n - t_{n+1} = (r_{n+1} - r_n)/c = \lambda/c$. In this interval the source moves a distance $wT = (w/c)\lambda$, so that the center of the sphere of radius r_n is displaced in the direction of the motion by the amount $(w/c)\lambda$, with respect to the center of the sphere of radius r_{n+1} (Fig. 5–10). It follows that the wave emitted in the forward direction has an apparent wavelength

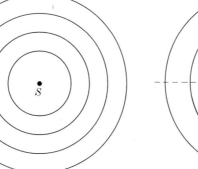

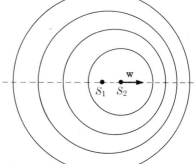

FIG. 5–9. Spherical waves from a point source at rest.

FIG. 5–10. Spherical waves from a point source in motion.

$$\lambda' = \lambda \left(1 - \frac{w}{c}\right), \tag{5-6}$$

and therefore an apparent frequency

$$\nu' = \frac{\nu}{1 - (w/c)}, \tag{5-7}$$

while the wave emitted in the backward direction has an apparent wavelength

$$\lambda' = \lambda \left(1 + \frac{w}{c}\right), \tag{5-8}$$

and an apparent frequency

$$\nu' = \frac{\nu}{1 + (w/c)}. \tag{5-9}$$

To obtain a general expression for the frequency observed at an arbitrary angle ϑ to the direction of the motion of the source, we can proceed as follows. Let S_1 be the position of the source at the time zero, S_2 the position at the time t, P the position of the stationary observer, and denote by r_1 and r_2 the distances $\overline{S_1 P}$ and $\overline{S_2 P}$, respectively (Fig. 5–11). We assume that the time t is long compared with the period, but sufficiently short so that $\overline{S_1 S_2} = wt \ll r_1$. The disturbance emitted by the source at the time zero reaches the observer at the time $t_1 = r_1/c$, and that emitted at the time t reaches the observer at the time $t_2 = t + r_2/c$. The wave train leaving the source during the time interval t, which contains $t/T = t\nu$ waves, is received by the observer during the time interval $t_2 - t_1 = t - (r_1 - r_2)/c$. Thus the apparent frequency is

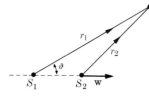

Fig. 5–11. Doppler effect due to motion of the source.

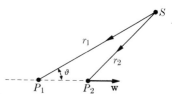

Fig. 5–12. Doppler effect due to motion of the observer.

$$\nu' = \frac{t\nu}{t - (r_1 - r_2)/c} \, . \tag{5–10}$$

Since we have assumed that $\overline{S_1 S_2} \ll r_1$, we can write, to a good approximation,

$$r_1 - r_2 = \overline{S_1 S_2} \cos \vartheta = wt \cos \vartheta;$$

hence Eq. (5–10) yields

$$\nu' = \frac{\nu}{1 - (w/c) \cos \vartheta} \, . \tag{5–11}$$

Note that (5–11) reduces to (5–7) for $\vartheta = 0$ and to (5–9) for $\vartheta = \pi$.

We have assumed so far that the observer is stationary and the source is in motion. Suppose now that the source is stationary and the observer moves with a velocity w in a direction forming an angle ϑ with the direction of the source (Fig. 5–12). Let P_1 be the position of the observer at the time t_1, P_2 his position at the time t_2, S the position of the source, and denote by r_1 and r_2 the distances $\overline{SP_1}$ and $\overline{SP_2}$, respectively. At the time t_1 the observer receives the disturbance emitted by the source at the time $t_1 - r_1/c$, and at time t_2 he receives the disturbance emitted at the time $t_2 - r_2/c$, so that in the time interval $t_2 - t_1$ he receives the wave train emitted during the time interval $(t_2 - r_2/c) - (t_1 - r_1/c) = t_2 - t_1 + (r_1 - r_2)/c$. This train contains $\nu[t_2 - t_1 + (r_1 - r_2)/c]$ waves, and thus the apparent frequency is

$$\nu'' = \frac{\nu[t_2 - t_1 + (r_1 - r_2)/c]}{t_2 - t_1} \, . \tag{5–12}$$

We assume again that $\overline{P_1 P_2} \ll r_1$; we can then write

$$r_1 - r_2 = \overline{P_1 P_2} \cos \vartheta = w(t_2 - t_1) \cos \vartheta,$$

and (5–12) yields

$$\nu'' = \nu \left(1 + \frac{w}{c} \cos \vartheta \right) . \tag{5–13}$$

We see that, regardless of whether the source or the observer is in motion, the apparent frequency (ν' or ν'') is greater than or smaller than the source frequency ν according as the source and the observer are approaching each other ($\vartheta < \pi/2$) or moving apart ($\vartheta > \pi/2$).

If we develop the expression $1/[1 - (w/c) \cos \vartheta]$ in a Taylor series, we can write Eq. (5–11) as

$$\nu' = \nu \left(1 + \frac{w}{c} \cos \vartheta + \frac{w^2}{c^2} \cos^2 \vartheta + \cdots \right). \tag{5–14}$$

Comparing this with Eq. (5–13), we see that while the differences $\nu' - \nu$ and $\nu'' - \nu$ contain terms proportional to w/c, the difference $\nu' - \nu''$ contains only terms proportional to the second and higher powers of w/c. If w is small compared with c, these terms are negligible, and the expressions for ν' and ν'' are practically equal. To this approximation, the Doppler shift depends only on the *relative* velocity of the source and the observer.

In the case of mechanical waves, such as sound, the medium that carries the waves establishes a preferred frame of reference. There is then a physical difference between the case in which the observer is at rest and the source is in motion, and that in which the source is at rest and the observer in motion. For light, however, all inertial frames of reference are physically equivalent, as we learned in the preceding section. Thus, in the case of light waves, the Doppler shift must depend only on the relative velocity of the source and the observer, and it follows that Eqs. (5–11) and (5–13), which give slightly different values for ν' and ν'', cannot be exactly correct. To obtain the rigorous expression for the apparent frequency we must use the relativity theory, which yields the result

$$\nu' = \nu'' = \frac{\nu[1 + (w/c) \cos \vartheta]}{\sqrt{1 - w^2/c^2}}. \tag{5–15}$$

This expression differs from (5–11) and (5–13) only by terms of the second and higher order in w/c. Since the relative velocity of the source and the observer is ordinarily very small compared with the velocity of light, Eqs. (5–11), (5–13), and (5–15) are equivalent for most practical purposes.

In the case of sound waves, the Doppler effect is often a conspicuous phenomenon. A familiar example is the way a train's whistle suddenly changes in pitch as the train passes by at high speed. However, since the velocity of light is much greater than the velocity of sound, the Doppler effect for light becomes noticeable only for exceedingly high velocities of the light source. Such high velocities are difficult to achieve on the earth, so long as one deals with macroscopic objects. However, it is comparatively easy to observe the Doppler effect in the laboratory by using as a light source a stream of rapidly moving positive ions. The experiment is performed using a discharge tube with a perforated cathode. The positive ions produced in the rarefied gas between the cathode and the anode are accelerated toward the cathode. Some of them pass through the perforations and continue to move with constant velocity in the field-free space behind the cathode, forming *canal rays*. The velocity of such ions is of the order of hundreds of kilometers per second, about 1/1000 the velocity of light and about 100 times the average muzzle velocity of a bullet, and the light emitted by these ions exhibits a distinct Doppler effect.

In connection with the influence of the Doppler effect on laboratory experiments, it should be mentioned that this effect is in part responsible for the lack of monochromaticity of light sources. Because of thermal agitation, at a given instant of time some of the atoms of the source are moving toward the observer, while others are moving away. The Doppler effect slightly increases the frequency of the light received from the former and decreases that received from the latter.

It is in the field of astronomy that the Doppler effect finds its most important applications, since the velocities of celestial objects are much greater than those attainable on the earth. For example, the effect has been used to determine the velocity of rotation of various regions on the surface of the sun, and it has also been used to measure that component of the velocity of stars and nebulae which is directed along the line of sight. By this method it was found that some nebulae are moving away from the earth with a velocity greater than 20,000 km/sec, since their spectral lines are shifted toward the red by more than 200 A. Another interesting astronomical application of the effect is the discovery and study of double stars whose components subtend an angle smaller than the limit of resolution of the telescope. The two components of a double star rotate about their common center of mass. At any given instant, the light coming from the component that is approaching the earth is shifted toward the higher frequencies, while the light coming from the component that moves away from the earth is shifted toward the lower frequencies. Thus in the spectrum of the double star each line is split into two lines whose separation is a periodic function of time, with a period equal to the period of revolution of the two stars.

5–5 Phase and group velocity. In empty space, the velocity of light has a unique and well-defined value; however, as we saw in Section 2–14, the velocity of sinusoidal light waves in a dispersive medium depends on their frequency. Now a light signal consists of a wave train of finite length, and we know from the results of Sections 3–14 and 3–15 that even if it is emitted by what we call a "monochromatic" source, such a train is not a pure sinusoidal wave, but may be regarded as the superposition of an infinite number

of sinusoidal waves of different
wavelengths. In a dispersive medium, therefore, each component of
the wave train will move with a
slightly different velocity, so that
the train will slowly change its shape

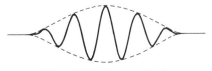

FIG. 5–13. A wave train.

as it moves, and a careful analysis is necessary to determine how its velocity
should be defined.

A simple experiment may serve to clarify this point. If we drop a stone
into a quiet pond and examine the circular surface wave originating from the
point where the stone hits the water, we see that it consists of a small number of nearly sinusoidal oscillations, so that its profile is a curve of the type
shown in Fig. 5–13. Let us now focus our attention on a given wave crest.
The crest moves forward with a certain velocity with respect to the stationary observer; in addition, by careful observation, we find that it moves
forward with respect to the wave train, so that it gradually approaches the
rear of the train. As it does so, its amplitude decreases until the crest
eventually fades away. Thus waves continually disappear at the front of
the train, while new waves appear at the rear. As a consequence, the train
as a whole moves at a lower speed than the individual waves. Apart from
the gradual motion of the individual waves with respect to the train, the
general profile of the train (i.e., the shape of the line connecting the crests of
successive waves) does not change appreciably over limited periods of time.
We can thus define a velocity of the train, or *group velocity*, as distinct from
the velocity of the individual waves in the train, or *phase velocity*.

To obtain a mathematical expression for the group velocity, let us assume
that at the time $t = 0$ all the sinusoidal waves are in phase at the point
$x = 0$. This is the point where the amplitude of oscillation of the resultant
disturbance is greatest, i.e., the point where the curve representing the profile of the group has a maximum. At a later time t, the various sinusoidal
waves will be in phase at a different point P, which determines the new
position of the maximum. If x is the distance of P from 0, the group velocity
is thus $v_g = x/t$.

Let E_1 and E_2 represent two of the sinusoidal waves into which we may
ideally resolve our wave train (Fig. 5–14). Since the two waves are in phase
at $t = 0$ and $x = 0$, E_1 and E_2 are given by expressions of the form

$$E_1 = A_1 \cos 2\pi \left(\nu_1 t - \frac{x}{\lambda_1} \right),$$

$$E_2 = A_2 \cos 2\pi \left(\nu_2 t - \frac{x}{\lambda_2} \right),$$

(5–16)

where ν_1 and ν_2 are the frequencies of the two waves, and $\lambda_1 = v_1/\nu_1$ and

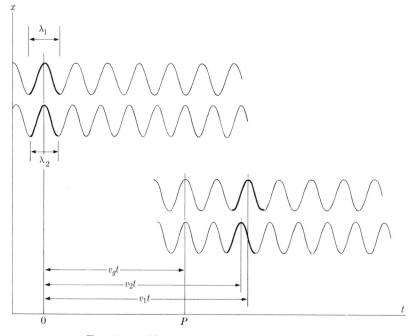

FIG. 5–14. Phase velocity and group velocity.

$\lambda_2 = v_2/\nu_2$ are the corresponding wavelengths. At the time t the two waves are in phase at the point whose abscissa x satisfies the equation

$$\nu_1 t - \frac{x}{\lambda_1} = \nu_2 t - \frac{x}{\lambda_2},$$

from which we obtain

$$\frac{t}{x} = \frac{1/\lambda_1 - 1/\lambda_2}{\nu_1 - \nu_2}. \tag{5–17}$$

As was pointed out in Section 3–14, if the wave train is long compared with the wavelength, the component sinusoidal waves have frequencies very close to a given value ν_0. In a nondispersive medium, the inverse wavelength $1/\lambda$ is proportional to the frequency ν; in a dispersive medium, it is a more complicated function of ν. In any case, if the difference $\nu_1 - \nu_2$ is sufficiently small, the right term of Eq. (5–17) may be taken to be equal to the derivative of $1/\lambda$ with respect to ν, computed at the frequency ν_0. Hence (5–17) becomes

$$\frac{t}{x} = \left[\frac{d(1/\lambda)}{d\nu} \right]_{\nu = \nu_0} \tag{5–18}$$

This equation does not contain ν_1 or ν_2. Thus we conclude that at the time t not only the two waves considered above, but all the sinusoidal waves that compose the train, are in phase at the same point x. According to our definition, x/t represents the group velocity v_g, and we obtain

$$\frac{1}{v_g} = \frac{d(1/\lambda)}{d\nu}.$$ (5–19)

Equation (5–19) may be written in several different ways. Let v be the phase velocity and $n = c/v$ the index of refraction, both quantities, according to our assumption, being functions of ν (or λ). Since

$$\frac{1}{\lambda} = \frac{\nu n}{c},$$

(5–19) becomes

$$\frac{1}{v_g} = \frac{n}{c} + \frac{\nu}{c}\frac{dn}{d\nu},$$

or

$$\frac{1}{v_g} = \frac{1}{v}\left(1 + \frac{\nu}{n}\frac{dn}{d\nu}\right).$$ (5–20)

If we consider that

$$\nu = v/\lambda,$$

and take the reciprocal of (5–19), we obtain

$$v_g = v + \frac{1}{\lambda}\frac{dv}{d(1/\lambda)},$$

or, since $d(1/\lambda) = -d\lambda/\lambda^2$,

$$v_g = v - \lambda\frac{dv}{d\lambda}.$$ (5–21)

In most materials, the index of refraction is an increasing function of the frequency. Equation (5–20) shows that in this case the group velocity of light is *smaller* than the phase velocity. If n is a constant, (5–20) yields

$$v_g = v = \frac{c}{n};$$

in this case, as we already know, the group and phase velocities are identical.

5–6 The velocity of light in matter. It is possible to determine the ratio of the velocity of light in a material substance to the velocity of light in vacuum by simply measuring the index of refraction of the substance in question. This measurement, however, is based upon the assumption that light is a wave phenomenon. A direct measurement of the velocity of light in material substances is thus an experiment of very great importance, for it provides a crucial test of this assumption. Indeed, as explained in Section 1–9, the wave model of light predicts that light travels faster in vacuum than in matter, whereas the corpuscular model of light makes an opposite prediction.

As we have already mentioned, the velocity of light in matter can be measured by the Foucault method described in Section 5–3. It is actually most convenient to compare the velocity in matter with the velocity in vacuum (or, for practical purposes, in air), and perform the experiment as shown schematically in Fig. 5–15.

In this figure, as in Fig. 5–5, S is the source, M a half-silvered glass plate, L a lens, and M_1 a rotating mirror which, with L, produces an image S_1. As M_1 rotates, S_1 moves along a curve on which there are now two concave mirrors, M_2 and M_3, instead of only one. If there is no condensed matter between the rotating mirror M_1 and either M_2 or M_3, the light rays reflected by M_2 and M_3 form images at the same point S_2'. As we explained in Section 5–2, the displacement of this point from the point S_2, where the image is formed when the mirror M_1 is stationary, is proportional to the transit time of the light between M_1 and M_2 (or M_1 and M_3) and back. Let us now place a tube filled with a transparent liquid, e.g., water, between M_1 and M_3. When M_1 rotates at high speed, we observe two images of the source, S_2' and S_2'', instead of only one, because now the time required by the

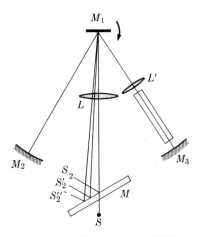

Fig. 5–15. Measurement of the velocity of light in matter.

light to travel between M_1 and M_2 is different from that required to travel between M_1 and M_3. We find that the image formed by the rays that have traversed the water is *more displaced* than the image formed by the rays that have traveled through air alone. We thus conclude, in agreement with the predictions of the wave theory, that the velocity of propagation of light in water is less than that in air (or vacuum). (To correct for the effect of refraction by the water column, it is necessary to place an auxiliary lens L' between M_1 and M_3; the additional retardation produced by this lens is negligible except in the most precise measurements.) For a quantitative interpretation of the experimental data, it should be noted that the velocity measured by this experiment is not the *phase velocity* but the *group velocity*. It is then found that, within the limit of experimental error, the velocity as directly determined agrees with that computed from the measured values of the index of refraction n and the quantity $dn/d\nu$.

5–1. Consider the rotating mirror experiment for the determination of the velocity of light, illustrated in Fig. 5–5. Suppose that the distance M_1M_2 is 20 m and the distance M_1S is 1 m. Compute the number of revolutions per second of the mirror M_1 for which the image S_2 undergoes a displacement of 0.7 mm.

5–2. In one of Michelson and Morley's measurements (Section 5–3) the effective path length of the rays between the half-silvered mirror N and each of the two mirrors M_1 and M_2 is $l = 11$ m. The experiment was performed with monochromatic light of wavelength $\lambda = 6000$ A. Assuming that the earth moves with a velocity of 30 km/sec with respect to the medium that propagates light waves, compute the expected shift of the observed interference pattern as the interferometer is rotated so that first one arm and then the other is parallel to the direction of motion of the earth. Express the shift as a fraction of the distance between maxima in the interference pattern.

5–3. Estimate the broadening of spectral lines due to the Doppler effect, for the two following sources: (a) atomic sodium gas at a temperature of 1800°C, and (b) helium gas at a temperature of 20°C. (The pertinent constants are: Boltzmann constant $k = 1.37 \times 10^{-16}$ erg/atom°K; mass of the helium atom $= 4 \times 1.66 \times 10^{-24}$ g; mass of sodium atom $= 23 \times 1.66 \times 10^{-24}$ g.)

5–4. The spectral lines of the galaxy NG 379 show a "red shift" $\Delta\lambda = 1.83\%$. Compute the radial velocity of the star relative to the earth.

5–5. The dispersion curve of a given kind of glass may be represented by (Cauchy's equation) $n = A + (B/\lambda^2)$,

where $A = 1.42$ and $B = 1.6 \times 10^6$ (angstroms)^2. Compute the phase and the group velocity of light in this glass at the wavelength $\lambda = 4000$ A.

5–6. A light source at the focal point of a parabolic mirror produces a plane wave of frequency ν. The amplitude of the wave is modulated (e.g., by means of a Kerr cell; see Section 6–16) in such a way that the optical disturbance at the origin is represented by $E_1 = A \cos 2\pi\nu_0 t \times \cos 2\pi\nu t$ ($\nu_0 \ll \nu$). The corresponding intensity is $I_1 = KA^2 \cos^2 2\pi\nu_0 t$. The light beam travels through a dispersive medium whose index of refraction n is a known function of frequency, to a mirror at a distance D which reflects it back to a detector located near the source. Considering the modulated wave as the superposition of two rigorously sinusoidal waves of slightly different frequencies ν_1 and ν_2, prove that the optical disturbance at the detector is given by an equation of the form

$$E_2 = A \cos 2\pi\nu_0(t - t') \times \cos 2\pi\nu(t - t''),$$

and the corresponding intensity by

$$I_2 = A^2 \cos^2 2\pi\nu_0(t - t') .$$

(a) Compute t' and t'', and discuss the physical meaning of the quantities $2D/t'$ and $2D/t''$.

(b) Suppose that the sensitivity of the detector is modulated in synchronism with the intensity of the light source, as in the experiment described in Fig. 5–6. For which values of D will the response of the detector be a maximun?

(c) Will the experiment described measure the phase or the group velocity of light?

CHAPTER 6

POLARIZATION AND CRYSTAL OPTICS

6–1 Polarization of light waves. By the study of interference and diffraction we have learned that the optical disturbance is a rapidly oscillating function of time whose form, in certain cases, approximates that of a sinusoidal function. However, we have not yet inquired into the character of the optical disturbance. Is it a scalar quantity, like the pressure change in a sound wave? Is it a vector quantity, like the displacement of the gas particles in a sound wave or the displacement of the water particles in a surface wave? If it is a vector quantity, does the vector point in the direction of propagation like the displacement in a sound wave, or does it point in a direction different from the direction of propagation, like the displacement in a surface wave?

It is clear that if the optical disturbance is a scalar quantity, or if it is a vector parallel to the direction of propagation, all planes through the same light ray are physically equivalent. If, on the other hand, the disturbance is a vector pointing in a direction different from the direction of propagation, the plane containing this vector might be expected to possess some distinctive property.

The question thus arises whether the infinite number of planes passing through the same light ray are physically distinguishable. This question can be answered by a simple experiment with a *sheet polarizer* (a commercial product manufactured by the Polaroid Corporation by a process we shall describe in Section 6–9), which is a sheet of transparent plastic widely used, e.g., in the manufacture of sunglasses. Let us hold a sheet polarizer before our eyes and look through it at a light source such as an incandescent lamp. If we rotate the sheet in its own plane we notice no change in the light intensity. We now place a second sheet polarizer between the light source and the eye (Fig. 6–1). If we rotate the second sheet in its own plane, keeping the first in a fixed position, we find that the light intensity changes periodically. The intensity is practically zero at two angular positions of the second sheet 180° apart, and it is a maximum at angular positions halfway between. If we actually measure the intensity I of the light that emerges from the second sheet polarizer, we find that it closely obeys a law of the following type:

$$I(\psi) = I_0 \cos^2 \psi, \qquad (6\text{–}1)$$

where I_0 is the maximum intensity and ψ is the angle of rotation of the second sheet, measured from the position at which the intensity is a maximum.

The very fact that the transmitted
intensity depends on the angular
position of the second sheet proves
that the optical disturbance is a vector quantity, whose direction does
not coincide with the direction of
propagation. We shall call this vector the *optical vector*. To explain in a
natural way the details of the above
experiment, as well as many other
observations, it is necessary to assume that *the optical vector of a plane*

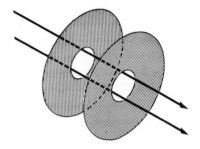

FIG. 6–1. A beam of light traversing
two sheet polarizers.

*light wave propagating in an isotropic medium is perpendicular to the direction
of propagation.*

From the above considerations, there develops the following picture.

Light waves are *transverse* waves (see Section 1–3). In the light coming
from an ordinary light source, the optical vector changes direction rapidly
and irregularly with time, while it always remains perpendicular to the direction of propagation. As we shall discuss later in more detail, this behavior is due to the incoherent superposition of the optical disturbances
coming from the many microscopic sources that form any ordinary light
source (see Section 3–7). The light under such conditions is called *natural*
or *unpolarized* light.

Consider a light wave incident perpendicularly upon a sheet polarizer.
The sheet transmits the light wave without appreciable absorption if the
optical vector is parallel to a certain preferred direction (the "transmission
axis"), while it absorbs it completely (or nearly so) if the optical vector
is perpendicular to this preferred direction. If the optical vector has
an intermediate direction, it may be regarded as the resultant of two vectors, one parallel and the other perpendicular to the transmission axis of the
sheet polarizer (Fig. 6–2). The sheet transmits the first component and absorbs the second so that, in all cases, the optical vector of the light wave
emerging from the filter is parallel to the transmission axis. We shall call
this wave *linearly polarized*, or *plane polarized*. We shall call the plane containing the direction of propagation and the optical vector the *plane of vibration*. Any optical device capable
of transmitting only linearly polarized light will be called a *polarization
filter*.

If the light incident upon the filter
is natural light, the intensity of the
linearly polarized wave emerging
from the filter does not change as the

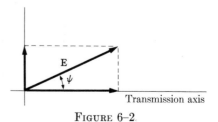

Transmission axis

FIGURE 6–2

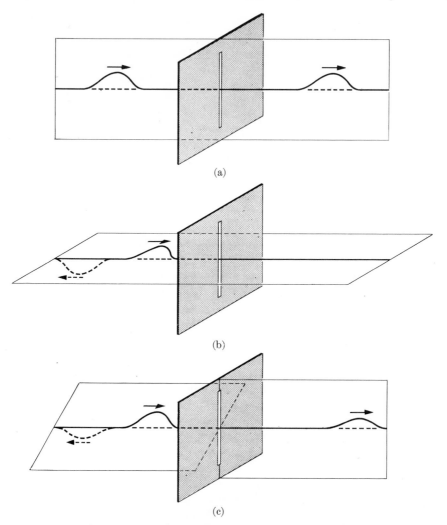

(a)

(b)

(c)

FIG. 6–3. Waves on a tube passing through a vertical slit: (a) a vertical disturbance is transmitted freely; (b) a horizontal disturbance is not transmitted; (c) a disturbance in an intermediate direction is partially transmitted.

filter rotates in its plane. Indeed, in the case of natural light, the rms component of the optical vector in any direction perpendicular to the direction of propagation is the same.

But suppose now that the linearly polarized light wave emerging from the first polarization filter is allowed to pass through a second filter. The amplitude of the wave transmitted by the second filter will be proportional to the cosine of the angle between the optical vector of the polarized wave and the transmission axis of the second filter (Fig. 6-2). This angle is equal to the angle ψ between the transmission axes of the two filters. The intensity of the light emerging from the second filter is proportional to the square of the amplitude (see Section 3-2) and is therefore proportional to $\cos^2 \psi$, as is found experimentally (Eq. 6-1).

The law expressed by (6-1) is called the *law of Malus*. When two polarization filters are arranged in the manner described above, the first filter is referred to as the *polarizer* and the second as the *analyzer*. An optical instrument consisting of a polarizer and an analyzer is called a *polariscope*.

We shall discuss later the physical nature of the sheet polarizer and of other polarization filters; for the moment, we shall confine our discussion to a mechanical analogy. Consider a rubber tube which, at a certain point, passes through a narrow slit (Fig. 6-3). A blow at one end of the tube, applied in the direction parallel to the slit, will start a wave which passes freely through the slit. A blow in the perpendicular direction, however, produces a wave that cannot pass through the slit. If the displacement in the incident wave is neither parallel nor perpendicular to the slit, the wave will be partially transmitted by the slit. Beyond the slit, the displacement will be parallel to the slit and will be equal in magnitude to the projection of the original displacement along the direction of the slit.

6-2 Superposition of polarized waves. Elliptical and circular polarization.

Consider two linearly polarized sinusoidal light waves of the same frequency traveling in the same direction. If their optical vectors are *parallel*, they combine into a single linearly polarized wave whose amplitude and phase are functions of the amplitudes and phases of the component waves (see Section 3-5). We propose to investigate the nature of the resultant wave in the case that the two optical disturbances are mutually *perpendicular*.

Consider a cartesian system of coordinates with the x-axis in the direction of propagation, the y-axis parallel to the optical vector of one wave, and the z-axis parallel to the optical vector of the other wave (Fig. 6-4). The optical vectors of the two waves are represented by expressions of the type

$$E_y = A_y \cos \left[\omega \left(t - \frac{x}{v} \right) + \varphi_1 \right],$$

$$E_z = A_z \cos \left[\omega \left(t - \frac{x}{v} \right) + \varphi_2 \right].$$

$$(6-2)$$

The functions E_y and E_z also represent the components of the resultant

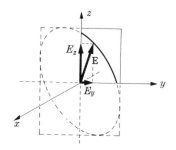

FIG. 6-4. Elliptical polarization.

optical vector **E** along the y- and z-axes. At a given point in space, this vector varies with time in both length and direction. Its tip describes a curve, of which Eqs. (6–2) are the parametric equations. To determine the shape of this curve, we need only eliminate t between the two equations. For this purpose we denote by $\varphi = \varphi_2 - \varphi_1$ the phase difference between the two oscillations and redefine the origin of time by putting $\omega t' = \omega(t - x/v) + \varphi_1$, so that Eqs. (6–2) become

$$E_y = A_y \cos(\omega t'),$$

$$E_z = A_z \cos(\omega t' + \varphi) = A_z \cos(\omega t') \cos \varphi - A_z \sin(\omega t') \sin \varphi. \tag{6–3}$$

From these equations, we obtain

$$\frac{E_z}{A_z} - \frac{E_y}{A_y} \cos \varphi = -\sin(\omega t') \sin \varphi,$$

$$\left(\frac{E_z}{A_z} - \frac{E_y}{A_y} \cos \varphi\right)^2 = \sin^2(\omega t') \sin^2 \varphi = \left[1 - \left(\frac{E_y}{A_y}\right)^2\right] \sin^2 \varphi,$$

and, after a few reductions,

$$\frac{E_y^2}{A_y^2} + \frac{E_z^2}{A_z^2} - 2 \frac{E_y}{A_y} \frac{E_z}{A_z} \cos \varphi = \sin^2 \varphi \tag{6–4}$$

This is the equation of an ellipse, and we thus conclude that the tip of the vector representing the resultant optical disturbance at a given point in space describes an ellipse in the plane perpendicular to the direction of propagation. We express this fact by saying that the wave is *elliptically polarized*.

Note that at any instant of time the *magnitude E* of the resultant optical disturbance is given by the equation

$$E^2 = E_y^2 + E_z^2. \tag{6-5}$$

It follows that the intensity I of the elliptically polarized wave equals the sum of the intensities I_y and I_z of the two linearly polarized waves vibrating in the perpendicular planes xy and xz:

$$I = I_y + I_z. \tag{6–6}$$

Equations (6–2) show that E_y varies from $+A_y$ to $-A_y$, and that E_z varies from $+A_z$ to $-A_z$. Hence the ellipse represented by these equations,

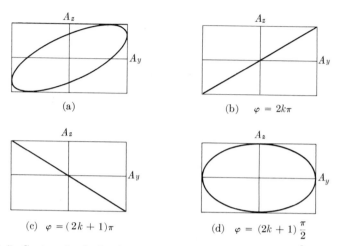

FIG. 6-5. States of polarization corresponding to different values of the phase difference φ.

or by Eq. (6–4,) is inscribed in a rectangle with sides of length $2A_y$ and $2A_z$ (Fig. 6–5a). If the two oscillations are in phase, i.e, if φ equals zero or an even multiple of π, the ellipse degenerates into a straight segment, coincident with the diagonal of the rectangle that lies in the first and third quadrants (Fig. 6–5b). Indeed, in this case Eqs. (6–3) yield

$$\frac{E_y}{A_y} = \frac{E_z}{A_z}.$$

If φ is an odd multiple of π, Eqs. (6–3) give

$$\frac{E_y}{A_y} = -\frac{E_z}{A_z}.$$

The resultant wave is again linearly polarized, but now the optical disturbance is parallel to the other diagonal of the rectangle, i.e., to that lying in the second and fourth quadrants (Fig. 6–5c).

If φ is an odd multiple of $\pi/2$, Eq. (6–4) becomes

$$\frac{E_y^2}{A_y^2} + \frac{E_z^2}{A_z^2} = 1, \tag{6–7}$$

which is the equation of an ellipse having its axes in the y- and z-directions (Fig. 6–5d). If, in particular, $A_y = A_z$, the ellipse reduces to a circle and the wave is said to be *circularly polarized*. In this case, the vector representing the optical disturbance at a given point in space rotates with uniform angular speed without change of magnitude.

In the case of elliptical or circular polarization we may inquire into the *direction of rotation* of the optical vector. For this purpose consider the positions of the optical vector at time $t' = 0$ and at time $t' = \tau$, where τ is a very small fraction of the period T. These positions are shown by the segments OP_1 and OP_2 in Fig. 6–6. From (6–3), we find

$$\text{at } t' = 0: \qquad E_y = A_y, \quad E_z = A_z \cos \varphi,$$

$$\text{at } t' = \tau: \qquad E_y = A_y \cos (\omega\tau), \quad E_z = A_z \cos (\varphi + \omega\tau).$$

We now recall that the cosine is a decreasing function of its argument if the argument lies between 0 and π, and an increasing function of its argument if the argument lies between 0 and $-\pi$. Thus, if we have $0 < \varphi < \pi$, E_z is a decreasing function of time at $t' = 0$, the point P_2 lies below the point P_1 (Fig. 6–6a), and the optical vector *rotates clockwise with respect to an observer toward whom the wave travels*. If, however, $-\pi < \varphi < 0$, E_z is an increasing function of time at $t' = 0$ and the optical vector rotates counterclockwise (Fig. 6–6b).

In conclusion, for a wave traveling in the direction of the x-axis of a right-handed cartesian frame of reference, we find that with respect to an observer facing the light source, the optical vector rotates clockwise or counterclockwise depending on whether the z-component leads or lags the y-component by a phase angle less than π. When the rotation is clockwise we speak of *right-handed* polarization. When the rotation is counterclockwise we speak of *left-handed* polarization. A phase difference φ is equivalent to a phase difference $\varphi \pm 2k\pi$, where k is an integer; thus, in particular, we shall have left-handed polarization if the z-component leads the y-component by a phase angle between π and 2π.

Just as two coherent linearly polarized waves with their planes of vibration perpendicular to each other give rise, in general, to an elliptically

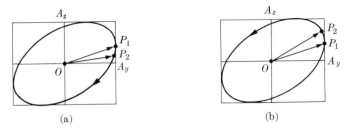

(a)   (b)

Fig. 6–6. (a) $0 < \varphi < \pi$; the optical vector rotates clockwise (right-handed polarization). (b) $\pi < \varphi < 2\pi$; the optical vector rotates counterlcockwise (left-handed polarization).

polarized wave, so, conversely, any elliptically polarized wave may be regarded as the resultant of two linearly polarized waves vibrating in two mutually perpendicular but otherwise arbitrary planes. Both the amplitudes and the phase difference of the two waves depend on the choice of these planes of vibration.

Consider lastly two coherent elliptically polarized waves traveling in the same direction. We can arbitrarily choose two orthogonal planes whose intersection is parallel to the direction of propagation, and decompose each elliptical wave into two linearly polarized waves vibrating in the two selected planes. We can now combine the waves that have a common plane of vibration, and are then left with two linearly polarized waves vibrating in mutually perpendicular planes. The resultant of these waves is an elliptically polarized wave. We thus conclude that two sinusoidal, coherent, elliptically polarized waves of the same frequency and traveling in the same direction combine, in general, into a single elliptically polarized wave.

The following special cases are worth mentioning. (a) Two coherent linearly polarized waves traveling in the same direction combine, in general, into an elliptically polarized wave, even if their planes of vibration are not mutually perpendicular. (b) A circularly polarized wave with clockwise rotation and a circularly polarized wave with counterclockwise rotation combine, in general, into an elliptically polarized wave. During each period, the rotating vectors of the component circularly polarized wave twice acquire the same direction (at angular positions 180° apart), and twice acquire opposite directions. The major axis of the resultant elliptical wave lies along the line on which the two component vectors are parallel, and the minor axis lies along the line on which the two component vectors are antiparallel (Fig. 6–7a). If, in particular, the two component circular waves have equal amplitudes, the resultant wave is linearly polarized (Fig.

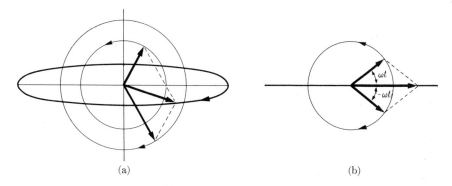

(a)   (b)

FIG. 6–7. Combination of two circularly polarized waves, one right-handed and one left-handed: (a) if the amplitudes are different, an elliptically polarized wave results; (b) if the amplitudes are equal, a linearly polarized wave results.

6–7b). Conversely, any linearly polarized wave may be regarded as the resultant of two circularly polarized waves of the same amplitude but with opposite sense of rotation and, in general, any elliptically polarized wave may be regarded as the resultant of a right-handed and a left-handed circularly polarized wave of different amplitudes.

We are now in a position to discuss in more detail the character of natural light (see preceding section).

Each wave train emitted by one of the many microscopic sources contained in any macroscopic source has a definite polarization (elliptical, circular, rectilinear). The individual wave trains combine into a single wave, which will, in general, be elliptically polarized. However, the shape of the ellipse, as well as the positions of its axes, changes irregularly and rapidly with time because each wave train is of short duration and because no correlation exists among the times of emission of the various wave trains.

From the previous discussion it follows that light from an ordinary source may also be regarded as the superposition of two linearly polarized waves vibrating in mutually perpendicular planes and whose phase difference changes rapidly and irregularly with time. The two planes, of course, can be chosen arbitrarily. We speak of *natural light* when the average amplitude of the two component waves is the same and when their phase difference φ changes in a completely random fashion (i.e., the average value of $\cos \varphi$ or $\sin \varphi$ is zero). If, on the other hand, the amplitudes of the two component waves are different (or if their phase difference does not vary completely at random), we say that the light is *partially polarized*. Partially polarized light may be regarded as the superposition of a wave of natural light and a wave of polarized light.

Sometimes the physical conditions of a source are such as to single out a certain preferred direction; for example, the source may lie in a magnetic or an electric field. In this case, the light from the source may be partially or even completely polarized (see Section 8–14). However, a simple symmetry argument shows that light coming from a source for which all directions are physically equivalent must be unpolarized.

6–3 Interference of polarized waves. Experimental determination of the plane of vibration. In Chapters 3 and 4 we developed the theory of interference and diffraction by treating the optical disturbance as if it were a scalar quantity. The results obtained there are not invalidated by the fact that, as we now know, the optical disturbance is, instead, a vector quantity. The reason why this is so will become clear from the discussion of a specific example.

Consider the experiment with the Fresnel mirrors, described in Section 3–7 (Fig. 3–10), and assume that the source S emits linearly polarized light. We may then regard the two images of S in the two mirrors (S_1 and S_2) as virtual oscillators, which at any one time vibrate in the same direction. At the point of interference P the wave from S_1 vibrates in the plane that passes through S_1P and is parallel to the direction of vibration of the source S_1. Similarly, the wave from the source S_2 vibrates in the plane that passes through S_2P and is parallel to the direction of vibration of the source S_2. Since the angle between S_1P and S_2P is very small, the optical vectors of the two waves are practically parallel and they add like scalar quantities.

If the light beam coming from the source S is elliptically polarized, we may consider it as the superposition of two linearly polarized light beams vibrating in mutually perpendicular planes, one of which may be the plane of the diagram. We now have four different waves meeting at each point P of the observation screen. Two of them, coming from the virtual sources S_1 and S_2, vibrate in the plane of the diagram. The other two, coming from the same virtual sources, vibrate in the plane perpendicular to the plane of the diagram. The two waves vibrating in the plane of the diagram combine in a single wave vibrating in the same plane. Similarly, the other two waves combine in a wave vibrating in a plane perpendicular to the plane of the diagram. We thus have at each point two mutually perpendicular optical disturbances, E_y and E_z. Let I_y and I_z be the corresponding intensities. The resultant optical disturbance is represented, in general, by an elliptically vibrating vector. The resultant intensity I is the sum of I_y and I_z, according to Eq. (6–6). The intensities I_y and I_z vary from point to point in the manner predicted by the theory of interference developed in Chapter 3, and so does the resultant intensity $I = I_y + I_z$.

The above conclusions apply also to the case of natural light. Indeed, a beam of natural light may also be regarded as the superposition of two linearly polarized beams, vibrating in mutually perpendicular planes. In general, the results obtained by treating the optical disturbance as a scalar quantity are valid whenever the interfering rays are parallel or nearly so. This was actually the case in all experimental situations discussed in Chapters 3 and 4. If, however, the interfering rays are not parallel, one must take into account the vector character of the optical disturbance in computing the resultant distribution of light intensity.

Consider the following experiment. A plane monochromatic light wave is incident at 45° upon a plane specular surface, e.g., a highly polished metal surface. It gives rise to a plane reflected wave, which travels in a direction perpendicular to that of the incident wave. Consider a plane parallel to the reflecting surface, a distance x from it (Fig. 6–8). The incident and the reflected rays meeting at a point P of this plane have a phase difference $\Delta\alpha$ that depends on x and on the phase change φ occurring at reflection. Since, starting from a given wave front such as AB, the incident ray travels the distance $\overline{BP} = x/\cos 45° = x\sqrt{2}$ before reaching P, while the reflected ray travels the distance $\overline{AC} + \overline{CP} = 2\overline{BP}$, the phase difference $\Delta\alpha$ is given by

$$\Delta\alpha = 2\pi \frac{x\sqrt{2}}{\lambda} + \varphi, \qquad (6\text{-}8)$$

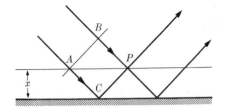

where λ is the wavelength.
The incident and the reflected
waves are in phase at those planes
for which $\Delta\alpha = 2\pi k$, where k is an
integer. The corresponding values
of x are given by the equation

FIG. 6-8. Interference of two polarized waves traveling at right angles.

$$\frac{x\sqrt{2}}{\lambda} + \frac{\varphi}{2\pi} = k. \qquad (6\text{-}9)$$

The incident and the reflected wave have opposite phases at those planes
for which $\Delta\alpha = 2\pi(k + \frac{1}{2})$; the corresponding values of x are given by the
equation

$$\frac{x\sqrt{2}}{\lambda} + \frac{\varphi}{2\pi} = k + \frac{1}{2}. \qquad (6\text{-}10)$$

It is instructive to examine several hypothetical cases.

Suppose, first, that the optical disturbance is a scalar quantity. Then we
should expect intensity maxima at the planes defined by (6–9) and intensity
minima at the planes defined by (6–10).

Suppose, next, that the optical disturbance is a vector parallel to the direction of propagation (like the displacement in a sound wave). The optical
disturbances corresponding to the incident and the reflected waves are then
mutually perpendicular vectors. Depending on the phase difference, the
resultant vibration may be rectilinear, elliptical, or circular (if the incident
and the reflected waves have equal intensity). However, the resultant intensity will be everywhere the same, and equal to the sum of the incident
and reflected intensities.

Consider, finally, the actual situation, namely, that of a wave vibrating
perpendicularly to the direction of propagation. Assume that the optical
vector is parallel to the reflecting surface, and therefore perpendicular to
the plane of incidence (defined as the plane containing the direction of
propagation and the normal to the reflecting surface). In this case, the
optical vectors of the incident and the reflected waves are everywhere
parallel. The resultant intensity has maxima at the planes defined by Eq.
(6–9) and minima at the planes defined by Eq. (6–10); i.e., the interference
pattern will be identical with that predicted under the assumption that the
optical disturbance is a scalar quantity. If, however, the wave vibrates in
the plane of incidence, then the optical vectors of the incident and of the
reflected waves are everywhere perpendicular, and the resultant intensity is
constant.

The observation of the interference pattern in the experiment outlined above is not an easy matter, mainly because the distance between the planes of maximum and minimum intensity is less than one wavelength, as shown by (6-9) and (6-10).

FIG. 6-9. Wiener's method for the observation of the interference between incident and reflected waves.

The problem, however, can be solved with a technique devised by Wiener. A very thin film of photographic emulsion is placed at a small angle to the reflecting surface, as shown in Fig. 6-9. If the incident light is in the appropriate state of polarization, the film, after development, will show a series of light and dark bands, the maximum darkening occurring along the lines where the plane of the film intersected the planes of maximum intensity.

This experiment was a very important one historically because it provided the first experimental determination of the plane of vibration of light waves. Most other polarization experiments, in fact, while proving the existence of linearly polarized light, do not furnish information about the actual direction of the vector representing the optical disturbance. For example, the experiment described in Section 6-1 shows that a sheet polarizer transmits only light waves whose optical vector is parallel to a certain preferred direction. It does not enable us to mark this preferred direction on the sheet. We can now do so by performing Wiener's experiment with light that has gone through the sheet polarizer. We repeat the experiment a number of times, rotating the sheet in its own plane between exposures of the photographic films, until the interference bands become sharpest or until they disappear completely. In the first instance the transmission axis of the polarizer will be the direction parallel to the reflecting surface. In the second instance, it will lie along the intersection of the plane of the sheet with the plane of incidence.

6-4 Reflection and refraction of polarized light. When a beam of linearly polarized light arrives at the surface of separation between two different transparent media, it splits into a reflected and a refracted beam, according to the ordinary laws of reflection and refraction. However, the distribution of intensity between the two beams depends not only on the angle of incidence, but also on the angle between the plane of vibration and the plane of incidence. When this angle is zero (i.e., when the optical vector, the direction of propagation, and the normal to the boundary surface are coplanar) the intensity of the refracted beam is a maximum and the intensity of the reflected beam a minimum. When, on the other hand, the angle is $\pi/2$ (i.e., when the optical vector is parallel to the boundary plane) the intensity of the refracted beam is a minimum and the intensity of the reflected beam a maximum. Moreover, when the incident beam vibrates in the plane of incidence, there exists a special angle of incidence for which the intensity of the reflected beam drops to zero. In this case the incident beam is totally refracted.

This particular angle of incidence is called the *polarization angle*. Its value, φ_p, is related to the indices of refraction of the two media, n_1 and n_2, by the following simple equation:

$$\tan \varphi_p = \frac{n_2}{n_1}. \qquad (6\text{--}11)$$

This law is known as *Brewster's law*. We shall later derive the above results from the electromagnetic theory of light (see Sections 8–5, 8–6, 8–7); for the moment, we accept them as experimental facts.

Suppose now that a beam of natural light is incident upon a surface of glass, or another transparent substance, at an angle equal to the polarization angle. The component vibrating in the plane of incidence is totally refracted. Therefore, the reflected beam is linearly polarized, with the optical vector parallel to the reflecting surface. We can therefore make use of reflection as a convenient means of producing linearly polarized light.

Note that if φ_p' is the angle of refraction corresponding to an angle of incidence equal to φ_p, Snell's law yields the equation

$$\frac{\sin \varphi_p}{\sin \varphi_p'} = \frac{n_2}{n_1},$$

which, together with Eq. (6–11), gives

$$\cos \varphi_p = \sin \varphi_p'.$$

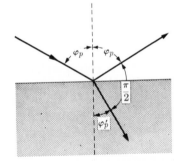

Fig. 6–10. Brewster's law.

Since the angle of reflection and the angle of incidence are equal, we reach the conclusion (Fig. 6–10) that the reflected beam is totally polarized when it and the refracted beam travel at right angles to each other.

A beam of natural light incident at an angle different from the polarization angle gives rise to a partially polarized reflected beam. The degree of polarization, of course, increases as the angle of incidence approaches the angle of polarization.

Sunlight reflected by a water surface and, to a smaller extent, that reflected by a road pavement, are partially polarized, with the optical vector vibrating preferentially in the horizontal plane. Sunglasses made with sheet polarizers that are arranged so as to transmit light waves vibrating in the

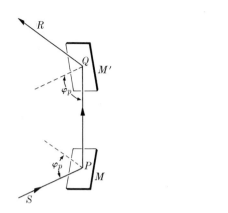
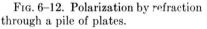

Fig. 6–11. Production and analysis   Fig. 6–12. Polarization by refraction
of polarized light by reflection.   through a pile of plates.

vertical plane are opaque to the reflected light and therefore effectively reduce the glare.

A simple polariscope can be made from two glass plates arranged as
shown schematically in Fig. 6–11. A beam of natural light is incident upon
a glass plate M at an angle equal to the polarization angle. The reflected,
linearly polarized beam falls upon a second glass plate M', at an angle equal
to the polarization angle. As the upper plate rotates about an axis parallel
to the beam that travels from M to M', the intensity of the beam reflected
by the plate M' changes periodically. It is a maximum when the plates M
and M' are perpendicular to the same plane (i.e., when the rays SP, PQ,
and QR in Fig. 6–11 are coplanar). It is zero when the two planes perpendicular to M and M' are perpendicular to each other (i.e., when the planes
SPQ and PQR are perpendicular). For intermediate positions, the intensity
varies according to the law of Malus (Eq. 6–1) and is therefore proportional
to the square of the cosine of the angle formed by the planes SPQ and PQR.

The refraction of natural light does not give rise to a totally polarized
beam because both the component vibrating in the plane of incidence and
the component vibrating in the plane perpendicular to the plane of incidence are always partially refracted. However, the former component is
refracted more strongly than the latter, and therefore the refracted beam is
partially polarized, with the vector representing the optical disturbance lying in the plane of incidence. The degree of polarization is a maximum when
the angle of incidence equals the polarization angle.

For all practical purposes, it is possible to obtain a light beam that is
completely polarized by using a pile of glass plates such as that shown
schematically in Fig. 6–12. The beam enters the first glass plate at an
angle equal to the polarization angle φ_p for the passage from air to glass.

Using Brewster's law, we can easily show that it will also leave the plane-parallel plate at an angle equal to the polarization angle φ_p' for the passage from glass to air. Likewise, the beam will enter and leave the subsequent plates at angles equal to φ_p and φ_p', respectively. Now, a partially polarized beam may be regarded as the superposition of a beam of natural light and of a linearly polarized beam. At each refraction, the polarized component passes undisturbed, while the unpolarized component becomes partially polarized. Thus the amount of unpolarized light decreases geometrically with the number of refractions.

6–5 A fundamental optical property of anisotropic media. Until now we have confined our attention to the propagation of light in isotropic media, i.e., substances whose optical properties are the same in all directions. Liquids, as well as amorphous solid substances such as glass and plastics, are usually isotropic because of the random distribution of the molecules. In many crystals, however, the optical as well as the other physical properties are different in different directions. This optical anisotropy, often referred to as *double refraction*, or *birefringence*, is due to the particular arrangement of the atoms in the crystalline lattice and produces many curious and interesting phenomena, which we propose now to investigate.

We start with a simple experiment. A parallel beam of monochromatic light passes through a polariscope formed, for example, by two sheet polarizers, and then falls upon a screen (Fig. 6–13). We rotate the analyzer until the light spot on the screen disappears. The transmission axis of the analyzer is then perpendicular to that of the polarizer (i.e., the polarizer and the analyzer are *crossed*). Between the analyzer and the polarizer we now insert a thin, plane-parallel plate cut from a birefringent crystal or ob-

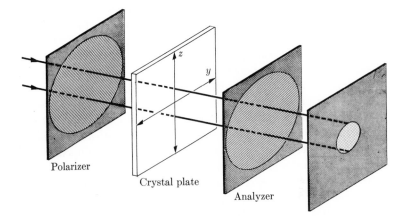

FIG. 6–13. A crystal plate between a polarizer and an analyzer.

tained by cleavage. The light on the screen will, in general, reappear. As we rotate the analyzer, the light intensity will change periodically between a maximum and a minimum, but will not become zero for any position of the analyzer. We thus conclude that the light emerging from the plate is no longer linearly polarized.

After removing the plate, we again place the analyzer and the polarizer in the crossed position, reinsert the birefringent plate, and rotate it in its own plane. For each complete turn, we find four positions, at 90° to one another, for which the light spot on the screen disappears. We conclude that the light now emerging from the plate has the same linear polarization as the light incident upon the plate. We can check this conclusion by rotating the analyzer and noting that the corresponding variation of the transmitted light intensity follows the law of Malus.

It is thus possible to trace on the plate two mutually perpendicular lines such that a linearly polarized light wave, vibrating in a direction parallel to either line, traverses the plate without changing its state of polarization. We call these lines the *axes of the plate*.

By generalizing this result, we can describe the fundamental property of an optically anisotropic medium as follows: *for every direction of propagation. there are only two waves, vibrating in one or the other of two mutually perpendicular planes, that preserve their state of polarization while traveling through the medium.*

Consider now a wave which, upon entering the plate, is linearly polarized, but does not vibrate in either of the two preferred directions. We may regard the incident wave as the superposition of two linearly polarized waves, vibrating in the two preferred directions. If the velocities of propagation of these two waves were the same, the two component waves, after traversing the plate, would recombine into a linearly polarized wave with the same plane of vibration as the incident wave. Since we know from experiment that this is not the case, i.e., since we know that the state of polarization of the wave changes on traversing the plate, we conclude that *the velocities of propagation in an anisotropic medium of the waves vibrating in the two preferred directions are different.* We can, of course, check this conclusion directly by measuring (e.g., with an interferometer) the velocities of propagation through a birefringent plate of the two waves whose planes of vibration contain one or the other of the two axes of the plate.

The above results can be derived from the electromagnetic theory of light and from a suitable atomic model of a birefringent medium (see Section 8–13).

Here we wish to mention only a mechanical analogue. Suppose that we have a long rod of elliptical cross section. If, at one end, we strike a blow in the direction of the minor axis of the ellipse, we produce a deformation parallel to this axis which travels with a given velocity along the rod, maintaining its original direction. A similar result is obtained by striking a blow in the direction of the major axis, but the velocity of propagation of the wave is greater than in the previous case. If we now strike a blow in a direction different from that of either axis, we shall find that the direction of the displacement changes as the wave travels along the rod. Indeed, after a certain distance, the wave will split into two separate deformations, one parallel to the major axis and one parallel to the minor axis, traveling with different velocities. Another mechanical model of a birefringent medium is described in Appendix 2(e).

We state explicity that in a plane wave traveling through an anisotropic medium the optical vector, in general, is not perpendicular to the direction of propagation. This point will be discussed further in Section 8–13.

6–6 Production of elliptically and circularly polarized light. We are now in a position to analyze in detail the change of polarization that occurs when an initially plane-polarized wave traverses a birefringent plate.

Let y and z be the axes of the plate (Fig. 6–14). Let n_y and n_z be the indices of refraction of the waves whose planes of vibrations are parallel to y and z, respectively; the corresponding velocities of propagation are c/n_y and c/n_z. Suppose, for example, that $n_y < n_z$, so that the velocity of propagation of the wave vibrating in the direction of the y-axis is greater than that of the wave vibrating in the direction of the z-axis.

Let **E** represent the optical vector of the linearly polarized light wave incident upon the plate, and ψ the angle formed by this vector with the y-axis. We decompose the incident wave (which we assume to be monochromatic) into two waves, with the planes of vibration parallel to the y- and z-axes, respectively. As they enter the plate, the incident wave and its two components have the same phase. Therefore, we may represent the magnitudes of the three corresponding optical vectors by equations of the following type:

$$E = A \cos 2\pi \frac{t}{T}, \qquad E_y = A_y \cos 2\pi \frac{t}{T}, \qquad E_z = A_z \cos 2\pi \frac{t}{T}, \quad (6\text{–}12)$$

where $\qquad A_y = A \cos \psi; \quad A_z = A \sin \psi.$

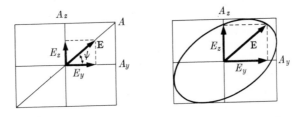

Fig. 6–14. Production of elliptically polarized light.

In the plate, the waves vibrating in the planes parallel to the two axes travel with two different velocities, c/n_y and c/n_z. If d is the thickness of the plate, the time necessary for traversing the plate is $n_y d/c$ for the first wave and $n_z d/c$ for the second. Therefore, as the two waves leave the plate, their optical vectors are represented by the following equations:

$$E_y = A_y \cos \frac{2\pi}{T}\left(t - \frac{n_y d}{c}\right) = A_y \cos 2\pi \left(\frac{t}{T} - \frac{n_y d}{\lambda_0}\right) ,$$

$$E_z = A_z \cos \frac{2\pi}{T}\left(t - \frac{n_z d}{c}\right) = A_z \cos 2\pi \left(\frac{t}{T} - \frac{n_z d}{\lambda_0}\right) ,$$

(6–13)

where λ_0 is the wavelength in vacuum. We see that the two emergent waves have different phases. Indeed, the oscillation parallel to the z-axis lags that parallel to the y-axis by a phase angle

$$\varphi = 2\pi \frac{d}{\lambda_0} (n_z - n_y).$$

(6–14)

As explained in Section 6–2, the two oscillations recombine to produce an elliptically polarized wave. We thus conclude that, in general, passage through a birefringent plate changes a plane-polarized wave into an elliptically polarized wave. The ellipse described by the optical vector of this wave is tangent to the rectangle whose sides are parallel to y and z and whose diagonal represents the rectilinear oscillation of the incident wave (Fig. 6–14).

If, in particular, $d(n_z - n_y) = \lambda_0/4$, then $\varphi = \pi/2$ and the axes of the ellipse coincide with the y- and z-directions. The ellipse is described counterclockwise. If, moreover, $\psi = 45°$, $A_y = A_z$ and the ellipse becomes a circle. A plate of thickness d such that $d(n_z - n_y) = \lambda_0/4$, that is, a plate in which the optical path lengths of the two waves vibrating in planes parallel to the two axes differ by $\lambda_0/4$, is called a *quarter-wave plate*. Thus, we can obtain circularly polarized light by placing along the path of a linearly polarized wave a quarter-wave plate with the axes at 45° to the plane of vibration of the incident wave.

If $d(n_z - n_y) = \lambda_0/2$ (*half-wave plate*), then $\varphi = \pi$ and the wave emerging from the plate is linearly polarized. The plane of vibration of the emergent wave and the plane of vibration of the incident wave are parallel to the two diagonals of the rectangle shown in Fig. 6–14, and therefore form an angle of 2ψ with each other.

If $d(n_z - n_y) = 3\lambda_0/4$, then $\varphi = 3\pi/2$ and the ellipse representing the vibration of the optical vector again has its axes in the y- and z-directions, as for $d(n_z - n_y) = \lambda_0/4$. The ellipse, however, is now described in the clockwise direction.

Lastly, if $d(n_z - n_y) = \lambda_0$, then $\varphi = 2\pi$ and the emergent wave has the same state of polarization as the incident wave.

If we continue to increase the thickness, we again pass through the same sequence of polarization states. In particular, a plate whose thickness satisfies the equation $d(n_z - n_y) = (4k + 1)\lambda_0/4$ behaves like a quarter-wave plate, and one whose thickness satisfies the equation $d(n_z - n_y) = (2k + 1)\lambda_0/2$ behaves like a half-wave plate.

6–7 Analysis of elliptically and circularly polarized light. If a beam of elliptically polarized light passes through a polarization filter, the intensity of the transmitted light changes as the filter rotates about an axis parallel to the incident beam. For each complete rotation of the filter there are two positions (180° from each other) at which the transmitted intensity is a maximum, and two positions (at 90° from the former) at which the transmitted intensity is a minimum. The maximum of the transmitted intensity is observed when the transmission axis of the filter is parallel to the major axis of the ellipse, and the minimum when the transmission axis is parallel to the minor axis.

If, on the other hand, the incident wave is circularly polarized, the intensity of light passing through the filter is the same for all positions of the filter.

In the above experiment, a beam of elliptically polarized light behaves exactly like a beam of partially polarized light, and a beam of circularly polarized light behaves like a beam of natural light. However, we can distinguish elliptically polarized light from partially polarized light, and cir-

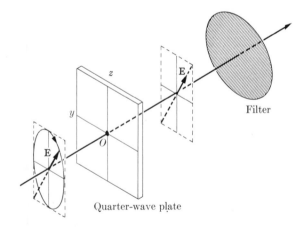

Fig. 6–15. Analysis of elliptically polarized light.

cularly polarized light from natural light, by using a quarter-wave plate in addition to a polarization filter.

In the case of elliptically polarized light, we first determine the directions of the major and minor axes of the ellipse by rotating the filter until the transmitted light reaches a maximum or a minimum. We then place the quarter-wave plate in front of the filter in such a way that its axes are parallel to the axes of the ellipse (Fig. 6–15). Suppose, for example, that the optical vector of the elliptically polarized wave rotates counterclockwise, and that the y-axis of the plate is parallel to the minor axis of the ellipse (Figs. 6–15 and 6–16). The incident wave may be regarded as the superposition of two linearly polarized waves, vibrating in the y- and z-directions, respectively. The second wave lags the first by a phase angle $\pi/2$, and the amplitudes of the two waves are equal to the half-sides of the rectangle shown in Fig. 6–16. If we assume, as before, that $n_y < n_z$, the quarter-wave plate produces an additional relative phase delay of $\pi/2$ of the second wave with respect to the first. Therefore the two waves, as they leave the plate, have a phase difference of π and combine into a linearly polarized wave. In Fig. 6–16, the plane of vibration of this wave is parallel to the diagonal of the rectangle that lies in the second and fourth quadrants.

Thus if, for example, the transmission axis of the filter is initially parallel to the minor axis of the ellipse, we obtain extinction of the beam by rotating the filter counterclockwise through an angle equal to the angle ψ that the plane of vibration of the wave emerging from the plate forms with the Oz-axis. The tangent of the angle ψ gives the ratio between the minor and the major axis of the ellipse (Fig. 6–16):

$$\tan \psi = A_y/A_z.$$

Circular polarization is a special case of elliptical polarization. From the above discussion, it follows that a quarter-wave plate changes a circularly polarized beam into a linearly polarized beam vibrating in a plane at 45° to the axes of the plate.

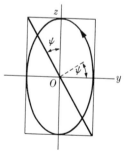

FIGURE 6–16.

6–8 Birefringent plate in white polarized light. We have assumed so far that the incident light is monochromatic, and we have seen that in this case the intensity of light passing through a polariscope with a birefringent plate between the polarizer and the analyzer depends on the thickness of the plate and on the angular positions of the polarizer and the analyzer relative

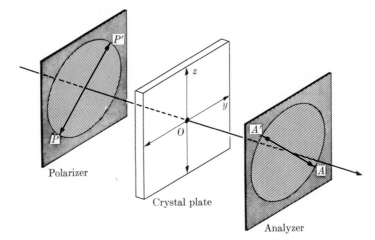

FIG. 6–17. Birefringent plate in white light.

to the axes of the plate. We now wish to investigate what happens when the incident light contains wavelengths continuously distributed throughout the visible spectrum, such as the "white" light emitted by an incandescent lamp.

Assume first that the transmission axes of the analyzer and the polarizer (PP' and AA' in Fig. 6–17) are at right angles to each other and at 45° to the axes of the plate (Oy and Oz). All rays whose wavelengths satisfy the condition

$$k\lambda_0 = d(n_z - n_y), \tag{6-15}$$

where k is an integer, leave the plate linearly polarized. Their plane of vibration is parallel to the transmission axis PP' of the polarizer, and therefore perpendicular to the transmission axis AA' of the analyzer. These rays are completely stopped by the analyzer.

The rays whose wavelengths satisfy the equation

$$(2k+1)\frac{\lambda_0}{2} = d(n_z - n_y) \tag{6-16}$$

also emerge from the plate linearly polarized, but their plane of vibration is perpendicular to the transmission axis of the polarizer. Therefore, these rays vibrate in a direction parallel to AA' and are transmitted by the analyzer without attenuation.

Lastly, the rays whose wavelengths are intermediate between those satisfying (6–15) or (6–16) emerge from the plate with an elliptical or circular polarization, and are partially transmitted by the analyzer. Thus in the spectrum of the light beam emerging from the analyzer, some wavelengths are missing [those that satisfy (6-15)] and some are particularly intense [those that satisfy (6-16)]. Consequently, the light will appear colored.

If the transmission axes of the polarizer and of the analyzer are parallel instead of perpendicular, and are still at 45° to the axes of the plate, Eq. (6-15) becomes the condition of minimum intensity, and Eq. (6-16) the condition of maximum intensity. The transmitted beam will then show the color complementary* to that observed in the previous case.

Let λ_1 and λ_2 be two neighboring wavelengths, each corresponding to a maximum of intensity. They satisfy the equations

$$k\lambda_1 = d(n_z - n_y),$$

$$(k + 1)\lambda_2 = d(n_z - n_y),$$

from which we obtain

$$\frac{\lambda_1}{\lambda_2} = 1 + \frac{1}{k} = 1 + \frac{\lambda_1}{d(n_z - n_y)},$$

and we see that, for a given value of λ_1, the ratio λ_1/λ_2 approaches 1 as d increases. Therefore, if the plate is thin, the dark and bright bands in the spectrum of the emergent light are wide, and the light appears distinctly colored. As the thickness of the plate increases, the bands become narrower and the coloring less noticeable. Indeed, for sufficiently large thicknesses, the light appears white to the unaided eye, and it is necessary to use a spectroscope in order to detect the dark and bright bands in the spectrum.

6-9 Dichroism. In some crystals the linearly polarized waves vibrating in the two preferred directions not only travel with different velocities, but also undergo different absorption. This phenomenon is known as *dichroism*. Natural light passing through a plate of a dichroic material becomes partially polarized. If the absorption coefficients of the crystal for the two waves are sufficiently different, and if the thickness of the plate is appropriately chosen, the transmitted light can be almost totally polarized.

Tourmaline is a well-known example of dichroic crystal. Its use as a polarization filter, however, has two important limitations: (1) tourmaline crystals can be obtained only in comparatively small samples, and (2) the absorption of tourmaline is not negligible even for waves vibrating in the direction of the transmission axis, and is strongly dependent on the wave-

---

*By definition, two colors are complementary when their combination produces white.

length. As a consequence, the polarized light transmitted by a tourmaline crystal has a bluish-green hue.

The synthetic crystal of sulphate of iodoquinine, or "herapathite," is a dichroic substance that transmits, with very little absorption, polarized light of all wavelengths. However, crystals of herapathite are mechanically very unstable and thus have no practical use as polarization filters.

The sheet polarizer manufactured by the Polaroid Corporation, and often mentioned in this chapter, is also a dichroic polarization filter. Among its advantages are availability in large sheets, high transparency for polarized light, and low cost. One early type consisted of a large number of small dichroic crystals embedded in a transparent plastic sheet; the special manu-facturing process ensured the parallel orientation of the individual crystals. A later type of sheet polarizer contains no crystals. It is made of a plastic material called polyvinyl-alcohol, whose molecules are exceedingly long. When a sheet of this material is stretched mechanically in one direction the long, tangled molecules straighten out and align themselves in the direction of the stretch. Addition of iodine gives strong dichroic properties to the sheet. Other types of sheet polarizers are made of pure plastics, without ad-dition of iodine.

A polarization filter may be characterized by two values, K_1 and K_2, which represent the ratios of transmitted to incident intensity for waves vibrating in the direction of the transmission axis and in the direction per-pendicular to the transmission axis, respectively (an "ideal" filter, of course, would have $K_1 = 1$, $K_2 = 0$). Table 6–1 gives the values of K_1 and K_2 for the so-called Polaroid H-sheet; this sheet makes an excellent polarization filter for practically all of the visible spectrum. Sheet polarizers for non-visible regions of the spectrum are also available.

TABLE 6–1

VALUES OF K_1 AND K_2, RELATIVE TO DIFFERENT WAVELENGTHS, FOR THE POLAROID H-SHEET.

Wavelength (A)	4000	5000	6000	7000
K_1	0.45	0.80	0.75	0.8
K_2	0.02	0.001	0.0000	0.0000

6–10 The Fresnel ellipsoid. Our next task is to find a rule that will enable us to determine, for each direction of propagation in a crystal, the planes of vibration and the velocities of the two waves discussed in the preceding sections.

An optically isotropic substance is characterized by a single parameter (the index of refraction), which determines the velocity of propagation.

However, in an optically anisotropic substance there is no single velocity of propagation and therefore no single index of refraction. It turns out, however, that we can describe the optical properties of such a substance completely by assigning three mutually perpendicular characteristic directions, Ox, Oy, and Oz, and three corresponding constants n_1, n_2, n_3, called the principal indices of refraction. The two plane waves traveling without change of their state of polarization in the direction of the x-axis have their planes of vibration parallel to the y- and z-axes, and their velocities of propagation are c/n_2 and c/n_3. The two waves traveling in the direction of the y-axis have their planes of vibration parallel to the z- and x-axes, and their velocities of propagation are c/n_3 and c/n_1, respectively. The two waves traveling in the direction of the z-axis have their planes of vibration parallel to the x- and y-axes, and their velocities of propagation are c/n_1 and c/n_2. Note that the velocities of propagation depend on the direction of vibration, not on the direction of propagation. Thus, for example, the wave vibrating in a direction parallel to the x-axis has the same velocity of propagation whether it travels in the y- or in the z-direction.

To determine the planes of vibration and the velocities of the two waves that are propagated in any direction different from Ox, Oy, or Oz, we use the following procedure. We first construct the ellipsoid whose three semiaxes are parallel to Ox, Oy, and Oz, and which have lengths equal to n_1, n_2, and n_3, respectively. The equation of this ellipsoid is

$$\frac{x^2}{n_1^2} + \frac{y^2}{n_2^2} + \frac{z^2}{n_3^2} = 1. \qquad (6\text{-}17)$$

Given the direction of propagation, we then construct a plane perpendicular to this direction (i.e., parallel to the corresponding wave fronts) and passing through the center of the ellipsoid. The intersection of the plane with the ellipsoid is an ellipse. The axes of this ellipse are parallel to the planes of vibration of the two plane waves that travel unchanged in the given direction. The lengths of the semiaxes are numerically equal to the two corresponding indices of refraction.

This general formulation of the laws of crystal optics was first discovered by Fresnel, on the basis of an elastic model of light. It can be rigorously derived from the electromagnetic theory of light, as we shall see in Section 8-13. For the moment we shall use it as a convenient expression of the empirical optical properties of birefringent substances, and we shall refer to the characteristic ellipsoid described above as the *Fresnel ellipsoid.**

---

*To avoid confusion, it should be noted that some authors use this term to designate the ellipsoid whose semiaxes are proportional to the velocities, rather than to the indices of refraction.

It is well known that crystals fall into different groups, depending on their symmetry properties.

For crystals belonging to the *cubic* system the three indices of refraction are equal ($n_1 = n_2 = n_3$), so that the Fresnel ellipsoid degenerates into a sphere. Since all sections of a sphere are circles, there are no preferred directions of vibration, and plane waves with an arbitrary state of polarization travel with equal velocities in all directions. The crystals belonging to the cubic system behave like optically isotropic substances, even though some of their other physical properties may depend on direction.

For crystals belonging to the *trigonal, hexagonal,* and *tetragonal* systems, two of the principal indices of refraction are equal, e.g., $n_2 = n_3$. The Fresnel ellipsoid is then an ellipsoid of revolution around the *optic axis* of the crystal. The crystals of these groups are called *uniaxial.*

The section of a Fresnel ellipsoid perpendicular to the axis is a circle of radius n_2. Therefore, all plane waves traveling in the direction of the optic axis preserve their states of polarization. For such waves the crystal behaves like an isotropic medium.

In all other directions, however, the crystal is birefringent. Given an arbitrary direction of propagation OA different from the optic axis, we intersect the Fresnel ellipsoid with a plane through its center and perpendicular to OA (Fig. 6–18). The intersection is an ellipse of which one axis, (MN) lies in the equatorial plane of the ellipsoid, while the other (PQ) lies in the plane containing the direction of propagation and the optic axis. These two axes are parallel to the planes of vibration of the two linearly polarized waves traveling in the direction OA. If we define the plane containing the direction of propagation and the optic axis as the *principal section* of the crystal relative to a given direction of propagation, we can say that of the two linearly polarized waves traveling in a given direction, one has its plane of vibration perpendicular and the other parallel to the corresponding principal section.

The index of refraction of the wave that vibrates perpendicularly to the principal section (and therefore to the optic axis) is equal to n_2, the radius of the equatorial section of the ellipsoid. The velocity of this wave is therefore c/n_2, and it has the same value for all directions of propagation. For this reason the wave vibrating in a direction perpendicular to the optic axis is called the *ordinary wave.*

The index of refraction of the

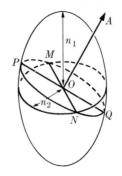

FIG. 6–18. The Fresnel ellipsoid for a positive uniaxial crystal.

wave that vibrates in the plane of the principal section is numerically equal to the semiaxis $\overline{OP}$ of the ellipse. This index of refraction is different for different directions of propagation; its value is always intermediate between n_1 and n_2. Thus, the wave vibrating in the plane of the principal section has a velocity that depends on the direction of propagation; for this reason it is called the *extraordinary wave.* *

When $n_2 < n_1$, the Fresnel ellipsoid is prolate. In this case the velocity of propagation of the extraordinary wave is less than that of the ordinary wave, and the crystal is called *positive*. When $n_2 > n_1$, the Fresnel ellipsoid is oblate, and the velocity of the extraordinary wave is greater than that of the ordinary wave. The crystal is then called *negative*.

For crystals belonging to the *orthorhombic, monoclinic,* and *triclinic* systems, the three axes of the Fresnel ellipsoid have different lengths. According to a well-known theorem of geometry, two planes pass through the center of such an ellipsoid, whose intersections with the ellipsoid are circles. These two planes contain the axis of intermediate length and are symmetrically oriented with respect to the other two axes. They are called the *circular sections* of the ellipsoid. Thus, in a crystal of the type now under consideration, instead of one, there are two directions in which all plane waves travel with the same velocity and without change in their states of polarization. These directions are perpendicular to the two circular sections of the Fresnel ellipsoid, and they are called the *principal optic axes* of the crystal. The crystal itself is called *biaxial*.

6–11 Wave surfaces in birefringent media. When diffraction phenomena are negligible, the propagation of light in birefringent media may be studied by means of the same Huygens' principle that, as we have seen in Chapter 1, forms the basis of geometrical optics in isotropic media.

To apply Huygens' principle, it is necessary to first determine the shape of the wave front corresponding to a point source in a homogeneous birefringent medium. The wave front, by definition, is the surface whose points are simultaneously reached by a light wave emitted at a given instant from the point source. In an isotropic medium, the velocity of propagation is the same in all directions and the wave front is spherical, as we well know. In an anisotropic medium, however, the wave front has a more complex shape because the velocity of propagation is different in different directions. Moreover, it will be represented by a double surface because, as we have seen, for each direction there are two possible velocities of propagation, corresponding to two waves with mutually perpendicular planes of vibration.

---

*Note that for the ordinary wave the optical vector is perpendicular to the direction of propagation. This is *not* so for the extraordinary wave (see Section 8–13).

To determine the wave front, consider one of the two linearly polarized waves corresponding to a given direction of propagation (Fig. 6–19). Let Σ be the position of the wave front at the time t; Σ_1 the position of the wave front at the time $t + \tau$. Huygens' principle states that Σ_1 is the envelope, at the time $t + \tau$, of the wavelets emitted from the various points of the surface Σ at the time t. If O is an arbitrary point of

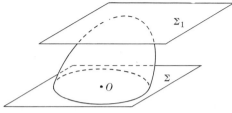

Fig. 6–19. Propagation of a wave front in a crystal (the construction shown in the figure refers to the extraordinary wave in a uniaxial crystal).

Σ, we thus conclude that Σ_1 is tangent to the wave front that develops from the point O during the time interval τ. It follows that this wave front may be determined by the following procedure. Imagine an infinite number of plane, unpolarized waves crossing at O in all directions at the time t. Each wave splits into two linearly polarized waves; with the help of the Fresnel ellipsoid, we determine the position of the various waves at the time $t + \tau$. The envelope of all these plane waves is a double surface representing the desired wave front.

Let us now consider the specific case of uniaxial crystals. Of the two linearly polarized waves corresponding to a given direction of propagation, the ordinary wave has a velocity independent of direction. This velocity is equal to c/n_2, according to the notation used in the preceding section. At the time $t + \tau$, the envelope of all the ordinary plane waves crossing at O at the time t is therefore a sphere of radius $c\tau/n_2$. The extraordinary wave, however, travels with different velocities in different directions. If, for example, the crystal is positive, the velocity of propagation of the extraordinary wave is greatest in the direction of the optic axis and smallest in the directions perpendicular to the optic axis. The maximum and minimum velocities are c/n_2 and c/n_1, respectively, and the maximum velocity is identical with the velocity of the ordinary wave. If, on the other hand, the crystal is negative, the velocity of propagation is a minimum in the direction of the optic axis and a maximum in the directions perpendicular to the optic axis; the velocities of the ordinary and of the extraordinary waves in the direction of the optic axis are again the same.

Since the velocity of propagation of the extraordinary wave depends only on the angle formed by the direction of propagation with the optic axis, at the time $t + \tau$ the envelope of all extraordinary plane waves is a surface of revolution around the optic axis. This surface is obviously symmetrical with respect to O. It intersects the optic axis at a distance from O equal to $c\tau/n_2$ and its equatorial section is a circle of radius $c\tau/n_1$. It can be shown that the surface in question is an ellipsoid, but we shall omit here the mathematical proof of this statement.

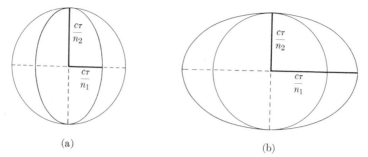

(a)   (b)

FIG. 6–20. Wave fronts in uniaxial crystals: (a) positive crystal; (b) negative crystal.

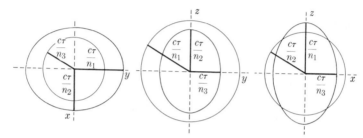

FIG. 6–21. Biaxial crystal. Intersections of the wave front with the coordinate planes.

To summarize, *the wave front developing from a point source in a uniaxial crystal consists of a sphere and of an ellipsoid of revolution around the optic axis. These two surfaces are tangent to each other at the points of intersection with the optic axis.*

If the crystal is positive, the ellipsoid is prolate and lies inside the sphere (Fig. 6–20a). If the crystal is negative, the ellipsoid is oblate and encloses the sphere (Fig. 6–20b).

In biaxial crystals, the shape of the wave front is more complex. If the

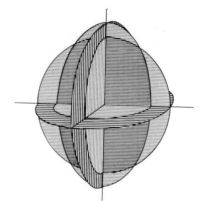

FIG. 6–22. Wave front in a biaxial crystal.

three characteristic directions are parallel to the x-, y-, and z-axes, respectively, of a cartesian frame of reference, the intersection of the wave front with each of the three coordinate planes consists of a circle and an ellipse. This is illustrated in Figs. 6–21 and 6–22. Note that, in this case, the wave front does not consist of two separate surfaces, but of a unique continuous surface folding upon itself and intersecting in a complicated manner.

6–12 Waves and rays in uniaxial crystals. We are now in a position to solve any problem of geometrical optics in birefringent media. For the sake of simplicity, we shall consider in detail only the case of uniaxial crystals.

The first question concerns the trajectories of rays. Consider an ordinary or extraordinary plane wave traveling in a given direction within a uniaxial crystal. The direction of propagation *of the wave* is, by definition, perpendicular to the plane of the wave, and the velocity of propagation is the distance between the wave fronts at the times t and $t + \tau$, divided by τ.

We now place, along the path of the wave and parallel to its plane, an opaque screen with an aperture whose dimensions are large compared with the wavelength, so that diffraction phenomena are negligible. To study the propagation of the wave beyond the aperture, we apply Huygens' principle: all points of the aperture, when reached by the advancing wave front, become the centers of secondary wavelets, whose envelope at some later time forms the new wave front. The construction is shown graphically in Fig. 6–23, both for the ordinary and for the extraordinary wave, and we see that, in either case, the envelope is a portion of the plane surface parallel to the incident wave. The points of contact between this plane surface and the wavelets originating from the border of the aperture form the boundary line of the wave front. Beyond the aperture, light is propagated within a cylinder whose lateral surface is tangent to the boundary of the aperture. The axis of this cylinder, which determines the direction of the ray, is parallel to the line that connects the center of a wavelet with the point of contact between the wavelet and the plane representing the wave front.

In the case of the ordinary wave, the secondary wavelets are spherical and the direction of the ray is perpendicular to the wave front.(Fig. 6–23a). Thus the ordinary wave and the corresponding ordinary ray travel in the same direction, as do waves and rays in isotropic media.

In the case of the extraordinary wave, however, the secondary wavelets are ellipsoids, and the *direction of propagation of the ray is usually different from that of the wave* (Fig. 6–23b). The velocities of propagation for the wave and for the ray are also different. Indeed, if Σ is the wave front at the time t and Σ_1 the wave front at the time $t + \tau$, the velocity v of the wave is equal to $\overline{ON}/\tau$, where $\overline{ON}$ is the distance between Σ and Σ_1 (Fig. 6–24). The velocity of propagation of the ray, however, which we shall denote by

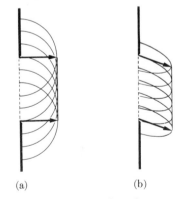

(a)   (b)

Fig. 6–23. Propagation of waves and rays in uniaxial crystals: (a) ordinary wave; (b) extraordinary wave.

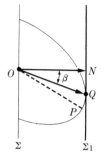

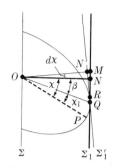

FIG. 6–24. The direction of propaga-   FIG. 6–25. Computation of β.
tion of the extraordinary wave (ON)
and of the extraordinary ray (OQ) in a
uniaxial crystal.

u, is equal to $\overline{OQ}/\tau$, where Q is the point of contact between Σ_1 and the wavelet centered at O. Therefore, if β is the angle between the directions of propagation of the wave and of the ray, the following equation holds:

$$\frac{v}{u} = \cos \beta. \tag{6-18}$$

Note that the direction of propagation of the extraordinary ray lies in the plane defined by the optic axis OP of the crystal, and by the perpendicular ON to the wave surface. This is the plane that we have defined as the principal section of the crystal, and that we have chosen as the plane of the drawing in Fig. 6–24. As we have seen, this is also the plane of vibration of the extraordinary ray.

––––––––––

To find a mathematical expression for the angle β, consider, in addition to Σ_1, another wave front, Σ_1', tangent to the ellipsoidal wavelet originating from O (Fig. 6–25). Suppose that the directions of propagation ON and ON' of these waves are coplanar with the optic axis and form a very small angle with each other. Let R be the intersection of Σ_1' with Σ_1, and M the intersection of ON' with Σ_1. Let χ and $\chi + d\chi$ be the angles formed by ON and ON' with the optic axis. From the similar triangles ONM and $RN'M$, we obtain

$$\frac{\overline{RM}}{\overline{OM}} = \frac{\overline{MN'}}{\overline{MN}}.$$

If $d\chi$ is sufficiently small, we can write, neglecting terms proportional to $(d\chi)^2$,

$$\overline{MN'} = \overline{NO} - \overline{N'O} = -dv \cdot \tau,$$

$$\overline{MN} = \overline{ON} \cdot d\chi = v \cdot \tau d\chi \,,$$

where v is the velocity of the wave propagated in the direction ON and $v + dv$ that of the wave propagated in the direction ON'. Moreover, as $d\chi$ goes to zero, R approaches Q and M approaches N, so that the ratio $\overline{RM}/\overline{OM}$ approaches $\overline{QN}/\overline{ON}$, that is, approaches $\tan \beta$ (Fig. 6–24). We thus obtain

$$\tan \beta = -\frac{1}{v}\frac{dv}{d\chi}. \tag{6–19}$$

Making use of the relation $v = c/n$, we may rewrite the above equation:

$$\tan \beta = \frac{1}{n}\frac{dn}{d\chi}. \tag{6–20}$$

Consider now the intersection of the Fresnel ellipsoid with the plane of the drawing. This is an ellipse whose axes are parallel and perpendicular to the optic axis and have lengths $2n_1$ and $2n_2$, respectively (Fig. 6–26). Let A and B be the intersections of Σ with this ellipse. $\overline{OA} = n$ represents the index of refraction of the wave Σ, and the segment OA forms an angle $\chi + \pi/2$ with the optic axis. Thus, from the equation of the ellipse in polar coordinates, we obtain

$$\frac{1}{n^2} = \frac{\sin^2 \chi}{n_1^2} + \frac{\cos^2 \chi}{n_2^2}. \tag{6–21}$$

Differentiation of the above equation yields

$$\frac{-dn}{n^3} = \left(\frac{1}{n_1^2} - \frac{1}{n_2^2}\right)\sin \chi \cos \chi \, d\chi.$$

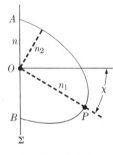

FIGURE 6–26.

From this equation, together with (6–20) and (6–21), it follows that

$$\tan \beta = \frac{(n_1^2 - n_2^2)\tan \chi}{n_1^2 + n_2^2 \tan^2 \chi}. \tag{6–22}$$

We shall make use of this relation in Section 8–13. Note that Eq. (6–22) is correct both in magnitude and in sign if we let χ_1 be the angle formed by the optic axis with the direction of the ray and if we define

$$\beta = \chi - \chi_1. \tag{6–23}$$

6–13 Refraction of waves and rays. We wish now to study the refraction of light at the surface of separation between air and a uniaxial crystal. For the sake of simplicity, we assume that the incident wave is plane and that the boundary is likewise a plane surface.

In Fig. 6–27, σ represents the intersection of the boundary surface and AB the intersection of the incident wave front with a plane perpendicular to the plane of the wave and to σ. To determine the refracted waves, we use a procedure like that used for the solution of the analogous problem in the case of isotropic media (Section 1–9). Consider the point A of the surface σ as the center of a secondary disturbance and con-

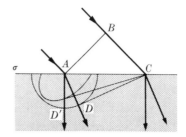

FIG. 6–27. Refraction of waves and rays in uniaxial crystals.

struct the wavelet that develops from A while the incident plane wave travels the distance BC. This wavelet consists, as we have seen, of two surfaces, one in the shape of a sphere, one in the shape of an ellipsoid. The two refracted wave fronts are the planes passing through C, perpendicular to the plane of incidence and tangent to the sphere and the ellipsoid, respectively. The wave tangent to the sphere is the ordinary wave; the wave tangent to the ellipsoid is the extraordinary wave.

The directions of the ordinary and extraordinary rays are those of the straight lines from A to the points of contact of the corresponding plane refracted wave fronts with the two surfaces of the wavelet. Note that while the point of contact with the spherical surface lies in the plane of incidence, the point of contact with the ellipsoid usually lies outside of this plane. Thus to a parallel beam of natural light incident upon the plane surface of the crystal, there correspond two refracted, linearly polarized beams of light traveling in different directions within the crystal. If the crystal is in the form of a plate with parallel surfaces, the two beams will emerge from the

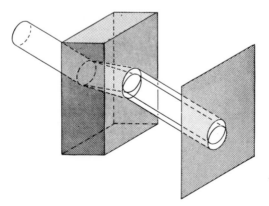

FIG. 6–28. Double refraction.

crystal in a direction parallel to that of the incident beam (see Fig. 6–28). If, moreover, the thickness of the plate is sufficiently great and the width of the incident beam sufficiently small, the two emergent beams will be completely separate. Thus the crystal plate will split the incident beam of natural light into two linearly polarized beams. This peculiar property gave rise to the term "birefringent," which we have used to describe an optically anisotropic substance. It explains the double image that we see when looking at an object through certain crystals.

It is easy to see that the ordinary ray follows Snell's law of refraction. However, the extraordinary ray does not. Indeed, the extraordinary ray remains in the plane of incidence only when the optic axis is parallel or perpendicular to this plane. Figures 6–29 and 6–30 illustrate these two cases. When the optic axis is perpendicular to the plane of incidence, the intersection of the secondary wavelet with the plane of incidence consists of two circles whose radii are proportional to c/n_2 and c/n_1, respectively. The first corresponds to the ordinary and the second to the extraordinary portion of the wavelet. In this case, both the ordinary and the extraordinary rays follow Snell's law, and if we call φ the angle of incidence and φ_2', φ_1' the angles of refraction of the ordinary and extraordinary rays, respectively, we obtain from the figure:

$$\overline{BC} = \overline{AC} \sin \varphi, \qquad \overline{AD} = \overline{AC} \sin \varphi_1', \qquad \overline{AD'} = \overline{AC} \sin \varphi_2',$$

from which it follows that

$$\frac{\sin \varphi}{\sin \varphi_1'} = \frac{\overline{BC}}{\overline{AD}} = n_1, \qquad \frac{\sin \varphi}{\sin \varphi_2'} = \frac{\overline{BC}}{\overline{AD'}} = n_2.$$

Let us also consider the special case where the incident wave front is parallel to the surface σ of the crystal. The various points of σ are then reached simultaneously by the disturbance, and the secondary wavelets

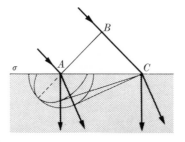

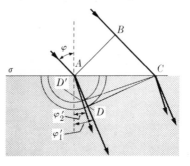

FIG. 6–29. Optic axis in the plane of incidence.

FIG. 6–30. Optic axis perpendicular to the plane of incidence.

originating from them have all the same dimensions at a given instant. Thus the common envelopes of the secondary wavelets are two plane surfaces parallel to the incident wave, representing the ordinary and extraordinary refracted waves. This is shown in Fig. 6–31, where the plane of the drawing contains the optic axis of the crystal and is perpendicular to the incident wave

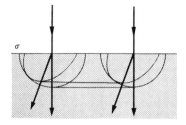

FIG. 6–31. Plane wave incident perpendicularly on a uniaxial crystal.

front. We immediately see that the ordinary ray continues in the direction of the incident ray; however, the extraordinary ray, in general, undergoes a deflection but remains in the plane of the drawing. If, in particular, the optic axis is parallel to the boundary surface, the extraordinary ray is undeflected but travels with a velocity different from that of the ordinary ray. If, lastly, the optic axis is perpendicular to the boundary surface, there is no reason to distinguish between ordinary and extraordinary rays because rays with arbitrary polarization travel through the crystal with equal velocities and without change of direction.

The propagation of waves and rays in biaxial crystals will not be discussed here in any detail. We wish only to remark that in these crystals neither of the two waves or rays, in general, follows the laws of ordinary geometrical optics. Therefore, both waves and both rays are *extraordinary*. As already pointed out in Section 6–9, a plane wave traveling in the direction of one of the two optic axes does not split into two waves. Even in this case, however, the crystal differs in its behavior from an optically isotropic substance because to the single plane wave traveling in the direction of an optic axis there corresponds an infinite number of rays, forming a cone. The discussion of this and other interesting and curious phenomena of crystal optics lies beyond the scope of the present volume.

6–14 The Nicol prism. The phenomenon of double refraction can be used for the production of linearly polarized light. Indeed, as pointed out in the preceding section, a birefringent plate of sufficiently great thickness will split a sufficiently narrow beam of natural light into two separate, linearly polarized beams.

However, to obtain wide beams of polarized light with crystals of reasonable thickness, it is necessary to resort to special devices. One of the best-known is the Nicol prism, which is made of Iceland spar, or calcite ($CaCo_3$). Iceland spar is a uniaxial crystal whose natural form is that of a rhombohedron, with the optic axis parallel to the axis of threefold symmetry. The lateral faces of a Nicol prism are natural cleavage surfaces, while the end

faces ($ADBC$ and $A'D'B'C'$ in Fig.
6–32) are cut artificially, parallel to
each other and in such a way that
the angles ABA' and $A'B'A$ are
equal to 68° (these angles would be
equal to 71° in the natural crystal).
The crystal is then cut along a plane
passing through A and A', and perpendicular to the short diagonal of
the end faces. The dimensions of the
prism are so chosen that this plane is
perpendicular to the plane that contains the optic axis of the crystal and
the normal to the end faces. The lat-

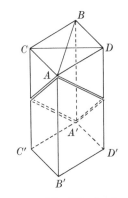

FIG. 6–32. The Nicol prism.

ter plane contains also the short diagonal of the end faces (AB in Fig. 6–32).
The two halves of the crystal are then cemented together with a thin layer
of Canada balsam.

A ray of natural light entering the prism through one of the end faces
splits into an ordinary and an extraordinary ray. The index of refraction of
the Canada balsam is greater than that of the extraordinary ray, but smaller
than that of the ordinary ray. Thus the extraordinary ray passes through
the prism, but the ordinary ray strikes the thin layer of Canada balsam at
such an angle that it is totally reflected, and consequently only the extraordinary ray emerges from the prism (Fig. 6–33). As we have seen, the
plane of vibration of the extraordinary ray is coincident with the principal
section of the crystal, and therefore contains the short diagonal of the end
faces.

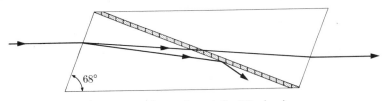

FIG. 6–33. Operation of the Nicol prism.

6–15 Rotation of the plane of vibration. Consider now the experimental
arrangements shown in Fig. 6–34. A parallel monochromatic beam of rays
passes through a polariscope formed by a polarizer P and an analyzer A,
and the analyzer is rotated until extinction is obtained. When a tube,
closed at its ends by plane parallel glass plates and containing a solution of
sugar in water, is placed between the polarizer and the analyzer, light reappears, indicating that the beam striking the analyzer is no longer linearly

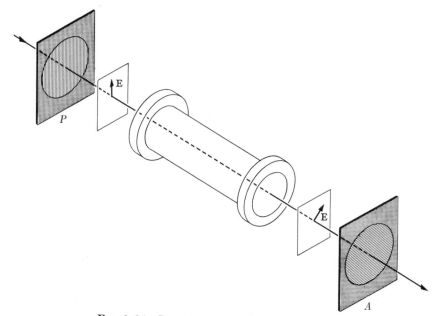

FIG. 6–34. Rotation of the plane of vibration.

polarized with the plane of vibration perpendicular to the transmission axis of the analyzer. However, if we now rotate the analyzer, we shall find a position where the intensity of the transmitted light goes to zero. Therefore, the light emerging from the sugar solution is still linearly polarized, but its plane of vibration has rotated through a certain angle. For a solution of given concentration, we find that the angle of rotation is proportional to the length of the tube. We thus conclude that the plane of vibration rotates progressively as the light beam travels through the solution.

Substances that exhibit the property described above are called *optically active*. They divide themselves into *dextrorotatory* and *levorotatory* substances, depending on whether the rotation of the plane of vibration occurs clockwise or counterclockwise with respect to an observer looking toward the oncoming light beam.

Solutions of many organic compounds are optically active. The activity, as measured by the angle of rotation per unit length, is, in general, proportional to the concentration. Thus the concentration of a solution of an optically active substance can be determined by measuring the rotation of the plane of polarization over a standard length of solution.

The optical activity of solutions depends on the spatial arrangement of atoms in the molecules of the dissolved substance; the shape of an optically active molecule differs from that of its specular image in the same way that a right-handed screw differs from a left-handed screw. This particular symmetry property is known as *enantiomorphism*. Generally, both enantio-morphic states of a given molecule exist, even though a natural organic compound may occur in only one of these states. Molecules with opposite enantiomorphic states exhibit optical activity of opposite sign. Therefore, a solution containing equal numbers of right-handed and left-handed molecules is optically inactive.

Some natural crystals are also optically active. In this case, the optical activity is connected with enantiomorphism in the crystal structure, which manifests itself also in the visible shape of the crystal. An important example is quartz, a uniaxial crystal for which the activity is a maximum when the light travels in the direction of the optic axis. In crystals, of course, the observation of the optical activity is usually complicated by the presence of birefringence.

The optical activity of a given substance depends on the wavelength and, in general, decreases as the wavelength increases. Thus, if a linearly polarized beam of white light traverses an optically active substance, rays of different wavelengths in the emergent beam will have different planes of vibration. Under these conditions, the analyzer cannot extinguish all wavelengths simultaneously. In general, the light passing through the analyzer will appear colored, and the color will change as the analyzer rotates.

Optical activity can be interpreted in a simple manner by assuming that in optically active substances *circularly polarized plane waves having opposite senses of rotation travel with different velocities.* As pointed out in Section 6–2, two parallel, circularly polarized waves of equal amplitude and equal frequency, but of opposite sense of rotation, combine into a linearly polarized wave. Indeed, any linearly polarized wave may be regarded as the superposition of a right-handed and a left-handed circular wave.

Consider a linearly polarized wave incident at $x = 0$ upon an optically active substance. Let ψ_r and ψ_l, at a given instant, be the angles formed by the optical vectors of the right-handed and of the left-handed circular components (OR and OL in Fig. 6–35) with the optical vector of the resultant incident linearly polarized wave OP. At the point of entrance into the optically active substance (Fig. 6–35a), ψ_r and ψ_l are given by

$$\psi_r = \omega t, \qquad \psi_l = -\omega t,$$

where we consider a rotation in the clockwise direction as positive and a rotation in the counterclockwise direction as negative.

Let n_r and n_l be the indices of refraction of the right-handed and left-handed components, respectively. The corresponding velocities of propagation are c/n_r and c/n_l, and the times necessary to travel a distance x in the optically active substance are $n_r x/c$ for the right-handed component and $n_l x/c$ for the left-handed component.

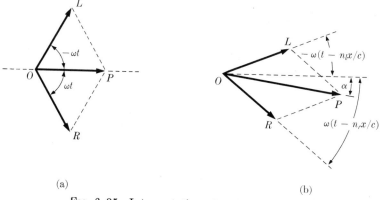

(a)

(b)

Fig. 6–35. Interpretation of optical activity.

Thus, at the time t and at the distance x from the point of entrance into the optically active medium, the angles ψ_r and ψ_l (which determine the positions of the optical vectors of the two circularly polarized waves) are given by

$$\psi_r(x,\,t) = \omega\left(t - \frac{n_r x}{c}\right), \qquad \psi_l(x,\,t) = -\omega\left(t - \frac{n_l x}{c}\right),$$

(see Fig. 6–35b).

Two vectors of equal length, forming angles ψ_r and ψ_l with a fixed direction, have a resultant that forms an angle $(\psi_r + \psi_l)/2$ with the same direction. Therefore the angle α formed by the optical vector of the resultant wave with the direction OP is given by

$$\alpha = \frac{\psi_r + \psi_l}{2} = \frac{\omega(n_l - n_r)x}{2c}$$

or

$$\alpha = \pi(n_l - n_r)\frac{x}{\lambda_0}, \qquad (6\text{–}24)$$

where λ_0 is the wavelength in vacuum. This angle is independent of t, which means that at each point of the active medium the two circularly polarized waves combine into a linearly polarized wave. However, α is proportional to x, indicating that the plane of vibration of this wave rotates gradually as the wave travels through the active medium. If $n_l > n_r$, α is positive, i.e., the rotation occurs clockwise with respect to an observer looking in the direction of the light source; therefore the substance is dextrorotatory. If $n_l < n_r$, α is negative and the substance is levorotatory.

6-16 Temporary birefringence and optical activity. Normally isotropic and optically inactive substances may become temporarily birefringent or optically active under the influence of external agents.

(a) *Mechanical birefringence.* A block of glass or of transparent plastic, when subjected to uniform compression at the two opposite surfaces, acquires the properties of a *negative* uniaxial crystal, with the optic axis in the direction of the compression. Under a uniform tension, on the other hand, the material acquires the properties of a *positive* uniaxial crystal. In either case, the difference between the two principal indices of refraction depends on the magnitude of the stress. Hence, if the stress is not uniform, the birefringence varies from point to point.

This phenomenon forms the basis of a method (called photoelastic stress analysis) for the study of stresses in mechanical structures such as bridges, beams, etc. A scale model of the structure, made of transparent plastic material, is placed between crossed polarization filters. The variable birefringence due to the mechanical stresses causes light to appear with different intensities at different points of the model (Fig. 6-36). Analysis of the polarization of the transmitted light yields accurate information on the magnitude and direction of the stresses. The same method can be used for the detection of internal stresses that may occur during the cooling process in the manufacture of glass.

(b) *The Kerr electrooptic effect.* When placed in a sufficiently strong electric field, most isotropic substances acquire the optical properties of uniaxial crystals, with the axis parallel to the lines of force. Nitrobenzene and nitrotoluene are among the substances in which this effect is prominent.

Figure 6-37 shows schematically a simple experimental arrangement for the study of electrical birefringence in liquids. The liquid is placed in a glass cell which contains two plane and parallel metal plates held at different voltages (Kerr cell). A beam of monochromatic light is sent through the cell so that it passes between the plates at right angles to the electric lines of force. Before entering the cell the beam traverses a polarization filter, with the transmission axis at 45° to the direction of the electric field. After passing through the cell, the beam is found to be elliptically polarized. Analysis of the elliptical polarization by the methods described in Section 6-7 yields the values of the difference between the two principal indices of refraction.

A Kerr cell placed between two crossed polarization filters acts as an "electrooptic shutter," which transmits light only when an electric field is established between the plates. Because of its great speed, the Kerr cell has important applications. It has been successfully used, for example, in measurements of the velocity of light (see Section 5-2).

The Kerr effect is due to anisotropy of the individual molecules of the liquid. In some substances the molecules are naturally anisotropic, and the electric field merely produces a partial alignment of the molecules in the di-

FIG. 6-36. Double refraction due to mechanical stress.

rection of the field.   In other substances, the molecules are naturally isotropic and become anisotropic under the influence of the electric field.

(c) *The Cotton-Mouton magnetooptic effect.* Some liquids become birefringent when placed in a magnetic field.   Nitrobenzene and carbon disulfide
are among these.   The effect is due to an orientation of the molecules in the
magnetic field.

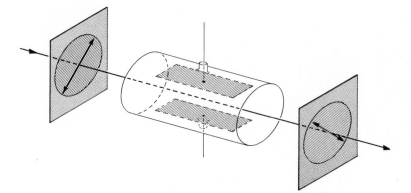

FIG. 6–37. A Kerr cell between crossed polarization filters.

(d) *The Faraday effect.* Glass and other transparent substances become optically active when placed in a magnetic field. The plane of polarization of a light wave whose direction of propagation is parallel to the field rotates clockwise or counterclockwise depending on whether the wave travels in the direction of the magnetic field or in the opposite direction. The theory of this effect will be discussed in Section 8–15.

PROBLEMS

In all the following problems it will be understood that the light wave travels in the direction of the positive x-axis of a right-handed frame of reference. If the medium is anisotropic, the y- and z-axes will be parallel to the planes of vibration of the two linearly polarized waves whose state of polarization remains unchanged during propagation, and n_y, n_z will represent the corresponding indices of refraction. Numerical data needed for the solution of the problems will be found in Tables A-4 and A-5 of the Appendix.

6–1. Describe the state of polarization of the waves represented by the following equations:

(a) $E_y = A \cos \omega \left(t - \dfrac{x}{v} \right),$

$E_z = A \sin \omega \left(t - \dfrac{x}{v} \right);$

(b) $E_y = A \cos \omega \left(t - \dfrac{x}{v} \right),$

$E_z = -A \cos \omega \left(t - \dfrac{x}{v} \right);$

(c) $E_y = A \cos \omega \left(t - \dfrac{x}{v} \right),$

$E_z = A \cos \left[\omega \left(t - \dfrac{x}{v} \right) - \dfrac{3}{4} \pi \right];$

(d) $E_y = A \cos \omega \left(t - \dfrac{x}{v} \right),$

$E_z = A \cos \left[\omega \left(t - \dfrac{x}{v} \right) + \dfrac{\pi}{4} \right].$

Specify the sense of rotation of the optical vector.

6–2. Two coherent, linearly polarized waves of amplitudes A and $\sqrt{2}A$ travel in the x-direction. The plane of vibration of the first wave is parallel to the y-axis, that of the second wave forms an angle of 45° with the y-axis; the second wave has a phase delay of 90° with respect to the first. Write the

equations describing the resultant wave, and discuss the state of polarization of this wave.

6–3. Write the equations describing the following waves:

(a) A linearly polarized wave whose plane of vibration lies at 45° to the y-axis. (b) A linearly polarized wave whose plane of vibration lies at 120° to the y-axis. (c) A wave with right-handed circular polarization. (d) A wave with right-handed elliptical polarization and with the major axis in the y-direction, this axis being twice the minor axis.

6–4. Consider the elliptically polarized wave described by

$E_y = A_y \cos \omega t,$

$E_z = A_z \cos(\omega t + \varphi).$

Prove that the angles χ formed by the two axes of the ellipse with the y- and z-axes satisfy

$$\tan 2\chi = \dfrac{2 \cos \varphi}{\left(\dfrac{A_y}{A_z} - \dfrac{A_z}{A_y} \right)}.$$

6–5. Two coherent, circularly polarized waves of amplitudes A and $2A$ travel in the x-direction. Describe the resultant wave, (a) assuming that both circularly polarized waves are right-handed, (b) assuming that the wave of amplitude A is right-handed, and that of amplitude $2A$ is left-handed.

307

6-6. Consider the wave represented by

$$E_y = A \cos 2\pi \left(\frac{t}{T} - \frac{x}{\lambda} \right),$$

$$E_z = A \cos 2\pi \left(\frac{t}{T} - \frac{x}{\lambda} + \frac{1}{8} \right).$$

Compute the magnitude of the optical vector and the angle formed by the optical vector with the y-axis at the times $t = 0$ and $t = T/4$ and at the points $x = 0$, $x = \lambda/4$, $x = \lambda/2$, $x = 3\lambda/4$, $x = \lambda$.

6-7. The wave described in Problem 6-6 is incident perpendicularly upon a sheet polarizer, and the sheet polarizer is rotated in its plane until the transmitted intensity is a maximum. (a) In which direction does the transmission axis of the polarizer lie? (b) Compute the ratio of the transmitted intensities observed with the sheet polarizer so oriented, and with the transmission axis of the sheet polarizer in the y-direction.

6-8. Compute the polarization angles for crown glass ($n = 1.520$), for flint glass ($n = 1.650$), and for water ($n = 1.33$).

6-9. Linearly polarized monochromatic light is incident perpendicularly upon a quarter-wave plate, the plane of vibration being at an angle ψ to the y-axis. Assume $n_y < n_z$. Determine the state of polarization of the transmitted light and the direction of rotation of the optical vector for the following values of ψ: (a) $\psi = \pi/4$, (b) $\psi = \pi/2$, (c) $\psi = 3\pi/4$.

6-10. A beam of monochromatic light is incident perpendicularly upon a polarization filter. It is found that when the polarization filter is rotated in its plane, the transmitted intensity changes periodically, going through two maxima and two minima for a rotation of 360°.

How can we determine whether the light is partially polarized or elliptically polarized?

6-11. A quarter-wave plate and a polarization filter are placed along the path of a beam of monochromatic light. Before entering the quarter-wave plate, the light has right-handed elliptical polarization; the ratio of major to minor axes is 4:1. No light is transmitted through the polarization filter. Show in a diagram the orientations of the axes of the plate and of the transmission axis of the filter with respect to the axes of the ellipse. Compute the angle formed by the transmission axis of the filter with the y-axis.

6-12. Mica cleaves naturally in planes perpendicular to the x-axis. The indices of refraction n_2 and n_3 of the two waves traveling in the direction of this axis are listed in Table A-4. Determine the thickness of a mica quarter-wave plate obtained by cleavage, for $\lambda = 5893$ A.

6-13. A beam of white, linearly polarized light is incident perpendicularly upon a plate of quartz 0.865 mm thick cut parallel to the optic axis. The plane of vibration is at 45° to the axes of the plate. The principal indices of refraction of quartz for sodium light are listed in Table A-4. Disregard the variation of $n_1 - n_2$ with wavelength. (a) Which wavelengths between 6000 and 7000 A emerge from the plate linearly polarized? (b) Which wavelengths emerge circularly polarized? (c) Suppose that the beam emerging from the plate passes through an analyzer whose transmission axis is perpendicular to the plane of vibration of the incident light. Which wavelengths are missing in the transmitted beam?

6-14. Determine the y- and z-axes and compute the corresponding indices of refraction n_y and n_z of a plane parallel plate of calcite (see Table A–4), assuming that the faces of the plate are (a) parallel to the optic axis, (b) perpendicular to the optic axis, and (c) at an angle of 30° to the optic axis.

6–15. A point source S of yellow light is placed within a calcite crystal. Determine the shape and compute the dimensions of the ordinary and extraordinary wave fronts which develop from S in 10^{-10} sec.

6–16. Solve Problem 6–15 for the case of a quartz crystal.

6–17. A plane parallel plate is cut from a calcite crystal. The plate is 2 cm thick and the optic axis lies in the plane of the plate. A parallel beam of natural yellow light is incident upon the plate at an angle of 45°, the plane of incidence being perpendicular to the optic axis. (a) Determine the directions of propagation within the crystal of the ordinary and the extraordinary waves and rays. (b) Compute the separation and determine the state of polarization of the ordinary and extraordinary rays as they emerge from the plate.

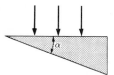

FIGURE 6–38.

6–18. A parallel beam of natural yellow light is incident perpendicularly upon a calcite prism (Fig. 6–38) whose edges are parallel to the optic axis. The refracting angle α is 20°. Determine the directions and states of polarization of the two rays emerging from the prism.

6–19. Refer to Problem 6–18 and Fig. 6–38. Compute the minimum and maximum values of the refracting angle α for which one of the two rays undergoes total reflection and the other does not. Specify the state of polarization of the ray emerging from the prism.

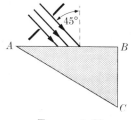

FIGURE 6–39.

6–20. ABC in Fig. 6–39 is the right cross section of a prism cut from a uniaxial crystal, whose optic axis is parallel to AB. A parallel beam of light limited by a diaphragm is incident upon the prism. The plane of incidence is parallel to the plane of the diagram. Show in a sketch how the directions of propagation of the ordinary and extraordinary waves and rays can be determined. Mark the path of the secondary light beam in the crystal, and the instantaneous positions of several wave fronts.

6–21. Refer to Problem 6–20 and Fig. 6–39. Let v be the velocity of the extraordinary wave, u the velocity of the extraordinary ray, and φ the angle of incidence *of the ray* upon the face of emergence from the prism. Compute the angle φ' at which this ray emerges from the crystal.

6–22. The indices of refraction of right-handed quartz for right-handed and left-handed circularly polarized waves traveling in the direction of the optic axis have the following values:

$\lambda = 3968$ A, $n_r = 1.55810$, $n_l = 1.55821$,

$\lambda = 7620$ A, $n_r = 1.53914$, $n_l = 1.53920$.

Compute the angles through which the planes of vibration of linearly polarized waves of wavelengths $\lambda = 3968$ A and $\lambda = 7620$ A are rotated on passing through a plate of quartz 2 mm thick, cut perpendicularly to the optic axis.

6–23. The *specific rotation* of an optically active solution is defined as the rotation produced by a 10-cm column of the liquid containing 1 gm of the active substance for every cm³ of solution. For diluted solutions, the specific rotation is nearly independent of concentration. The values of the specific rotation of sucrose solutions for different wavelengths are listed in Table A–5. Compute the difference between the indices of refraction of a 10% solution of sucrose for right-handed and left-handed circularly polarized waves for the following wavelengths:

$$\lambda = 4358 \text{ A}, \lambda = 5461 \text{ A}, \lambda = 6708 \text{ A}.$$

FIGURE 6–40.

6–24. A narrow beam of linearly polarized monochromatic light is incident upon a piece of quartz cut as shown in Fig. 6–40. The optic axis of the quartz is parallel to the incident beam and the normal to the exit face is at 37° to the axis. Determine the angular separation of the two beams emerging from the quartz.

6–25. The difference Δn between the two principal indices of refraction of a liquid placed in an electric field of intensity E is given by $\Delta n = jE^2\lambda$, where λ is the wavelength in vacuum. If E is measured in volt/cm and λ in cm, the constant j has the value $j = 4.0 \times 10^{-12}$ for carbon disulfide, and $j = 400 \times 10^{-12}$ for nitrobenzene. A Kerr cell is placed between two polarization filters with

their transmission axes at right angles to each other and at 45° to the direction of the electric field. The plates are 5 cm long and 0.7 cm apart, and are kept at a potential difference of 10,000 volts. The cell is filled first with carbon disulfide and then with nitrobenzene. Compute the fractions of the incident intensities passing through the polarization filters and the cell in the two experiments (disregard absorption and reflection losses).

6–26. *Fresnel-Arago experiment.* Consider Young's interference experiment (see Problem 3–12), whose arrangement is shown schematically in Fig. 6–41, where S is a point (or line) source of monochromatic unpolarized light, S_1 and S_2 are two small holes (or narrow slits) acting as coherent synchronous sources, and Σ is the plane on which the interference fringes are observed. Let P_0 be the position of the interference maximum of order zero, and P_1, P_{-1} the positions of the interference maxima of the first order.

(a) A polarization filter F is placed in front of the source. What change, if any, will be observed in the appearance of the interference fringes?

(b) Two additional polarization filters, F_1 and F_2, are placed in front of the openings S_1 and S_2; their transmission axes are at 90° to each other and at 45° to the transmission axis of F. What is now the intensity distribution on the plane of observation Σ? Describe the state of polarization of the light at P_0, at P_1, and at the three intermediate points P', P'', P''' which divide the segment P_0P_1 into four equal parts.

(c) A fourth polarization filter, F', is placed in front of the observation plane Σ. Its transmission axis is parallel to that of the polarization filter F. Compare the interference pattern now ob-

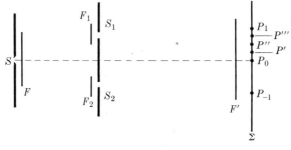

FIGURE 6-41.

served with that observed without the polarization filters F_1, F_2, and F'.

(d) The polarization filter F is rotated in its plane through 90°. Describe the corresponding change in the interference pattern observed on Σ.

(e) The polarization filter F is now removed. Will any interference fringes appear on Σ?

6-27. Refer to the experimental arrangement described in Problem 6-26.

(a) A quarter-wave plate is placed in front of each of the openings S_1 and S_2. The z-axis of one plate is parallel to the y-axis of the other, and for both plates $n_y < n_z$. A polarization filter F is placed between the source and the quarter-wave plates. Describe how the appearance of the interference fringes on Σ changes as the filter rotates through 360° in its plane.

(b) The transmission axis of the polarization filter F is at 45° to the y- and z-axes of the quarter-wave plates. How do the intensity and the state of polarization of the light vary as we move from P_0 to P_1?

(c) Without changing the orientation of F, we place a second polarization filter F' in front of the plane of observation Σ. The transmission axis of F' is parallel to that of F. Describe the interference pattern observed on Σ.

(d) How does the interference pattern change if the polarization filter F

is rotated through 90° in its plane?

(e) What happens if we remove the filter F, keeping F' and the quarter-wave plates in place?

(f) What happens if we also remove the filter F'?

6-28. Refer again to the experimental arrangement described in Problem 6-26. Two plates cut perpendicularly to the optic axis of a right-handed and a left-handed quartz crystal, respectively, are placed in front of the openings S_1 and S_2. The thickness of either plate is such as to rotate the plane of vibration of a linearly polarized wave through 45°. A polarization filter F is placed between the source and the quartz plates.

(a) Determine the intensity and the state of polarization of the light at P_0, at P_1, and at three intermediate points P', P'', P''' dividing the segment P_0P_1 into four equal parts.

(b) Describe the interference pattern observed when a second polarization filter F', with its transmission axis parallel to that of F, is placed in front of the observation screen.

(c) What happens if F' is rotated through 45°?

(d) What happens if F' is again rotated through 45°, so that its transmission axis is perpendicular to that of F?

(e) What happens if both F and F' are removed?

CHAPTER 7

ELECTROMAGNETIC THEORY OF LIGHT

7-1 The physical nature of light waves. Throughout this book we have gradually widened the scope of our study by taking into consideration new aspects of the phenomenon of light. As a consequence, our concept of light waves has gradually become increasingly definite and specific.

We started from the assumption that light waves consist of a succession of very short pulses, traveling with different velocities in different media, and capable of being reflected at the boundary surface between two media. We found that this assumption explained the rectilinear propagation of light in homogeneous isotropic media, and accounted adequately for all other phenomena of *geometrical optics*. Subsequently, the analysis of *interference* effects taught us that the optical disturbance in a monochromatic light wave is actually a sinusoidal function of time. By making use of the concept of sinusoidal waves we were also able to explain quantitatively the deviations from the laws of geometrical optics, i.e., the *diffraction* phenomena. Lastly, the phenomenon of *polarization* and the study of the propagation of light in crystals led us to the conclusion that the optical disturbance is a vector quantity and that, in isotropic media, this vector is perpendicular to the direction of propagation.

However, what we have achieved so far amounts to no more than a detailed description of the *kinematic* properties of light waves. We have not yet attempted to relate these properties to the dynamic properties of the medium that carries the light waves.

As already pointed out, the wave theory of light was suggested by mechanical analogies, and we can construct a model describing light as an elastic wave propagated by a medium (the "ether") having dynamic properties similar to those of ordinary matter. This model easily explains the phenomena of geometrical optics, interference, and diffraction, which are common features of all wave motions. However, the transverse character of light waves, which we were forced to recognize in order to explain polarization phenomena, places the mechanical model under a severe strain. If the "ether," permeating the whole universe, is a substance similar to ordinary matter, it must be regarded as an exceedingly tenuous fluid, for it offers no apparent resistance to the motion of the planets and of other celestial bodies. On the other hand, fluid substances cannot transmit transverse waves; only solid substances can do so. Moreover, ordinary solids transmit both transverse and longitudinal waves, while there appears to be no longitudinal component of light waves. An additional difficulty is the very great speed of propagation of light, which can be explained only if we make extreme assumptions about the density and the elastic properties of the "ether."

All these difficulties were solved when Maxwell suggested that light was not a mechanical but an electromagnetic phenomenon. In this chapter we shall outline the electromagnetic theory of light and show how the kinematic properties of light waves can be derived in a very direct way from the dynamic properties of the electromagnetic field.

7–2 The fundamental laws of electromagnetism. For the convenience of the reader, we summarize briefly the fundamental laws of electromagnetism:

(a) *Electric fields* are produced by electric charges and by varying magnetic fields. Correspondingly, the electric intensity **E** is determined by two laws: *Gauss' law*, stating that the flux of the electric intensity through a closed surface S is proportional to the total charge enclosed by this surface, and *Faraday's law* of electromagnetic induction, stating that the integral of the electric intensity along a closed path is proportional to the rate of change of the magnetic flux linked by this path.

The numerical factors appearing in the equations depend on the choice of the system of units; in what follows we shall use the rationalized mks system.

(1) Gauss' law, in vacuum, is expressed by

$$\epsilon_0 \int_S E_n \, dS = \int_V \rho \, dV, \qquad (7\text{–}1)$$

where $\epsilon_0 = 8.85 \times 10^{-12}$ farad/m, E_n is the component of **E** perpendicular to the element of area dS (positive if **E** points in the outward direction with respect to the closed surface S), V is the volume enclosed by the surface S, and ρ is the volume density of electric charge.

If a dielectric is present, in addition to the effect of the "free" charges, the effect of the *polarization* of the dielectric must also be considered. The polarization is described by the *polarization vector* **P**, defined as the resultant of the electric dipole moments of the individual molecules contained in the unit volume. It can be proved that the electric field produced by the molecular dipoles is equal to the field produced by a charge distributed with a density ρ_P that satisfies the following equation:

$$\int_V \rho_P \, dV = - \int_S P_n \, dS. \qquad (7\text{–}2)$$

If we now indicate by ρ the density of "free" electric charges alone, we must replace Eq. (7–1) with the following:

$$\epsilon_0 \int_V E_n \, dS = \int_V \rho \, dV + \int_V \rho_P \, dV,$$

or

$$\epsilon_0 \int_S E_n \, dS = \int_V \rho \, dV - \int_S P_n \, dS. \qquad (7\text{–}3)$$

(2) Faraday's induction law is expressed by the equation

$$\oint_s E_s \, ds = -\frac{d}{dt} \int_S B_n \, dS, \qquad (7\text{–}4)$$

where S is a surface bounded by the closed line s, B_n is the component of the magnetic induction $\mathbf{B}$ perpendicular to the element of area dS, and E_s is the component of $\mathbf{E}$ parallel to the line element ds. The positive direction of the perpendicular to the surface S and the positive sense of travel along the line s bear the same relation to each other as the direction of advance and the sense of rotation of a right-handed screw.

(3) Since there is no magnetic counterpart of the electric charge, the flux of $\mathbf{B}$ through any *closed surface* is always zero:

$$\int_S B_n \, dS = 0. \qquad (7\text{–}5)$$

From this theorem it follows that the fluxes of $\mathbf{B}$ through two different open surfaces having the same boundary line are equal. Therefore $\oint_s E_s ds$, as given by (7–4), has a definite value despite the arbitrariness in the choice of the surface S.

(b) *Magnetic fields* are produced by electric currents and by varying electric fields.

(1) Magnetic fields due to electric currents obey *Ampere's circuital law*, stating that, in vacuum, the integral of the magnetic induction vector $\mathbf{B}$ along a closed line is proportional to the total current linked by this line. Ampere's law is expressed by

$$\frac{1}{\mu_0} \oint_s B_s \, ds = \int_S j_n \, dS, \qquad (7\text{–}6)$$

where $\mu_0 = 4\pi \times 10^{-7}$ henry/m and j_n is the component perpendicular to dS of the vector $\mathbf{j}$ representing the space density of current. In this equation the convention regarding signs is the same as in Eq. (7–4).

(2) The magnetic effects of varying electric fields can be described by saying that a varying electric field is equivalent to an electric current whose density $\mathbf{j}_E$ is proportional to the rate of change of the electric field. More exactly,

$$\mathbf{j}_E = \epsilon_0 \frac{\partial \mathbf{E}}{\partial t}. \tag{7-7}$$

Thus when there are varying electric fields in addition to electric currents, Ampere's circuital law must be modified as follows:

$$\frac{1}{\mu_0} \oint_s B_s \, ds = \int_S \left(j_n + \epsilon_0 \frac{\partial E_n}{\partial t} \right) dS. \tag{7-8}$$

Note that the integral of the right side of this equation has the same value for all surfaces S with the same boundary line s. Indeed, from Gauss' theorem and from the principle of conservation of electric charges, it follows that the flux of the vector $\mathbf{j} + \epsilon_0(\partial \mathbf{E}/\partial t)$ across any closed surface is zero.

(3) If material substances are present, we must consider two other kinds of currents, in addition to the current due to the motion of free charges.

In the first place, any change in the dielectric polarization of the medium produces a current whose density $\mathbf{j}_P$ equals the rate of change of the polarization vector $\mathbf{P}$:

$$\mathbf{j}_P = \frac{\partial \mathbf{P}}{\partial t}. \tag{7-9}$$

In the second place, there are currents due to the motion of electrons along their atomic or molecular orbits, and to the rotation of the electrons around their axes (spin). These microscopic currents are responsible for the magnetic properties of matter, which are usually described by the magnetization vector $\mathbf{M}$. Except in the case of ferromagnetic substances, the magnetization is very small and has a negligible effect on the propagation of electromagnetic waves. To avoid unnecessary complications, we shall here neglect the microscopic currents giving rise to magnetization; then the current density in Eq. (7–8) consists of two terms: the current due to the motion of "free" charges alone, and the polarization current, $\mathbf{j}_P$, given by (7–9). If we now call $\mathbf{j}$ the "free" current, (7–8) becomes

$$\frac{1}{\mu_0} \oint_s B_s \, ds = \int_S \left(j_n + \frac{\partial P_n}{\partial t} + \epsilon_0 \frac{\partial E_n}{\partial t} \right) dS. \tag{7-10}$$

Equations (7–3), (7–4), (7–5), and (7–10) are the fundamental equations of the electromagnetic field (if magnetization can be neglected). They are known as *Maxwell's equations*, and are sufficient to determine the electromagnetic field completely if ρ and $\mathbf{j}$ are given and if the electric properties of the medium are known, i.e., if the relation between $\mathbf{P}$ and $\mathbf{E}$ is given.

We can express Maxwell's equations in a more convenient form by defining two auxiliary vectors, i.e., the electric displacement $\mathbf{D}$:

$$\mathbf{D} = \epsilon_0 \, \mathbf{E} + \mathbf{P}, \tag{7-11}$$

and the magnetic intensity $\mathbf{H}$:

$$\mathbf{H} = \frac{\mathbf{B}}{\mu_0}. \tag{7-12}$$

With these notations, we obtain

$$\int_S D_n \, dS = \int_V \rho \, dV, \tag{7-13}$$

$$\oint_s E_s \, ds = - \int_S \frac{\partial B_n}{\partial t} \, dS, \tag{7-14}$$

$$\int_S B_n \, dS = 0, \tag{7-15}$$

$$\oint_s H_s \, ds = \int_S \frac{\partial D_n}{\partial t} \, dS + \int_S j_n \, dS. \tag{7-16}$$

Equations (7–13) through (7–16) have general validity, and they are also valid when magnetization is taken into account. In this case, however, Eq. (7–12) must be replaced by

$$\mathbf{H} = \frac{\mathbf{B}}{\mu_0} - \mathbf{M}. \tag{7-17}$$

In isotropic substances, and for constant or slowly varying electric fields, the vectors $\mathbf{P}$ and $\mathbf{E}$ are usually parallel and proportional in magnitude to each other. The vector $\mathbf{D}$ is then proportional to the vector $\mathbf{E}$ also, and the following equation holds:

$$\mathbf{D} = \epsilon \mathbf{E}, \tag{7-18}$$

where ϵ is a scalar quantity independent of $\mathbf{E}$, called the *dielectric permittivity* of the medium. In inhomogeneous media, ϵ may vary from point to point. In vacuum, it reduces to the constant ϵ_0 defined previously. The quantities ϵ_0 and μ_0 are sometimes referred to as the electric permittivity and the magnetic permeability of vacuum. The quantity

$$\kappa = \frac{\epsilon}{\epsilon_0} \tag{7-19}$$

is called the *dielectric constant*.

(c) *Electromagnetic fields* are capable of developing heat and of performing work against mechanical or chemical forces, which means that electromagnetic fields possess energy. This energy is distributed in space with a density u given by

$$u = \tfrac{1}{2}(\mathbf{E} \cdot \mathbf{D} + \mathbf{H} \cdot \mathbf{B}), \tag{7-20}$$

where the dots indicate scalar products.

A point charge e moving with velocity $\mathbf{w}$ in an electromagnetic field experiences a force

$$\mathbf{F} = e(\mathbf{E} + \mathbf{w} \times \mathbf{B}), \tag{7-21}$$

where $\mathbf{E}$ and $\mathbf{B}$ are the electric intensity and the magnetic induction at the point occupied by the charge, and the cross indicates a vector product. Note that in the computation of $\mathbf{E}$ and $\mathbf{B}$ the electromagnetic effects of the charge e are disregarded.

7-3 Plane electromagnetic waves in isotropic and homogeneous dielectrics. Consider the electromagnetic field in a region of space occupied by an *isotropic* and *homogeneous* dielectric. We assume that the density of charge, ρ, and the density of electric current, $\mathbf{j}$, are everywhere zero. Equations (7-13) through (7-16) can then be rewritten as follows:

$$\int_S E_n \, dS = 0, \tag{7-22}$$

$$\oint_s E_s \, ds = -\mu_0 \int_S \frac{\partial H_n}{\partial t} \, dS, \tag{7-23}$$

$$\int_S H_n \, dS = 0, \tag{7-24}$$

$$\oint_s H_s \, ds = \epsilon \int_S \frac{\partial E_n}{\partial t} \, dS. \tag{7-25}$$

In this case, Maxwell's equations become symmetrical with respect to $\mathbf{E}$ and $\mathbf{H}$ [except for a difference of sign in (7-23) and (7-25)].

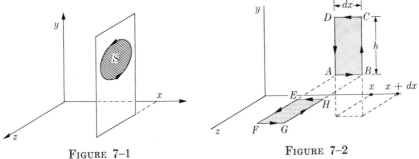

FIGURE 7–1   FIGURE 7–2

We choose an arbitrary system of rectangular cartesian coordinates, x, y, z, and we propose to prove that there exists a solution of the above equations such that *the electric intensity* **E** *and the magnetic intensity* **H** *depend only on the time t and on the coordinate x.*

(1) Consider first an area S parallel to the yz-plane (Fig. 7–1). Since, according to our assumption, **E** is constant in this plane, the integral of **E** along the boundary of S vanishes (if the magnitude and the direction of a force are the same at all points, the work of the force along any closed path is zero). Therefore, Eq. (7–23) yields

$$\int_S \frac{\partial H_x}{\partial t}\, dS = 0.$$

Since, moreover, H_x has the same value at all points of the surface S, we conclude that

$$\frac{\partial H_x}{\partial t} = 0.$$

In a similar manner, we can prove [from Eq. 7–25] that

$$\frac{\partial E_x}{\partial t} = 0.$$

(2) We next apply Faraday's induction law, as expressed by Eq. (7–23), to a rectangle $ABCD$ (Fig. 7–2) formed by two infinitesimal segments parallel to the x-axis (AB, CD) and by two segments of length h parallel to the y-axis (BC and DA). Let x be the x-coordinate of the segment DA, and $x + dx$ that of the segment BC. According to our assumption, **E** has a constant value **E**(x) along the segment DA, and a different constant value **E**$(x + dx)$ along the segment BC.

The left term of (7–23), representing the integral of **E** along the line $ABCD$, reduces to the sum of four terms, corresponding to the sides of the rectangle $ABCD$:

Side BC: $E_y(x + dx) \cdot h$ (in going from B to C, we travel a distance h in the direction of the positive y-axis; E_y has the constant value $E_y(x + dx)$ on the segment BC).

Side CD: $-\overline{E}_x \cdot dx$ ($\overline{E}_x$ is some average value of E_x over the infinitesimal segment CD; the minus sign comes from the fact that in going from B to C we travel in the direction of the negative x-axis).

Side DA: $-E_y(x) \cdot h$.

Side AB: $\overline{E}_x \cdot dx$ ($\overline{E}_x$ has the same value as in the term corresponding to the side CD, because E_x depends only on x).

The two terms corresponding to CD and AB cancel and we thus obtain

$$\oint_s E_s \, ds = h[E_y(x + dx) - E_y(x)],$$

or

$$\oint_s E_s \, ds = \frac{\partial E_y}{\partial x} h \, dx.$$

The integral on the right side of (7–23), representing the flux of the vector $d\mathbf{H}/dt$ through the surface $ABCD$, is given by

$$\int_S \frac{\partial H_n}{\partial t} \, dS = \frac{\partial H_z}{\partial t} h \, dx.$$

Therefore (7–23) yields

$$\frac{\partial E_y}{\partial x} = -\mu_0 \frac{\partial H_z}{\partial t}.$$

(3) In a similar way, considering a rectangle $EFGH$ with sides parallel to the z- and x-axes (Fig. 7–2), we obtain

$$\frac{\partial E_z}{\partial x} = \mu_0 \frac{\partial H_y}{\partial t}.$$

(4) From Eq. (7–25) we can derive two equations similar to those just obtained, in which ϵ replaces $-\mu_0$ and the vectors $\mathbf{E}$ and $\mathbf{H}$ are interchanged.

(5) We can obtain two additional equations from (7–22) and (7–24). For this purpose, we choose a closed surface S in the shape of a parallelepiped $ABCDA'B'C'D'$, with sides parallel to the coordinate axes (Fig. 7–3). Let x and $x + dx$ be the

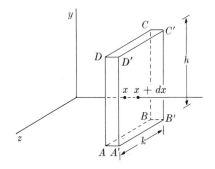

FIGURE 7–3

x-coordinates of the two planes ($ABCD$ and $A'B'C'D'$) perpendicular to the x-axis (dx is an infinitesimal length). Let h and k be the lengths of the sides parallel to the y- and z-axes, respectively. The flux of $\mathbf{E}$ through $A'B'C'D'$ is $E_x(x + dx)hk$. The flux of $\mathbf{E}$ through $ABCE$ is $-E_x(x)hk$. Thus the total outgoing flux through the two opposite surfaces of the parallelepiped perpendicular to the x-axis is

$$[E_x(x + dx) - E_x(x)]hk = \frac{\partial E_x}{\partial x} hk \, dx.$$

Since $\mathbf{E}$ depends only on x, the fluxes of $\mathbf{E}$ through the two surfaces $AA'B'B$ and $DD'C'C$ (which are perpendicular to the y-axis) are equal in magnitude and opposite in sign, and therefore cancel. The same is true of the fluxes through the surfaces $BCC'B'$ and $ADD'A'$. Therefore, (7–22) yields the following result:

$$\frac{\partial E_x}{\partial x} = 0.$$

Similarly, Eq. (7–24) yields

$$\frac{\partial H_x}{\partial x} = 0.$$

As a summary of the above results, we can write the following system of differential equations:

$$\text{(a)} \quad \frac{\partial H_x}{\partial x} = 0, \qquad \text{(b)} \quad \frac{\partial E_x}{\partial x} = 0,$$

$$\text{(c)} \quad \frac{\partial H_x}{\partial t} = 0, \qquad \text{(d)} \quad \frac{\partial E_x}{\partial t} = 0,$$

$$\text{(e)} \quad \mu_0 \frac{\partial H_y}{\partial t} = \frac{\partial E_z}{\partial x}, \qquad \text{(f)} \quad \epsilon \frac{\partial E_y}{\partial t} = -\frac{\partial H_z}{\partial x},$$

$$\text{(g)} \quad \mu_0 \frac{\partial H_z}{\partial t} = -\frac{\partial E_y}{\partial x}, \qquad \text{(h)} \quad \epsilon \frac{\partial E_z}{\partial t} = \frac{\partial H_y}{\partial x}.$$

$$(7\text{–}26)$$

The above equations have been obtained under the assumption that $\mathbf{E}$ and $\mathbf{H}$ are independent of y and z. With essentially similar methods, we can handle the more general case in which $\mathbf{E}$ and $\mathbf{H}$ depend on all three space coordinates, x, y, and z. We quote the result, omitting the proof:

(a) $\dfrac{\partial H_x}{\partial x} + \dfrac{\partial H_y}{\partial y} + \dfrac{\partial H_z}{\partial z} = 0,$

(b) $\dfrac{\partial E_x}{\partial x} + \dfrac{\partial E_y}{\partial y} + \dfrac{\partial E_z}{\partial z} = 0,$

(c) $-\mu_0 \dfrac{\partial H_x}{\partial t} = \dfrac{\partial E_z}{\partial y} - \dfrac{\partial E_y}{\partial z},$

(d) $\epsilon \dfrac{\partial E_x}{\partial t} = \dfrac{\partial H_z}{\partial y} - \dfrac{\partial H_y}{\partial z},$

(e) $-\mu_0 \dfrac{\partial H_y}{\partial t} = \dfrac{\partial E_x}{\partial z} - \dfrac{\partial E_z}{\partial x},$

(f) $\epsilon \dfrac{\partial E_y}{\partial t} = \dfrac{\partial H_x}{\partial z} - \dfrac{\partial H_z}{\partial x},$

(g) $-\mu_0 \dfrac{\partial H_z}{\partial t} = \dfrac{\partial E_y}{\partial x} - \dfrac{\partial E_x}{\partial y},$

(h) $\epsilon \dfrac{\partial E_z}{\partial t} = \dfrac{\partial H_y}{\partial x} - \dfrac{\partial H_x}{\partial y}.$

$$(7\text{--}27)$$

For the benefit of the reader experienced in vector calculus, we recall that Eqs. (7–27) may be written more compactly as follows:

$$\text{div } \mathbf{H} = 0, \qquad \text{div } \mathbf{E} = 0,$$

$$-\mu_0 \frac{\partial \mathbf{H}}{\partial t} = \text{curl } \mathbf{E}, \qquad \epsilon \frac{\partial \mathbf{E}}{\partial t} = \text{curl } \mathbf{H}.$$

$$(7\text{--}28)$$

Returning to the special case in which the field vectors depend only on x, we note that Eqs. (7–26a, b, c, d) indicate that the x-components of $\mathbf{E}$ and $\mathbf{H}$ are constant both in time and in space. Since we are not interested here in static electric or magnetic fields, we can assume that

$$E_x = 0, \qquad H_x = 0. \tag{7–29}$$

Of the remaining four equations, two contain E_y and H_z and two contain E_z and H_y. Thus, E_y and H_z are independent of E_z and H_y, and we can consider the behavior of the field components E_y and H_z separately from that of the field components E_z and H_y.

The two equations containing E_y and H_z are

$$\mu_0 \frac{\partial H_z}{\partial t} = -\frac{\partial E_y}{\partial x}, \qquad \epsilon \frac{\partial E_y}{\partial t} = -\frac{\partial H_z}{\partial x}. \tag{7–30}$$

To understand the physical significance of these equations, consider two planes, perpendicular to the x-axis and at an infinitesimal distance dx from each other. The first of equations (7–30) means that the time rate of change of H_z in the space between the two planes depends on the difference between the values of E_y at these planes. Similarly, the second of equations (7–30) means that the time rate of change of E_y in the space between the two planes depends on the difference between the values of H_z at these planes. Thus one can say that the electric field existing in the immediate neighborhood of a given point is the direct cause of the changes that occur in the intensity of the magnetic field at this point. Similarly, the magnetic field existing in the immediate neighborhood of a given point is the cause of the changes in the electric intensity. This means that the electromagnetic disturbance is propagated from point to point, each point of the medium being influenced only by conditions existing in its immediate vicinity.

We are faced here with a situation very similar to that encountered in the case of mechanical waves. For example, in a sound wave the pressure difference between the two boundaries of a layer of air causes the velocity of this layer to change, and the pressure in the layer changes because the velocities of the two boundary surfaces are different (see Sections 1–3, 1–5). This similarity suggests a close, though purely formal, relationship between the propagation of electromagnetic disturbances and the propagation of mechanical waves.

To obtain a mathematical expression for the dependence of E_y and H_z on x and t, we differentiate the first of Eqs. (7–30) with respect to x and the second with respect to t:

$$\mu_0 \frac{\partial^2 H_z}{\partial t \partial x} = -\frac{\partial^2 E_y}{\partial x^2}, \qquad \epsilon \frac{\partial^2 E_y}{\partial t^2} = -\frac{\partial^2 H_z}{\partial x \partial t}.$$

By eliminating $\partial^2 H_z/\partial t \partial x = \partial^2 H_z/\partial x \partial t$ between the two equations above, we obtain

$$\frac{\partial^2 E_y}{\partial x^2} = \epsilon \mu_0 \frac{\partial^2 E_y}{\partial t^2}. \tag{7–31}$$

This is the well-known differential equation of wave motion in one dimension [see Appendix 2, Eq. (A2–5)]. We can easily verify that any function of the form

$$E_y(x, t) = f_1 \left(t - \frac{x}{v} \right) \tag{7–32}$$

satisfies this equation, provided the constant v is suitably chosen. Indeed, by successive differentiations, we obtain

$$\frac{\partial E_y}{\partial t} = \dot{f}_1, \qquad \frac{\partial E_y}{\partial x} = -\frac{1}{v} \dot{f}_1,$$

$$\frac{\partial^2 E_y}{\partial t^2} = \ddot{f}_1, \qquad \frac{\partial^2 E_y}{\partial x^2} = \frac{1}{v^2} \ddot{f}_1, \tag{7–33}$$

where we have used the symbols $\dot{f}_1$ and $\ddot{f}_1$ to indicate, respectively, the first and the second derivatives of the function f_1 with respect to its argument

$(t - x/v)$ [we refer the reader to Appendix 2 for further details on the mathematical procedure].

Equation (7–31), together with the last two of Eqs. (7–33), now yields

$$\frac{1}{v^2}\ddot{f}_1 = \epsilon\mu_0\ddot{f}_1.$$

We thus recognize that (7–32) is a solution of (7–31) if v satisfies

$$v = \frac{1}{\sqrt{\epsilon\mu_0}}. \tag{7–34}$$

In Section 1–3 we discussed in detail the physical significance of an equation of the type of (7–32). We showed that this equation represents a wave traveling in the direction of the positive x-axis without change of shape and with constant velocity v. In the case now being considered, the velocity of propagation is related to the electric and magnetic properties of the medium by (7–34).

If in the first of equations (7–30) we introduce the expression for E_y given by the second of equations (7–33), we obtain

$$\frac{\partial H_z}{\partial t} = \frac{1}{v\mu_0}\dot{f}_1\left(t - \frac{x}{v}\right) = \sqrt{\frac{\epsilon}{\mu_0}}\dot{f}_1\left(t - \frac{x}{v}\right).$$

Therefore, neglecting a possible constant magnetic field, we conclude that H_z is given by

$$H_z(x, t) = \sqrt{\frac{\epsilon}{\mu_0}}f_1\left(t - \frac{x}{v}\right) = \sqrt{\frac{\epsilon}{\mu_0}}E_y(x, t). \tag{7–35}$$

As pointed out above, E_y and H_z are independent of E_z and H_y. Thus there exists a solution of the Maxwell equations in which E_z and H_y are everywhere zero, and E_y and H_z are given by Eqs. (7–32) and (7–35). *This solution describes a plane electromagnetic wave traveling in the direction of the positive x-axis, such that the electric intensity E is everywhere parallel to the y-axis and the magnetic intensity H is everywhere parallel to the z-axis.* The wave is therefore *linearly polarized.* The directions of **E** and **H** are related to the sense of propagation by the rule of the right-handed screw; the sense of propagation and the direction of the rotation through the smallest angle that will make **E** parallel to **H** bear to each other the same relation as the sense of advance and the direction of rotation of a right-handed screw, (Fig. 7–4).

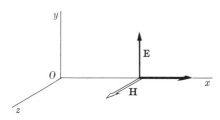 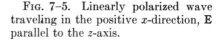

FIG. 7–4. Linearly polarized wave traveling in the positive x-direction, $\mathbf{E}$ parallel to the y-axis.

FIG. 7–5. Linearly polarized wave traveling in the positive x-direction, $\mathbf{E}$ parallel to the z-axis.

The two Eqs. (7–26) that contain E_z and H_y may be treated in a similar manner. Elimination of H_y yields the differential equation

$$\frac{\partial^2 E_z}{\partial x^2} = \epsilon \mu_0 \frac{\partial^2 E_z}{\partial t^2}. \qquad (7\text{--}36)$$

This equation has the same form as (7–31) and therefore admits a solution of the type

$$E_z(x, t) = f_2(t - x/v). \qquad (7\text{--}37)$$

The corresponding expression for H_y is

$$H_y(x, t) = -\sqrt{\frac{\epsilon}{\mu_0}} f_2\left(t - \frac{x}{v}\right) = -\sqrt{\frac{\epsilon}{\mu_0}} E_z(x, t). \qquad (7\text{--}38)$$

Equations (7–37) and (7–38), with $E_y = 0$ and $H_z = 0$, represent a *plane, linearly polarized electromagnetic wave, traveling in the direction of the positive x-axis, such that $\mathbf{E}$ is parallel to the z-axis and $\mathbf{H}$ is parallel to the y-axis* (Fig. 7–5).

The most general solution corresponding to a plane wave traveling in the direction of the positive x-axis is a superposition of the two solutions just discussed. In such a wave, the y- and z-components of $\mathbf{E}$ and $\mathbf{H}$ are simultaneously different from zero, and are given by Eqs. (7–32), (7–35), (7–37), and (7–38). The direction of $\mathbf{E}$ and of $\mathbf{H}$ change, in general, with time and with position; therefore, the wave is not linearly polarized. However, $\mathbf{E}$ and $\mathbf{H}$ at a given point and at a given instant are still perpendicular to each other, which is easily proved by showing that the scalar product of $\mathbf{H}$ and $\mathbf{E}$ vanishes:

$$\mathbf{E} \cdot \mathbf{H} = E_x H_x + E_y H_y + E_z H_z$$

$$= -\sqrt{\frac{\epsilon}{\mu_0}} f_1\left(t - \frac{x}{v}\right) f_2\left(t - \frac{x}{v}\right) + \sqrt{\frac{\epsilon}{\mu_0}} f_2\left(t - \frac{x}{v}\right) f_1\left(t - \frac{x}{v}\right) = 0.$$

It will be recognized that the directions of **E** and **H** and the direction of propagation are still related by the rule of the right-handed screw.

In addition to the solution represented by Eq. (7–32), Eq. (7–31) also has solutions of the form

$$E_y(x, t) = g_1 \left(t + \frac{x}{v} \right), \qquad (7\text{--}39)$$

where v is again given by (7–34) [see Appendix 2]. The corresponding expression for the magnetic field is found to be

$$H_z(x, t) = -\sqrt{\frac{\epsilon}{\mu_0}} \, g_1 \left(t + \frac{x}{v} \right) = -\sqrt{\frac{\epsilon}{\mu_0}} \, E_y(x, t). \qquad (7\text{--}40)$$

Equations (7–39) and (7–40) describe *a plane linearly polarized wave traveling in the direction of the negative x-axis* (see Section 1–3) *such that the electric intensity* **E** *is everywhere parallel to the y-axis and the magnetic intensity* **H** *is everywhere parallel to the z-axis* (Fig. 7–6).

Similarly, Eq. (7–36) has solutions of the form

$$E_z(x, t) = g_2 \left(t + \frac{x}{v} \right). \qquad (7\text{--}41)$$

The corresponding expression for H_y is

$$H_y(x, t) = \sqrt{\frac{\epsilon}{\mu_0}} \, g_2 \left(t + \frac{x}{v} \right) = \sqrt{\frac{\epsilon}{\mu_0}} \, E_z(x, t). \qquad (7\text{--}42)$$

Equations (7–41) and (7–42) represent *a plane linearly polarized wave traveling in the direction of the negative x-axis such that* **E** *is parallel to the z-axis and* **H** *is parallel to the y-axis* (Fig. 7–7).

Superposition of the wave represented by Eqs. (7–39) and (7–40) and the wave represented by (7–41) and (7–42) gives the most general plane wave traveling in the direction of the negative x-axis.

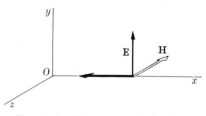

FIG. 7–6. Linearly polarized wave traveling in the negative x-direction, **E** parallel to the y-axis.

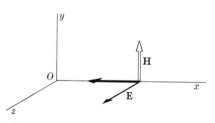

FIG. 7–7. Linearly polarized wave traveling in the negative x-direction, **E** parallel to the z-axis.

Finally, the most general solution of Maxwell's equations, in which $\mathbf{E}$ and $\mathbf{H}$ depend only on x and t, corresponds to the superposition of two plane waves traveling in opposite directions along the x-axis.

7–4 The Poynting vector. In Section 7–2 we mentioned the fact that the energy of electromagnetic fields is distributed in space with a density u given by Eq. (7–20). We wish now to investigate the flow of electromagnetic energy associated with the propagation of plane waves.

For this purpose, we consider a volume bounded by a cylindrical surface whose axis is parallel to the x-axis, and by two plane surfaces S_1 and S_2 perpendicular to this axis. Let A be the common area of S_1 and S_2, and let x_1 and x_2 be their x-coordinates (Fig. 7–8). For the sake of simplicity, we assume that $E_z = 0$, $H_y = 0$, that is, we consider a linearly polarized wave. Since E_y and H_z depend only on x, the total electromagnetic energy contained in the cylindrical volume is

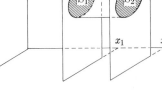

$$U = A \int_{x_1}^{x_2} \frac{\epsilon E_y^2 + \mu_0 H_z^2}{2}\, dx.$$

The rate of change of U with time is given by

FIGURE 7–8

$$\frac{dU}{dt} = A \int_{x_1}^{x_2} \left(\epsilon E_y \frac{\partial E_y}{\partial t} + \mu_0 H_z \frac{\partial H_z}{\partial t} \right) dx.$$

This equation, together with Eqs. (7–30), yields

$$\frac{dU}{dt} = A \int_{x_1}^{x_2} \left(-E_y \frac{\partial H_z}{\partial x} - H_z \frac{\partial E_y}{\partial x} \right) dx = -A \int_{x_1}^{x_2} \frac{\partial}{\partial x}(E_y H_z)\, dx,$$

from which we obtain

$$\frac{dU}{dt} = A[(E_y H_z)_{x=x_1} - (E_y H_z)_{x=x_2}]. \tag{7–43}$$

We shall make the natural assumption that the electromagnetic energy of a plane electromagnetic wave travels in the direction of propagation of the wave. Thus the energy flux through the lateral surface of the cylinder is zero, and the principle of conservation of the energy is satisfied if the quantity $E_y H_z$ is interpreted as the energy flux per unit area in the direction of propagation. Equation (7–43) then states that the change per unit time in the energy contained in the cylindrical volume equals the amount of energy per unit time that enters this volume through the plane surface S_1 at x_1, minus the amount of energy per unit time that leaves the volume through the plane surface S_2 at x_2.

Thus, if we indicate the energy flux per unit area by S_x, we obtain

$$S_x = E_y H_z. \qquad (7\text{--}44)$$

Similarly, in the case of a wave whose electric vector is parallel to the z-axis and whose magnetic vector is parallel to the y-axis, we obtain

$$S_x = -E_z H_y. \qquad (7\text{--}45)$$

An arbitrary plane wave traveling in the direction of the x-axis may be regarded as the superposition of two waves whose electric vectors are parallel to the y-axis and to the z-axis, respectively. Therefore the general expression for the energy flux per unit area in a wave traveling along the x-axis is

$$S_x = E_y H_z - E_z H_y. \qquad (7\text{--}46)$$

Note that Eqs. (7–44), (7–45), and (7–46) are valid both for waves traveling in the positive direction and for waves traveling in the negative direction. In the former case, S_x is positive, in the latter it is negative.

The results presented above are a special case of Poynting's theorem, which states that *in an electromagnetic field the energy flux per unit area is represented by a vector* **S**, *called the Poynting vector, which is given by*

$$\mathbf{S} = \mathbf{E} \times \mathbf{H},$$

where the cross indicates the vector product. We shall omit the general proof of this theorem.

7–5 Light as electromagnetic waves. We shall now compare the theoretical description of electromagnetic waves presented in the previous sections with the experimental properties of light waves.

It is important to remark that in the development of the theory we have assumed that **D** is, at all times, parallel and proportional to **E**, so that we can define the dielectric permittivity ϵ by the equation $\mathbf{D} = \epsilon\mathbf{E}$. This assumption is certainly correct for the case of a vacuum, where no polarization effects occur, but may not be correct for material substances, at least when we are dealing with rapidly varying fields.

We shall begin by considering the behavior of electromagnetic waves and of light in vacuum, and we immediately find two strong arguments in favor of the assumption that light consists of electromagnetic waves: (1) In a plane electromagnetic wave the electric intensity $\mathbf{E}$ and the magnetic intensity $\mathbf{H}$ are perpendicular to the direction of propagation. Thus the transverse character of light waves, which is very difficult to explain by any elastic theory of light, is easily understood if light waves are electromagnetic waves. (2) The second argument is the excellent agreement between the experimental value of the velocity of light in empty space, c, and the computed value of the velocity of electromagnetic waves in empty space, $1/\sqrt{\epsilon_0\mu_0}$. Indeed, in Section 5–2 the most accurate optical determination of the velocity of light is given as

$$c = 299792.7 \pm 0.25 \text{ km/sec},$$

while the best value of $1/\sqrt{\epsilon_0\mu_0}$, as obtained from static electromagnetic measurements of the constants ϵ_0 and μ_0 by Rosa and Dorsey, is*

$$1/\sqrt{\epsilon_0\mu_0} = 299784 \pm 10 \text{ km/sec}.$$

It may be added that precise direct measurements of the velocity of propagation of electromagnetic waves of wavelengths in the centimeter range give values† ranging from

$$c = 299789.3 \pm 0.8 \text{ km/sec}$$

to

$$c = 299792.7 \pm 0.25 \text{ km/sec}.$$

We shall thus adopt the view that light waves are electromagnetic waves and shall proceed to discuss a number of optical phenomena on this basis.

From the study of interference (Chapter 3) we have come to the conclusion that in a monochromatic wave the optical disturbance is a sinusoidal function of time. Thus, in vacuum, the equations of a plane electromagnetic wave representing monochromatic light are of the following form:

---

*See R. T. Birge, *Rev. Mod. Phys.*, **13**, p. 233 (1941).
†See J. F. Mulligan, *Am. J. Phys.*, **20**, p. 165 (1952).

$$E_y = A_y \cos \left[\omega \left(t - \frac{x}{c} \right) + \varphi_y \right],$$

$$E_z = A_z \cos \left[\omega \left(t - \frac{x}{c} \right) + \varphi_z \right],$$

$$H_y = - \sqrt{\frac{\epsilon_0}{\mu_0}} A_z \cos \left[\omega \left(t - \frac{x}{c} \right) + \varphi_z \right] \qquad (7\text{--}48)$$

$$= \sqrt{\frac{\epsilon_0}{\mu_0}} A_z \cos \left[\omega \left(t - \frac{x}{c} \right) + \varphi_z + \pi \right],$$

$$H_z = \sqrt{\frac{\epsilon_0}{\mu_0}} A_y \cos \left[\omega \left(t - \frac{x}{c} \right) + \varphi_y \right].$$

These equations are a special case of the more general equations (7–32), (7–37), (7–38), and (7–35). It is here assumed that the waves travel in the direction of the positive x-axis. The y-component of $\mathbf{E}$ and the z-component of $\mathbf{H}$ are everywhere in phase, while the z-component of $\mathbf{E}$ and the y-component of $\mathbf{H}$ have opposite phase. Between the z- and the y-components of $\mathbf{E}$ there is an arbitrary phase difference $\varphi_z - \varphi_y$; the corresponding phase difference between the y- and the z-components of $\mathbf{H}$ is $\pi + \varphi_z - \varphi_y$. Recalling the results obtained in Section 6–2 on the superposition of coherent sinusoidal waves vibrating in mutually perpendicular planes, we conclude that, in general, the endpoints of the vectors representing $\mathbf{E}$ and $\mathbf{H}$ describe elliptical curves. As in all plane electromagnetic waves, of course, the vectors $\mathbf{E}$ and $\mathbf{H}$ are mutually perpendicular at all times, and perpendicular to the direction of propagation. Hence Eqs. (7–48) describe, in general, a monochromatic, elliptically polarized plane wave traveling in the direction of the positive x-axis.

Linear and circular polarization are special cases of elliptical polarization. The wave is linearly polarized if $\varphi_z = \varphi_y$, or if $\varphi_z - \varphi_y$ is an integral multiple of π, and also if either A_z or A_y is zero. If, for example, $A_z = 0$,

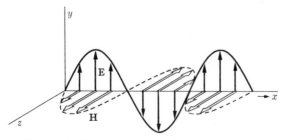

FIG. 7–9. Linearly polarized sinusoidal wave.

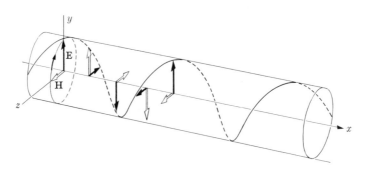

FIG. 7–10. Circularly polarized wave.

then the electric vector is everywhere parallel to the y-axis, and the magnetic vector is everywhere parallel to the z-axis (Fig. 7–9).

The wave is circularly polarized if $A_y = A_z$, and $\varphi_z - \varphi_y$ is an odd multiple of $\pi/2$ (Fig. 7–10).

The square of the electric intensity at the time t is given by

$$E^2 = E_y^2 + E_z^2 = A_y^2 \cos^2\left[\omega\left(t - \frac{x}{c}\right) + \varphi_y\right] + A_z^2 \cos^2\left[\omega\left(t - \frac{x}{c}\right) + \varphi_z\right].$$

Remembering that the average value of the $\cos^2$ functions, computed over a time interval long compared with the period of the waves, is $1/2$ (Section 3–2), we find the following expression for the mean square value of E:

$$(E^2)_{\mathrm{av}} = \tfrac{1}{2}(A_y^2 + A_z^2). \qquad (7\text{–}49)$$

Similarly, the mean square value of **H** is

$$(H^2)_{\mathrm{av}} = \frac{\epsilon_0}{2\mu_0}(A_y^2 + A_z^2). \qquad (7\text{–}50)$$

The Poynting vector **S** is directed along the x-axis and its magnitude is given by

$$S = S_x = E_y H_z - E_z H_y, \qquad (7\text{–}51)$$

or

$$S_x = \sqrt{\frac{\epsilon_0}{\mu_0}}\left\{A_y^2 \cos^2\left[\omega\left(t - \frac{x}{c}\right) + \varphi_y\right] + A_z^2 \cos^2\left[\omega\left(t - \frac{x}{c}\right) + \varphi_z\right]\right\}.$$

$$(7\text{–}52)$$

In the case of circular polarization, S_x has the constant value $\sqrt{\epsilon_0/\mu_0}\, A_y^2$. In all other cases, S_x is a rapidly varying function of time whose instantaneous value cannot be observed experimentally. The time average of S_x, however, is a measurable quantity. Indeed, $(S_x)_{\mathrm{av}}$ is proportional to the intensity I of the traveling electromagnetic wave, according to the definition of I given in Section 3–1. From (7–52) we find the following expression for $(S_x)_{\mathrm{av}}$:

$$(S_x)_{\mathrm{av}} = \frac{1}{2} \sqrt{\frac{\epsilon_0}{\mu_0}}\, (A_y^2 + A_z^2). \tag{7–53}$$

Comparing this equation with (7–49) and (7–50), we see that $(S_x)_{\mathrm{av}}$, and therefore the intensity of the wave, is proportional to the mean value of E^2 or the mean value of H^2.

The energy of an electromagnetic wave is distributed in space with a density

$$u = \tfrac{1}{2}(\epsilon_0 E^2 + \mu_0 H^2),$$

or, from Eqs. (7–48),

$$u = \epsilon_0 \left\{ A_y^2 \cos^2 \left[\omega \left(t - \frac{x}{c} \right) + \varphi_y \right] + A_z^2 \cos^2 \left[\omega \left(t - \frac{x}{c} \right) + \varphi_z \right] \right\}. \tag{7–54}$$

The average value of u is therefore

$$(u)_{\mathrm{av}} = \frac{\epsilon_0}{2}\, (A_y^2 + A_z^2). \tag{7–55}$$

Equations (7–53) and (7–55) yield

$$(S_x)_{\mathrm{av}} = \frac{(u)_{\mathrm{av}}}{\sqrt{\epsilon_0 \mu_0}} = u_{\mathrm{av}} c. \tag{7–56}$$

Thus far we have considered plane electromagnetic waves traveling in the direction of the x-axis. We now wish to find the expression for a plane wave traveling in an arbitrary direction. Without essential loss of generality, we may restrict ourselves to the case of a linearly polarized wave, for an arbi-

trary elliptically polarized wave can
always be regarded as the superposition of two linearly polarized waves.
Let **k** be a vector of unit length
pointing in the direction of propaga-
tion of the wave, and let γ_x, γ_y, and
γ_z be the components of **k** along the
x-; y- and z-axes, respectively. These
quantities, of course, are the direction cosines, i.e., the cosines of the
angles made by the direction of

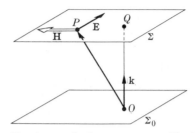

Fig. 7–11. A plane wave traveling in
the direction **k**.

propagation with the three coordinate axes.

Plane electromagnetic waves are characterized by the condition that **E**
and **H** are functions only of t and of the distance from a fixed plane. For a
wave traveling in the direction of the x-axis, the fixed plane is the yz-
plane, and the distance from this plane is the x-coordinate. In other words,
the planes of constant phase are those for which $x = \text{const.}$ For a wave
traveling in the direction of the vector **k**, the planes of constant phase are
those perpendicular to **k**. Thus **E** and **H** at an arbitrary point P must be
functions of t and of the distance of P from a fixed plane Σ_0 perpendicular
to **k**. Without loss of generality, we may assume that this plane passes
through the origin O of our coordinate system. Let **r** be the position vector
of the point P, that is, the vector represented by the segment OP (Fig.
7–11). Consider the plane Σ passing through P and perpendicular to **k** (and
therefore parallel to Σ_0). Let Q be the intersection of this plane with the
straight line through O, parallel to **k**. The distance of P from Σ_0 is equal
to $\overline{OQ}$ and this length, in turn, is equal to $\mathbf{r} \cdot \mathbf{k}$, where the dot indicates a
scalar product. We conclude that the expression $t - x/c$ that appears in the
equations for a wave traveling in the direction of the x-axis, must now be
replaced with the expression $t - (\mathbf{r} \cdot \mathbf{k}/c)$. Thus in a plane linearly polarized
sinusoidal electromagnetic wave traveling in the direction of the unit vector
k, the vector **E** is given by an equation of the following type:

$$\mathbf{E} = \mathbf{A} \cos\left[\omega\left(t - \frac{\mathbf{r} \cdot \mathbf{k}}{c}\right) + \varphi\right]. \tag{7–57}$$

In this equation, **A** is a vector perpendicular to **k**. Since **r** has the components x, y, z, and **k** has the components γ_x, γ_y, γ_z, we have

$$\mathbf{r} \cdot \mathbf{k} = \gamma_x x + \gamma_y y + \gamma_z z. \tag{7–58}$$

In some of the mathematical developments to follow, it is convenient to use the complex representation of the sinusoidal functions and to write (7–57) as

$$\mathbf{E} = \mathbf{A} \exp\left\{ i \left[\omega \left(t - \frac{\mathbf{r} \cdot \mathbf{k}}{c} \right) + \varphi \right] \right\}, \qquad (7\text{–}59)$$

or

$$\mathbf{E} = \mathbf{A} \exp\left(i\varphi \right) \exp\left(i\omega t \right) \exp\left(-2\pi i \frac{\mathbf{r} \cdot \mathbf{k}}{\lambda} \right), \qquad (7\text{–}60)$$

where $\lambda = 2\pi c/\omega$ is the wavelength.

Considering Eqs. (7–48) and remembering that the direction of propagation, the direction of $\mathbf{E}$, and the direction of $\mathbf{H}$ bear to one another the same relation as the x-, y-, and z-axes in a right-handed cartesian coordinate system, we obtain the following equations:

$$\mathbf{H} = \sqrt{\frac{\epsilon_0}{\mu_0}}\, \mathbf{k} \times \mathbf{E}, \qquad (7\text{–}61)$$

$$\mathbf{S} = \mathbf{E} \times \mathbf{H} = \sqrt{\frac{\epsilon_0}{\mu_0}}\, E^2 \mathbf{k}, \qquad (7\text{–}62)$$

where the symbol $\times$ indicates a cross product. The expression for the mean energy flux per unit area is

$$(S)_{\text{av}} = \frac{1}{2} \sqrt{\frac{\epsilon_0}{\mu_0}}\, A^2. \qquad (7\text{–}63)$$

Visible light includes only a small portion of the electromagnetic spectrum, extending approximately from a wavelength (in vacuum) of 8000 A (extreme red) to a wavelength of 4000 A (extreme violet). Beyond the extreme red, in order of increasing wavelength, are the infrared rays, the microwaves, and the ordinary radio waves. Beyond the extreme violet, in order of decreasing wavelength, are the ultraviolet rays, the x-rays, and the γ-rays (see Table 7–1). The classification of electro-

TABLE 7–1

APPROXIMATE LIMITS OF THE VARIOUS PORTIONS OF THE ELECTROMAGNETIC SPECTRUM.

	Wavelengths in vacuum		
	m	cm	A
Radio broadcast	-10^4 -10^3 -10^2		
Short radio waves	-10 -1 -10^{-1}	10^2 10 1	
Infrared		10^{-1} 10^{-2} 10^{-3}	10^6 10^5
Visible		10^{-4}	10^4
Ultraviolet			10^3 10^2
X-rays and γ-rays			10 1

magnetic waves is somewhat arbitrary, and is based essentially on the different methods used for the production and detection of the different radiations.

In this volume we deal mainly with visible light. Many of the properties discussed here apply also to waves outside the visible range, but the behavior of electromagnetic waves of wavelength much shorter or much longer than that of visible light is quite different with respect to their interactions with matter, where the dimensions of atoms establish a natural scale of wavelengths.

7–6 Radiation from an accelerated charge. So far, we have considered only the propagation of electromagnetic waves, and have ignored the question of how these waves are actually produced. We now turn our attention to this problem.

Electromagnetic waves are variable electromagnetic fields, and it is therefore clear that they must originate from moving electric charges. Actually, the electromagnetic disturbance produced by a given system of moving charges could be computed by solving Maxwell's equations, with the assumption that the vector **j** (which describes the currents arising from the motion of electric charges) is a known function of time. This approach, however, involves considerable mathematical difficulty, and we shall follow instead an indirect method, suggested originally by J. J. Thompson, which is at the same time simpler mathematically and more illuminating from the physical point of view. The argument will be based on the two following premises:

THEOREM 1. *Electromagnetic disturbances are propagated with a finite velocity, which in empty space is* $c = 1/\sqrt{\epsilon_0 \mu_0}$. This statement is a direct result of Maxwell's equations. We have proved its validity in the special case of plane waves; we shall omit here the general proof, but we wish to stress one of its consequences. Consider a point charge moving in empty space; let O be its instantaneous position and let $r = \overline{OP}$ be its distance from a fixed point P (r is, of course, a function of time). The electromagnetic field produced by the moving charge at the point P at time t is entirely determined by the position of the charge at the earlier time t':

$$t' = t - r(t')/c, \qquad (7\text{–}64)$$

and by the quantities that characterize the motion of the point charge at the same time t'. In the above equation, the quantity $r(t')$ is the distance of P from O at the time t', when the electromagnetic disturbance leaves the charge, hence $r(t')/c$ represents the time of travel of the electromagnetic disturbance from O to P. Since r is assumed to be a known function of time,

Eq. (7–64) determines t' implicitly. However, in most of the cases of interest to us, the charge remains in the immediate vicinity of a fixed point; r, then, may be regarded as the (constant) distance of this point from the point P of observation.

THEOREM 2. *The electric field produced by a point charge moving in empty space along a straight line and with constant velocity small compared with the velocity of light is practically identical to the electric field produced by the same charge at rest.* A moving charge, of course, produces both an electric field $\mathbf{E}$ and a magnetic field $\mathbf{H}$. The above statement means that if the charge passes through the point O at the time t, we can compute $\mathbf{E}$ *at the given time t* and at all points of space by assuming that the charge is at rest at O. The proof of this statement which, as already mentioned, applies only to charges moving with a *constant velocity w $\ll$ c*, appears in Appendix 3. It is shown there that the electric field of the moving charge differs from the electric field of the stationary charge by quantities of the order of $(w/c)^2$.

With the help of the two above theorems we shall now investigate the following problem. A point charge q has been moving for some time in empty space along a straight line with the constant velocity w ($w \ll c$). Within a short time interval Δt, beginning at $t = t'$, the velocity is increased with a constant acceleration to a new value $w + \Delta w$, which then remains constant. We shall consider Δw and Δt as infinitesimal quantities of the same order, so that the acceleration

$$a = \frac{\Delta w}{\Delta t} \qquad (7\text{–}65)$$

is a finite quantity. What is the electromagnetic field in the space surrounding the charge?

Let O and O' be the points occupied by the charge at the times t' and $t' + \Delta t$, respectively (Fig. 7–12). Apart from infinitesimal quantities of higher order, we then have

$$\overline{OO'} = w\,\Delta t. \qquad (7\text{–}66)$$

For a given value of $t > t'$, consider a sphere centered at O, of radius

$$r_0 = c(t - t'), \qquad (7\text{–}67)$$

and a sphere centered at O', of radius $r_0 - \Delta r$, where

$$\Delta r = c\,\Delta t. \qquad (7\text{–}68)$$

Since the velocity of the charge is small compared with the velocity of light, the distance $\overline{OO'}$ between the centers of the two spheres is small compared

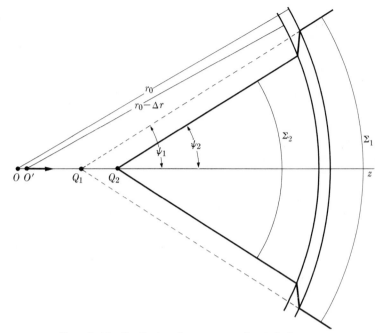

FIG. 7–12. Radiation from an accelerated charge.

with the difference Δr between their radii. In other words, the two spheres are practically concentric.

Consider first the region outside the sphere of radius r_0. A signal traveling with velocity c that reaches a point of this region at the time t has left the moving charge at a time prior to t', that is, at a time when the charge was still moving with the constant velocity w. From Theorem 1 we conclude that, at the time t, the electric field outside the sphere of radius r_0 is the same as if the charge were still moving with the original constant velocity w. From Theorem 2 we know that this field is practically identical to that of a stationary charge q located at the point Q_1 where the charge would have been at time t if it had not been accelerated. Thus the electric lines of force outside the sphere of radius r_0 are straight lines diverging from Q_1 (Fig. 7–12).

Consider next the region inside the sphere of radius $r_0 - \Delta r$. A signal traveling with velocity c that reaches a point of this region at time t has left the moving charge at a time when this was already moving with the new velocity $w + \Delta w$. From Theorem 1 it follows that at the time t the field inside the sphere of radius $r_0 - \Delta r$ is the same as if the charge had always been moving with the velocity $w + \Delta w$. Theorem 2 then tells us that the lines of force inside the sphere of radius $r_0 - \Delta r$ are straight lines diverging from the point Q_2, where the moving charge actually is at the time t.

There remains the task of determining the field in the shell between the two spheres, i.e., in the region of space from which one "sees" the charge in the process of being accelerated. For this purpose, let us follow a line of force originating from the charge at an angle ψ_2 to the direction of motion (to be called henceforth the z-axis, see Fig. 7-12). Beyond the sphere of radius r_0, this line of force is a straight line passing through Q_1. Let ψ_1 be the angle between this line and the z-axis. To determine the relation between ψ_1 and ψ_2, we consider the surface of revolution described by the line of force as it rotates about the z-axis. We then apply Gauss' theorem to the volume enclosed by this surface and by two portions of spherical surfaces, Σ_1 and Σ_2, centered at Q_1 and at Q_2, respectively, whose radii R_1 and R_2 are chosen in such a way that Σ_2 lies inside the sphere of radius $r_0 - \Delta r$ and Σ_1 lies outside the sphere of radius r_0 (Fig. 7-12). Since there are no charges in this volume, and since there is no flux through the lateral surface, the flux entering the volume through Σ_2 equals the flux leaving the volume through Σ_1. The areas of Σ_1 and Σ_2 are $2\pi R_1^2(1 - \cos \psi_1)$ and $2\pi R_2^2(1 - \cos \psi_2)$. The electric intensities at these two surfaces are $q/(4\pi\epsilon_0 R_1^2)$ and $q/(4\pi\epsilon_0 R_2^2)$, respectively. Hence Gauss' law yields

$$\frac{q}{4\pi\epsilon_0 R_1^2} 2\pi R_1^2(1 - \cos \psi_1) = \frac{q}{4\pi\epsilon_0 R_2^2} 2\pi R_2^2(1 - \cos \psi_2).$$

From this equation, it follows that

$$\psi_2 = \psi_1,$$

i.e., the two straight portions of the line of force are parallel to each other.

The results obtained so far may be graphically pictured as follows:

We represent the electric field of a point charge by means of a certain number of lines of force, diverging radially from the charge. If the point charge moves with constant velocity, the lines of force participate in the motion, as if they were rigid wires attached to the charge. If, however, the charge suddenly changes its velocity from w to $w + \Delta w$, there appears in each moving line of force a sharp double bend which travels along the line of force with the speed of light (with respect to an observer at rest). On the far side of the bend, the lines of force continue to move as a rigid system with the initial velocity w, ignoring the change in the velocity of the charge. On the near side of the bend, however, the lines of force diverge radially from the point charge and participate in its motion, thus traveling with the velocity $w + \Delta w$.

Note that as t increases, the distance between Q_1 and Q_2 increases, and so does the lateral distance between the two straight sections of each line of force. However, the distance over which the bend occurs is a constant, and after a sufficient length of time the two angles of the double bend become practically right angles, so that the electric field in the shell between the spheres of radii r_0 and $r_0 - \Delta r$ is practically at right angles to the direction of propagation.

We now have a graphical solution of the problem. There remains only the task of giving an analytic expression to our results. From our previous analysis it follows that an *infinitesimal* change of velocity Δw occurring during the *infinitesimal* time interval Δt does not produce a *finite* change in the electric field *except* in the infinitesimal shell between the spheres of radii r_0 and $r_0 - \Delta r$. In this volume, from which we "see" the charge in the process of being accelerated, the infinitesimal change of velocity produces a *finite* change in the electric field. However, within as well as without the shell, the component of the field in the radial direction with respect to the instantaneous position of the charge undergoes no finite change.

Let us now introduce a spherical system of coordinates with the center at the point O occupied by the charge at the time zero, and with the polar axis in the direction of motion (Fig. 7–13). Let ϑ be the angle from the polar axis, and let φ be the azimuthal angle, measured from an arbitrary fixed plane through the polar axis.

In Fig. 7–13, $Q_2 \, ACD$ represents a line of force at the time t; AC is the portion of this line that lies within the infinitesimal shell from which the charge is seen in the process of being accelerated. Let B and H be the points where the straight lines OA and Q_2A intersect the outer surface of the infinitesimal shell.

From the figure, we see that since the electric field in the shell is in the direction of the segment AC, the ϑ- and r-components of $\mathbf{E}$ satisfy the equation

$$\frac{E_\vartheta}{E_r} = \frac{\overline{CB}}{\overline{AB}} \, . \tag{7–69}$$

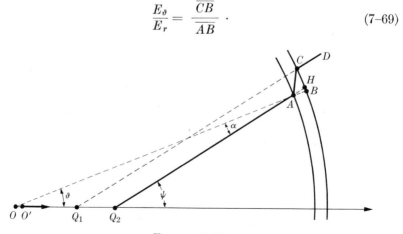

FIGURE. 7–13

If we denote by α the angle OAQ_2 and neglect infinitesimal quantities of order higher than the first, we have

$$\overline{AB} = \Delta r, \tag{7–70}$$

$$\overline{CH} = \overline{Q_1Q_2}\,\frac{\sin\psi}{\cos\alpha}, \tag{7–71}$$

$$\overline{HB} = \Delta r\,\tan\alpha, \tag{7–72}$$

$$\overline{Q_1Q_2} = \Delta w(t - t') = \frac{\Delta w}{c}\,r_0. \tag{7–73}$$

The angle α is of the order of magnitude of w/c. Since we have consistently neglected terms of the order of $(w/c)^2$, we can write

$$\cos\alpha = 1, \qquad \tan\alpha = \alpha.$$

Equations (7–71), (7–72), and (7–73) then yield

$$\overline{CB} = \overline{CH} + \overline{HB} = \frac{\Delta w}{c}\,r_0\sin\psi + \Delta r\cdot\alpha,$$

and consequently,

$$\frac{\overline{CB}}{\overline{AB}} = \frac{r_0\sin\psi}{c^2}\,a + \alpha, \tag{7–74}$$

where we have made use of the equations $\Delta r = c\,\Delta t$ and $a = \Delta w/\Delta t$.

On the other hand, if $R = \overline{Q_2A}$ is the distance from the point of observation to the instantaneous position of the charge, we have

$$E_r = \frac{q}{4\pi\epsilon_0 R^2}\cos\alpha,$$

or, by again putting $\cos\alpha = 1$,

$$E_r = \frac{q}{4\pi\epsilon_0 R^2}. \tag{7–75}$$

Equations (7–69), (7–74), and (7–75) then yield

$$E_\vartheta = \frac{q}{4\pi\epsilon_0 R^2}\left(\frac{r_0\sin\psi}{c^2}\,a + \alpha\right). \tag{7–76}$$

Equations (7–75) and (7–76) are correct in the limit for $\Delta w = 0$, and to the extent that w^2/c^2 is negligible compared with unity. To avoid mathematical complications, we now assume that not only w^2/c^2, but also w/c is negligible compared with unity, and we evaluate the above equations in the limit of $w/c = 0$. In this limit, α vanishes, ψ becomes equal to ϑ, R becomes equal to r_0, and we obtain

$$E_r = \frac{q}{4\pi\epsilon_0 r_0^2}, \qquad E_\vartheta = \frac{q\sin\vartheta}{4\pi\epsilon_0 c^2 r_0}\, a. \qquad (7\text{–}77)$$

These results can be extended to the case in which the charge undergoes acceleration during several separate intervals of time and, in the limit, to the case where the charge moves with an arbitrary, continuous acceleration. Indeed, according to Theorem 1, the field at the point P and at the time t depends only on the position, the velocity, and the acceleration of the charge at the time $t' = t - r/c$, where r is the distance between the charge and the point of observation at the time t'. Thus the field at P at time t is the same as if the charge had been moving with a constant velocity w until *almost* the time $t' = t - r/c$, and as if at the time t' it was in the process of being accelerated from w to $w + a\ \Delta t$. We can therefore apply Eqs. (7–77) directly to our case by replacing r_0 with r and by interpreting a as the instantaneous value of the acceleration at the time $t' = t - r/c$. It must be understood, also, that the origin of the polar system of coordinates is at the point occupied by the charge at the time t'.

From Eqs. (7–77), we see that E_ϑ is proportional to the acceleration and varies as the *inverse distance* of the point of observation from the charge; E_r, however, varies as the *inverse square* of this distance. Thus, at sufficiently large distances, E_r becomes negligible compared with E_ϑ, and the electric field is described by the following set of equations:

$$E_r(r,\ \vartheta,\ \varphi,\ t) = 0,$$

$$E_\vartheta(r,\ \vartheta,\ \varphi,\ t) = \frac{q\sin\vartheta}{4\pi\epsilon_0 c^2 r}\, a_{t-r/c}, \qquad (7\text{–}78)$$

$$E_\varphi(r,\ \vartheta,\ \varphi,\ t) = 0.$$

This is the *radiation field*. The last equation signifies that the electric intensity lies in the plane containing the point of observation and the trajectory of the particle, and the subscript $t - r/c$ in the second equation indicates that the acceleration must be computed at the time $t - r/c$.

In the above system of equations we recognize the characteristic description of a disturbance propagated by spherical waves with velocity c from a point source (see Section 1–4). We see that the magnitude of the disturbance is inversely proportional to the distance from the source, and is proportional to a function of $t - r/c$. The electric vector representing the disturbance is everywhere perpendicular to the direction of propagation, and for given r and t, its magnitude varies as sin ϑ. It is thus a maximum in the direction perpendicular to the polar axis and zero in the direction of the polar axis.

Over a volume of space of sufficiently small dimensions and sufficiently removed from the source, the electric field described by Eqs. (7–78) is practically identical to that of a plane wave. It is thus natural that in the radiation field of an accelerated charge, the magnetic and the electric vectors should bear to each other the same relation as in a plane wave. We accept this conclusion here, omitting, for the sake of simplicity, its rigorous proof. It then follows, since in a plane wave the direction of propagation and the directions of $\mathbf{E}$ and $\mathbf{H}$ are mutually perpendicular, that in the radiation field of an accelerated charge only the φ-component of $\mathbf{H}$ is different from zero. Thus the lines of the vector $\mathbf{H}$ are circles with their centers on the polar axis. In a plane wave traveling in the direction of the positive x-axis of a right-handed cartesian frame of reference, E_y and H_z have the same sign. Since, in a polar frame of reference, the vectors pointing in the directions of increasing r, ϑ, and φ bear to one another the same relation as the vectors pointing in the directions of the positive x-, y-, and z-axes, we conclude that H_φ and E_ϑ have the same sign (Fig. 7–14). Moreover, the magnitude of $\mathbf{H}$ and the magnitude of $\mathbf{E}$ are in the ratio of $\sqrt{\epsilon_0/\mu_0}$, as they are in a plane wave. Thus the magnetic field is described by the following set of equations:

$$H_r(r, \vartheta, \varphi, t) = 0,$$

$$H_\vartheta(r, \vartheta, \varphi, t) = 0, \qquad (7\text{–}79)$$

$$H_\varphi(r, \vartheta, \varphi, t) = \sqrt{\frac{\epsilon_0}{\mu_0}} E_\vartheta(r, \vartheta, \varphi, t).$$

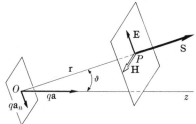

Thus far in our discussion we have assumed that the charge is moving with arbitrary acceleration along a straight line. The results obtained, however, are valid also in the more general case of a curved trajectory, but in this case we must take the axis of our system of polar coordinates parallel to the acceleration vector, so that ϑ, in (7–78) and (7–79), represents the angle between the direction of the acceleration and the line of sight.

FIG. 7–14.   Electromagnetic wave produced by an accelerated charge.

It is interesting to compute the Poynting vector $\mathbf{S} = \mathbf{E} \times \mathbf{H}$ describing the energy flux. We recognize immediately that in the radiation field, **S** points radially away from the accelerated charge, so that only its r-component, S_r, is different from zero. The magnitude of S_r is given by

$$S_r = E_\vartheta H_\varphi = \frac{q^2 \sin^2 \vartheta}{(4\pi)^2 \epsilon_0 c^3 r^2} a^2_{t-r/c}. \tag{7-80}$$

If we compute the total energy flux Φ across a sphere of radius r centered at O, we find

$$\Phi = \int_0^\pi S_r 2\pi r^2 \sin \vartheta \, d\vartheta = \frac{q^2 a^2_{t-r/c}}{8\pi\epsilon_0 c^3} \int_0^\pi \sin^3 \vartheta \, d\vartheta,$$

or

$$\Phi = \frac{q^2 a^2_{t-r/c}}{6\pi\epsilon_0 c^3}. \tag{7-81}$$

In (7–81), r appears only in the expression $a_{t-r/c}$, which means that the total energy flux through a sphere of radius r at time t equals the total energy flux through a larger sphere of radius r_1 at the later time t_1 such that $r_1 - r = c(t_1 - t)$. Thus the electromagnetic energy of the wave spreads out in space with the velocity c. Although it is clear from the foregoing, we point out explicitly that Φ *represents the amount of radiant energy emitted by the accelerated charge per unit time.*

Before closing this section we recapitulate our conclusions, using a slightly different and more concise notation. The problem is to determine the radiation field of a moving charge q at a point P and at the time t.

Let O be the position of the charge at the time $t - r/c$ ($r = \overline{OP}$), and $\mathbf{a}_{t-r/c}$ the acceleration of the charge at the same time. We consider the vector $q\mathbf{a}_{t-r/c}$ (Fig. 7–14), which is parallel or antiparallel to $\mathbf{a}_{t-r/c}$ depending on whether q is positive or negative. We also consider the component of this vector perpendicular to the line of sight OP, to be called $q(\mathbf{a}_n)_{t-r/c}$, and the unit vector **k** pointing along the line of sight from O to P. If ϑ is the angle between the vector $q\mathbf{a}_{t-r/c}$ and the line of sight, the magnitude of the vector $q(\mathbf{a}_n)_{t-r/c}$ is $|q\mathbf{a}_{t-r/c}| \sin \vartheta$.

The electric field is represented by the vector

$$\mathbf{E} = -\frac{q(\mathbf{a}_n)_{t-r/c}}{4\pi\epsilon_0 c^2 r} \tag{7-82}$$

and is thus antiparallel and proportional in magnitude to the vector $q(\mathbf{a}_n)_{t-r/c}$. The magnetic field **H** has the magnitude

$$|\mathbf{H}| = \sqrt{\frac{\epsilon_0}{\mu_0}} |\mathbf{E}|, \tag{7-83}$$

and is perpendicular to **E** and to **k**. Therefore

$$\mathbf{H} = \sqrt{\frac{\epsilon_0}{\mu_0}}\, \mathbf{k} \times \mathbf{E}. \tag{7-84}$$

The Poynting vector is

$$\mathbf{S} = \mathbf{E} \times \mathbf{H}$$

or

$$\mathbf{S} = \frac{q^2 (\mathbf{a}_n)^2_{t-r/c}}{(4\pi)^2 \epsilon_0 c^3 r^2}\, \mathbf{k}. \tag{7-85}$$

In the next chapter we shall see how the general results obtained in this section may be applied to the process of light emission by charged particles in atoms and molecules.

7-1. Compute the rms value of E at a distance of 1 m from a 100-watt bulb. (Consider the bulb as a point source, and assume that the power emitted goes entirely into visible and invisible electromagnetic radiation.)

7-2. The electric field of an electromagnetic wave in vacuum is represented by (in the mks system)

$$E_x = 0,$$
$$E_y = 0.5 \cos\left[2\pi \times 10^8 \left(t - \frac{x}{c}\right)\right],$$
$$E_z = 0.$$

(a) Determine the wavelength, the state of polarization, and the direction of propagation. (b) Compute the magnetic field of the wave. (c) Compute the instantaneous value and the mean value of the energy flux per unit area.

7-3. Solve (a), (b), and (c) of Problem 7-2 for the wave represented by

$$E_x = 0,$$
$$E_y = 0.5 \cos\left[4\pi \times 10^7 \left(t - \frac{x}{c}\right)\right],$$
$$E_z = 0.5 \sin\left[4\pi \times 10^7 \left(t - \frac{x}{c}\right)\right].$$

7-4. A plane sinusoidal linearly polarized light wave of wavelength $\lambda = 5000$ A travels in vacuum in the direction of the x-axis. The mean energy flux per unit area is 0.1 watt/m^2 and the plane of vibration is parallel to the y-axis. Write the equations describing the electric and magnetic fields of this wave.

7-5. A plane sinusoidal linearly polarized light wave of wavelength $\lambda = 5000$ A travels in vacuum. The mean energy flux is 0.1 watt/m^2. The direction of propagation lies in the xy-plane at 45° to the x-axis. The plane of vibration is parallel to the z-axis. Write the equations describing the electric and magnetic fields of this wave.

7-6. Solve Problem 7-5, assuming that the plane of vibration is perpendicular to the z-axis.

7-7. Consider a plane linearly polarized wave, traveling in vacuum, represented by

$$E_y = A \exp\left[2\pi i\left(\frac{t}{T} - \frac{x}{\lambda}\right)\right],$$

and consider a rectangular loop of wire of resistance R with two sides of length a parallel to the y-axis, and two sides of length b forming an angle θ with the x-axis. (a) Compute the sinusoidal current i induced in the loop as a function of θ. (b) For what value of θ is the rms value of the current a maximum? (Assume that R is sufficiently large so that the perturbation of the field due to i may be neglected.) Discuss separately the cases $b < \lambda/2$, $b > \lambda/2$.

7-8. In Problem 7-7 assume $(i)_{rms} = 10^{-6}$ amp, $a = 10$ m, $b = 5$ m, $R = 10^7$ ohms, $\theta = 0, \lambda = 40$ m. Compute the energy flux of the wave in watts/m^2.

7-9. Two sinusoidal linearly polarized plane waves, both of frequency ν and amplitude A and vibrating in the same plane, travel in opposite directions in empty space. Take the direction of propagation as the x-axis.

Compute (as functions of t and x) (a) the resultant electric field $\mathbf{E}$, (b) the resultant magnetic field $\mathbf{H}$, (c) the energy density u, (d) the Poynting vector $\mathbf{S}$.

Compute also (as functions of x), (e) the time average of $\mathbf{E}^2$, (f) the time average of u, (g) the time average of $\mathbf{S}$.

7–10. Discuss Problem 7–9 under the assumption that the two waves are polarized in mutually perpendicular planes.

7–11. Two sinusoidal waves, both of frequency ν and amplitude A, travel in vacuum in the directions of the x-axis and y-axis, respectively. The electric fields of both waves are parallel to the z-axis. Compute (a) the components of the electric field $\mathbf{E}$, (b) the components of the magnetic field $\mathbf{H}$, (c) the energy density u, (d) the components of the Poynting vector $\mathbf{S}$, (e) the mean values of u and $\mathbf{S}$. (f) Determine the planes in which the mean value of $\mathbf{E}^2$ is a maximum or a minimum. (g) Determine the planes in which the vector $\mathbf{H}$ performs circular oscillations.

7–12. Discuss parts (a), (b), (c), (d), (e), and (f) of Problem 7–11 under the assumption that the magnetic fields of the two waves are parallel to the z-axis.

7–13. Discuss the Fresnel double-mirror interference experiment on the basis of the electromagnetic theory of light. The following steps are suggested: Assume that the light source consists of a microscopic oscillator vibrating along a line parallel to the intersection of the two mirrors. Consider the two specular images of the source, S_1, S_2, as two coherent microscopic oscillators. Consider a point P in the plane containing S_1, S_2, and perpendicular to the intersection of the mirrors. Let O be the midpoint of the segment $S_1 S_2$; r the distance of P from

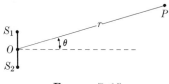

Figure 7-15

O; and $\pi/2 - \theta$ the angle between OP and S_1S_2 (Fig. 7–15). Assume that $r \gg \overline{S_1S_2}$. (a) Compute the resultant electric field at P as a function of r, θ, and $h = \overline{S_1S_2}$. (b) Compute the resultant magnetic field. (c) Compute the resultant Poynting vector.

7–14. A proton is injected into a uniform magnetic field $\mathbf{B}$ with a velocity $\mathbf{w}$ at right angles to the lines of force. Neglecting first energy loss by radiation, we find that the proton describes a circular orbit with an angular velocity ω independent of w. Assuming $w \ll c$, compute the fractional energy loss due to radiation during one revolution. After what time will the energy of the proton be $1/e$ of its initial value?

7–15. Solve Problem 7–14 numerically, assuming $B = 1$ weber/m^2 (proton mass: 1.67×10^{-27} kg; proton charge: 1.6×10^{-19} coul).

7–16. Electrons emitted with zero velocity from a plane electrode at ground potential are accelerated in vacuum toward a second plane electrode parallel to the first and held at a positive potential V_0. Let h be the separation of the electrodes, and assume a uniform electric field between them. Upon reaching the positive electrode, the electrons are brought to rest, with constant deceleration, in a distance δ. Compute the energies radiated during acceleration and deceleration as fractions of the energy with which the electrons would strike the positive electrode in the absence of radiation.

7–17. Solve Problem 7–16 numerically, assuming

$$h = 10 \text{ cm}, \quad \delta = 10^{-8} \text{ cm},$$

$$V_0 = 10^4 \text{ volts}$$

(electron mass: 9.1×10^{-31} kg; electron charge: 1.6×10^{-19} coul).

7–18. Two plane conducting plates are placed in an evacuated vessel, a distance $2h$ from each other. They are at a negative potential $-V_0$ with respect to a plane grid parallel to the plates and placed halfway between them. An electron, injected with zero velocity at a distance x_0 from the grid, will begin to oscillate in the direction perpendicular to the plates. Determine the fractional energy loss in one oscillation. Determine the electric field, the magnetic field, and the Poynting vector of the radiation field at a distance $r \gg x_0$

from the electron and at an angle θ to the direction of the motion of the electron (assume a uniform field between the grid and each of the plates; assume that the grid and the plates have sufficiently low conductivity so that their presence does not appreciably disturb the radiation field).

7–19. A point charge q has been moving with constant velocity w along a straight line until the time $t = t_0$. In the short time interval from $t = t_0$ to $t = t_0 + \Delta t$, a force perpendicular to the trajectory changes the direction of motion without changing the magnitude of the velocity. After the time $t_0 + \Delta t$, the electron again moves with velocity w along a straight line forming an angle $\Delta\alpha$ with the initial trajectory. Compute the radiation field, following a procedure similar to that used in Section 7–6.

Radioastronomy. *The development of sensitive microwave receivers has revealed a variety of radio waves arriving upon the earth from outer space. A point source of radio waves is referred to as a radio star. Many radio stars coincide with visible celestial objects (stars, distant galaxies). Radio waves originate also from the gas clouds (mostly hydrogen) filling our galaxy. The total incoming radiation consists of monochromatic waves superposed on a continuous spectrum. Among the former, the 21-cm wavelength radiation originating from atomic hydrogen has been extensively investigated. A typical radiotelescope consists of a parabolic mirror with a receiving antenna at the focal point. The receiver can be tuned so as to repond only to frequencies in a very narrow interval.*

7–20. The largest radiotelescopes in existence or under construction in 1956 include a telescope 250 ft in diameter at Manchester, England, a telescope 83 ft in diameter in Holland, a telescope 50 ft in diameter at the Naval Research Laboratory in Washington, D. C., and a telescope 60 ft in diameter at Harvard University in Cambridge, Massachusetts. Compute the limits of resolution of these telescopes for radio waves of 1.5 m wavelength.

7–21. A radiotelescope, at an altitude h over the surface of the sea, points toward the horizon (Fig. 7–16). The receiver is tuned to a frequency of 200 megacycles. Waves from a pointlike radio star near the horizon reach the detector both directly and after reflection at the water's surface. Compute the intensity of the radiation detected by the telescope as a function of the angle α characterizing the height of the radio star above the horizon. Assume that the receiving antenna is horizontal.

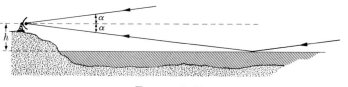

FIGURE 7–16

7–22. Suppose that the radiotelescope in the previous problem has a diameter of 3 m and is located at an altitude $h = 3000$ m. Evaluate the minimum angular diameter $\Delta\alpha$ of a radio source that can be distinguished from a pointlike source if the time variation of the signal received by the telescope is recorded as the source rises above the horizon. Compare with the limit of resolution of the radiotelescope.

7–23. A radiotelescope built by the Commonwealth Scientific and Industrial Research organization near Sydney, Australia, consists of 600 evenly spaced dipoles forming a linear array 1500 ft long. With cables of equal length the outputs of the 600 dipoles are brought to an adding circuit, giving a signal proportional to the rms value of the algebraic sum of the electric field strengths at the locations of the various dipoles. Suppose that the receivers are tuned to a frequency of 300 megacycles. Compute and plot the output signal of the adding circuit as a function of the angle θ formed by the line on which the dipoles are arranged with the line pointing toward the radio star. Evaluate the limit of resolution of the array.

7–24. The galactic volume is roughly in the shape of a flat disk, about 100,000 light years in diameter, rotating about an axis through its center (Fig. 7–17). The period of rotation increases gradually from the center to the periphery, as shown in Fig. 7–18. The earth lies about 30,000 light years from the galactic center. A radiotelescope points at 45° to the direction of the galactic center, in the galactic plane (Fig. 7–18). Considering Doppler effect, plot the frequency of the 21-cm hydrogen line detected by the telescope, as a function of the distance of the source from the earth. (In Fig. 7–17 assume clockwise rotation.)

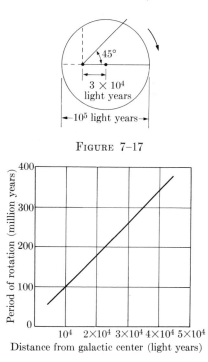

FIGURE 7–17

Distance from galactic center (light years)

FIGURE 7–18

CHAPTER 8

LIGHT AND MATTER

8-1 The process of light emission. Light is a consequence of the motions of the electrically charged particles that form the atoms and the molecules of the light source. Motions of electrons within the atoms, rigid rotations of polar molecules (i.e., of molecules in which the centers of gravity of the positive and negative charges do not coincide), and vibrations of atoms within molecules contribute, in different measure, to the process of light emission and to other optical phenomena.

Classical physics cannot adequately describe the behavior of atoms and molecules; a rigorous theory of the interactions between light and matter is a problem of quantum physics. In the present book we do not intend to deal with this problem but wish to present only what may be called a "model theory" of the optical properties of matter.

For this purpose we shall replace the actual molecules with an ensemble of harmonic oscillators. Each oscillator will be an *electric dipole*, formed by two material particles carrying charges of opposite sign, equal in magnitude to the charge of the electron ($e = 1.602 \times 10^{-19}$ coulomb). We shall assume that the two particles attract each other with a force proportional to their separation. Thus, if the particles are a certain distance apart, and are then released from rest, they will execute harmonic oscillations, one with respect to the other. In computing this motion, we shall take no account of the coulomb interaction between the two particles, nor shall we concern ourselves with the fact that, according to this model, the particles would collide twice during each complete oscillation.*

We shall consider two different groups of oscillators, one corresponding to the motions of electrons in the atoms (*electronic oscillators*), and one corresponding to the rigid rotations and internal vibrations of the molecules (*molecular oscillators*).

---

*We could build a classical model in which this difficulty does not arise and in which, moreover, the coulomb attraction provides the required restoring force. This model, suggested by J. J. Thomson, pictures the oscillator as a sphere of uniformly distributed positive charge, containing a pointlike negative charge. The negative charge is in equilibrium at the center of the sphere and, when displaced from this position, is acted upon by a force proportional to the displacement and directed toward the center.

In the electronic oscillators the negatively charged particle will be an electron, while the positively charged particle will have a mass large compared with that of the electron. In the molecular oscillators both the positive and the negative particles will have masses of the order of atomic masses, and therefore much larger than the mass of the electron. However, to simplify the calculations, we shall again assume that one of the two particles is much heavier than the other. For both kinds of oscillators, then, we need consider only the motion of the lighter particle, while the heavier particle acts essentially as a fixed center of attraction.

One might question the value of a theory based on the admittedly crude model described above. The truth of the matter is that, so long as we remain within the framework of classical physics, this model is forced upon us by the experimental facts, in particular by the emission of almost perfectly sinusoidal light waves by luminescent gases. Indeed, of all classical systems, the harmonic oscillator is the only one whose frequency is independent of amplitude, and hence no other classical model can reconcile the sharpness of the spectral lines emitted by certain light sources with the fact that, at any given time, the various molecules of a light source must be in different states of excitation, and that this state of excitation must change with time.

It turns out that the classical model of the harmonic oscillator accounts remarkably well for a number of experimental observations, and it is extremely valuable in clarifying the relationship among such different phenomena as emission, absorption, dispersion, scattering, etc. Thus the study of the emission of electromagnetic waves by harmonic electric oscillators, and of the action of electromagnetic waves on harmonic electric oscillators, is not merely a formal exercise. Rather, it provides an intuitive foundation for the understanding of the more rigorous results of quantum theory.

In what follows we shall focus our attention upon electronic oscillators, but the results will be valid for molecular oscillators as well, provided we take into account the difference in mass of the oscillating particles in the two systems.

We assume first that at $t = 0$ the electron is at rest at a distance b from the fixed center of attraction. The subsequent motion of the electron will then occur along a straight line passing through this point. If

$$F = -kz \qquad (8\text{--}1)$$

is the force acting on the electron when its distance from the center of attraction is z, the differential equation of the motion is

$$m \frac{d^2z}{dt^2} = -kz. \qquad (8\text{--}2)$$

It is well known (and we can check by direct substitution) that this equation has the following solution:

$$z = b \cos \omega_0 t, \qquad (8\text{--}3)$$

where we have placed

$$\omega_0 = \sqrt{k/m}, \qquad (8\text{--}4)$$

and have made use of the initial conditions $z = b$ and $dz/dt = 0$ at $t = 0$. At the time t, the electron and the positive charge form a dipole whose moment is given by

$$p = -ez = p_0 \cos \omega_0 t, \qquad (8\text{--}5)$$

where

$$p_0 = -eb. \qquad (8\text{--}6)$$

Note that p is positive or negative depending on whether the dipole moment points in the positive or negative z-direction.

If the electron has initially a certain velocity, as well as a certain displacement, and if the direction of the velocity does not coincide with the direction of the displacement, the subsequent motion of the electron does not occur along a straight line, but in the plane containing the center of attraction and the initial direction of the velocity. By taking this plane as the yz-plane, we can write the differential equations of motion as

$$m\frac{d^2y}{dt^2} = -ky, \qquad m\frac{d^2z}{dt^2} = -kz. \qquad (8\text{--}7)$$

The general solution of these equations is

$$y = b_1 \cos (\omega_0 t + \varphi_1), \qquad z = b_2 \cos (\omega_0 t + \varphi_2), \qquad (8\text{--}8)$$

where the amplitudes b_1, b_2 and the phases φ_1, φ_2 are determined by the coordinates of the electron, and by the components of its velocity at the time $t = 0$. The components of the electric dipole moment are

$$p_y = p_{0y} \cos (\omega_0 t + \varphi_1), \qquad p_z = p_{0z} \cos (\omega_0 t + \varphi_2), \qquad (8\text{--}9)$$

where

$$p_{0y} = -eb_1, \qquad p_{0z} = -eb_2. \qquad (8\text{--}10)$$

From what we have learned in Section 6–2, we conclude that in this general case the electron moves in an elliptical orbit.

According to our model, in the quiescent state the electron is at its equilibrium position, which coincides with the position of the positive charge. Light emission occurs when the electron is displaced from its equilibrium position by an external agency, such as a collision due to thermal agitation or the impact of a fast-moving particle. The electron then begins to oscillate and consequently emits electromagnetic radiation until the energy acquired in the excitation process is completely dissipated or until its motion is disturbed, e.g., by another collision. As we shall see in the next section, the energy radiated during one oscillation turns out to be a very small fraction of the energy present in the oscillating dipole. Moreover, in gases, collisions between molecules occur relatively seldom, so that an excited dipole can emit a fairly long train of sinusoidal waves before its oscillatory motion is disturbed. Therefore, light emitted by gaseous sources is highly monochromatic (see Section 3–14). In condensed matter, however, the oscillatory motions of individual dipoles is continuously disturbed by the nearby presence of other dipoles. Consequently, the light emitted by an incandescent solid or liquid exhibits a continuous spectrum of wavelengths.

In what follows we shall confine our attention to the emission of light by gases. To a first approximation, we can then neglect all external perturbations, as well as the damping due to the radiation process.

Note that the amplitude of the oscillations is of the order of atomic dimensions (i.e., of the order of 10^{-8} cm) and is therefore very small compared with the wavelength (of the order of 5×10^{-5} cm for visible light). Therefore in applying the formulas for the computation of the radiation field (Section 7–6) we can regard the origin O of our frame of reference as coincident with the fixed positive charge rather than with the moving electron.

From the general expression for the electric field of an accelerated charge (Eq. 7–82), it follows that $\mathbf{E}$ is proportional to the component of the acceleration vector perpendicular to the line of sight (the proportionality factor is negative if the charge is positive, and positive if the charge is negative). On the other hand, in a harmonic oscillator the acceleration vector is proportional in magnitude and opposite in direction to the vector representing the instantaneous displacement of the moving particle from the equilibrium position. We therefore conclude that the line described by the tip of the vector $\mathbf{E}$ has the same shape as the projection of the trajectory of the electron on a plane perpendicular to the line of sight. In other words, *the apparent shape of the electron orbit, as seen from a point in space, represents the state of polarization of the electromagnetic wave received at this point.* In the general case, the electron orbit is an ellipse. Since the projection of an ellipse on a plane is, in general, another ellipse, we recognize that the light wave is, in general, elliptically polarized. Linear and circular polarizations occur as special cases.

Note that for an electron performing linear or elliptical oscillations, the vectors representing the acceleration **a** and the electric dipole moment **p** are related by

$$-e\mathbf{a} = \frac{d^2\mathbf{p}}{dt^2}, \tag{8-11}$$

or, since the components of **p** are sinusoidal functions of time (Eq. 8-9),

$$-e\mathbf{a} = -\omega_0^2\mathbf{p}. \tag{8-12}$$

With $q = -e$, the general expression for **E** (Eq. 7-82) now becomes

$$\mathbf{E} = \frac{\omega_0^2}{4\pi\epsilon_0 c^2 r}\,(\mathbf{p}_n)_{\,t-r/c}, \tag{8-13}$$

where $(\mathbf{p}_n)_{\,t-r/c}$ represents the component perpendicular to the line of sight of the vector **p**, taken at the time $t - r/c$. We see that **E** is always *parallel* to the vector $(\mathbf{p}_n)_{\,t-r/c}$.

We now wish to consider in some detail the electromagnetic waves produced (a) by a linear oscillator, and (b) by a circular oscillator.

(a) *Linear oscillator.* We describe the field in a polar frame of reference with the polar axis z in the direction of the oscillations (Fig. 8-1). The electric dipole moment is parallel to the z-axis, **E** is tangent to the meridian circle, and **H** is tangent to the parallel circle; hence the wave is everywhere linearly polarized.

If the oscillations of the electric dipole are represented by Eq. (8-5), and if ϑ is the angle of the line of sight with the polar axis, the ϑ-component of **E** is expressed by

$$E_\vartheta = \frac{p_0\omega_0^2 \sin \vartheta}{4\pi\epsilon_0 c^2 r}\cos \omega_0\left(t - \frac{r}{c}\right). \tag{8-14}$$

The other components of **E** are zero.

The only component of the Poynting vector different from zero is the r-component, given by

$$S_r = \frac{p_0^2\omega_0^4 \sin^2 \vartheta}{16\pi^2 \epsilon_0 c^3 r^2}\cos^2 \omega_0\left(t - \frac{r}{c}\right). \tag{8-15}$$

Since the average value of $\cos^2 \omega_0(t - r/c)$ is $\frac{1}{2}$, the mean value of S_r at the distance r from the oscillating dipole and at the angle ϑ to the direction of oscillation is

$$(S_r)_{\text{av}} = \frac{p_0^2\omega_0^4 \sin^2 \vartheta}{32\pi^2 \epsilon_0 c^3 r^2}, \tag{8-16}$$

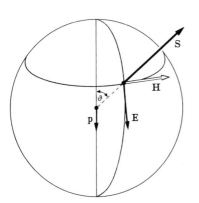

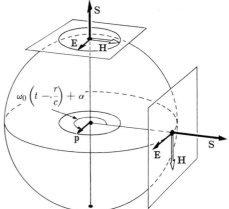

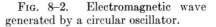

FIG. 8–1.   Electromagnetic wave   FIG. 8–2.   Electromagnetic wave
generated by a linear oscillator.   generated by a circular oscillator.

and we see that the intensity [which is proportional to $(S_r)_{av}$] is zero along
the polar axis, i.e., in the direction of the axis of the dipole, and is a maximum in the equatorial plane.

(b) *Circular oscillator.* In this case the electric dipole moment **p** has a
constant magnitude p_0 and rotates with a constant angular velocity,
ω_0 (Fig. 8–2). At a given point in space the wave is, in general, elliptically
polarized.

In the plane of the orbit, the ellipse reduces to a straight segment, i.e., the
wave is linearly polarized. The electric field lies in the plane of the orbit.
Thus, in a polar frame of reference with the polar axis perpendicular to the
plane of the orbit, only the component of **E** corresponding to the azimuthal
angle Φ is different from zero. The angle formed by **p** with the line of sight
at the time t is represented by an expression of the type $\omega_0 t + \alpha$. Hence E_Φ
is given by

$$E_\Phi = \frac{p_0\omega_0^2}{4\pi\epsilon_0 c^2 r} \sin\left[\omega_0\left(t - \frac{r}{c}\right) + \alpha\right].$$
(8–17)

The instantaneous magnitude of the Poynting vector is

$$S_r = \frac{p_0^2\omega_0^4}{16\pi^2\epsilon_0 c^3 r^2} \sin^2\left[\omega_0\left(t - \frac{r}{c}\right) + \alpha\right].$$
(8–18)

The mean value of the energy flux per unit area is

$$(S_r)_{av} = \frac{p_0^2\omega_0^4}{32\pi^2\epsilon_0 c^3 r^2}.$$
(8–19)

Along the axis of the orbit the ellipse becomes a circle. In this case, $\mathbf{p}$ is perpendicular to the line of sight. The electric vector $\mathbf{E}$ is given by

$$\mathbf{E} = \frac{\omega_0^2}{4\pi\,\epsilon_0 c^2 r}\,\mathbf{p}_{\,t-r/c}. \tag{8-20}$$

The Poynting vector is constant in time, and its magnitude is given by

$$S = \frac{p_0^2 \omega_0^4}{16\pi^2 \epsilon_0 c^3 r^2}. \tag{8-21}$$

The results described above apply both to electronic oscillators and to molecular oscillators. The main difference between the two lies in the values of the characteristic frequency ω_0, which, being inversely proportional to the square root of the mass of the oscillating particle (Eq. 8-4), is much smaller for the molecular oscillators than for the electronic oscillators. Indeed, the characteristic frequencies of molecular oscillators are usually in the distant infrared, while the characteristic frequencies of electronic oscillators are mostly in the ultraviolet range or beyond.

8-2 Damping of the oscillating dipoles. As pointed out in the preceding section, the energy loss due to the emission of electromagnetic waves by an oscillating electron causes a gradual damping of the oscillations. We now propose to compute this effect.

In the general case of elliptical oscillations, the kinetic energy of the electron at time t is given by

$$\frac{1}{2}\,m\left[\left(\frac{dy}{dt}\right)^2 + \left(\frac{dz}{dt}\right)^2\right] = \frac{1}{2}\,m\omega_0^2[b_1^2\,\sin^2\,(\omega_0 t + \varphi_1) + b_2^2\,\sin^2\,(\omega_0 t + \varphi_2)];$$

the potential energy at the same time is

$$\tfrac{1}{2}\,k(y^2 + z^2) = \tfrac{1}{2}\,m\omega_0^2[b_1^2\,\cos^2\,(\omega_0 t + \varphi_1) + b_2^2\,\cos^2\,(\omega_0 t + \varphi_2)];$$

and thus the total energy is

$$W = \tfrac{1}{2}\,m\omega_0^2(b_1^2 + b_2^2). \tag{8-22}$$

In the special case of linear oscillations ($b_2 = 0$, $b_1 = b$) the above equation becomes

$$W = \tfrac{1}{2}\,m\omega_0^2 b^2. \tag{8-23}$$

According to Eq. (7–81), the instantaneous rate of energy loss due to radiation is

$$\Phi = \frac{e^2}{6\pi\epsilon_0 c^3}\, a^2,$$

where $a = |\mathbf{a}|$ is the magnitude of the acceleration vector. Since

$$a^2 = \left(\frac{d^2 y}{dt^2}\right)^2 + \left(\frac{d^2 z}{dt^2}\right)^2 = \omega_0^4[b_1^2 \cos^2 (\omega_0 t + \varphi_1) + b_2^2 \cos^2 (\omega_0 t + \varphi_2)],$$

we obtain

$$\Phi = \frac{e^2 \omega_0^4}{6\pi\epsilon_0 c^3}\, [b_1^2 \cos^2 (\omega_0 t + \varphi_1) + b_2^2 \cos^2 (\omega_0 t + \varphi_2)]. \quad (8\text{--}24)$$

Since the average value of the $\cos^2$ function is $\frac{1}{2}$, we obtain from (8–24) the following expression for the *average* energy loss per unit time, i.e., for the average power radiated by the oscillating dipoles:

$$(\Phi)_{av} = \frac{e^2(b_1^2 + b_2^2)\omega_0^4}{12\pi\epsilon_0 c^3}. \quad (8\text{--}25)$$

Introducing the amplitudes of oscillation of the components of the electric dipole moment (Eqs. 8–10), we can write (8–25) as

$$(\Phi)_{av} = \frac{(p_{0y}^2 + p_{0z}^2)\omega_0^4}{12\pi\epsilon_0 c^3}. \quad (8\text{--}26)$$

If we denote the period by T_0, the wavelength by λ_0 (i.e., if we put $\lambda_0 = cT_0 = 2\pi c/\omega_0$, and define

$$r_e = \frac{e^2}{4\pi\epsilon_0 mc^2}, \quad (8\text{--}27)$$

we can also write (8–25) as

$$(\Phi)_{av} = \frac{8\pi^2}{3}\frac{r_e}{\lambda_0}\frac{W}{T_0}, \quad (8\text{--}28)$$

where W is given by (8–22). Note that the quantity r_e has the dimension of length. If the oscillating particle is an electron, we have $e = 1.602 \times 10^{-19}$ coul, and $m = 9.105 \times 10^{-28}$ gm, and Eq. (8–27) yields

$$r_e = 2.818 \times 10^{-13} \text{cm}.$$

This length plays an important role in many problems of atomic physics, and is often referred to as the *classical radius of the electron*.* From (8–28), and remembering that λ_0 for visible light is of the order of 5×10^{-5} cm, we find that the fractional energy loss during one oscillation,

$$\frac{T_0}{W}\left(-\frac{dW}{dt}\right)_{\text{av}} = \frac{T_0(\Phi)_{\text{av}}}{W},$$

is of the order of 1.5×10^{-7}, and is therefore a very small number, as stated in the previous section. If we put

$$\tau_r = \frac{3}{8\pi^2}\frac{\lambda_0}{r_e}T_0, \tag{8–29}$$

we obtain for the variable energy W of the oscillating dipole the following differential equation:

$$-\frac{dW}{dt} = (\Phi)_{\text{av}} = \frac{W}{\tau_r}. \tag{8–30}$$

whose solution is

$$W = W_0 \exp\left(-t/\tau_r\right). \tag{8–31}$$

Here t is the time measured from the instant when the excitation occurs and W_0 is the initial value of the excitation energy. It is evident that *the energy of the oscillating dipole decreases exponentially with time*. Its value is reduced to $1/e$ of the initial value after a time equal to τ_r.** The length of the wave train emitted during this time is $\tau_r c$ and it is of the order of 300 cm for visible light. This length is greater than the length of wave trains computed from the observed lack of monochromaticity of real light sources (Section 3–14), which means that ordinarily the length of wave trains emitted by excited atoms is not limited by radiation damping, but rather by such external disturbances as collisions with other atoms.†

---

*To justify the name, note that the energy stored in the electric field produced by a charge e uniformly distributed over a spherical surface of radius r_e is of the order of magnitude of the rest energy of the electron, mc^2 (in fact, it is equal to $mc^2/2$).

**Note that the amplitude of oscillation is proportional to the square root of the energy. Therefore, the amplitude b at the time t is related to the initial amplitude b_0 by the equation $b(t) = b_0 \exp\left(-t/2\tau_r\right)$, and the amplitude is reduced to $1/e$ of the initial value in a time equal to $2\tau_r$.

†The Doppler effect also contributes to the width of spectral lines; see Section 5–4.

We can formally represent the damping of the oscillating dipoles due to both radiation and collisions by introducing into the equations of motion (Eq. 8–2 or Eqs. 8–7) a fictitious *frictional force*, i.e., a force proportional and opposite to the velocity. We may consider this force as the sum of two terms: $f_r = -h_r(dz/dt)$, corresponding to radiation damping; and $f_c = -h_c(dz/dt)$, corresponding to collision damping. For the case of the linear oscillator, for example, in place of Eq. (8–2) we shall write

$$m \frac{d^2z}{dt^2} = -kz - (h_r + h_c) \frac{dz}{dt}.$$ (8–32)

Since the fractional energy loss during one oscillation is small, we may compute h_r by equating the average work per unit time done by the oscillating particle against the force f_r to the average rate of energy loss by radiation, $(\Phi)_{av}$ (Eq. 8–28). The work per unit time done against the force $f_r = -h_r(dz/dt)$ is

$$-f_r \frac{dz}{dt} = h_r \left(\frac{dz}{dt}\right)^2 = h_r b^2 \omega_0^2 \sin^2 \omega_0 t,$$

and, remembering Eq. (8–23), the average value of this quantity is

$$\left(-f_r \frac{dz}{dt}\right)_{av} = \frac{h_r b^2 \omega_0^2}{2} = \frac{h_r W}{m}.$$ (8–33)

From the equation

$$\left(-f_r \frac{dz}{dt}\right)_{av} = (\Phi)_{av},$$

we then obtain

$$h_r = \frac{m(\Phi)_{av}}{W},$$

and therefore (Eq. 8–30)

$$h_r = m/\tau_r.$$ (8–34)

Similarly, we find that the work per unit time done against the frictional force f_c corresponding to collision damping has the average value

$$\left(-f_c \frac{dz}{dt}\right) = \frac{h_c W}{m}.$$ (8–35)

Thus, if we take into account both frictional forces, f_r and f_c, the differential equation for the oscillation energy W becomes

$$-\frac{dW}{dt} = \frac{h_r + h_c}{m}\, W, \tag{8-36}$$

whose solution is

$$W = W_0 e^{-t/\tau},$$

where

$$\tau = \frac{m}{h_r + h_c}. \tag{8-37}$$

Note that the work done against the frictional force f_c is transformed into heat, whereas, as we already know, the work done against the force f_r goes into radiation energy.

8–3 Forced oscillations of atomic electrons. The presence of matter affects the propagation of light in many ways. The most common and noticeable effects are the following:

(1) The velocity of propagation is smaller in a material medium than in empty space, and is different in different media. The change in the velocity of light at the surface of separation between the media gives rise to the phenomena of *reflection* and *refraction*, as discussed in detail in Chapter 2.

(2) Part of the energy of light is transformed into heat, i.e., the light beam is partially *absorbed*.

(3) The light is partially *scattered*, i.e., deflected away from the original direction of propagation.

Absorption and scattering produce a gradual attenuation of a light beam as it travels through matter. In the so-called transparent substances the attenuation is quite small unless the thickness traversed by the light beam is very great. However, in any actual material medium both absorption and scattering always occur to some degree, and therefore no medium, except the absolute vacuum, is perfectly transparent.

The three effects mentioned above depend on frequency. The frequency dependence of the index of refraction is known as *dispersion* (see Section 2–14). The frequency dependence of absorption is responsible for the color of most objects; for example, white light passing through a piece of ruby glass becomes red because the glass absorbs the green and blue rays much more strongly than the red ones. A piece of red cloth owes its color to a similar effect, because the light rays penetrate some distance into the dyed fibers before being diffused back. Sometimes, however, the color of a surface is due to selective reflection rather than to selective absorption of certain wavelengths; this is true in the case of several metals, e.g., copper or gold. The frequency dependence of scattering accounts for the blue color of the sky.

In the previous sections we have interpreted light emission as a radiation process of freely oscillating electric dipoles. We shall now apply the same model of the microscopic dipoles to the discussion of the phenomena that accompany the passage of light through matter. We shall see that we can understand these phenomena by considering the *forced oscillations* of the dipoles in the rapidly varying electric fields of the light waves. The power required to maintain the forced oscillations is supplied by the incident wave, which is therefore gradually attenuated as it propagates through the material medium. The incoherent superposition of the secondary waves emitted by the oscillating dipoles is responsible for the phenomenon of scattering. The coherent interference of these secondary waves with the incident wave results in a decrease of the velocity of propagation.

As a preliminary step toward a quantitative discussion of the general ideas outlined above, we shall investigate here the behavior of an isolated oscillator in the electromagnetic field of a sinusoidal wave.

The force experienced by the moving charge in such a field is given by the expression $\pm e(\mathbf{E} + \mathbf{w} \times \mathbf{B})$, where the first term represents the effect of the electric field and the second term the effect of the magnetic field; we leave open the possibility that the charge may have either sign. For an electromagnetic wave in vacuum, the magnitude of $\mathbf{B}$ is $1/c$ times the magnitude of $\mathbf{E}$. Since the velocity w of the moving charge is always very small compared with the velocity of light c, the second term is very small compared with the first, and will be neglected in the following computations.

We are thus left with the problem of studying the motion of a charged particle acted upon by an elastic restoring force (responsible for the free oscillations), a frictional force (responsible for the damping), and an external sinusoidal force (due to the electric field of the wave).

The qualitative features of this motion are well known. When the initially quiescent particle is reached by the light wave, it goes through a transient period and eventually settles in a state of steady forced oscillations. The frequency of the oscillations is identical to the frequency of the incident wave. The amplitude of the oscillations depends on the difference between the frequency of this incident wave and the characteristic frequency of the free oscillations, and is a maximum when the two frequencies are equal, i.e., when the incident wave is in *resonance* with the natural frequency of the oscillating charge. At frequencies appreciably different from the resonant frequency a small amount of damping does not appreciably affect the amplitude of the oscillations and can often be neglected. At the resonant frequency, however, damping always plays an essential role because it alone limits the amplitude of the forced oscillations.

For a quantitative study of the phenomena described above, we consider a plane, sinusoidal, linearly polarized wave traveling in the x-direction and with the electric vector in the z-direction. We take the origin of our frame of reference at the equilibrium position of the charged particle. The oscilla-

360 LIGHT AND MATTER [CHAP. 8

tions of the charged particle will occur along the z-axis, and the equation of motion is of the following form:

$$m \frac{d^2 z}{dt^2} = -kz - (h_r + h_c) \frac{dz}{dt} \pm eA \cos \omega t. \qquad (8\text{--}38)$$

On the right side of this equation, the first term represents the elastic restoring force, the second represents the frictional force (due to the combined effects of radiation damping and collisions; see Section 8–2), and the third represents the force due to the electric field of the light wave (of amplitude A and angular frequency ω).

Remembering the definition of ω_0 (Eq. 8–4) and that of τ (Eq. 8–37), and introducing as a new variable the electric dipole moment

$$p = \pm ze, \qquad (8\text{--}39)$$

we can rewrite Eq. (8–38) as

$$\frac{d^2 p}{dt^2} + \frac{1}{\tau} \frac{dp}{dt} + \omega_0^2 p = \frac{e^2}{m} A \cos \omega t. \qquad (8\text{--}40)$$

We are interested only in the solution of this equation corresponding to the steady-state motion, i.e., the solution representing a simple sinusoidal motion of constant amplitude. We have mentioned above that the angular frequency of this sinusoidal motion equals the angular frequency ω of the external force, so that we can write

$$p = p_0 \cos (\omega t - \varphi). \qquad (8\text{--}41)$$

We now wish to check that a function of this type actually satisfies Eq. (8–40) and to determine the values of the quantities p_0 and φ. We could simply insert the expression for p given by Eq. (8–41) into Eq. (8–40) and compute the values of p_0 and φ for which the resulting equation is satisfied at all values of t. However, we achieve the desired result more readily by making use of the vector representation of sinusoidal functions. In Fig. 8–3 the vector of length p_0 represents the sinusoidally varying dipole moment p. Since $dp/dt = -\omega p_0 \sin (\omega t - \varphi) = \omega p_0 \cos (\omega t - \varphi + \pi/2)$, the function dp/dt is represented by a vector of length ωp_0 rotated in the positive direction (i.e., counterclockwise) by an amount $\pi/2$ with respect to the vector representing the function p. By repeating the same argument, we find that the function d^2p/dt^2 is represented by a vector of length $\omega^2 p_0$ pointing in the direction opposite to that of the vector that represents the function p.

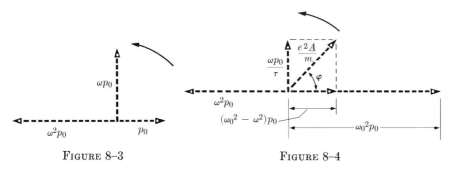

FIGURE 8–3   FIGURE 8–4

With these results in mind, we can immediately translate the differential equation (8–40) into a vector equation, as shown in Fig. 8–4. A vector of length $\omega_0^2 p_0$ represents the function $\omega_0^2 p$. A vector of length $\omega^2 p_0$, directly opposite to the former, represents the function d^2p/dt^2. The vector representing the function $(1/\tau)\,dp/dt$ has a length $(\omega/\tau)p_0$ and is at right angles to the other two vectors. The resultant of the three vectors has a magnitude

$$\sqrt{(\omega_0^2 - \omega^2)^2 p_0^2 + (\omega/\tau)^2 p_0^2}.$$

According to Eq. (8–40), this quantity equals the length $(e^2/m)A$ of the vector that represents the function $(e^2/m)A \cos \omega t$. We thus obtain

$$p_0 = \frac{(e^2/m)A}{\sqrt{(\omega_0^2 - \omega^2)^2 + \omega^2/\tau^2}}, \qquad (8\text{–}42)$$

which determines the amplitude of oscillation p_0 of the dipole moment. From Fig. 8–4 we also find that the difference of phase φ between the oscillations of the dipole moment and those of the electric field obey the equation

$$\tan \varphi = \frac{\omega}{\tau(\omega_0^2 - \omega^2)}. \qquad (8\text{–}43)$$

Note that the oscillations of the dipole always *lag* those of the electric field.

Equation (8–42) shows that p_0 is a maximum when $\omega = \omega_0$, as already pointed out. At $\omega = \omega_0$, p_0 acquires the value

$$(p_0)_{\max} = (e^2\tau/m\omega)A, \qquad (8\text{–}44)$$

and we see that $(p_0)_{\max}$ becomes greater as the damping becomes smaller. Indeed, for a given frequency, $(p_0)_{\max}$ is proportional to τ, the time after which the energy of a freely oscillating dipole is reduced to $1/e$ of its initial value.

In gases, damping is often very small, that is, τ is large. Thus, unless ω is very close to ω_0, the term $(\omega/\tau)^2$ in (8–42) is negligible compared with the term $\omega_0^2 - \omega^2$, and this equation becomes

$$p_0 = \frac{(e^2/m)A}{|\omega_0^2 - \omega^2|}.\qquad(8\text{–}45)$$

In other words, when damping is small the amplitude of the forced oscillations is practically the same as for an undamped oscillator, except in the immediate neighborhood of resonance.

Equation (8–43) shows that φ is smaller than $\pi/2$ for frequencies *below* the resonant frequency, and greater than $\pi/2$ for frequencies *above* the resonant frequency. In the case of small damping, the absolute value of $\tan \varphi$ is always very small except in the immediate neighborhood of the resonant frequency. Thus the electric field and the oscillations of the dipole have practically the same phase when $\omega < \omega_0$, and have practically opposite phase when $\omega > \omega_0$. The smaller the damping, the more suddenly the transition from $\varphi = 0$ to $\varphi = \pi$ occurs. As an illustration of the above results, Figs. 8–5 and 8–6 show the quantities p_0^2 and $\tan \varphi$ as functions of $(\omega - \omega_0)/\omega$, for two different values of τ.

8–4 The propagation of light waves in homogeneous dielectrics. Dispersion. The propagation of light in material substances is inherently a very complex phenomenon. Indeed, the electromagnetic disturbance at any point of the medium results from the combined effects of the primary wave coming from the light source and the secondary waves due to the forced oscillations of the microscopic dipoles. Yet many optical phenomena can be explained by a simple theory in which the secondary waves do not appear explicitly.

In this section we shall consider the propagation of light waves in a homogeneous dielectric, under the assumption that the damping of the microscopic oscillators is small and their characteristic frequency is far from that of the incident wave. Then, as we have seen in the preceding section, the oscillations of the microscopic dipoles occur with a phase difference of either 0 or π with respect to the oscillations of the external field. In both cases the dipole moments of the individual oscillations are, at all times, proportional to the intensity of the external field, the proportionality constant being positive or negative, as the case may be. It follows that the polarization vector **P** (which represents the resultant dipole moment per unit volume of the dielectric) is also proportional to the electric field $\mathbf{E}_e$ acting upon the dipoles.

Suppose first that all microscopic oscillators are identical, and let N be their number per unit volume. Considering Eq. (8–45) and remembering

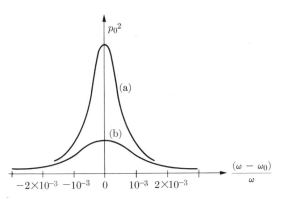

FIG. 8–5. p_0^2 vs. $(\omega - \omega_0)/\omega$ for two different values of τ: (a) $\tau = 1000/\omega_0$; (b) $\tau = 500/\omega_0$.

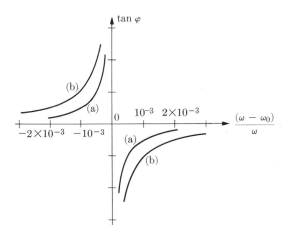

FIG. 8–6. tan φ vs. $(\omega - \omega_0)/\omega$ for two different values of τ: (a) $\tau = 1000/\omega_0$; (b) $\tau = 500/\omega_0$.

that φ is zero when $\omega < \omega_0$ and π when $\omega > \omega_0$, we find that

$$\mathbf{P} = \frac{N(e^2/m)}{\omega_0^2 - \omega^2}\, \mathbf{E}_e \qquad (8\text{–}46)$$

gives both the correct magnitude and the correct direction of the vector $\mathbf{P}$.

If, on the other hand, the material under consideration contains oscillators of several different frequencies, ω_{0i}, Eq. (8–46) must be replaced by the following:

$$\mathbf{P} = \left(\sum \frac{N_i(e^2/m_i)}{\omega_{0i}^2 - \omega^2} \right) \mathbf{E}_e, \qquad (8\text{–}47)$$

where N_i represents the number per unit volume of oscillators of characteristic frequency ω_{0i} and mass m_i.

The above results are completely unambiguous only for gases. In the case of liquids or solids there is a possibility that some of the microscopic oscillators will be strongly damped, although this difficulty is not very serious because the most effective oscillators in the phenomena here discussed are the electronic oscillators, and these are not greatly affected by the presence of neighboring molecules even in condensed matter.

A question may also be raised about the actual value of the electric field E_e acting upon the individual oscillators. The so called electric field E in a polarized dielectric is the resultant of the external field and of the field produced by the polarization (Sections 7–2), but E is not identical to the field E_e acting upon an individual dipole because in computing E_e the contribution of the dipole itself must be disregarded. In gases, where the field due to the polarization is small compared with the external field, the difference between E_e and E is negligible. In condensed matter, it turns out that E_e may differ appreciably from E, but is always proportional to E, and so in Eqs. (8–46) and (8–47) we should put $E_e = \text{const} \times E$. On the other hand, a constant factor is of no great concern to us, since N and N_i are essentially arbitrary constants, to be determined by experiment. In what follows we shall neglect this factor and simply substitute E for E_e in our analysis.

If the vector P and the vector E are proportional to each other at all times, then the displacement vector $D = \epsilon_0 E + P$ is also proportional to E, and we can define a dielectric permittivity ϵ by means of the equation

$$\epsilon E = D = \epsilon_0 E + P \qquad (8\text{–}48)$$

(see Section 7–2). From this equation, together with (8–47) we obtain

$$\epsilon = \epsilon_0 + \sum \frac{N_i(e^2/m_i)}{\omega_{0i}^2 - \omega^2}. \qquad (8\text{–}49)$$

Note that we cannot speak of a dielectric permittivity in the case of an arbitrary rapidly varying field, but only for a field that varies sinusoidally with time, because in the general case the instantaneous value of P is *not* proportional to the instantaneous value of E. Note also that in the case of a sinusoidally varying field *the permittivity turns out to be a function of the frequency* ω.

From the general theory developed in Section 7–3, it now follows that there exist solutions of Maxwell equations representing plane sinusoidal waves in the material media considered here. In other words, *the medium will propagate plane sinusoidal waves without changing their shape, but will not so propagate plane waves of any other kind.*

The velocity of propagation of the sinusoidal waves is determined by the electric permittivity of the medium (Eq. 7–34). Introducing the index of refraction $n = c/v$, we have

$$n = \sqrt{\epsilon/\epsilon_0},\qquad(8\text{–}50)$$

and therefore, from (8–49),

$$n^2 = 1 + \frac{e^2}{\epsilon_0}\sum_i \frac{N_i/m_i}{\omega_{0i}^2 - \omega^2}.\qquad(8\text{–}51)$$

This equation contains the solution of our problem. As pointed out at the outset, this solution has been obtained under the assumption that the wave frequency is appreciably different from the characteristic frequencies ω_{0i} of the microscopic oscillators. Equation (8–51) shows that when this is the case, the index of refraction n increases gradually with increasing frequency. This behavior is known as *normal dispersion*.

The behavior of the index of refraction in the neighborhood of one of the characteristic frequencies will be discussed later. Here we wish to remark that when the wave frequency becomes greater than all the characteristic frequencies (which happens only at frequencies far beyond the visible range), the index of refraction n becomes *smaller than* 1, which means that the phase velocity of the wave becomes *greater* than the velocity of light in empty space. There seems to be here a contradiction to the fundamental law stating that no velocity greater than the velocity of light in vacuum can occur in nature (see Section 5–3). The contradiction, of course, is only an apparent one, since c/n represents the *phase velocity* of the wave, whereas the velocity of propagation of an electromagnetic signal coincides with the *group velocity* (Section 5–5). At frequencies higher than the characteristic frequencies the group velocity differs considerably from the phase velocity because of the rapid variation of the index of refraction with frequency, and is always smaller than the velocity of light in vacuum.

At sufficiently low frequencies, ω becomes negligible compared with all characteristic frequencies ω_{0i}, and n acquires a value independent of ω, given by the equation

$$n^2 = 1 + \frac{e^2}{\epsilon_0}\sum \frac{N_i}{m_i\omega_{0i}^2} = 1 + \frac{e^2}{\epsilon_0}\sum \frac{N_i}{k_i},\qquad(8\text{–}52)$$

where we have made use of the equation $\omega_{0i}^2 = k_i/m_i$ (see Eq. 8–4). The value of n^2 given by (8–52) coincides with that of the static dielectric constant ($\kappa = \epsilon/\epsilon_0$) of the medium.

Optically transparent substances contain dipoles whose characteristic frequencies lie *outside* the visible ranges. Often such characteristic frequencies fall into two groups: one located in the ultraviolet, including the proper frequencies of electronic oscillators, and one located in the infrared, including the proper frequencies of molecular oscillators. Equation (8–51) shows that for $\omega \gg \omega_{0i}$ the contribution of a given oscillating dipole varies as $1/m_i\omega^2$, and thus decreases rapidly with increasing frequency. Therefore molecular dipoles of large mass and low characteristic frequency do not contribute effectively to the index of refraction in the optical range, the physical reason being that their large inertia prevents them from following the rapidly varying fields of light waves. Thus the index of refraction for visible light is determined mainly by the properties of the electronic oscillators. However, all dipoles, both of high and of low characteristic frequency, contribute to the static dielectric constant and to the index of refraction at low frequencies (up to those corresponding to the microwave or to the infrared spectrum). This explains the apparent contradiction between the large value of the static dielectric constant of water ($\kappa \approx 80$) and the small value of the index of refraction of water in the visible range ($n \approx 1.33$).

From our discussion it becomes clear that the physical reason why only sinusoidal waves travel without deformation in matter is that atoms behave like harmonic electric oscillators. It is the presence of such microscopic oscillators that enables a prism to sort out the various monochromatic components in a beam of white light. The peculiarly privileged role that sinusoidal waves appear to play stems from the fact that the free oscillations of electric charges in the atoms have a sinusoidal character.*

8–5 Reflection and refraction at the boundary between two transparent media. We now proceed to investigate, from the point of view of the electromagnetic theory of light, the phenomena of reflection and refraction that occur at the boundary between two dielectrics.

We shall consider sinusoidal light waves, so that we may assign to each dielectric a definite dielectric permittivity, ϵ_1 and ϵ_2. We shall assume that the two media are separated by a plane surface, and we shall take this surface as the yz-plane of a cartesian frame of reference. We shall assume that the negative x-axis lies in the medium of dielectric permittivity ϵ_1, and the positive x-axis in the medium of dielectric permittivity ϵ_2.

The electromagnetic fields in the two media are related to each other by certain conditions that must be satisfied at the surface of separation between the two media (i.e., at the surface $x = 0$). To find these boundary conditions, we consider the rectangle $ABCD$ shown in Fig. 8–7, such that sides BC, DA are parallel to the x-axis, while the sides AB, CD lie on opposite sides of the boundary surface and are parallel to the y-axis. Let Δy be the common length of the segments AB and CD, and Δx the common length

---

* For a mechanical model of a dispersive medium, see Appendix 2(d).

of the sides BC and DA. We now apply to this rectangle Faraday's induction law, expressed by Eq. (7–14):

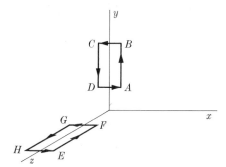

$$\oint E_s \, ds = -\int \frac{\partial B_z}{\partial t} \, dS.$$

At the limit for $\Delta x = 0$ the right side of this equation goes to zero because the area of integration vanishes and the integrand, $\partial B_z/\partial t$, is everywhere finite. Let us assume that Δy is sufficiently small so that **E** does not

FIG. 8–7.   Determination of the boundary conditions.

change appreciably along the segment AB or along the segment CD, and let us call E_{2y} and E_{1y}, respectively, the y-components of **E** on these two segments. Then the integral on the left side reduces to the sum of two terms:

$$\oint E_s \, ds = -E_{1y} \, \Delta y + E_{2y} \, \Delta y,$$

and we obtain

$$-E_{1y} \, \Delta y + E_{2y} \, \Delta y = 0,$$

or

$$E_{1y} = E_{2y}. \tag{8–53}$$

Similarly, application of the circuital law (Eq. 7–16) to the same rectangle $ABCD$ yields

$$H_{1y} = H_{2y}. \tag{8–54}$$

Two additional equations follow from the application of Eqs. (7–14) and (7–16) to the rectangle $EFGH$ (see Fig. 8–7):

$$E_{1z} = E_{2z}, \tag{8–55}$$

$$H_{1z} = H_{2z}. \tag{8–56}$$

Equations (8–53) through (8–56) show that *the components of the electric intensity and of the magnetic intensity parallel to the surface of separation between the two media are continous across this surface.*

The phenomena of reflection and refraction are direct consequences of the boundary conditions established above. In each of the two media there exist solutions of Maxwell's equations that represent arbitrary combinations of plane sinusoidal waves, traveling with the characteristic velocities $v_1 = 1/\sqrt{\epsilon_1\mu_0}$ and $v_2 = 1/\sqrt{\epsilon_2\mu_0}$, respectively. The boundary conditions, however, restrict the acceptable solutions in such a way that only a definite combination of plane waves in one of the two media may coexist with a given combination of plane waves in the second medium. In particular, as we shall see, we cannot usually satisfy the boundary conditions by assuming the existence of only one plane wave in the first medium (the incident wave) and only one plane wave in the second medium (the refracted wave). Indeed, with some exceptions that we shall discuss below, the boundary conditions require the presence in the first medium of both a refracted and a reflected wave. Formally, the phenomena here discussed are entirely similar to the reflection and transmission of mechanical waves at points of discontinuity [see Section 1–5 and Appendix 2(f)].

For a mathematical discussion of the problem, we choose, as before, the surface of separation between the two media as the yz-plane, and we take the y-axis in the plane containing the direction of propagation of the incident wave. Thus the xy-plane is coincident with the plane of incidence. If φ is the angle of incidence, the cosines of the angles that the direction of propagation of the incident wave forms with the coordinate axes (Fig. 8–8) are

$$\gamma_x = \cos\,\varphi, \qquad \gamma_y = \cos\left(\frac{\pi}{2} - \varphi\right) = \sin\,\varphi, \qquad \gamma_z = 0.$$

We assume the incident wave to be linearly polarized in an arbitrary plane. Remembering Eqs. (7–57) and (7–58), and making use of the complex representation of sinusoidal functions, we can write the following expression for the electric intensity $\mathbf{E}$ of this wave:

$$\mathbf{E} = \mathbf{A}\,\exp\left\{i\omega\left(t - \frac{x\,\cos\,\varphi + y\,\sin\,\varphi}{v_1}\right)\right\}. \qquad (8\text{–}57)$$

If A_y and A_z are the y- and z-components of the constant vector $\mathbf{A}$, the y- and z-components of $\mathbf{E}$ have the following expressions:

$$E_y = A_y\,\exp\left\{i\omega\left(t - \frac{x\,\cos\,\varphi + y\,\sin\,\varphi}{v_1}\right)\right\}, \qquad (8\text{–}58)$$

$$E_z = A_z\,\exp\left\{i\omega\left(t - \frac{x\,\cos\,\varphi + y\,\sin\,\varphi}{v_1}\right)\right\}. \qquad (8\text{–}59)$$

We do not wish to make *a priori* assumptions about the amplitude, the direction of propagation, or even the frequency of the refracted and re-

flected waves, so we write the equations for the y- and z-components of the
$\mathbf{E}$ vector of these waves in the following form:*

refracted wave:

$$E'_y = A'_y \exp\left\{i\omega'\left(t - \frac{\gamma'_x x + \gamma'_y y + \gamma'_z z}{v_2}\right)\right\}, \qquad (8\text{-}60)$$

$$E'_z = A'_z \exp\left\{i\omega'\left(t - \frac{\gamma'_x x + \gamma'_y y + \gamma'_z z}{v_2}\right)\right\}; \qquad (8\text{-}61)$$

reflected wave:

$$E''_y = A''_y \exp\left\{i\omega''\left(t - \frac{\gamma''_x x + \gamma''_y y + \gamma''_z z}{v_1}\right)\right\}, \qquad (8\text{-}62)$$

$$E''_z = A''_z \exp\left\{i\omega''\left(t - \frac{\gamma''_x x + \gamma''_y y + \gamma''_z z}{v_1}\right)\right\}. \qquad (8\text{-}63)$$

Since the y-component of the electric field is $E_y + E''_y$ in the first medium
and E'_y in the second, the boundary condition (8–53) yields

$$\text{at } x = 0: \qquad E_y + E''_y = E'_y. \qquad (8\text{-}64)$$

Similarly, we obtain

$$\text{at } x = 0: \qquad E_z + E''_z = E'_z. \qquad (8\text{-}65)$$

With the help of Eqs. (8–58) through (8–63), Eqs. (8–64) and (8–65) become

$$A_y \exp\left\{i\omega\left(t - \frac{y \sin\varphi}{v_1}\right)\right\} + A''_y \exp\left\{i\omega''\left(t - \frac{\gamma''_y y + \gamma''_z z}{v_1}\right)\right\}$$

$$= A'_y \exp\left\{i\omega'\left(t - \frac{\gamma'_y y + \gamma'_z z}{v_2}\right)\right\}, \qquad (8\text{-}66)$$

$$A_z \exp\left\{i\omega\left(t - \frac{y \sin\varphi}{v_1}\right)\right\} + A''_z \exp\left\{i\omega''\left(t - \frac{\gamma''_y y + \gamma''_z z}{v_1}\right)\right\}$$

$$= A'_z \exp\left\{i\omega'\left(t - \frac{\gamma'_y y + \gamma'_z z}{v_2}\right)\right\}. \qquad (8\text{-}67)$$

---

*For the sake of simplicity, however, we introduce no phase factors. As we
shall see, these are unnecessary in the present case.

For $t = 0$, $y = 0$, $z = 0$ the above equations yield

$$A_y + A_y'' = A_y', \tag{8-68}$$

$$A_z + A_z'' = A_z'. \tag{8-69}$$

Moreover, since (8–66) and (8–67) must be satisfied for all values of the variables t, y, and z, we conclude that the coefficients of each variable in the exponents of the various terms are identical. We thus obtain the following equations:

$$\omega = \omega' = \omega'', \tag{8-70}$$

$$\frac{\sin \varphi}{v_1} = \frac{\gamma_y'}{v_2} = \frac{\gamma_y''}{v_1}, \tag{8-71}$$

$$0 = \gamma_z' = \gamma_z''. \tag{8-72}$$

Equations (8–70) state the almost obvious fact that the frequencies of the reflected and refracted waves are identical to that of the incident wave. Equations (8–72) show that the directions of propagation of the reflected and of the refracted waves lie in the xy-plane, i.e., in the plane of incidence, in agreement with the law stated in Section 1–1.

If φ'' is the angle of reflection and φ' the angle of refraction, we have the following relations (Fig. 8–8):

$$\gamma_x' = \cos \varphi',$$

$$\gamma_y' = \cos \left(\frac{\pi}{2} - \varphi' \right) = \sin \varphi',$$

$$\gamma_x'' = \cos \left(\pi - \varphi'' \right) = -\cos \varphi'',$$

$$\gamma_y'' = \cos \left(\frac{\pi}{2} - \varphi'' \right) = \sin \varphi''.$$

With the help of these equations, Eqs. (8–71) yield

$$\frac{\sin \varphi}{v_1} = \frac{\sin \varphi'}{v_2} = \frac{\sin \varphi''}{v_1},$$

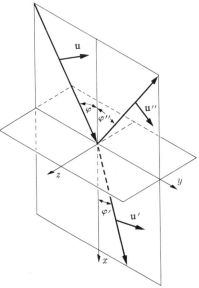

Fig. 8–8. Reflection and refraction of electromagnetic waves at the boundary between two dielectrics.

or
$$\varphi'' = \varphi, \tag{8–73}$$

$$\frac{\sin \varphi}{\sin \varphi'} = \frac{v_1}{v_2}. \tag{8–74}$$

Equation (8–73) expresses the law of reflection and (8–74) the law of refraction (Snell's law; see Sections 1–1 and 1–9). If n_1 and n_2 are the indices of refraction of the two media:

$$n_1 = \frac{c}{v_1} = \sqrt{\frac{\epsilon_1}{\epsilon_0}}, \qquad n_2 = \frac{c}{v_2} = \sqrt{\frac{\epsilon_2}{\epsilon_0}}, \tag{8–75}$$

(8–74) may be rewritten as

$$\frac{\sin \varphi}{\sin \varphi'} = \frac{n_2}{n_1}. \tag{8–76}$$

Note that the equations of the refracted and reflected waves now become

$$E_y' = A_y' \exp\left\{ i\omega\left(t - \frac{x\cos\varphi' + y\sin\varphi'}{v_2} \right) \right\},$$

$$E_z' = A_z' \exp\left\{ i\omega\left(t - \frac{x\cos\varphi' + y\sin\varphi'}{v_2} \right) \right\},$$

$$E_y'' = A_y'' \exp\left\{ i\omega\left(t + \frac{x\cos\varphi - y\sin\varphi}{v_1} \right) \right\}, \tag{8–77}$$

$$E_z'' = A_z'' \exp\left\{ i\omega\left(t + \frac{x\cos\varphi - y\sin\varphi}{v_1} \right) \right\}.$$

Since $\sin \varphi'$ cannot be greater than 1, Eq. (8–74) can be satisfied only if

$$\frac{v_2}{v_1} \sin \varphi < 1, \tag{8–78}$$

which is always the case when $v_2 < v_1$. If, however, $v_2 > v_1$, the above condition implies that the angle of incidence φ must be smaller than a limiting angle φ_0 given by

$$\sin \varphi_0 = \frac{v_1}{v_2} = \frac{n_2}{n_1}. \tag{8–79}$$

When φ is greater than φ_0, the refracted wave does not exist, i.e., the incident wave undergoes *total reflection* (see Section 1–1).

We shall discuss the phenomenon of total reflection in the next section. For the time being, we shall assume that the inequality (8–78) is satisfied, and proceed to investigate the relationship between the amplitudes and the intensities of the incident, the reflected, and the refracted waves.

We shall discuss separately the case where the electric vectors of the three waves lie in the plane of incidence (the xy-plane; see Fig. 8–9), and when they lie in the plane perpendicular to it (the xz-plane; see Fig. 8–10). The study of these two cases will give us the general solution of our problem, since an arbitrarily polarized wave can always be regarded as the superposition of two waves, vibrating in the two perpendicular planes considered above.

(a) *Vector* **E** *in the plane of incidence.* Let A, A', and A'' be the magnitudes of the amplitude vectors **A**, **A**', and **A**'' of the incident, the refracted, and the reflected waves. We consider the quantities A, A', and A'' positive if the corresponding vectors are oriented as shown by the unit vectors **u**, **u**', **u**'' in Fig. 8–8, negative in the opposite case. We then find that

$$A_y = A \cos \varphi, \qquad A'_y = A' \cos \varphi', \qquad A''_y = A'' \cos \varphi,$$

$$A_z = A'_z = A''_z = 0.$$

(8–80)

Equation (8–68) yields

$$A \cos \varphi + A'' \cos \varphi = A' \cos \varphi',$$

or

$$A + A'' = \frac{\cos \varphi'}{\cos \varphi} A'.$$

(8–81)

The magnetic fields of the incident, refracted, and reflected waves are parallel to the z-axis. Considering the relationship between the direction of **E**, the direction of **H**, and the direction of propagation, we find that if the electric vectors of the three waves are in the direction of the vectors **u**, **u**', and **u**'' in Fig. 8–8, the vector **H** is in the direction of the positive z-axis for the incident and the refracted waves, and in the direction of the negative z-axis for the reflected wave. Thus the following equations hold:

$$H_z = \sqrt{\frac{\epsilon_1}{\mu_0}} A \exp \left\{ i\omega \left(t - \frac{x \cos \varphi + y \sin \varphi}{v_1} \right) \right\},$$

$$H'_z = \sqrt{\frac{\epsilon_2}{\mu_0}} A' \exp \left\{ i\omega \left(t - \frac{x \cos \varphi' + y \sin \varphi'}{v_2} \right) \right\},$$

(8–82)

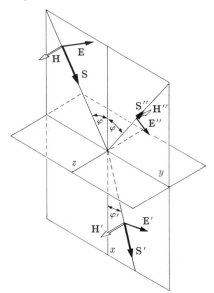

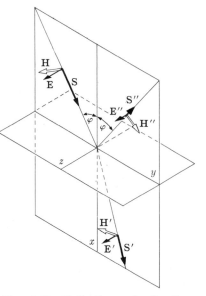

FIG. 8–9. Reflection and refraction of electromagnetic waves; **E** in the plane of incidence.

FIG. 8–10. Reflection and refraction of electromagnetic waves; **E** perpendicular to the plane of incidence.

$$H''_z = - \sqrt{\frac{\epsilon_1}{\mu_0}} A'' \exp \left\{ i\omega \left(t + \frac{x \cos \varphi - y \sin \varphi}{v_1} \right) \right\}.$$

The boundary conditions for the magnetic field,

$$H_z + H''_z = H'_z, \tag{8-83}$$

yields

$$\sqrt{\frac{\epsilon_1}{\mu_0}} A - \sqrt{\frac{\epsilon_1}{\mu_0}} A'' = \sqrt{\frac{\epsilon_2}{\mu_0}} A',$$

or

$$n_1 (A - A'') = n_2 A'. \tag{8-84}$$

Taking Snell's law (Eq. 8–76) into consideration, the last equation can also be written

$$A - A'' = \frac{\sin \varphi}{\sin \varphi'} A'. \tag{8-85}$$

Equations (8–81) and (8–85) may be solved for A' and A'', and yield

$$A' = \frac{2 \sin \varphi' \cos \varphi}{\sin \varphi' \cos \varphi' + \sin \varphi \cos \varphi} A, \qquad (8\text{-}86)$$

$$A'' = \frac{\sin \varphi' \cos \varphi' - \sin \varphi \cos \varphi}{\sin \varphi' \cos \varphi' + \sin \varphi \cos \varphi} A. \qquad (8\text{-}87)$$

It is easily verified that these equations are equivalent to

$$A' = \frac{2 \sin \varphi' \cos \varphi}{\sin (\varphi + \varphi') \cos (\varphi - \varphi')} A, \qquad (8\text{-}88)$$

$$A'' = -\frac{\tan (\varphi - \varphi')}{\tan (\varphi + \varphi')} A. \qquad (8\text{-}89)$$

(b) *Vector* **E** *perpendicular to the plane of incidence.* In this case the electric vectors are parallel to the z-axis and the magnetic vectors lie in the xy-plane (Fig. 8–10). Let A, A', and A'' be the amplitudes of oscillation of the electric vectors of the incident, refracted, and reflected waves. We consider these quantities as positive or negative depending upon whether the corresponding vectors **A**, **A**', and **A**'' are in the direction of the positive or of the negative z-axis. Thus

$$A_z = A, \quad A'_z = A', \quad A''_z = A'', \qquad A_y = A'_y = A''_y = 0, \qquad (8\text{-}90)$$

and the boundary conditon for E_z (Eq. 8–69) yields

$$A + A'' = A'. \qquad (8\text{-}91)$$

The amplitudes of oscillation of the magnetic vectors are $-\sqrt{\epsilon_1/\mu_0}\, A$, $-\sqrt{\epsilon_2/\mu_0}\, A''$, and $\sqrt{\epsilon_1/\mu_0}\, A'$. Here positive amplitudes indicate that the corresponding amplitude vectors are oriented in the direction of the vectors **u**, **u**', **u**'' (Fig. 8–8), negative amplitudes indicate the opposite orientation. The y-components of the magnetic fields are thus

$$H_y = -\sqrt{\frac{\epsilon_1}{\mu_0}}\, A \cos \varphi \exp \left\{ i\omega \left(t - \frac{x \cos \varphi + y \sin \varphi}{v_1} \right) \right\},$$

$$H'_y = -\sqrt{\frac{\epsilon_2}{\mu_0}}\, A' \cos \varphi' \exp \left\{ i\omega \left(t - \frac{x \cos \varphi' + y \sin \varphi'}{v_2} \right) \right\}, \qquad (8\text{-}92)$$

$$H''_y = \sqrt{\frac{\epsilon_1}{\mu_0}}\, A'' \cos \varphi \exp \left\{ i\omega \left(t + \frac{x \cos \varphi - y \sin \varphi}{v_1} \right) \right\}.$$

The boundary condition for the magnetic field,

$$H_y + H_y'' = H_y',$$ (8–93)

then yields

$$-\sqrt{\frac{\epsilon_1}{\mu_0}}\cos\varphi\cdot(A - A'') = -\sqrt{\frac{\epsilon_2}{\mu_0}}\cos\varphi'\cdot A',$$

or

$$n_1\cos\varphi\cdot(A - A'') = n_2\cos\varphi'\cdot A'.$$ (8–94)

This equation may also be written as

$$A - A'' = \frac{\sin\varphi}{\sin\varphi'}\frac{\cos\varphi'}{\cos\varphi}A'.$$ (8–95)

Equations (8–91) and (8–95) yield

$$A' = \frac{2\sin\varphi'\cos\varphi}{\sin\varphi\cos\varphi' + \sin\varphi'\cos\varphi}A,$$ (8–96)

$$A'' = \frac{\sin\varphi'\cos\varphi - \sin\varphi\cos\varphi'}{\sin\varphi\cos\varphi' + \sin\varphi'\cos\varphi}A,$$ (8–97)

or

$$A' = \frac{2\sin\varphi'\cos\varphi}{\sin(\varphi + \varphi')}A,$$ (8–98)

$$A'' = -\frac{\sin(\varphi - \varphi')}{\sin(\varphi + \varphi')}A.$$ (8–99)

Equations (8–88), (8–89), (8–98), and (8–99) were first obtained by Fresnel, on the basis of an elastic theory of light. They contain the complete solution of our problem when the refracted ray exists, i.e., when the inequality (8–78) is satisfied.

For the case of perpendicular incidence, $\varphi = 0$, $\varphi' = 0$, and Fresnel equations give an undetermined result. To investigate this case, it is most convenient to return to the boundary conditions [Eqs. (8–81) and (8–84)], which now become

$$A + A'' = A', \qquad A - A'' = \frac{n_2}{n_1}A'.$$

From these equations, we obtain

$$A' = \frac{2n_1}{n_1 + n_2}A, \qquad A'' = \frac{n_1 - n_2}{n_1 + n_2}A.$$ (8–100)

The *reflectance* ρ^2 is the ratio of the intensities of the reflected and incident waves. Since the intensity is proportional to the square of the amplitude, we have

$$\rho^2 = \left(\frac{A''}{A}\right)^2. \tag{8-101}$$

Thus, for example, in the case of perpendicular incidence, we obtain

$$\rho^2 = \left(\frac{n_1 - n_2}{n_1 + n_2}\right)^2. \tag{8-102}$$

8-6 Some consequences of Fresnel's formulas. Identification of the optical vector. We now wish to discuss some of the consequences of the equations derived in the preceding section.

Equations (8-88) and (8-98) show that A and A' always have the same sign. We thus conclude that the electric fields of the incident and of the refracted waves are always *in phase* at the boundary surface. To discuss the phase relation between the incident and the reflected waves, we must consider separately the cases where n_1 is smaller or larger than n_2, and the cases where the electric vector lies in the plane of incidence and in the plane perpendicular to it.

(1a) $n_1 < n_2$, **E** *in the plane of incidence.* In this case, $\varphi > \varphi'$, and Eq. (8-89) then shows that A'' and A have opposite signs when $\varphi + \varphi' < \pi/2$, and the same sign when $\varphi + \varphi' > \pi/2$. In the first case, the electric fields of the incident and the reflected waves have opposite phase at the boundary surface; in the second they have the same phase.

(1b) $n_1 < n_2$, **E** *perpendicular to the plane of incidence.* Equation (8-99) shows that in this case A'' and A always have opposite signs. Thus the electric fields of the incident and of the reflected waves have opposite phase at the boundary surface.

(2a) $n_1 > n_2$, **E** *in the plane of incidence.* In this case, the electric fields of the incident and of the reflected waves have the same phase if $\varphi + \varphi' < \pi/2$, and have opposite phase if $\varphi + \varphi' > \pi/2$.

(2b) $n_1 > n_2$, **E** *perpendicular to the plane of incidence.* In this case, the electric fields of the incident and of the reflected waves are always in phase at the boundary surface.

As an illustration of the above conclusions, the graphs in Figs. 8-11 and 8-12 represent the quantities A'/A and A''/A as functions of the angle of incidence φ for the cases where **E** is parallel and perpendicular to the planes of incidence, computed under the assumption that $n_2/n_1 = 1.5$ and $n_2/n_1 = 1/1.5$, respectively.

We have considered so far the phase relations between the electric fields. If we examine the equations describing the magnetic fields [Eqs. (8-82) and

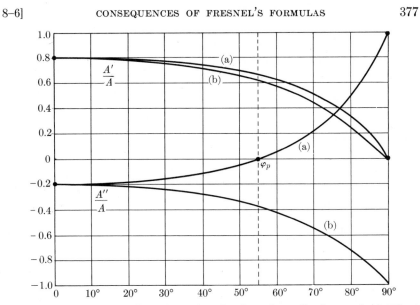

FIG. 8–11. Ratios of the refracted and reflected amplitudes to the incident amplitude, computed for $n_2/n_1 = 1.5$. (a) **E** in plane of incidence, (b) **E** perpendicular to plane of incidence.

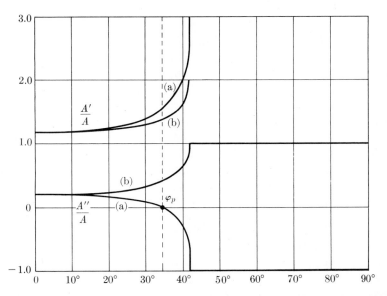

FIG. 8–12. Ratios of the refracted and reflected amplitudes to the incident amplitude, computed for $n_2/n_1 = 1/1.5$. (a) **E** in the plane of incidence, (b) **E** perpendicular to the plane of incidence.

(8–92)], we find that H_z and H''_z (or H_y and H''_y) have the same sign at the boundary surface when A and A'' have opposite signs, and vice versa. We thus conclude that when the electric fields of the incident and reflected waves have opposite phase, the magnetic fields are in phase, and that when the electric fields are in phase, the magnetic fields have opposite phase.

A singular case arises when $\varphi + \varphi' = \pi/2$. Then $\tan(\varphi + \varphi')$ goes to infinity and Eq. (8–89) shows that if $\mathbf{E}$ lies in the plane of incidence, the amplitude of the reflected wave vanishes. Thus the wave is totally refracted.

In this result we find a theoretical justification of Brewster's law, presented in Section 6–4 as an experimental fact. We recall that from the condition of perpendicularity between the reflected and refracted rays it follows that the Brewster angle φ_p satisfies

$$\tan \varphi_p = \frac{n_2}{n_1}. \tag{8–103}$$

In Section 6–3 we described an experiment by which the direction of the optical vector of a light wave can be determined. In Section 6–4 we found that light incident at the Brewster angle φ_p is totally refracted when the optical vector lies in the plane of incidence. On the other hand, from the theory developed above we have obtained the result that an electromagnetic wave incident at the Brewster angle φ_p is totally refracted when the electric vector lies in the plane of incidence. We thus reach the important conclusion that the optical vector must be identified with the electric vector $\mathbf{E}$. This means, of course, that the effects by which light manifests itself (chemical changes in a photographic plate, heating of a thermocouple, etc.) are due to the electric field of the light wave rather than to its magnetic field.

It follows, in particular, that the phase relations between the optical disturbances of the incident and reflected waves at the boundary surface are identical to the phase relations between the electric vectors of the two waves. Thus, for example, the reflection at normal or nearly normal incidence is or is not accompanied by a phase reversal, depending on whether the index of refraction of the second medium, n_2, is greater or smaller than that of the first, n_1. We have repeatedly made use of this property in the interpretation of interference phenomena (see, e.g., Section 3–8). It should be pointed out, however, that often the results would have been the same if the phase change had occurred when $n_2 < n_1$ instead of when $n_2 > n_1$. For example, in the experiment of Newton's rings (Section 3–8) one of the two interfering rays is reflected at the boundary between air and glass, the other at the boundary between glass and air. The position of the interference fringes does not depend on whether it is the first or the second ray that undergoes phase reversal at reflection, but only on the fact that one of the rays does and the other does not.

*8–7 Total reflection. We have specifically excluded from our previous considerations the case where the second medium has a smaller index of refraction than the first, and where the angle of incidence is greater than the limiting angle for total reflection, φ_0, given by Eq. (8–79). When $\varphi > \varphi_0$, a refracted wave in the ordinary sense does not exist, for we cannot find an angle of refraction φ' that satisfies Snell's law (Eq. 8–76). In other words, we cannot fulfill the boundary conditions at the surface of separation between the two media by assuming that the electric and magnetic fields in the second medium depend on the time and space coordinates through a function of the type

$$\exp\left\{i\omega\left(t - \frac{x\cos\varphi' + y\sin\varphi'}{v_2}\right)\right\}$$

(see Eqs. 8–77).

In order to remove the restriction that φ should be smaller than φ_0, we must consider a somewhat more general solution of Maxwell's equations. We shall again assume that in the first medium the electromagnetic field may be represented as the superposition of an incident and a reflected sinusoidal wave. Thus, for example, the y-component of the electric vector has the expression $E_y + E_y''$, where

$$E_y = A_y \exp\left\{i\omega\left(t - \frac{x\cos\varphi + y\sin\varphi}{v_1}\right)\right\},$$

$$E_y'' = A_y'' \exp\left\{i\omega\left(t + \frac{x\cos\varphi - y\sin\varphi}{v_1}\right)\right\},$$

(8–104)

and the z-component of the magnetic field has the expression $H_z + H_z''$, where

$$H_z = \sqrt{\frac{\epsilon_1}{\mu_0}}\,E_y, \qquad H_z'' = -\sqrt{\frac{\epsilon_1}{\mu_0}}\,E_y''.$$

(8–105)

We shall also assume that the components of the electric and magnetic fields in the second medium depend on the time and space coordinates through a function of the type

$$\exp\left\{-i\omega\left(t - \frac{\gamma_x' x + \gamma_y' y}{v_2}\right)\right\},$$

and thus we shall write, e.g.:

$$E_y' = A_y' \exp\left\{i\omega\left(t - \frac{\gamma_x' x + \gamma_y' y}{v_2}\right)\right\}.$$

(8–106)

However, we shall *not* require that γ'_x and γ'_y be the sine and cosine of a given angle, respectively.

(a) Our first task will be to investigate the properties of an electromagnetic field of the general type described by Eq. (8–106). From this equation, we find

$$\frac{\partial E'_y}{\partial t} = i\omega E'_y, \qquad \frac{\partial^2 E'_y}{\partial t^2} = -\omega^2 E'_y,$$

$$\frac{\partial E'_y}{\partial x} = -\frac{i\omega\gamma'_x}{v_2} E'_y, \qquad \frac{\partial^2 E'_y}{\partial x^2} = -\frac{\omega^2(\gamma'_x)^2}{v_2^2} E'_y,$$

$$\tag{8–107}$$

$$\frac{\partial E'_y}{\partial y} = -\frac{i\omega\gamma'_y}{v_2} E'_y, \qquad \frac{\partial^2 E'_y}{\partial y^2} = -\frac{\omega^2(\gamma'_y)^2}{v_2^2} E'_y,$$

$$\frac{\partial E'_y}{\partial z} = 0, \qquad \frac{\partial^2 E'_y}{\partial z^2} = 0.$$

Similar relations hold for the other components of the electric and magnetic fields.

From Maxwell's equations in the differential form (Eq. 7–27), we can easily prove that the components of the electric and magnetic fields satisfy equations of the type

$$\frac{\partial^2 E'_y}{\partial t^2} = v_2^2 \left(\frac{\partial^2 E'_x}{\partial x^2} + \frac{\partial^2 E'_y}{\partial y^2} + \frac{\partial^2 E'_z}{\partial z^2} \right). \tag{8–108}$$

This equation is a generalization of the wave equation (7–31) to the case where the electric field depends on all three coordinates x, y, z, instead of being a function of x alone. [cf. Appendix 2(h)].

Equation (8–108), together with equations (8–107), yields the following equation:

$$(\gamma'_x)^2 + (\gamma'_y)^2 = 1. \tag{8–109}$$

Equation (7–27b):

$$\frac{\partial E'_x}{\partial x} + \frac{\partial E'_y}{\partial y} + \frac{\partial E'_z}{\partial z} = 0,$$

together with (8–107), yields the following relation between E'_x and E'_y:

$$\gamma'_x E'_x + \gamma'_y E'_y = 0. \tag{8–110}$$

Equation (7–27g):

$$\frac{\partial H'_z}{\partial t} = \frac{1}{\mu_0}\left[\frac{\partial E'_x}{\partial y} - \frac{\partial E'_y}{\partial x}\right],$$

together with (8–107), yields

$$H'_z = \frac{1}{\mu_0 v_2}\left[-\gamma'_y E'_x + \gamma'_x E'_y\right],$$

or, considering (8–110),

$$H'_z = \frac{1}{\mu_0 v_2 \gamma'_x}\left[(\gamma'_x)^2 + (\gamma'_y)^2\right] E'_y.$$

Remembering that $v_2 = 1/\sqrt{\epsilon_2\mu_0}$ and making use of (8–109), we finally obtain

$$H'_z = \frac{1}{\gamma'_x}\sqrt{\frac{\epsilon_2}{\mu_0}}\, E'_y. \tag{8–111}$$

By a similar procedure, we find

$$H'_y = -\gamma'_x \sqrt{\frac{\epsilon_2}{\mu_0}}\, E'_z. \tag{8–112}$$

The boundary conditions for the y- and z-components of the electric field at $x = 0$ yield

$$\frac{\sin\varphi}{v_1} = \frac{\gamma'_y}{v_2},$$

or

$$\gamma'_y = \frac{n_1}{n_2}\sin\varphi. \tag{8–113}$$

If $\sin\varphi < n_2/n_1$ (i.e., if $\varphi < \varphi_0$), then $\gamma'_y < 1$, and Eq. (8–109) shows that γ'_x is a real number, and that we can find an angle φ' such that $\gamma'_x = \cos\varphi'$, $\gamma'_y = \sin\varphi'$. We thus come back to the case treated in Section 8–5: Eq. (8–106) is then the equation of a sinusoidal wave; Eq. (8–110) indicates that the electric vector is perpendicular to the direction of propagation; Eqs. (8–111) and (8–112) become equivalent to the second of Eqs. (8–82) and to the second of Eqs. (8–92), respectively.

If, however, $\sin\varphi > n_2/n_1$, then (8–109) shows that γ'_x is an imaginary number:

$$\gamma'_x = \pm i\sqrt{(\gamma'_y)^2 - 1}. \tag{8–114}$$

By substituting this expression for γ'_x in (8–106), we find

$$E'_y = A'_y \exp\left\{i\omega\left(t - \frac{\gamma'_y y}{v_2}\right)\right\} \exp\left\{\pm \frac{\omega}{v_2}\sqrt{(\gamma'_y)^2 - 1}\, x\right\}. \qquad (8\text{–}115)$$

Thus E'_y varies *sinusoidally* in the y-direction, but varies *exponentially* in the x-direction. It either increases or decreases with increasing x, depending on whether we take the $+$ or $-$ sign before the radical in (8–114). If the second medium extends to infinity in the direction of the positive x-axis, the first alternative is ruled out by the condition that E'_y must be everywhere finite. *Thus we must choose the negative sign* in (8–114) and (8–115), and we may write the latter equation as follows:

$$E'_y = A'_y \exp\left\{i\omega\left(t - \frac{\gamma'_y y}{v_2}\right)\right\} \exp\left(-\frac{x}{\xi}\right), \qquad (8\text{–}116)$$

where γ'_y is given by (8–113), and ξ is given by

$$\xi = \frac{v_2}{\omega\sqrt{(\gamma'_y)^2 - 1}}. \qquad (8\text{–}117)$$

Equations similar to (8–116) hold for the other components of the electric and magnetic vectors; e.g.:

$$E'_z = A'_z \exp\left\{i\omega\left(t - \frac{\gamma'_y}{v_2}\right)\right\} \exp\left(-\frac{x}{\xi}\right).$$

If $\lambda_2 = 2\pi v_2/\omega$ is the wavelength in the second medium, (8–117) becomes

$$\xi = \frac{\lambda_2}{2\pi\sqrt{(\gamma'_y)^2 - 1}}. \qquad (8\text{–}118)$$

The quantity ξ has the dimensions of a length, and represents the distance from the boundary at which the intensities of the electric and magnetic fields are reduced to $1/e$ of their values at the boundary. Except for the case that γ'_y is close to one, i.e., except in the immediate vicinity of the limiting angle for total reflection, ξ is of the order of λ. We thus conclude that *the electromagnetic field penetrates into the second medium, although only to a very small depth.*

(b) We shall now proceed to determine the amplitude of the reflected wave, following step by step the method used in Section 8–5.

We first consider the case where the electric field of the incident wave lies in the plane of incidence, i.e., in the xy-plane. The magnetic field is then parallel to the z-direction. Let A and A'' be, as before, the amplitudes of oscillation of the electric fields of the incident and reflected waves, respectively, so that $A_y = A \cos \varphi$, $A''_y = A'' \cos \varphi$. The corresponding magnetic fields are parallel to the z-direction, and their amplitudes of oscillation are $\sqrt{\epsilon_1/\mu_0}\, A$ and $-\sqrt{\epsilon_1/\mu_0}\, A''$. The boundary conditions

$$E_y + E''_y = E'_y, \qquad H_z + H''_z = H'_z, \qquad \text{at } x = 0,$$

together with Eqs. (8–111) and (8–115), yield

$$(A + A'') \cos \varphi = A'_y,$$

$$\sqrt{\frac{\epsilon_1}{\mu_0}}\, (A - A'') = \frac{1}{\gamma'_x} \sqrt{\frac{\epsilon_2}{\mu_0}}\, A'_y.$$

Upon elimination of A'_y, and remembering that $\sqrt{\epsilon_2/\epsilon_1} = n_2/n_1$, we obtain

$$A'' = -A\, \frac{1 - (n_1/n_2)(\gamma'_x/\cos \varphi)}{1 + (n_1/n_2)(\gamma'_x/\cos \varphi)}. \qquad (8\text{–}119)$$

If we replace γ'_x with $\cos \varphi'$, Eq. (8–119) becomes identical to (8–87). In the case now under consideration, γ'_x is the imaginary number $-i\sqrt{(\gamma'_y)^2 - 1}$. Thus we may write

$$\frac{n_1}{n_2}\, \frac{\gamma'_x}{\cos \varphi} = -ih,$$

where h is the real number

$$h = \frac{n_1}{n_2}\, \frac{\sqrt{(\gamma'_y)^2 - 1}}{\cos \varphi}, \qquad (8\text{–}120)$$

and (8–119) becomes

$$A'' = -A\, \frac{1 + ih}{1 - ih}. \qquad (8\text{–}121)$$

Equation (8–121) shows that the ratio between the amplitudes of the reflected and incident waves is a complex number. To understand the physical significance of this result, we write the complex number in the polar form; i.e., we put

$$\frac{1 + ih}{1 - ih} = \frac{1 - h^2 + 2ih}{1 + h^2} = \rho e^{i\psi_1}. \qquad (8\text{–}122)$$

We thus recognize that if the electric field of the incident wave is represented by

$$E = A \exp\left\{i\omega\left(t - \frac{x\cos\varphi + y\sin\varphi}{v_1}\right)\right\},$$

that of the reflected wave is represented by

$$E'' = -\rho A \exp\left\{i\left[\omega\left(t + \frac{x\cos\varphi - y\sin\varphi}{v_1}\right) + \psi_1\right]\right\}.$$

Contrary to the case considered previously, the reflected and incident waves now have at the boundary surface a phase difference ψ_1, which is, in general, neither 0 nor π. From (8–122), we find

$$\tan\psi_1 = \frac{2h}{1 - h^2},$$

which is equivalent to

$$\tan\frac{\psi_1}{2} = h.$$

This equation, together with the definition of φ_0 (Eq. 8–79) and with Eqs. (8–113) and (8–120), yields, after some transformations,

$$\tan\frac{\psi_1}{2} = \frac{\sqrt{\sin^2\varphi - \sin^2\varphi_0}}{\sin^2\varphi_0\cos\varphi}. \tag{8–123}$$

The ratio between the amplitudes of the reflected and incident waves is given by ρ. From (8–122), we find

$$\rho^2 = \left(\frac{1 + ih}{1 - ih}\right)\left(\frac{1 - ih}{1 + ih}\right) = 1. \tag{8–124}$$

Thus the amplitude of the reflected wave is identical with that of the incident wave; the incident wave is *totally reflected.*

The fact that the whole energy of the incident wave is found in the reflected wave does not contradict the existence of an electromagnetic field in the second medium. Indeed, this field does not represent an ordinary electromagnetic wave and does not carry energy across the boundary surface. In other words, its energy flux in the direction perpendicular to this surface is zero, as we can easily prove by showing that the average value of the x-component of the Poynting vector vanishes.

The case of a wave vibrating in the plane perpendicular to the plane of incidence can be similarly treated, and for the amplitude of the reflected wave we obtain the following expression:

$$A'' = \frac{1 + ik}{1 - ik}\, A, \tag{8-125}$$

where

$$k = \frac{n_2}{n_1}\, \frac{\sqrt{(\gamma_y')^2 - 1}}{\cos\varphi}. \tag{8-126}$$

Equation (8-125) differs from (8-97) because $\gamma_x' = -i\sqrt{(\gamma_y')^2 - 1}$ replaces $\cos\varphi'$. Again we find that the reflected and incident waves have equal intensities and that reflection occurs with a certain change of phase ψ_2, so that, if the electric field of the incident wave is represented by

$$E_z = A\,\exp\left\{i\left[\omega\left(t - \frac{x\cos\varphi + y\sin\varphi}{v_1}\right)\right]\right\},$$

that of the reflected wave is represented by

$$E_z'' = A\,\exp\left\{i\left[\omega\left(t + \frac{x\cos\varphi - y\sin\varphi}{v_1}\right) + \psi_2\right]\right\}.$$

The phase angle ψ_2 is given by

$$\tan\frac{\psi_2}{2} = k = \frac{\sqrt{\sin^2\varphi - \sin^2\varphi_0}}{\cos\varphi}. \tag{8-127}$$

For a given angle of incidence the phase changes given by (8-123) and (8-127) are different, and are related by

$$\frac{\tan(\psi_2/2)}{\tan(\psi_1/2)} = \sin^2\varphi_0 = \left(\frac{n_2}{n_1}\right)^2.$$

Consider now the total reflection of a linearly polarized wave vibrating in a plane neither coincident nor perpendicular to the plane of incidence. This wave may be regarded as the superposition of two waves, in phase with each other, vibrating respectively in the plane of incidence and in the plane perpendicular to it. The two waves undergo different phase changes at reflection and therefore recombine into an elliptically polarized wave. Thus, in general, total reflection changes a linearly polarized wave into an elliptically polarized wave.

As we have seen, the electromagnetic theory of light predicts that when total reflection occurs, the electromagnetic field penetrates for a very small distance into the second medium. Various experiments have been devised to demonstrate the existence of this "penetrating wave." One can, for example, use a totally reflecting glass prism, as described in Section 1-1, and cover the face on which total reflection occurs with a very light layer of lamp black. This face then appears illuminated because each particle of carbon in the oscillatory field of the penetrating wave becomes the center of a scattered light wave (see Section 8–8). The presence of the lamp black, of course, disturbs the electromagnetic field to some extent, so that the equations derived previously do not apply exactly. The reflected wave now has a slightly smaller intensity than the incident wave, and the difference accounts for the intensity of the scattered light.

We have assumed so far that the second medium extends to infinity in the direction of the positive x-axis. In practice, our conclusions will hold provided the thickness of the second medium is large compared with the wavelength. If this is not the case, the theory as developed above ceases to be valid, and we find that total reflection will no longer occur.

Consider, for example, two pieces of glass separated by a thin air film. A light wave incident upon the air film at an angle greater than the critical angle for total reflection will nevertheless be partially transmitted if the thickness of the air film is comparable to the wavelength. Physically, the situation may be described as follows. The electromagnetic field that penetrates into the air film still has an appreciable intensity at the farther surface of the film. Here it changes again into an ordinary light wave that travels in the glass beyond the air space.

For the mathematical formulation of the problem, we must recall that when reflection occurs with $\varphi > \varphi_0$ at the surface of an air film of limited thickness, the electromagnetic field which penetrates into the air does not need to remain finite as x tends to infinity. Thus its mathematical expression may contain a term that *increases* exponentially with x, whereas in the case considered previously only a term that decreases exponentially with x appeared. On the other hand, the electromagnetic field in the air film must now join smoothly with the electromagnetic fields of two ordinary sinusoidal waves at both surfaces.

We shall not develop the theory outlined above in detail, but shall mention a simple experiment that demonstrates the partial transmission of a light wave through the barrier of a thin air film. This experiment uses two totally reflecting prisms, one of which has the hypotenuse face slightly convex. The two prisms are arranged as shown in Fig. 8–13, so that the hypotenuse surfaces touch at one point. If we look at a broad light source through the two prisms, we see, centered at the point of contact, a spot of light surrounded by several interference

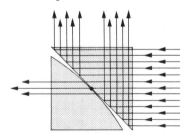

FIG. 8–13. The light beam does not undergo total reflection near the point of contact between the hypotenuse surfaces of the two prisms.

rings. At the center, of course, the light is transmitted without attenuation because an air space of zero thickness is no air space at all.

The reader who undertakes the study of quantum mechanics will find some interesting analogies between the phenomena analyzed here and those encountered in the discussion of the passage of a material particle through a potential barrier.

8–8 Scattering. In discussing the phenomenon of scattering we must carefully distinguish between homogeneous and heterogeneous media. In heterogeneous media, scattering is often a conspicuous effect and has a comparatively trivial explanation. For example, the light shaft that appears when a sunbeam enters a darkened room through a hole in the shutters is due to diffraction of sunlight by particles of dust. Crudely, these particles behave like small opaque obstacles distributed at random.

Scattering in homogeneous materials is a far less noticeable, but more interesting, effect. As pointed out in Section 8–3, it is a manifestation of the secondary waves arising from the forced oscillations of the microscopic electric dipoles.

For the sake of simplicity, we shall assume that the incident light is linearly polarized, e.g., with the electric vector in the y-direction. The electric moment of each microscopic dipole will then be parallel to the y-direction and in the steady state condition its magnitude will vary sinusoidally with a circular frequency ω, equal to that of the incident wave.

The electromagnetic wave emitted by the oscillating dipole has the properties described in Section 8–1. Its intensity is a maximum in the equatorial plane of the dipole, i.e., in the plane perpendicular to the electric vector **E** of the incident wave, and vanishes in the direction of **E**. We can compute the average power radiated by the oscillating dipole, $(\Phi_s)_{\mathrm{av}}$, by means of Eq. (8–26), putting $\omega_0 = \omega$, $p_{0z} = 0$ (because the dipole moment is parallel to the y-axis), and replacing p_{0y} with the quantity p_0 given by Eq. (8–45) (we assume here that damping is negligible). We thus obtain

$$(\Phi_s)_{\mathrm{av}} = \frac{e^4 \omega^4}{12\pi \epsilon_0 c^3 m^2 (\omega_0^2 - \omega^2)^2} A^2. \tag{8–128}$$

Note that in this equation ω_0 is the resonant frequency of the dipole, and ω is the frequency of the incident wave.

The ratio of $(\Phi_s)_{\mathrm{av}}$ to the average energy flux per unit area of the incident wave $(S)_{\mathrm{av}}$ is a quantity σ_s with the dimensions of an area:

$$\sigma_s = \frac{(\Phi_s)_{\mathrm{av}}}{(S)_{\mathrm{av}}}. \tag{8–129}$$

We call this quantity the *scattering cross section* of the dipole because the energy transferred from the incident to the scattered wave by the oscillating dipole during a given interval of time equals the energy of the incident wave falling upon the area σ_s during the same time interval. If we remember the expression for the energy flux per unit area in a plane wave (Eq. 7–53) and consider that in the present case $A_y = A$, $A_z = 0$, we obtain

$$\sigma_s = \frac{e^4}{6\pi \epsilon_0^2 c^4 m^2 (\omega_0^2/\omega^2 - 1)^2}. \tag{8–130}$$

This equation shows that the scattering cross section decreases as the mass of the oscillating charged particle increases. Therefore, the scattering cross sections of the heavy molecular oscillators are completely negligible compared with those of the electronic oscillators. In other words, only the forced oscillations of atomic electrons contribute appreciably to the phenomenon of scattering. Remembering the definition of the classical radius of the electron, r_e (Eq. 8–27), we find the following expression for the scattering cross section of an electronic oscillator:

$$\sigma_s = \frac{8}{3} \frac{\pi r_e^2}{(\omega_0^2/\omega^2 - 1)^2}. \tag{8–131}$$

This quantity is of the order of magnitude of the "classical cross section" πr_e^2 of the electron, except when the frequency of the wave is close to the resonant frequency of the dipole.

In the field of a linearly polarized plane wave, the electrons of the various molecules of matter execute forced oscillations along parallel lines, with definite phase differences that depend on the position along the direction of propagation of the wave.

The secondary waves emitted by the various oscillators interfere with one another, and the resultant disturbance at any particular point depends on the phase difference between these waves. To bring out an important point in connection with the phase relationship between the secondary waves, we begin by considering two identical oscillators A and B, separated by a small distance d, which are excited by the wave coming from a distant source S, and whose secondary waves are observed at a distant point P (Fig. 8–14a). If l is the difference between the geometrical paths SBP and SAP, and λ is the wavelength, the phase difference between the two secondary waves at P is $2\pi l/\lambda$. For a given value of d, l depends on the angle ϑ between the direction of the incident rays and the direction of observation, and on the orientation of the line AB connecting the two atomic oscillators. In particular, if $\vartheta = \pi/2$, l has a maximum value equal to $\sqrt{2}\, l$ when A and B are coplanar with S and P, and the line AB forms an angle of $\pi/4$ with the direction of its incident rays (Fig. 8–14b).

As ϑ decreases, the maximum value of l decreases, and becomes zero when ϑ becomes equal to 0, i.e., when secondary waves are observed in the forward direction. In this case, the secondary waves originating from A and B arrive at P with the same phase, and this is true irrespective of the orientation of the line AB (Fig. 8–14c).

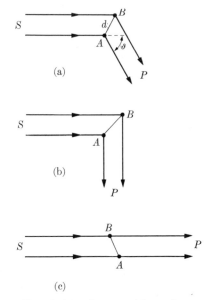

It now becomes easy to visualize the phenomena that will arise from the superposition of the secondary waves originating from large numbers of microscopic oscillators.

In the forward direction, the secondary waves are in phase with one another and bear a definite phase relationship to the primary wave. The interference between the primary and the secondary waves simply produces a change in the velocity of

FIG. 8–14. Superposition of waves from two scattering centers A and B.

propagation. We have already studied this effect in Section 8–4, and we shall investigate it later in more detail (Section 8–9).

In the other directions, however, the phase difference between the secondary waves depends on the relative positions of the atoms. We shall first consider *gases*. Here the atoms are distributed at random, and therefore, *for directions of observations sufficiently far from the forward direction*, we should also expect a random distribution in the phases of the secondary waves arriving at a given point from the individual microscopic oscillators. As explained in Section 3–16, the superposition of a large number of sinusoidal vibrations with randomly distributed phases gives rise to a vibration whose amplitude squared equals the sum of the amplitudes squared of the component vibrations. Thus *the total intensity of the light*, scattered at a sufficiently large angle to the direction of the incident beam, *is simply equal to the sum of the intensities of the scattered individual waves.*

For the sake of simplicity, we shall assume here that all microscopic oscillators of the gas under consideration are identical, so that all of them have the same scattering cross section, σ_s, for a given frequency of the incident light wave. We now consider a light beam of cross-sectional area S traversing a layer of gas of thickness h. If N is the number of oscillators per unit volume, the number of atomic oscillators in the illuminated portion of the gas layer is NSh, and the energy per unit time of the scattered radiation originating from this volume is $\sigma_s N Sh I$, where I is the intensity of the incident radiation (Eq. 8–129). We thus recognize that the quantity

$$\mu_s = N\sigma_s \tag{8–132}$$

represents the fractional energy per unit path length abstracted from the incident beam and transferred to the scattered radiation. This quantity may be called the *attenuation coefficient for scattering*.

In most gases the damping of the atomic oscillators is sufficiently small so that we can use for σ_s the expression given by (8–131), provided ω is not too close to ω_0. Moreover, the natural frequency ω_0 often lies in the ultraviolet, so that, for visible light, $\omega < \omega_0$. From (8–131) we then see that the intensity of the scattered light *increases with increasing frequency*. Indeed, if ω is sufficiently far from ω_0, $(\omega_0/\omega)^2$ is large compared with unity and (8–131) becomes approximately equivalent to the following:

$$\sigma_s = \frac{8}{3}\pi r_e^2 \left(\frac{\omega}{\omega_0}\right)^4. \tag{8–133}$$

In this case the intensity of the scattered light is proportional to the fourth power of the frequency, i.e., is inversely proportional to the fourth power of the wavelength.

Scattering by the air molecules is mainly responsible for the illumination of the sky on a cloudless day. In the absence of scattering the sky would appear black, as it does at very high altitudes where the residual atmospheric pressure is a small fraction of that existing near sea level. The blue color of the sky arises from the preferential scattering of the short wavelengths, as explained above; the same phenomenon accounts for the red color of the sun at sunset or at sunrise. Indeed, when the sun is near the horizon, the sun's rays reach the surface of the earth after traversing a very large thickness of air, and the short wavelengths are strongly attenuated by scattering.

The theory developed here makes definite predictions concerning the polarization and the intensity distribution of the scattered light. Assume first that the incident light is linearly polarized. The atomic dipoles will then vibrate in the direction parallel to the electric vector of this wave. The scattered light observed in any direction will be linearly polarized with the electric vector in the plane that contains the direction of observation and the electric vector of the incident wave (Fig. 8–15a). For a given angle ϑ between the direction of propagation of the incident wave and the direction of observation, the intensity of the scattered light will be a maximum when the electric vector of the incident wave, $\mathbf{E}$, is perpendicular to the plane containing the direction of propagation of this wave and the direction of

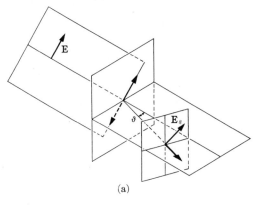

(a)

(b)

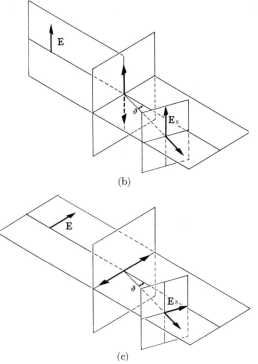

(c)

FIG. 8–15. Polarization of scattered light.

observation (Fig. 8–15b), and a minimum when **E** lies in this plane (Fig. 8–15c). In the latter case, the intensity of the scattered light vanishes if the direction of observation is perpendicular to the incident beam.

If the incident light is not polarized, the scattered light will still appear completely polarized to an observer looking in a direction perpendicular to the incident beam. The intensity, of course, will be the same in all such directions. However, for all other directions of observation the scattered light will appear partially polarized. The theoretical predictions concerning the polarization of scattered light can be verified qualitatively by looking at different regions of the sky through a polarization filter.

So far, we have confined our discussion to gases. In liquids and, to a greater extent, in solids, molecules are distributed with a certain degree of regularity and therefore we cannot assume random distribution for the phase of the secondary waves arising from the individual oscillators. The partial coherence of the secondary waves observed at a certain angle to the primary beam results in a strong reduction of the intensity of scattered light*. This is why liquids and solids do not scatter light much more strongly than gases, even though the number of scattering centers per unit volume is thousands of times greater in condensed matter than in gases. This point will become clearer from the discussion at the end of the following section.

*8–9 The function of the secondary waves in the phenomena of reflection and refraction. We have repeatedly stated that the various effects observed when light passes through matter are due, in the last analysis, to the secondary electromagnetic waves arising from the forced oscillations of the microscopic dipoles. However, in dealing with phenomena such as reflection and refraction, we have used a procedure that does not recognize explicitly the function of the secondary waves. In so doing, we have by-passed the mathematical difficulties inherent in the complexity of the phenomena under discussion, but, at the same time, we have lost sight of the physical mechanism responsible for these phenomena. It is thus desirable to analyze some of the phenomena already discussed from a more direct point of view.

(a) We begin by considering a thin, plane layer of matter containing a number of identical dipoles, and a plane linearly polarized electromagnetic wave, incident perpendicularly upon the material layer. We denote by x and y the direction of propagation and the direction of vibration, respectively. In the field of the incident wave, the dipoles execute forced oscillations in the y-direction. If the thickness δx of the layer is small compared with the wavelength λ, all the oscillations of the dipoles have practically the same phase. We describe these oscillations by

$$p = p_0 \cos \omega t, \qquad (8\text{–}134)$$

giving the electric dipole moment of each oscillator as a function of time.

---

*We concluded in Section 4–20 that a *"perfect crystal"* is completely transparent to all wavelengths large compared with the separation of the scattering centers.

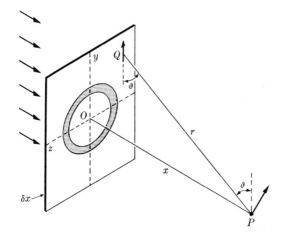

FIG. 8–16. Secondary wave from a thin plane layer of scattering centers.

The oscillating electric field produced at P by a dipole located at the point Q (Fig. 8–16) is perpendicular to PQ and lies in the plane passing through PQ and parallel to the y-axis. Its amplitude is inversely proportional to the distance $r = \overline{PQ}$ and proportional to $\sin \vartheta$, where ϑ is the angle that QP forms with the y-axis. The y-component of this field thus has an amplitude proportional to $\sin^2 \vartheta$.

We now propose to compute the resultant electric field δE_s produced at P by all the oscillating dipoles in the layer under consideration. For this purpose, we follow a procedure closely similar to that used in the discussion of diffraction phenomena (see Section 4–2). Let O be the point where the perpendicular through P to the plane of the material layer intersects this plane (Fig. 8–16) and let x be the distance $\overline{OP}$. We draw in the plane of the layer a series of circles centered at O, each circle at a distance from P that exceeds that of the preceding circle by a constant amount Δr. We assume Δr to be small compared with the wavelength. In this manner we have sub-divided the material layer into a central circular disk surrounded by a series of circular zones. The area of the central disk is given by

$$\Delta\sigma = \pi[(x + \Delta r)^2 - x^2],$$

or, considering that Δr is very small compared with x,

$$\Delta\sigma = 2\pi x\,\Delta r. \tag{8–135}$$

The secondary waves originating from the various dipoles of a given zone extending from r to $r + \Delta r$ arrive at P essentially in phase with one another. Their interference produces an oscillating electric field which, on grounds of symmetry, is seen to be parallel to the electric field of the incident wave (i.e., parallel to the y-axis). The amplitude of the field is proportional to the average value of $\sin^2 \vartheta$ for the zone under consideration. This average value is a decreasing function of r, and corresponds to the *obliquity factor* q considered in Section 4–2. An argument analogous to that developed in Section 4–2 then shows that the amplitude of the disturbance arising from the elementary zone decreases slowly with increasing r. We see, also, that the electric fields produced at P by two neighboring zones have a phase difference of $2\pi\, \Delta r/\lambda$.

To find the resultant field produced at P by all the oscillating dipoles, we must add the contributions of the various zones. Using the vector representation of sinusoidal functions, we plot, one after the other, segments of slowly decreasing length, each forming with the preceding one an angle equal to $2\pi\, \Delta r/\lambda$. At the limit for $\Delta r = 0$, the broken line becomes a tightly wound spiral similar to the vibration spiral discussed in Section 4–2 (Fig. 8–17).

The resultant field, δE_s, is represented by the vector AZ, where A is the starting point and Z is the center of the spiral.

In Fig. 8–17, let A' be the point of the vibration spiral corresponding to the boundary of the central disk (for which $r_0 < r < r_0 + \Delta r$), so that the infinitesimal vector $A A'$ represents the disturbance originating from this disk. The disk has a volume equal to $\Delta\sigma \cdot \delta x$ and, if N is the number of oscillators per unit volume, it contains $N\, \Delta\sigma \cdot \delta x$ oscillators. The point P lies practically on the equatorial plane of all these oscillators. Remembering the equation that describes the wave of a linear oscillator (Eq. 8–14) and making use of (8–135), we then find that the oscillating electric field produced at P by the dipoles contained in the central disk has the expression

$$\Delta\sigma \cdot \delta x\, \frac{N p_0 \omega^2}{4\pi\,\epsilon_0 c^2 x}\, \cos\omega\left(t - \frac{x}{c}\right) = \Delta r \cdot \delta x\, \frac{P_0 \omega^2}{2\,\epsilon_0 c^2}\, \cos\omega\left(t - \frac{x}{c}\right),$$

where p_0 represents the amplitude of oscillations of the individual dipoles (Eq. 8–134) and $P_0 = N p_0$ represents the amplitude of oscillation of the polarization vector $\mathbf{P} = N\mathbf{p}$. We thus conclude that the length of the vector $A A'$ is

$$\overline{A A'} = \frac{P_0 \omega^2}{2\,\epsilon_0 c^2}\, \Delta r \cdot \delta x. \quad (8\text{–}136)$$

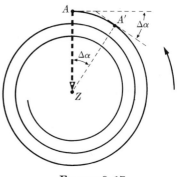

FIGURE 8–17

From Fig. 8–17, we see that

$$\frac{\overline{AA'}}{\overline{AZ}} = \Delta\alpha = 2\pi\,\frac{\Delta r}{\lambda}, \qquad (8\text{–}137)$$

where $\Delta\alpha$ is the phase difference between the waves reaching P from the edge and from the center of the disk.

From (8–136) and (8–137), we then find that the length of the vector $\overline{AZ}$ is

$$\overline{AZ} = \frac{\overline{AA'}}{\Delta\alpha} = \frac{P_0\omega^2\lambda}{4\pi\,\epsilon_0 c^2}\,\delta x,$$

or, since $\omega = 2\pi c/\lambda$,

$$\overline{AZ} = \frac{\pi P_0}{\epsilon_0}\,\frac{\delta x}{\lambda}. \qquad (8\text{–}138)$$

Note that $\overline{AZ}$ is independent of x, and also that the vector $\overline{AZ}$ is perpendicular to the vector AA'. Hence the field of the complete secondary wave, δE_s, oscillates with a phase lag of $\pi/2$ with respect to the field of the wave originating from the central disk alone. Remembering the expression for this field (Eq. 8–14), we obtain the following expression for δE_s:

$$\delta E_s = \frac{\pi P_0}{\epsilon_0}\,\frac{\delta x}{\lambda}\,\cos\left[\omega\left(t - \frac{x}{c}\right) - \frac{\pi}{2}\right]. \qquad (8\text{–}139)$$

We have assumed so far that $x > 0$, i.e., that the point P lies to the right of the layer of oscillating dipoles. If $x < 0$, we obtain, by exactly the same procedure,

$$\delta E_s = \frac{\pi P_0 \delta x}{\epsilon_0 \lambda}\,\cos\left[\omega\left(t + \frac{x}{c}\right) - \frac{\pi}{2}\right]. \qquad (8\text{–}140)$$

We thus arrive at the following conclusions: The interference of the secondary waves originating from the coherent oscillations of the dipoles in the plane material layer of thickness δx considered here produces two plane waves of equal amplitude that travel in opposite directions with velocity c. The two waves leave the source layer with a phase lag of $\pi/2$ with respect to the oscillations of the atomic dipoles. If the characteristic frequency of the dipoles is greater than the wave frequency, and if the damping is negligible, the atomic dipoles oscillate in phase with the incident wave. The secondary waves and the primary wave then have a phase difference of $\pi/2$ at the layer.

The wave traveling in the backward direction represents the wave *reflected* by the material layer. As the thickness of the layer, δx, goes to zero, the intensity of the reflected wave goes to zero as $(\delta x)^2$. We would obtain the same result by considering the destructive interference of the waves reflected by the two surfaces of a film of vanishing thickness (see Section 3–8).

The wave traveling in the forward direction combines with the incident wave. Since the vectors representing the two waves are at right angles to each other, and since the amplitude of the secondary wave is very small compared with that of the incident wave, the resultant wave has practically the same amplitude as the incident wave. However, it lags the incident wave by a small phase angle equal to the ratio of the amplitudes of the two waves (Fig. 8–18).

This is, qualitatively at least, in agreement with our previous results, showing that the velocity of propagation of an electromagnetic wave is smaller in matter than in vacuum. The present example, however, does not lend itself to an actual computation of the velocity in matter because the phenomena are here complicated by multiple reflections in the thin layer.

(b) We shall now turn our attention to the phenomena that occur when a plane, linearly polarized wave is incident perpendicularly upon the plane surface of separation between a vacuum and a refractive medium. To avoid complications resulting from multiple reflections, we assume that the material medium has a very large thickness and is slightly absorbing, so that the wave is practically extinguished before it reaches the second boundary. The point of view that we have taken in the present discussion leads to the following interpretation of the phenomena of reflection and refraction.

The incident wave travels unperturbed in the material medium, with constant velocity c. The forced oscillations of the atomic dipoles produce secondary waves, which also travel with velocity c and which interfere with one another and with the incident wave. Both the reflected and the refracted waves are the result of these interference phenomena.

If we try to discuss the problem quantitatively, we meet a characteristic difficulty due to the fact that the oscillations of the dipoles are determined by the total electric field existing inside the material and this, in turn, is affected by the oscillations of the dipoles. Thus we cannot solve the problem by a straightforward computation, but must resort to an indirect consistency argument.

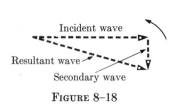

FIGURE 8–18

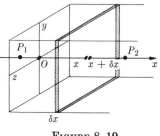

FIGURE 8–19

We shall therefore start from the assumption that the interference of the primary and secondary waves produces in the material medium a plane wave traveling with a constant velocity $v = c/n$ which, however, we leave undetermined. We then seek an equation that determines this velocity, as well as the amplitude relations between the incident, reflected, and refracted waves.

We select a cartesian frame of reference with the origin on the boundary surface, and with the x-axis in the direction of propagation (Fig. 8–19). We denote by E, E', and E'' the electric fields corresponding to the incident, refracted, and reflected waves. Their expressions are of the following type:

$$E = A \cos \omega \left(t - \frac{x}{c} \right),$$

$$E' = A' \cos \omega \left(t - \frac{x}{v} \right), \qquad (8\text{–}141)$$

$$E'' = A'' \cos \omega \left(t + \frac{x}{c} \right).$$

The constants A and ω are given, but v, A', and A'' are unknown quantities.

We now subdivide the material medium into layers parallel to the boundary surface, all of the same thickness, $\delta x \ll \lambda$.

We consider first a point P_1 in the empty space. If the medium were perfectly transparent, all the secondary waves originating from the various elementary layers would have the same amplitude at P. Because of the assumed slight absorption, the amplitude is a very slowly decreasing function of the distance of the elementary layer from the boundary. The atomic dipoles oscillate in phase with the refracted wave, whose velocity of propagation is v, and therefore the oscillations in a given layer occur with an average time delay $\delta x/v$ with respect to those of the preceding layer. Since the secondary waves are propagated with velocity c, the total time delay between the secondary waves arriving at P from two neighboring layers is $\delta x/v + \delta x/c$. The corresponding phase delay is

$$\delta\alpha = 2\pi \frac{\delta x}{T} \left(\frac{1}{v} + \frac{1}{c} \right) = 2\pi(n + 1)\frac{\delta x}{\lambda}, \qquad (8\text{–}142)$$

where we have made use of the identities $\lambda = cT$ and $n = c/v$.

The reflected wave is the resultant of the secondary waves here considered. To find this resultant, we construct a broken line formed by segments of gradually decreasing length, each making the same angle $\delta\alpha$ with the preceding one. At the limit, $\delta x = 0$, the broken line becomes a tightly wound spiral (Fig. 8–20). With the usual argument, we conclude that the resultant wave is represented by the vector LK, where L is the starting point of the spiral and K is its center.

Consider now the infinitesimal segment LL' corresponding to the infinitesimal layer adjacent to the boundary surface. The length $\overline{LL'}$ represents the amplitude of the electric field, δE_s, originating from this layer, and is thus equal to the quantity $\overline{AZ}$ given by Eq. (8–138). Thus $\overline{LL'}$ is given by

$$\overline{LL'} = \frac{\pi P_0}{\epsilon_0} \frac{\delta x}{\lambda}. \tag{8–143}$$

From Fig. 8–20, we see that

$$\frac{\overline{LL'}}{\overline{LK}} = \delta\alpha, \tag{8–144}$$

where $\delta\alpha$ is the phase difference between the waves arriving at P from the points at $x = 0$ and $x = \delta x$, respectively, and is given by (8–142). We then find that the amplitude of the reflected wave is

$$A'' = \overline{LK} = \frac{\overline{LL'}}{\delta\alpha} = \frac{1}{2(n+1)} \frac{P_0}{\epsilon_0}. \tag{8–145}$$

From the definitions for $\mathbf{D}$ and ϵ [Eqs. (7–11) and (7–18)], it follows that the ratio of the polarization to electric field strength equals the difference between the dielectric permittivity of the medium and that of the vacuum. Since the oscillations of the atomic dipoles are caused by the electric field of the refracted wave, whose amplitude we have called A', we can write

$$P_0 = (\epsilon - \epsilon_0)A', \tag{8–146}$$

and Eq. (8–145) becomes

$$A'' = \left(\frac{\epsilon}{\epsilon_0} - 1\right) \frac{A'}{2(n+1)}. \tag{8–147}$$

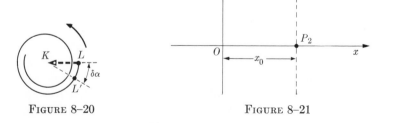

FIGURE 8–20   FIGURE 8–21

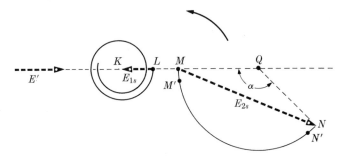

FIGURE 8-22

In Fig. 8-20 we note that the vectors LK and LL' are mutually perpendicular, which shows that the reflected wave has a phase delay of $\pi/2$ with respect to the secondary wave originating from the infinitesimal layer between
$x = 0$ and $x = \delta x$. This, in turn, has a phase delay of $\pi/2$ with respect to
the refracted wave at $x = 0$. Thus, in agreement with previous results, we
find that the reflected and refracted waves have opposite phase at the
boundary.

We can use an analogous procedure to compute the secondary disturbance
at a point P_2 of the material medium (Figs. 8-19 and 8-21). Let x_0 be the
abscissa of this point. We consider separately the resultant secondary wave
arising from the oscillating dipoles that lie beyond the plane $x = x_0$, and
that arising from the dipoles that lie between the planes $x = 0$ and $x = x_0$;
E_{1s} and E_{2s} are the electric fields of these two waves.

E_{1s} is identical to the electric field of the reflected wave considered previously. Its amplitude is therefore the quantity A'' given by Eq. (8-145) and
its phase is opposite to that of the refracted wave E' at $x = x_0$ (Fig. 8-22).
To find the contribution E_{2s} of the portion of the medium between $x = 0$
and $x = x_0$, we must again construct the appropriate vibration curve. If
x_0 is not too large, absorption can be neglected, and we can assume that all
the disturbances arriving at P_2 from the various infinitesimal layers of
equal thickness δx have the same amplitude. The difference of phase between the waves originating in two neighboring layers is now

$$\delta\alpha = 2\pi(n - 1)\frac{\delta x}{\lambda}. \tag{8-148}$$

The vibration curve (Fig. 8-22) becomes an arc MN of a circle, where M is
the point corresponding to the plane at $x = x_0$ and N is the point corresponding to the plane at $x = 0$. The secondary wave E_{2s} is represented in
amplitude and phase by the vector MN.

An argument analogous to that developed previously shows that the
radius of the circle is

$$\overline{QM} = \left(\frac{\epsilon}{\epsilon_0} - 1 \right) \frac{A'}{2(n-1)}. \tag{8-149}$$

The secondary wave coming from the infinitesimal layer between $x = x_0$ and $x = x_0 - \delta x$ (represented by the infinitesimal segment MM' of the vibration curve) has a phase delay of $\pi/2$ with respect to refracted waves. It lags the wave originating in the infinitesimal layer between $x = 0$ and $x = \delta x$ (represented by the infinitesimal segment $N'N$ of the vibration curve) by a phase angle

$$\alpha = 2\pi(n-1)\frac{x_0}{\lambda}. \tag{8-150}$$

This angle represents the angle between the tangents to the vibration curve at M and N, respectively. It also represents the angle subtended at the center by the arc MN.

To complete our task, we must now solve the equation

$$E' = E + E_{1s} + E_{2s}, \tag{8-151}$$

which says that the refracted wave results from the interference of the incident wave with the secondary waves originating from the atomic dipoles.

For this purpose we draw from a point R a vector RS representing the refracted wave E' (Fig. 8–23). This vector has the (unknown) length A'. To it we add a vector ST representing $-E_{1s}$. The latter vector is parallel to the former, and its length is

$$\frac{(\epsilon/\epsilon_0) - 1}{2(n+1)} A'.$$

Thus the function $E' - E_{1s}$ is represented by a vector RT of length

$$\left(1 + \frac{(\epsilon/\epsilon_0) - 1}{2(n+1)} \right) A'.$$

Note that this length is independent of x_0. On the other hand, for $x_0 = 0$, E_{2s} obviously vanishes, so that $E' - E_{1s}$ becomes equal to E. We thus conclude that the length of the vector representing $E' - E_{1s}$ is equal to the length of the vector representing E, or

$$\left(1 + \frac{(\epsilon/\epsilon_0) - 1}{2(n+1)} \right) A' = A. \tag{8-152}$$

In the general case ($x_0 \neq 0$), the electric field of the incident wave at x_0 leads the electric field of the refracted wave by a phase angle $\alpha = 2\pi(n-1)x_0/\lambda$. Thus E is represented by a vector RU of length A rotated in the positive direction by an angle α with respect to the vector

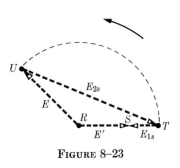

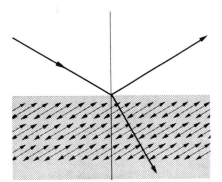

FIGURE 8–23

FIG. 8–24. Interpretation of Brewster's law.

RS. The vector UT then represents the function $E' - E_{1s} - E = E_{2s}$. Comparison of Figs. 8–23 and 8–22 shows that $\overline{RU} = \overline{QM}$ or (see Eq. 8–149)

$$\frac{(\epsilon/\epsilon_0) - 1}{2(n - 1)} A' = A. \tag{8-153}$$

From (8–152) and (8–153), we obtain

$$n^2 = \frac{\epsilon}{\epsilon_0}, \tag{8-154}$$

$$A' = \frac{2(n - 1)}{n^2 - 1} A = \frac{2}{n + 1} A, \tag{8-155}$$

and (8–147) now becomes

$$A'' = \frac{n - 1}{2} A' = \frac{n - 1}{n + 1} A. \tag{8-156}$$

The above equations determine the velocity of propagation in the medium, as well as the amplitudes of the reflected and refracted waves. They are identical to equations previously obtained [see Eqs. (8–50) and (8–100)].

(c) Using similar methods, we could discuss the reflection and refraction of waves incident at an oblique angle at the boundary surface between a vacuum and a material medium, but we shall not attempt to do so here. We do, however, wish to remark that the model of the oscillating dipoles provides a simple physical interpretation of Brewster's law (see Sections 6–4 and 8–6). Indeed, when the angle of incidence is equal to the Brewster angle, the angle between the refracted ray and the reflected ray (if the latter exists) is $\pi/2$. If the incident wave vibrates in the plane of incidence, the refracted wave does also, and the oscillations of the dipoles occur in the direction of the reflected ray (see Fig. 8–24). Since the intensity of the wave emitted by a linear oscillator is zero in the direction of oscillation, no reflected wave exists in these circumstances.

The considerations developed in this section enable us to clarify an apparent paradox. On the one hand we have concluded that in a perfect dielectric an electromagnetic wave is propagated without attenuation. On the other hand, we know that scattering always occurs to some extent, and it alone produces some attenuation. It now appears that the arguments leading to the conclusion that the refracted wave is propagated without attenuation are based on the tacit assumption that the oscillating dipoles are distributed with absolute uniform density in the dielectric, for in our computation of the secondary waves, we have neglected the possibility of local fluctuations in the density of the dipoles. Actually, fluctuations do occur, especially in gases, because of the random distribution in space of the molecules. These fluctuations are responsible for the scattering, and it is because of them that our computation of the refracted wave is not rigorous. It follows from statistical theory that the fluctuations in the number of gas molecules contained in an element of volume are proportional in magnitude to the square root of the density. On this ground, one might expect the *amplitude* of the scattered wave to be also proportional to the square root of the density, and the *intensity* of the scattered wave to be proportional to the density. We have seen that this is exactly what happens in the case of gases.

8–10 Absorption, resonance, anomalous dispersion. We have already pointed out that when a light wave traverses matter part of its energy goes into the production of scattered radiation, and part is changed into heat (true absorption). In both phenomena, the energy loss may be attributed to frictional forces, opposite in direction to the motion of the oscillating particle and proportional in magnitude to its velocity. The same frictional forces, of course, are also responsible for the damping of the free oscillations discussed in Section 8–2.

We have seen that the work done against the frictional forces in one oscillation is proportional to the square of the amplitude of oscillation (Eq. 8–33). In many substances, the dissipative forces are small, and the absorption is correspondingly small except in the vicinity of one of the characteristic frequencies where, as already noted, the amplitude of the forced oscillations becomes very large and the substance exhibits strong absorption. This phenomenon is called *resonance absorption* because of the obvious similarity with the phenomenon of acoustic resonance, whereby a tuning fork is set in oscillation by a sound wave of frequency equal to its characteristic frequency.

In Section 8–3 we found a general expression for the amplitude p_0 of the forced oscillations of a dipole of characteristic frequency ω_0 in the field of a wave of frequency ω (Eq. 8–42). The behavior of p_0^2 in the vicinity of ω_0 is shown in Fig. 8–5 for two different values of the damping constant. It is evident that as the damping decreases, the interval of the frequency in which p_0^2 is large and therefore the absorption is strong, becomes narrower. Thus in solids and liquids, where damping is relatively large, the absorption bands are broad, whereas in gases, where the damping is usually small, the absorption bands are narrow and reduce to the so-called *absorption lines.* For example, the black Fraunhofer lines in the spectrum of solar radiation are due to resonance absorption by the gases of the solar atmosphere of the continuous spectrum emitted by the hot solar surface.

When the damping due to collisions between molecules is large compared with the radiation damping, most of the absorbed energy goes into heating the absorbing substance. When, however, collision damping is small compared with radiation damping, most of the absorbed energy is re-emitted in the form of radiation (resonance radiation). This phenomenon occurs prominently in diluted gases. It can be easily demonstrated by means of an evacuated glass vessel containing a piece of sodium metal. When the sodium is heated, it develops sodium vapor, which has a strong absorption line in the yellow (strictly speaking, two lines close to each other). In a strong beam of white light the sodium vapor becomes luminescent, emitting yellow light of the frequency corresponding to its absorption line.

In the neighborhood of a characteristic frequency, also, the index of refraction exhibits an anomalous behavior. As the frequency of the light wave increases gradually from a value slightly lower to a value slightly higher than the characteristic frequency, the index of refraction increases rapidly, passes through a maximum, then drops suddenly to a low value, and eventually increases again (Fig. 8–25). Thus in the immediate vicinity of a characteristic frequency the index of refraction *decreases* with increasing frequency instead of increasing as is usually the case. This behavior is known as *anomalous dispersion*. It is physically explained by the fact that as the wave frequency overtakes the characteristic frequency, the phase difference between the oscillations of the atomic dipoles and those of the wave field changes rapidly from a value close to 0 to a value close to π (see Section 8–3, Fig. 8–6). As the damping decreases, the change becomes more abrupt and the curve of the anomalous dispersion becomes steeper. For zero damping there would be a mathematical discontinuity in the curve representing n as a function of ω; this situation is approached in the case of gases, whose absorption lines are very narrow.

Anomalous dispersion may be demonstrated by the following sim-

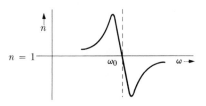

Fig. 8–25. Anomalous dispersion in the neighborhood of a characteristic frequency.

ple experiment. A narrow beam of white light passes through a glass prism that spreads the incident light beam into a fanlike beam with the red rays on one side and the violet rays on the other. We now place along the path of this beam a hollow glass prism filled with a solution of fuchsine, with the refracting edge perpendicular to the refracting edge of the first prism, so that the two prisms will deflect the light rays in mutually perpendicular planes. Fuchsine has a strong narrow absorption band in the visible spectrum, and exhibits anomalous dispersion in the neighborhood of this band. On a screen placed beyond the second prism a pattern of the shape shown in Fig. 8–26 appears.

The reader will note that our theory, based on the model of the microscopic harmonic oscillators, predicts a close correspondence between the *emission* and the *absorption* properties of a given substance. Indeed, the characteristic frequencies of the microscopic oscillators determine both the frequencies of the light waves that are strongly absorbed by the substance and those of the light waves that the same substance can emit when its molecules are excited by some external agency. Moreover, when the damping of the microscopic oscillators is small, the theory predicts that both the emission lines and the absorption lines should be narrow. In other words, if the substance is capable of emitting nearly monochromatic light, it will also absorb only light waves within a narrow frequency interval. On the other hand, a large damping of the microscopic oscillators results in broad emission bands and broad absorption bands.

To some extent, these predictions are borne out by experiment. For example, sodium vapor exhibits strong absorption at frequencies exactly identical to those of the two narrow emission lines in the yellow region of the spectrum. There are, however, exceptions in the sense that not *all* emission lines appear also as absorption lines. These exceptions point to an essential limitation in the validity of our model.

*8–11 Optical properties of metals. The two most characteristic optical properties of metals are their opacity and the high reflecting power of their polished surfaces. Both of these properties are explained by the fact that metals are good electrical conductors.

Consider first the ideal case of a perfect conductor. Inside the conductor the electric field is zero, because any finite electric field would produce an infinitely large electric current. To study the reflection of a light wave at the boundary of the conductor, we follow the same pro-

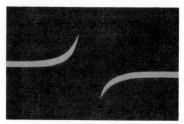

FIGURE 8–26

cedure used in the study of reflection and refraction at the boundary between two dielectrics (see Section 8–5). We again find that the directions of propagation of the incident and reflected waves lie in one plane with the perpendicular to the reflecting surface, and form equal angles φ with this perpendicular. The boundary conditions for the electric field now require that the tangential components of the electric fields of the incident and reflected waves cancel each other at the boundary surface. Thus, using the same notations introduced in Section 8–5, we find

$$A_y = -A_y'', \qquad A_z = -A_z''. \tag{8–157}$$

If we now consider that the electric vector is perpendicular to the direction of propagation, and that the x-, y-, and z-components of the unit vector pointing in the direction of propagation are $\gamma_x = \cos\varphi$, $\gamma_y = \sin\varphi$, $\gamma_z = 0$ for the incident wave, and $\gamma_x'' = -\cos\varphi$, $\gamma_y'' = \sin\varphi$, $\gamma_z'' = 0$ for the reflected wave, we have

$$A_x\gamma_x + A_y\gamma_y + A_z\gamma_z = 0, \qquad A_x''\gamma_x'' + A_y''\gamma_y'' + A_z''\gamma_z'' = 0,$$

or

$$A_x\cos\varphi + A_y\sin\varphi = 0, \qquad A_x''\cos\varphi - A_y''\sin\varphi = 0. \tag{8–158}$$

These equations, together with Eqs. (8–157), give $A_x'' = A_x$ and therefore

$$A_x^2 + A_y^2 + A_z^2 = A_x''^2 + A_y''^2 + A_z''^2.$$

Thus the amplitude of the reflected wave is equal to the amplitude of the incident wave. In other words, the surface of a perfect conductor acts as a perfect reflector.

To investigate the optical behavior of real metals, it is necessary to examine the physical nature of these substances more closely. The electrical conductivity of metals is due to the presence of electrons of charge $-e$, which are not permanently bound to individual atoms, but are free to wander from one atom to another. To represent bound electrons, we have introduced the harmonic electronic oscillators (Section 8–1). We shall now assume that conduction electrons behave like *charged material particles immersed in a viscous medium*. Thus an electron moving with a velocity **w** will experience a frictional force $-h_e\mathbf{w}$, where h_e is a constant. The equation of motion of a conduction electron in an external electric field **E** is then

$$m\frac{d\mathbf{w}}{dt} + h_e\mathbf{w} = -e\mathbf{E}. \tag{8–159}$$

Suppose, for example, that $\mathbf{E}$ is the sinusoidally varying field of a linearly polarized electromagnetic wave:

$$\mathbf{E} = \mathbf{A} \cos \omega t. \tag{8-160}$$

After an initial transitory period, each conduction electron will execute linear oscillations with the angular frequency ω, and $\mathbf{w}$ will be a sinusoidal function of time of the type

$$\mathbf{w} = \mathbf{w}_0 \cos (\omega t + \varphi). \tag{8-161}$$

In this case, (8–159) becomes

$$-m\omega \mathbf{w}_0 \sin (\omega t + \varphi) + h_e \mathbf{w}_0 \cos (\omega t + \varphi) = -e\mathbf{A} \cos \omega t. \tag{8-162}$$

By means of this equation or, more simply, by using the vector representation of sinusoidal functions, we can determine $\mathbf{w}_0$ and φ. Here we wish only to remark that the ratio between the amplitudes of oscillation of the two sinusoidal terms on the left side of (8–162) is $m\omega/h_e$. Thus, if the frictional forces are sufficiently large and if the frequency is not too high, the first term is negligible compared with the second. In this case the external force, $-e\mathbf{E}_i$ is, at all times, practically equal to the frictional force $h_e\mathbf{w}$:

$$h_e\mathbf{w} = -e\mathbf{E}. \tag{8-163}$$

For the sake of simplicity, we shall assume in what follows that the conditions for the validity of (8–163) are satisfied.

By definition, the density of current, $\mathbf{j}$, is given by

$$\mathbf{j} = -N_e e\mathbf{w}, \tag{8-164}$$

where N_e is the number of conduction electrons per unit volume of the metal. We see that if (8–163) holds, $\mathbf{j}$ is proportional to $\mathbf{E}$, that is, $\mathbf{j}$ obeys Ohm's law. Indeed, if σ is the conductivity, then

$$\mathbf{j} = \sigma\mathbf{E},$$

and we obtain

$$\sigma = \frac{N_e e^2}{h_e}. \tag{8-165}$$

We recall that, as we go from a dielectric to a conductor, the first three Maxwell's equations [Eqs. (7–22), (7–23), and (7–24)] remain unchanged, while in the fourth (Eq. 7–25) the vector $\epsilon(\partial \mathbf{E}/\partial t)$ must be replaced by the vector $\epsilon(\partial \mathbf{E}/\partial t) + \mathbf{j} = \epsilon(\partial \mathbf{E}/\partial t) + \sigma\mathbf{E}$.

Let us inquire about the possibility of satisfying Maxwell's equations in a metal with a set of functions $E_x, E_y, E_z, H_x, H_y, H_z$, that depend only on the x-coordinate and on time. By exactly the same procedure followed in the case of a dielectric (see Section 7–3), we find the following system of equations:

$$\text{(a)} \quad \frac{\partial H_x}{\partial x} = 0, \qquad\qquad \text{(b)} \quad \frac{\partial E_x}{\partial x} = 0,$$

$$\text{(c)} \quad \frac{\partial H_x}{\partial t} = 0, \qquad\qquad \text{(d)} \quad \frac{\partial E_x}{\partial t} = 0,$$

$$\text{(e)} \quad \mu_0 \frac{\partial H_y}{\partial t} = \frac{\partial E_z}{\partial x}, \qquad\qquad \text{(f)} \quad \epsilon \frac{\partial E_y}{\partial t} + \sigma E_y = -\frac{\partial H_z}{\partial x},$$

$$\text{(g)} \quad \mu_0 \frac{\partial H_z}{\partial t} = -\frac{\partial E_y}{\partial x}, \qquad\qquad \text{(h)} \quad \epsilon \frac{\partial E_z}{\partial t} + \sigma E_z = \frac{\partial H_y}{\partial x}.$$

$$(8\text{–}166)$$

These equations are identical to (7–26), except for the extra terms σE_y and σE_z appearing in (f) and (h). From (a), (b), (c) and (d), we again conclude that the vectors $\mathbf{E}$ and $\mathbf{H}$ are perpendicular to the x-axis. We also find that of the four equations where E_y, E_z, H_y, H_z appear, two contain only E_y and H_z, and the other two only E_z and H_y. Thus we can find a special solution for which $E_z = 0, H_y = 0, E_u \neq 0, H_z \neq 0$.

We shall try to satisfy the two equations containing E_y and H_z by assuming that they depend on x and t through a function *formally* similar to that appearing in the equation of a sinusoidal wave; i.e., we shall take

$$E_y = A_y \exp\left\{ i\omega \left(t - \frac{n'x}{c} \right) \right\}, \qquad (8\text{–}167)$$

where n' is a constant to be appropriately chosen. An equation with a different coefficient but the same exponential term will represent H_z.

From the assumed functional dependence of E_y and H_z on t and x, it follows that

$$\frac{\partial E_y}{\partial x} = -\frac{i\omega n'}{c} E_y, \qquad \frac{\partial E_y}{\partial t} = i\omega E_y,$$

$$\frac{\partial H_z}{\partial x} = -\frac{i\omega n'}{c} H_z, \qquad \frac{\partial H_z}{\partial t} = i\omega H_z.$$

$$(8\text{–}168)$$

With the help of these equations, (f) and (g) of Eq. (8–166) become

$$\epsilon i\omega E_y + \sigma E_y = \frac{i\omega n'}{c} H_z,$$

$$\mu_0 i\omega H_z = \frac{i\omega n'}{c} E_y.$$

$$(8\text{–}169)$$

From the second of the above equations (remembering that $c = 1/\sqrt{\epsilon_0\mu_0}$), we obtain

$$H_z = \frac{n'}{\mu_0 c} E_y = \sqrt{\frac{\epsilon_0}{\mu_0}}\, n' E_y. \qquad (8\text{-}170)$$

Substitution of (8-170) into the first of equations (8-169) yields

$$\epsilon i\omega E_y + \sigma E_y = i\omega\epsilon_0 (n')^2 E_y,$$

or

$$(n')^2 = \frac{\epsilon}{\epsilon_0} + \frac{\sigma}{i\omega\epsilon_0}, \qquad (8\text{-}171)$$

which shows that n' is a complex quantity. If we put

$$n' = n(1 - i\eta), \qquad (8\text{-}172)$$

we obtain

$$n^2(1 - \eta^2) = \frac{\epsilon}{\epsilon_0}, \qquad (8\text{-}173)$$

$$2n^2\eta = \frac{\sigma}{\omega\epsilon_0}. \qquad (8\text{-}174)$$

Substitution of (8-172) into (8-167) yields

$$E_y = A_y \exp\left\{i\omega\left(t - \frac{nx}{c}\right)\right\} \exp\left(-\frac{\mu x}{2}\right), \qquad (8\text{-}175)$$

where we have, for brevity, written

$$\mu = \frac{2\omega n\eta}{c}. \qquad (8\text{-}176)$$

We conclude that it is indeed possible to find solutions of Maxwell's equations in which the electric and the magnetic fields depend only on t and x. The particular solution given by (8-175) and (8-170), together with $E_z = 0$, $H_y = 0$, represents a transverse wave with the electric vector in the y-direction and the magnetic vector in the z-direction. At any given point, E_y and H_z vary sinusoidally with time, with the angular frequency ω. At a given instant, the dependence on x is represented by the product of a sinusoidal function $(e^{-i\omega nx/c})$ and an exponential function with negative coefficient $(e^{-\mu x/2})$. Thus our equations describe a sinusoidal wave that is gradually attenuated as it travels in the x-direction. The attenuation, of course, is due to the Joule effect, whereby the energy of the wave is progressively changed into heat in the conducting medium.

Since the intensity I of the wave is proportional to the square of the amplitude, we find from (8–175) that I is given by

$$I = I_0 e^{-\mu x}, \qquad (8\text{--}177)$$

where I_0 is the intensity at $x = 0$. Thus μ represents the *absorption coefficient*, i.e., the inverse thickness of a metal layer that reduces the intensity in the ratio of 1 to $1/e$.

Equation (8–170), together with (8–172), shows that the ratio of the magnetic to electric intensity at any given point is a complex quantity, which means that in a metal the magnetic and electric fields oscillate with a certain difference of phase φ. Indeed, (8–172) shows that φ satisfies

$$\tan \varphi = \eta.$$

The reader will recall that in a dielectric, on the other hand, the oscillations of the electric and magnetic vectors have equal or opposite phase.

Equations (8–173) and (8–174) determine the optical constants n and η in terms of the electrical constants σ and ϵ. Elimination of n yields

$$\frac{2\eta}{1 - \eta^2} = \frac{\sigma}{\omega \epsilon},$$

which has the solution

$$\eta = -\frac{\omega \epsilon}{\sigma} + \sqrt{\left(\frac{\omega \epsilon}{\sigma}\right)^2 + 1}\,. \qquad (8\text{--}178)$$

This equation, together with (8–174), yields

$$n^2 \eta^2 = \frac{1}{2}\left[-\frac{\epsilon}{\epsilon_0} + \sqrt{\left(\frac{\epsilon}{\epsilon_0}\right)^2 + \left(\frac{\sigma}{\omega \epsilon_0}\right)^2}\right]. \qquad (8\text{--}179)$$

Note that for $\sigma = 0$, η becomes zero and Eq. (8–173) goes over into (8–50). Thus the theory of the propagation of electromagnetic waves in a dielectric developed in Section 8–4 is a special case of the more general theory developed here.

We shall now investigate the reflection of light waves at the surface of separation between a vacuum and a metal, limiting ourselves, for the sake of simplicity, to the case of normal incidence. We assume, moreover, that the incident wave is linearly polarized, with the electric vector in the y-direction. The electric fields of the incident, refracted, and reflected waves are then represented by equations of the following form:

$$E_y = A \exp \left\{ i\omega \left(t - \frac{x}{c} \right) \right\},$$

$$E_y' = A' \exp \left\{ i\omega \left(t - \frac{nx}{c} \right) \right\} \exp \left(- \frac{\mu x}{2} \right), \qquad (8\text{–}180)$$

$$E_y'' = A'' \exp \left\{ i\omega \left(t + \frac{x}{c} \right) \right\}.$$

The boundary condition for the electric field yields

$$A + A'' = A'. \qquad (8\text{–}181)$$

The boundary condition for the magnetic field, with the help of (8–170) and (8–172), yields

$$A - A'' = n(1 - i\eta)A'. \qquad (8\text{–}182)$$

Upon elimination of A' between (8–181) and (8–182), we obtain

$$A'' = \frac{1 - n + in\eta}{1 + n - in\eta} A. \qquad (8\text{–}183)$$

Thus the ratio between the amplitudes of the electric fields of the reflected and incident waves at the boundary surface is a complex number. If we write this number as $\rho e^{i\alpha}$, that is, if we put

$$\rho \epsilon^{i\alpha} = \frac{1 - n + in\eta}{1 + n - in\eta}, \qquad (8\text{–}184)$$

we obtain

$$\rho^2 = \frac{(n - 1)^2 + n^2\eta^2}{(1 + n)^2 + n^2\eta^2}, \qquad (8\text{–}185)$$

and

$$\tan \alpha = \frac{2n\eta}{1 - n^2 - n^2\eta^2}. \qquad (8\text{–}186)$$

Note that since the intensity of a wave is proportional to the square of the amplitude, ρ^2 represents the ratio of the reflected to the incident intensity, or the reflectance (see Section 8–5).

We shall not carry out the computation for the case of oblique incidence. We wish only to point out that the phase difference between the reflected and the incident waves depends not only on the angle of incidence, but also on the direction of vibration. Therefore, in general, metallic reflection will change a linearly polarized wave into an elliptically polarized wave.

If we use for σ the electric conductivity of the metal determined from experiments on stationary or slowly varying currents, we find that the dimensionless quantity $\sigma/\omega\epsilon_0$ is a number large compared with unity even for values of ω as large as those corresponding to visible light. For example, for copper, $\sigma = 5.8 \times 10^7$ ohm^{-1} m^{-1}. With $\epsilon_0 = 8.85 \times 10^{-12}$ farad/m, and taking $\omega = 3.2 \times 10^{15}$ sec^{-1} (corresponding to the yellow light of sodium, 5890 A wavelength), we obtain $\sigma/\omega\epsilon_0 \approx 2000$. Even though the dielectric constant of metals cannot be measured directly, it is safe to assume that for metals as well as for dielectrics, ϵ/ϵ_0 is of the order of unity, and is therefore small compared with the value of $\sigma/\omega\epsilon_0$ computed above. Therefore, Eqs. (8–178) and (8–179) give, to good approximation,

$$\eta \approx 1 \quad \text{and} \quad n \approx \frac{\sigma}{2\omega\epsilon_0}. \qquad (8\text{--}187)$$

On the other hand, n and η can be determined experimentally, e.g., from a measurement of the absorption coefficient μ (Eq. 8–176) and of the reflectance ρ^2 (Eq. 8–185). If we use infrared rays or electromagnetic waves of still greater wavelengths, we find that the experimental values of these constants agree well with those given by Eqs. (8–187). For wavelengths corresponding to those of visible light, however, the theoretical and experimental values differ by a large factor. In the case of copper, for example, the value of $n\eta$ for the yellow sodium light deduced from the static conductivity of the metal is about 1000, whereas the value of the same quantity deduced from the measured value of the attenuation length is 2.66.

The reason for this disagreement lies in the fact that for frequencies as high as those corresponding to visible light, the inertia of the conduction electrons cannot be neglected. Therefore, the effective conductivity of the metal no longer coincides with the static conductivity, nor is the current in phase with the electric field, as we assumed in developing the theory.

Note that for many metals n turns out to be smaller than unity, which means that the corresponding velocity of propagation of the wave, c/n, is greater than c, in contrast with the fundamental postulate of the relativity theory. We encountered a similar apparent paradox in Section 8–4. Here again the difficulty disappears if we consider that the velocity of propagation of a light signal is not the phase velocity, but the group velocity.

8–12 Momentum and angular momentum of electromagnetic waves. We have seen in Section 7–4 that electromagnetic waves carry energy, and that the energy flux is represented by the Poynting vector **S**. This means that energy is transferred from an electromagnetic wave to any material object that absorbs the wave (in part or completely).

A transfer of mechanical energy is often accompanied by a transfer of *momentum*. For example, if one shoots bullets into a target, the target absorbs both energy and momentum and, if free to move, acquires a velocity in the direction of the velocity of the oncoming projectiles.

In some cases, a transfer of mechanical energy is accompanied by a transfer of *angular momentum*. This happens, for instance, if the bullets of the previous example are spinning about a longitudinal axis. When stopped by the target, the bullets transfer to the target their angular momentum. If the target is free to rotate, it will acquire an angular velocity about an axis parallel to the axis of rotation of the projectiles.

The question arises whether electromagnetic waves, too, give a certain amount of linear momentum, and perhaps a certain amount of angular momentum, to a material object by which they are absorbed. If they do, we shall conclude that they carry linear momentum and angular momentum in addition to energy.

To investigate these questions from a theoretical point of view, we use a fairly idealized absorber, whose physical characteristics we shall choose in such a way as to simplify the calculations. Yet the results will have general validity because the properties of electromagnetic fields are obviously independent of the properties of whatever device we may use to investigate them.

Consider a plane electromagnetic wave traveling in vacuum, and an absorber in the shape of a plane sheet of conducting material of thickness small compared with the wavelength and of infinite lateral extent, placed perpendicular to the direction of propagation of the wave.

The conducting sheet will partially reflect, partially transmit, and partially absorb the incident wave. We select a cartesian system of coordinates with the origin on the conducting sheet and the x-axis in the direction of propagation of the incident wave (Fig. 8–27). We assume, for the moment, that the incident wave is linearly polarized, with the electric vector in the xy-plane. The reflected and transmitted waves are similarly polarized. Thus in each of the three waves, only the y-component of the electric field and the z-component of the magnetic field are different from zero. In particular, we represent the incident wave by

$$E_y = A \cos \omega \left(t - \frac{x}{c} \right), \quad (8\text{–}188)$$

$$B_z = \mu_0 H_z = \frac{1}{c} E_y. \quad (8\text{–}189)$$

In accordance with the model introduced in the preceding section, we assume that the conduction is due to the presence of electrons of charge $-e$ whose motion is opposed by strong viscous forces, so that the

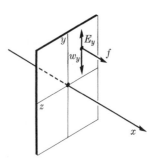

FIG. 8–27. Radiation pressure.

velocity of an individual electron, $w_y = dy/dt$, at any instant of time is proportional to the instantaneous value of the force acting on it.

For the sake of simplicity, we also assume that the conductivity is small, so that the sheet absorbs and reflects only a small fraction of the incident energy. In the computation of the reflection and absorption we can then take the electric field in the sheet as equal to that of the incident wave. That is, if the incident wave is represented by Eq. (8–188), the electric field in the sheet ($x = 0$) is

$$E_y = A \cos \omega t. \tag{8–190}$$

The corresponding instantaneous velocity of the electrons is

$$w_y = -\frac{e}{h_e} E_y \tag{8–191}$$

(Eq. 8–163). Work is done by the *electric field* of the incident wave on each moving electron at a rate

$$q = -eE_y w_y = \frac{e^2}{h_e} E_y^2, \tag{8–192}$$

per unit time. On the other hand, the *magnetic field* of the incident wave acts upon each moving electron with a force

$$f = -ew_y B_z = -\frac{e}{c} w_y E_y \tag{8–193}$$

(Eq. 8–189), or

$$f = \frac{e^2 E_y^2}{h_e c} = \frac{q}{c}. \tag{8–194}$$

This force is in the x-direction, i.e., in the direction of propagation of the incident wave. Since the electron cannot leave the sheet, the force is transmitted to the sheet.

To summarize, if N is the number of electrons per unit area of the sheet, we find that the sheet absorbs energy from the wave at a rate Nq per unit area. This energy is converted into Joule heat. At the same time, the sheet is subject to a force equal to Nf per unit area. If the sheet is free to move, it will acquire a momentum in the direction of the positive x-axis. By Newton's second law, the quantity Nf represents the rate of change of momentum per unit area of the absorber, and we conclude that a transfer of energy from the wave to the conducting sheet is accompanied by a transfer of momentum. It is natural to interpret this result by saying that the electromagnetic wave itself carries both energy and momentum, and from Eqs. (8–192) and (8–194) we see that *the ratio between the energy and the momentum of the electromagnetic wave equals the velocity of light.*

According to Eqs. (7–20), the energy of an electromagnetic wave is distributed in space with a density

$$u = \tfrac{1}{2}(\epsilon_0 E^2 + \mu_0 H^2) = \epsilon_0 E^2 \qquad (8\text{–}195)$$

per unit volume. It follows that the momentum of an electromagnetic wave is distributed with a density

$$p = \frac{u}{c}, \qquad (8\text{–}196)$$

and is directed in the sense of the propagation. Thus the momentum per unit volume, considered as a vector, is parallel to the Poynting vector $\mathbf{S} = \mathbf{E} \times \mathbf{H}$ and is related to $\mathbf{S}$ by the equation

$$\mathbf{p} = \frac{\mathbf{S}}{c^2}. \qquad (8\text{–}197)$$

In the above considerations we have neglected the reflected wave, a procedure which needs justification, since a reflected wave of appreciable intensity would carry an appreciable momentum, opposite in direction to that of the incident wave. If Eq. (8–196) is correct, we would expect that the momentum transferred to the conducting sheet should equal the absorbed energy *plus twice the reflected energy* divided by the velocity of light.

It turns out that reflection can be neglected in the present case because, as we shall prove, for infinitesimal conductivity of the sheet the absorbed energy is an infinitesimal quantity of the first order, while the reflected energy is an infinitesimal quantity of the second order.

We can prove the above statement by the following argument. First we rewrite (8–191):

$$\frac{dy}{dt} = -\frac{e}{h_e} A \cos \omega t.$$

By integrating this equation we find that each electron executes harmonic oscillations around a fixed position in the y-direction, represented by

$$y - y_0 = -\frac{Ae}{h_e \omega} \sin \omega t,$$

or

$$y - y_0 = -\frac{Ae}{h_e \omega} \cos \left(\omega t - \frac{\pi}{2} \right),$$

where y_0 is the value of y at $t = 0$.

Each oscillating electron radiates as an electric dipole with a moment

$$-e(y - y_0) = \frac{Ae^2}{h_e\omega} \cos\left(\omega t - \frac{\pi}{2}\right). \qquad (8\text{–}198)$$

As shown in Section 8–9, the oscillating dipoles produce two secondary waves E_{ys} traveling in opposite directions, which start from the conducting sheet with a phase delay of $\pi/2$ with respect to the oscillations of the dipoles. These, in turn, have a phase delay of $\pi/2$ with respect to the incident wave [compare Eqs. (8–190) and (8–198)]. Hence, on the conducting sheet each of the secondary waves is opposite in phase to the incident wave. The equations of the secondary waves are of the following form:

$$\text{for } x > 0: \quad E_{ys} = -A_s \cos \omega \left(t - \frac{x}{c}\right),$$

$$\text{for } x < 0: \quad E_{ys} = -A_s \cos \omega \left(t + \frac{x}{c}\right).$$

The secondary wave that travels in the backward direction ($x < 0$) represents the reflected wave. It has an amplitude A_s and an intensity proportional to A_s^2.

The secondary wave that travels in the forward direction has everywhere a phase opposite to that of the incident wave. The amplitude of the transmitted wave is $A - A_s$ and its intensity is proportional to $(A - A_s)^2$.

The ratio of the *reflected* to the incident energy is therefore $(A_s/A)^2$. On the other hand, the ratio of the *absorbed* to the incident energy is

$$\frac{A^2 - (A - A_s)^2 - A_s^2}{A^2} = \frac{2A_s}{A} - \frac{2A_s^2}{A^2}.$$

It follows that the reflected energy varies as A_s^2, while the absorbed energy varies as A_s.

The momentum of electromagnetic waves manifests itself as a *radiation pressure* whenever an electromagnetic wave is (totally or partially) reflected or absorbed.

The pressure of radiation from terrestrial sources is a small effect which can be demonstrated only by very delicate experiments. In astrophysical phenomena, however, radiation pressure plays a prominent role. For example, it is believed that the tail of a comet is due to the radiation pressure of sunlight pushing the gases that surround the comet away from the sun.

So far, we have considered only linearly polarized waves, but it is readily apparent that the effects are the same with light of any arbitrary state of polarization, or with natural light. However, another effect comes into play for elliptically or circularly polarized waves because, as we shall presently show, the absorption of such a wave is accompanied by the transfer of a certain amount of angular momentum from the wave to the absorber.

As before, consider a thin sheet of low conductivity placed perpendicular to the direction of propagation of the wave and assume that the wave is a sinusoidal, circularly polarized wave. The vector $\mathbf{E}$ then has a constant magnitude and rotates with constant angular velocity ω in the plane of the wave. In the conducting sheet, each electron is acted upon by a force $-e\mathbf{E}$. As a result of this force and of the viscous forces opposing the motion, the electron acquires a velocity

$$\mathbf{w} = -\frac{e}{h_e}\,\mathbf{E}. \qquad (8\text{-}199)$$

Like $\mathbf{E}$, $\mathbf{w}$ has a constant magnitude and rotates with a constant angular velocity ω. A motion in which the velocity vector is constant in magnitude and rotates with constant angular velocity in a plane is a circular motion. We thus conclude that each charge describes a circle whose radius r is determined by

$$w = \frac{e}{h_e}\,E = \omega r,$$

where E is the magnitude of $\mathbf{E}$, and w the magnitude of $\mathbf{w}$. From this equation, we obtain

$$r = \frac{eE}{h_e\omega}. \qquad (8\text{-}200)$$

With respect to the center of the circle, the electric force $-e\mathbf{E}$ acting on the charge $-e$ exerts a torque $\boldsymbol{\vartheta}$ given by

$$\boldsymbol{\vartheta} = -e\,\mathbf{r}\times\mathbf{E}, \qquad (8\text{-}201)$$

where $\mathbf{r}$ is the vector from the center of the circle to the instantaneous position of the electron. The magnitude of this torque is

$$|\boldsymbol{\vartheta}| = eEr = \frac{e^2E^2}{h_e\omega}. \qquad (8\text{-}202)$$

It can be easily shown that $|\boldsymbol{\vartheta}|$ represents also the time average of the torque with respect to any other point of the sheet.

We conclude that the partial absorption of a circularly polarized wave develops a torque on the absorbing sheet. If the absorbing sheet is free to rotate about an axis perpendicular to its plane, it will acquire an angular momentum about this axis. With respect to an observer looking toward the oncoming wave, the rotation occurs clockwise or counterclockwise depending on whether the wave has right-handed or left-handed circular polarization (see Section 6-2).

From the above results it follows that a circularly polarized wave carries angular momentum as well as energy and linear momentum, so that, for such a wave, we can define an angular momentum per unit volume, τ. The vector τ is parallel or antiparallel to the direction of propagation, depending on whether the circular polarization is left-handed or right-handed. From the expressions of $|\vartheta|$ and q (Eqs. 8–203 and 8–192), we find that the ratio between the density of angular momentum and the density of energy has the following value:

$$\frac{|\tau|}{u} = \frac{1}{\omega}. \qquad (8\text{–}203)$$

Note that linearly polarized waves have zero angular momentum because under the action of a linearly polarized wave the charges in the conducting sheet execute linear oscillations, and the average torque of the force acting on each charge is zero.

*8–13 Electromagnetic waves in anisotropic dielectrics. We have studied thus far the propagation of electromagnetic waves in homogeneous isotropic substances. To explain the optical properties of crystals, we must now investigate the propagation of electromagnetic waves in homogeneous anisotropic dielectrics.

The electric anisotropy of crystals arises from the fact that the polarizability is different in different directions. A simple model will help to clarify this point. Suppose that the positive charges occupy fixed positions in the crystal lattice, while the negative charges are tied to the positive ones by elastic forces. Suppose, however, that the restoring forces are different in three mutually perpendicular directions, $O\xi$, $O\eta$, $O\zeta$. An electric field parallel to any one of these directions will produce a polarization parallel to the field, but the ratio of polarization to the electric field strength will be different for the three different directions:

$$P_\xi = \chi_1 E_\xi, \qquad P_\eta = \chi_2 E_\eta, \qquad P_\zeta = \chi_3 E_\zeta. \qquad (8\text{–}204)$$

An electric field acting in a direction different from any of the three principal directions $O\xi$, $O\eta$, and $O\zeta$, may be resolved into its three orthogonal components, E_ξ, E_η, E_ζ. Each component separately produces a corresponding polarization P_ξ, P_η, P_ζ, as given by Eqs. (8–204). The resultant of these three mutually perpendicular vectors is the resultant polarization vector. In general, *the polarization vector* $\mathbf{P}$ *is not parallel to the electric field strength* $\mathbf{E}$.

The electric displacement $\mathbf{D}$ is the vector sum of $\epsilon_0\mathbf{E}$ and $\mathbf{P}$:

$$\mathbf{D} = \epsilon_0\mathbf{E} + \mathbf{P}.$$

We thus conclude that in the dielectric under consideration, $\mathbf{D}$ is parallel to

E only if **E** lies in one of the three principal directions $O\xi$, $O\eta$, or $O\zeta$. In all other cases, **D** and **E** have different directions.* The three orthogonal components of **D** are related to the three orthogonal components of **E** by the following equations:

$$D_\xi = \kappa_1 \epsilon_0 E_\xi, \qquad D_\eta = \kappa_2 \epsilon_0 E_\eta, \qquad D_\zeta = \kappa_3 \epsilon_0 E_\zeta, \qquad (8\text{-}205)$$

where

$$\kappa_1 = 1 + \frac{\chi_1}{\epsilon_0}, \qquad \kappa_2 = 1 + \frac{\chi_2}{\epsilon_0}, \qquad \kappa_3 = 1 + \frac{\chi_3}{\epsilon_0}. \qquad (8\text{-}206)$$

The constants κ_1, κ_2, and κ_3 are called the three principal dielectric constants.

It is important to note that *the electrical properties of the model discussed above apply to all anisotropic dielectrics satisfying the following conditions:* (1) *The displacement is a linear function of the electric field strength*, which means that if the field strength $\mathbf{E}_1$ produces the displacement $\mathbf{D}_1$ and the field strength $\mathbf{E}_2$ produces the displacement $\mathbf{D}_2$, then the field strength $\mathbf{E}_1 + \mathbf{E}_2$ produces the displacement $\mathbf{D}_1 + \mathbf{D}_2$. (2) *The substance exhibits no asymmetry that makes it possible to distinguish a right-handed form from a left-handed form* (as discussed in Section 4–15, this kind of asymmetry is connected with optical activity). In other words, for all crystals that satisfy the above conditions, we can determine three mutually perpendicular principal directions, $O\xi$, $O\eta$, $O\zeta$, and three corresponding principal dielectric constants, κ_1, κ_2, κ_3, such that Eqs. (8–205) are satisfied. This result is a consequence of the general theory of tensors; however, we shall not attempt here to give its mathematical proof.

Maxwell's equations (7–13, 7–14, 7–15, 7–16), of course, are valid in anisotropic as well as in isotropic media. The only difference between the two cases lies in the relationship between **D** and **E**.

We now propose to investigate the propagation of plane waves in anisotropic dielectrics, and we look for solutions of Maxwell's equations in which the electric and magnetic vectors are functions only of x and t. In this case, as shown in Section 7–3, Maxwell's equations become

(a) $\dfrac{\partial H_x}{\partial x} = 0,$ (b) $\dfrac{\partial D_x}{\partial x} = 0,$ (c) $\dfrac{\partial H_x}{\partial t} = 0,$

(d) $\dfrac{\partial D_x}{\partial t} = 0,$ (e) $\mu_0 \dfrac{\partial H_y}{\partial t} = \dfrac{\partial E_z}{\partial x},$ (f) $\dfrac{\partial D_y}{\partial t} = -\dfrac{\partial H_z}{\partial x},$

(g) $\mu_0 \dfrac{\partial H_z}{\partial t} = -\dfrac{\partial E_y}{\partial x},$ (h) $\dfrac{\partial D_z}{\partial t} = \dfrac{\partial H_y}{\partial x}.$ (8-207)

---

*Unless two of the constants χ_1, χ_2, χ_3 are equal.

As in the isotropic case, we conclude that

$$D_x = 0, \qquad H_x = 0.$$

Thus **D** and **H** are perpendicular to the direction of propagation, but, since **E** is no longer parallel to **D**, the electric field may now have a component perpendicular to the wave front.

We now wish to inquire whether Eqs. (8–207) have solutions representing linearly polarized waves. Assume, for example, that the vector **H**, which is perpendicular to the direction of propagation, lies in the z-direction ($H_y = 0$). It then follows that $\partial E_z/\partial x$ and $\partial D_z/\partial t$ are zero, E_z is independent of x, and D_z is independent of t. Since, in a plane wave, E_z and D_z are functions of $t - x/v$ or $t + x/v$, we conclude that E_z and D_z are constant both in time and in space, and may be taken as zero. Therefore **E** and **D** lie in the xy-plane. Similarly, we conclude that if **H** lies in the y-direction, E_y and D_y are zero, so that **E** and **D** lie in the xz-plane. Thus, (a) in a *linearly polarized wave, the vector* **E**, *the vector* **D**, *and the direction of propagation are coplanar.*

For the sake of simplicity, we shall now continue under the assumption that two of the principal dielectric constants are equal, e.g.:

$$\kappa_2 = \kappa_3.$$

As we shall see, this corresponds to the case of uniaxial crystals. Anticipating this result, we shall refer to the ξ-axis as the optic axis of the crystal. All the directions perpendicular to the optic axis are equivalent, and we are therefore free to choose as η- and ζ-axes any two mutually perpendicular directions in the plane normal to the ξ-axis. In particular, given the electric field **E**, we may take either the η- or the ζ-axis in the plane parallel to the optic axis and the instantaneous direction of the vector **E**. In the first case $E_\zeta = 0$ and, from Eqs. (8–205), $D_\zeta = 0$; in the second case $E_\eta = 0$, $D_\eta = 0$. Therefore, (b) *in uniaxial crystals the vector* **E**, *the vector* **D**, *and the optic axis are coplanar.*

For any given direction of propagation there are only two linearly polarized waves which satisfy both conditions (a) and (b):

(1) The wave whose electric vector is perpendicular to the optic axis; in this case **E** and **D** are parallel and are thus obviously coplanar with any other direction (Fig. 8–28). This is the wave that we have called the *ordinary wave* in Section 6–10.

(2) The wave whose electric vector lies in the plane that contains the optic axis and the direction of propagation (Fig. 8–29). This is the wave that we have called the *extraordinary wave* in Section 6–10.

After determining the two possible planes of vibration of the waves traveling in a given direction, we turn to the problem of computing their velocities of propagation.

We select a cartesian frame of reference with the x-axis in the direction of propagation, and such that the xz-plane contains the axis of the crystal. Then the ordinary wave vibrates in the xy-plane, and the extraordinary wave vibrates in the xz-plane. We also assume that the η-axis (which is an arbitrary line perpendicular to the optic axis $O\xi$) is coincident with the y-axis (see Figs. 8–28, 8–29).

In the case of the ordinary wave (Fig. 8–28), $E_z = 0$, $D_z = 0$, $H_y = 0$, $H_x = 0$, $E_x = 0$, and $D_y = \kappa_2\epsilon_0 E_y$. Equations (8–207 f, g) become

$$\frac{\partial H_z}{\partial x} = -\kappa_2\epsilon_0 \frac{\partial E_y}{\partial t}, \qquad \frac{\partial E_y}{\partial x} = -\mu_0 \frac{\partial H_z}{\partial t}. \qquad (8\text{–}208)$$

Elimination of H_z between these two equations yields

$$\frac{\partial^2 E_y}{\partial x^2} = \kappa_2\epsilon_0\mu_0 \frac{\partial^2 E_y}{\partial t^2}, \qquad (8\text{–}209)$$

which is the equation of a wave traveling with the velocity

$$v = \frac{1}{\sqrt{\kappa_2\epsilon_0\mu_0}} = \frac{c}{\sqrt{\kappa_2}}. \qquad (8\text{–}210)$$

Therefore we obtain the following expression for the index of refraction of the ordinary wave:

$$n_2 = \sqrt{\kappa_2}. \qquad (8\text{–}211)$$

In the case of the extraordinary wave (Fig. 8–29), $E_y = 0$, $D_y = 0$, $H_z = 0$, $H_x = 0$, $D_x = 0$, but $E_x \neq 0$. Only parts (e) and (h) of (8–207),

$$\frac{\partial E_z}{\partial x} = \mu_0 \frac{\partial H_y}{\partial t}, \qquad \frac{\partial H_y}{\partial x} = \frac{\partial D_z}{\partial t}, \qquad (8\text{–}212)$$

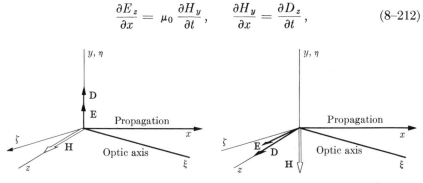

FIG. 8–28. E, D, and H in the ordinary wave.   FIG. 8–29. E, D, and H in the extraordinary wave.

are not identically zero. If we define the quantity κ by means of the equation

$$\kappa = \frac{D_z}{\epsilon_0 E_z}, \qquad (8\text{–}213)$$

we obtain from (8–212),

$$\frac{\partial^2 E_z}{\partial x^2} = \kappa \epsilon_0 \mu_0 \frac{\partial^2 E_z}{\partial t^2}. \qquad (8\text{–}214)$$

This is the equation of a wave traveling with the velocity

$$v = \frac{1}{\sqrt{\kappa \epsilon_0 \mu_0}} = \frac{c}{\sqrt{\kappa}}. \qquad (8\text{–}215)$$

Therefore the index of refraction of the extraordinary wave has the value

$$n = \sqrt{\kappa}. \qquad (8\text{–}216)$$

To compute κ we note that $\mathbf{D}$ is parallel to the z-axis and that both $\mathbf{E}$ and $\mathbf{D}$ lie in the $\xi\zeta$-plane (Figs. 8–29 and 8–30). We can therefore express the scalar product of $\mathbf{E}$ and $\mathbf{D}$ in either of the two following forms:

$$\mathbf{E} \cdot \mathbf{D} = E_z D_z$$

or

$$\mathbf{E} \cdot \mathbf{D} = E_\xi D_\xi + E_\zeta D_\zeta.$$

From these equations and from (8–213), we obtain

$$\frac{1}{\kappa} = \epsilon_0 \frac{E_z}{D_z} = \epsilon_0 \frac{E_z D_z}{D_z^2} = \epsilon_0 \frac{E_\xi D_\xi + E_\zeta D_\zeta}{|\mathbf{D}|^2},$$

or, remembering Eqs. (8–205),

$$\frac{1}{\kappa} = \frac{1}{\kappa_1} \frac{D_\xi^2}{|\mathbf{D}|^2} + \frac{1}{\kappa_2} \frac{D_\zeta^2}{|\mathbf{D}|^2}. \qquad (8\text{–}217)$$

If we denote by χ the angle between the optic axis (the ξ-axis) and the direction of propagation (the x-axis; see Fig. 8–29) and remember that $\mathbf{D}$ is parallel to the z-axis, we have

$$D_\xi = |\mathbf{D}| \sin \chi, \qquad D_\zeta = |\mathbf{D}| \cos \chi, \qquad (8\text{–}218)$$

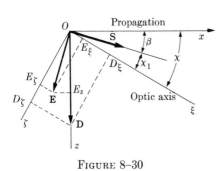

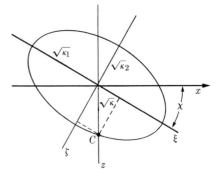

FIGURE 8–30

FIG. 8–31. Computation of the index of refraction of the extraordinary wave.

and (8–217) becomes

$$\frac{1}{\kappa} = \frac{\sin^2 \chi}{\kappa_1} + \frac{\cos^2 \chi}{\kappa_2}, \tag{8–219}$$

which determines κ for any given direction of propagation.

We can give a simple graphical interpretation of this result. On the z-axis we plot a point C at the distance $\sqrt{\kappa}$ from the origin (Fig. 8–31), whose ξ- and ζ-coordinates are

$$\xi = \sqrt{\kappa} \sin \chi, \qquad \zeta = \sqrt{\kappa} \cos \chi.$$

From Eq. (8–219), we then see that ξ and ζ satisfy the equation

$$\frac{\xi^2}{\kappa_1} + \frac{\zeta^2}{\kappa_2} = 1, \tag{8–220}$$

and we conclude that as we change the direction of propagation, i.e., as we change the angle χ, the point C describes an ellipse. The semiaxes of this ellipse are parallel to the ξ- and ζ-axes, respectively, and their lengths are κ_1 and κ_2. The ellipse represented by (8–220) is the intersection with the xz- (or $\xi\zeta$-) plane of the ellipsoid of revolution around the ξ-axis, represented by

$$\frac{\xi^2}{\kappa_1} + \frac{\eta^2}{\kappa_2} + \frac{\zeta^2}{\kappa_2} = 1 \tag{8–221}$$

(Fig. 8–32). The intersection of this ellipsoid with the plane perpendicular to the direction of propagation (i.e., the yz-plane) is an ellipse whose semiaxes are parallel to the y- and z-directions, respectively, and whose lengths are $\sqrt{\kappa_2}$ and $\sqrt{\kappa}$.

These results fully justify the method we introduced in Section 6–10 for determining the planes of vibration and the velocities of propagation of the ordinary and extraordinary waves in uniaxial crystals. Indeed, the ellipsoid defined by Eq. (8–221) is identical to the Fresnel ellipsoid.

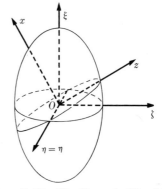

FIG. 8–32. The Fresnel ellipsoid.

The Poynting vector of the extraordinary wave, $\mathbf{S} = \mathbf{E} \times \mathbf{H}$, is not perpendicular to the plane of the wave because $\mathbf{E}$ does not lie in this plane. The vector $\mathbf{S}$ represents the energy flux. Therefore one should anticipate that the direction of $\mathbf{S}$ coincides with that of the ray, as determined in Section 6–12, and it is readily seen that this is actually the case. In the first place, the ray lies in the plane containing the optic axis, $OP = O\xi$, and the direction of propagation of the wave, $Ox = ON$ (see Figs. 6–25 and 8–31). The same is true of the vector $\mathbf{S}$, for $\mathbf{S}$ is perpendicular to $\mathbf{H}$, and $\mathbf{H}$ is perpendicular to both $O\xi$ and Ox. Moreover, the angle between Ox and $\mathbf{S}$ is equal to the angle between $\mathbf{D}$ and $\mathbf{E}$. The ξ- and ζ-components of $\mathbf{D}$ are given by Eqs. (8–218) in terms of the angle χ between Ox and $O\xi$, therefore the ξ- and ζ-components of $\mathbf{E}$ are

$$E_\xi = \frac{|\mathbf{D}|}{\epsilon_0 \kappa_1} \sin \chi, \qquad E_\zeta = \frac{|\mathbf{D}|}{\epsilon_0 \kappa_2} \cos \chi. \qquad (8\text{–}222)$$

The angle χ, between the optic axis and the vector $\mathbf{S}$ (which is perpendicular to $\mathbf{E}$) is then given by

$$\tan \chi_1 = \frac{E_\xi}{E_\zeta} = \frac{\kappa_2}{\kappa_1} \tan \chi,$$

and it follows that

$$\tan (\chi - \chi_1) = \frac{\tan \chi - \tan \chi_1}{1 + \tan \chi \tan \chi_1}$$

$$= \frac{(\kappa_1 - \kappa_2) \tan \chi}{\kappa_1 + \kappa_2 \tan^2 \chi}.$$

If $\beta = \chi - \chi_1$ is the angle between $\mathbf{D}$ and $\mathbf{E}$, which is equal to the angle between Ox and $\mathbf{S}$, and if we put $\kappa_1 = n_1^2$, $\kappa_2 = n_2^2$, we obtain

$$\tan \beta = \frac{(n_1^2 - n_2^2) \tan \chi}{n_1^2 + n_2^2 \tan \chi}. \qquad (8\text{–}223)$$

This equation is identical to (6–22), giving the angle between ON and the direction of propagation of the ray. We thus conclude that the ray is parallel to **S**.

8–14 The Zeeman effect and the Stark effect. If light is an electromagnetic disturbance due to the motions of the charged particles of which atoms and molecules are composed, one would logically predict that the properties of a light source are modified by the presence of a magnetic or an electric field. This prediction is borne out by experiment. The effect of a magnetic field on the emission lines of gases was first observed by Zeeman, and the corresponding effect of an electric field was discovered by Stark and by Lo Surdo. These effects provided a striking confirmation of the electromagnetic theory of light and played an important role in the development of atomic physics.

Let us examine the effect of the magnetic field on the basis of our model theory. According to this theory, each atom of a light source contains one or more electrons attracted toward a fixed center by forces proportional to the displacements. In the absence of any external field, the electrons describe elliptical orbits. The elliptical motion of a given electron may be regarded as the superposition of three linear harmonic oscillations, occurring along the x-, y-, and z-axes of an arbitrarily chosen cartesian frame of reference. The oscillations along the y- and z-axes combine into an elliptical motion which, in turn, may be regarded as the superposition of two circular motions of opposite sense and, in general, of different amplitudes. We are thus justified in replacing, ideally, each oscillator with *three coherent oscillators, one of which executes linear oscillations along the x-axis while the other two execute circular oscillations of opposite sense in the yz-plane* (see Fig. 8–33).*

For the sake of simplicity, we assume that in the absence of an external field the source emits monochromatic light, which means that the proportionality constant k between the elastic force and the displacement is the same for all electronic oscillators. The value of k is related to the mass m of the electron and to the angular frequency ω_0 of the oscillations by

$$\omega_0 = \sqrt{\frac{k}{m}} \qquad (8\text{–}224)$$

(see Eq. 8–4).

---

*To make a more rigorous argument, one should also remark that the electromagnetic field of the wave produced by two or more charges of equal magnitudes, moving with accelerations $\mathbf{a}_1$, $\mathbf{a}_2$, ... in a region of space of dimensions small compared with the wavelength, is identical to the field of the wave produced by a single charge of the same magnitude, whose acceleration is the vector sum of $\mathbf{a}_1$, $\mathbf{a}_2$, ...

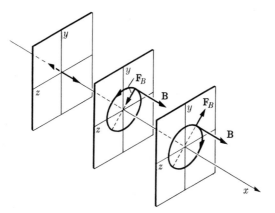

FIG. 8–33. Interpretation of the Zeeman effect.

For circular oscillations, i.e., for particles moving with constant angular velocity ω_0 on circles of radius r, the above equation may be deduced directly from the condition of equality between the elastic force kr and the product of the mass m times the centripetal acceleration $\omega_0^2 r$:

$$kr = m\omega_0^2 r.$$

Let us now assume that the light source is placed in a magnetic field $\mathbf{B}$ parallel to the x-axis and pointing in the positive x-direction. The magnetic field acts on each moving electron (of charge $-e$ and velocity $\mathbf{w}$) with a force $\mathbf{F}_B$ given by

$$\mathbf{F}_B = -e\mathbf{w} \times \mathbf{B} \qquad (8\text{–}225)$$

(see Eq. 7–21). This force vanishes if $\mathbf{w}$ is parallel to $\mathbf{B}$, i.e., parallel to the x-axis. Hence we conclude that electrons vibrating in the direction of the x-axis are not affected by the magnetic field and continue to execute linear oscillations with their characteristic frequency ω_0.

The motions of the electrons describing circular orbits in the yz-plane, however, are modified. We shall presently verify that these electrons will still move along circular orbits, but with angular velocities different from ω_0.

Let us consider an electron rotating counterclockwise with respect to the positive x-direction (Fig. 8–33). Let r be the radius of the circle, ω_1 the angular velocity, and therefore $|\mathbf{w}| = \omega_1 r$ the linear velocity. If B is the magnitude of the vector $\mathbf{B}$, the magnetic field acts on the electron with a force of magnitude $eB\omega_1 r$ pointing toward the center of the circle. The resultant of this force and the elastic force kr is a centripetal force of magnitude $kr + eB\omega_1 r$. Since the resultant force is equal to the mass times the centripetal acceleration, we can write

$$kr + eB\omega_1 r = m\omega_1^2 r$$

or, recalling Eq. (8–224),

$$eB\omega_1 = m(\omega_1^2 - \omega_0^2). \tag{8–226}$$

Similarly, if ω_2 is the angular velocity of an electron rotating clockwise with respect to the positive x-axis (Fig. 8–33), the resultant centripetal force acting upon this electron is $kr - eB\omega_2 r$, and we obtain

$$kr - eB\omega_2 r = m\omega_2^2 r,$$

or

$$eB\omega_2 = m(\omega_0^2 - \omega_2^2). \tag{8–227}$$

Equations (8–226) and (8–227) determine the new angular velocities of the two sets of electronic oscillators. We see that $\omega_1 > \omega_0$ and $\omega_2 < \omega_0$. If B is sufficiently small, the differences $\omega_1 - \omega_0$ and $\omega_0 - \omega_2$ become small compared with ω_0. Neglecting quantities of the order of $(\omega_1 - \omega_0)^2/\omega_0^2$ and $(\omega_0 - \omega_2)^2/\omega_0^2$, we have

$$\omega_1^2 - \omega_0^2 = 2\omega_1(\omega_1 - \omega_0),$$

$$\omega_0^2 - \omega_2^2 = 2\omega_2(\omega_0 - \omega_2),$$

and we can rewrite (8–226) and (8–227):

$$\omega_1 - \omega_0 = \omega_0 - \omega_2 = \frac{eB}{2m}. \tag{8–228}$$

Thus we see that the magnetic field increases the angular velocity of the electrons rotating counterclockwise with respect to the direction of the magnetic field by an amount

$$\Delta\omega = \frac{eB}{2m}, \tag{8–229}$$

and decreases the angular velocity of the electrons rotating clockwise by the same amount.

Suppose now that we analyze with a spectroscope the light emitted by the source. In the absence of the field, we observe, in all directions, unpolarized light of a single frequency, ω_0. In the presence of the field, however, we obtain different results for different directions of observation.

(a) If we look in a direction *perpendicular* to the magnetic field (e.g., in the z-direction; see Fig. 8–33) we see three spectral lines. The middle line is due to light waves of angular frequency ω_0 emitted by the electrons oscillating in the direction of the x-axis. This light is linearly polarized, with the plane of vibration parallel to the magnetic field. The other two lines are due to the light waves of angular frequencies $\omega_0 + \Delta\omega$ and $\omega_0 - \Delta\omega$ emitted by the electrons rotating counterclockwise and clockwise in a plane perpendicular to the magnetic field. These waves are linearly polarized, with the plane of vibration perpendicular to the magnetic field.

(b) Let us suppose next that we look in the direction of the magnetic field, for example, with the vector **B** pointing toward us. Since the linear oscillators do not radiate in the direction of their motion, we shall see only the two spectral lines due to the electrons rotating counterclockwise and clockwise in the yz-plane. The line of angular frequency $\omega_0 + \Delta\omega$ will show left-handed circular polarization, and the lines of angular frequency $\omega_0 - \Delta\omega$ will show right-handed circular polarization.

The theory developed here is only partially borne out by the observations. When the source is placed in a magnetic field, some spectral lines split into a triplet, as theoretically predicted, and the separations of the components, as well as their states of polarization, agree accurately with the results of our theory (*normal Zeeman effect*). Many spectral lines, however, behave in an anomalous manner, often splitting into complicated multiplets under the influence of a magnetic field (*anomalous Zeeman effect*). This disagreement between theory and experiment is due to a fundamental limitation of our model, and can be removed only by the exact quantum-mechanical treatment of the phenomenon.

The effect of an electric field on the emission lines of gases is qualitatively similar to that of a magnetic field. Here, too, a single spectral line splits into a multiplet consisting of characteristically polarized components. However, a discussion of this effect on the basis of our model does not prove profitable and we shall therefore omit further details.

8–15 The Faraday effect. As already mentioned in Section 6–16, optically inactive substances become active when placed in a magnetic field parallel to the direction of propagation of the light wave (Faraday effect). The theory of this effect is closely related to the theory of the Zeeman effect developed in the preceding section.

For the sake of simplicity, we again assume that all electronic oscillators have the same angular frequency ω_0. We then consider a circularly polarized monochromatic wave of angular frequency ω traveling in the direction of the x-axis of a cartesian frame of reference. In the absence of a magnetic field, the forces acting upon a given electron are the elastic force and the force $-e\mathbf{E}$ due to the electric field **E** of the wave. Since **E** remains constant in magnitude and rotates with the constant angular velocity ω, the electron, in the steady state condition, will be forced to describe a circular orbit with the same angular velocity ω. The radius r of this orbit is determined by the condition that the resultant force should equal the product of the mass times the centripetal acceleration. If $\mathbf{r}$ is the vector from the center of the circle to the instantaneous position of the electron, the elastic force is $-k\mathbf{r}$ and the centripetal acceleration is $-m\omega^2\mathbf{r}$. We thus obtain the equation

$$-e\mathbf{E} - k\mathbf{r} = -m\omega^2\mathbf{r} \qquad (8\text{--}230)$$

or, recalling the expression for ω_0 (Eq. 8–224):

$$\mathbf{r} = -\frac{e/m}{\omega_0^2 - \omega^2}\,\mathbf{E}.$$

The electric dipole moment of each oscillator has the expression

$$\mathbf{p} = -e\mathbf{r} = \frac{e^2/m}{\omega_0^2 - \omega^2}\,\mathbf{E}. \qquad (8\text{--}231)$$

If N is the number of oscillators per unit volume, the polarization vector is given by

$$\mathbf{P} = N\mathbf{p} = \frac{Ne^2/m}{\omega_0^2 - \omega^2}\,\mathbf{E}. \qquad (8\text{--}232)$$

This equation, as we might have anticipated, is identical to that expressing the relation between $\mathbf{P}$ and $\mathbf{E}$ for a linearly polarized wave (Eq. 8–46).

Let us suppose now that the substance is placed in a magnetic field $\mathbf{B}$ parallel to the x-axis and pointing, for example, in the positive direction. Upon each moving electron the magnetic field will exert a force directed along the radius of the circular orbit, and equal to $-eB\omega\mathbf{r}$ if the electron rotates counterclockwise (i.e., if the light wave has left-handed circular polarization) or to $+eB\omega\mathbf{r}$ if the rotation is clockwise. In place of (8–230), we now have

$$-e\mathbf{E} \mp eB\omega\mathbf{r} - k\mathbf{r} = -m\omega^2\mathbf{r},$$

which yields

$$\mathbf{r} = -\frac{e/m}{\omega_0^2 - \omega^2 \pm eB\omega/m}\,\mathbf{E},$$

and therefore

$$\mathbf{P} = \frac{Ne^2/m}{\omega_0^2 - \omega^2 \pm eB\omega/m}\,\mathbf{E}, \qquad (8\text{--}233)$$

$$\mathbf{D} = \epsilon_0\mathbf{E} + \mathbf{P} = \epsilon_0\mathbf{E} + \frac{Ne^2/m}{\omega_0^2 - \omega^2 \pm eB\omega/m}\,\mathbf{E}. \qquad (8\text{--}234)$$

In (8–233) and (8–234) the $+$ sign refers to left-handed polarization, the $-$ sign to right-handed polarization. In both cases the light wave is assumed to travel in the direction in which the magnetic field is pointing. For light waves traveling in the opposite sense, the signs would be inverted.

Equation (8–234) shows that in the presence as well as in the absence of the magnetic field, $\mathbf{D}$ is at all times proportional and parallel to $\mathbf{E}$. We can thus define a permittivity ϵ by means of the equation $\mathbf{D} = \epsilon\mathbf{E}$, and we obtain

$$\epsilon = \epsilon_0 + \frac{Ne^2/m}{\omega_0^2 - \omega^2 \pm eB\omega/m}. \tag{8–235}$$

From this equation we find that the indices of refraction corresponding to left-handed and right-handed polarization, n_l and n_r, are given by

$$n_l^2 = 1 + \frac{Ne^2/\epsilon_0 m}{\omega_0^2 - \omega^2 + eB\omega/m},$$

$$n_r^2 = 1 + \frac{Ne^2/\epsilon_0 m}{\omega_0^2 - \omega^2 - eB\omega/m}, \tag{8–236}$$

whereas the index of refraction n of the medium in the absence of the magnetic field is given by

$$n^2 = 1 + \frac{Ne^2/\epsilon_0 m}{\omega_0^2 - \omega^2}. \tag{8–237}$$

From (8–236) and (8–237), we obtain

$$\frac{1}{n_l^2 - 1} - \frac{1}{n^2 - 1} = \frac{1}{n^2 - 1} - \frac{1}{n_r^2 - 1} = \frac{\epsilon_0 B\omega}{Ne}.$$

Since $n - n_l \ll n$ and $n_r - n \ll n$, we have, to good approximation,

$$\frac{1}{n_l^2 - 1} - \frac{1}{n^2 - 1} = \frac{n^2 - n_l^2}{(n^2 - 1)^2} = \frac{2n}{(n^2 - 1)^2} (n - n_l)$$

and, similarly,

$$\frac{1}{n^2 - 1} - \frac{1}{n_r^2 - 1} = \frac{2n}{n^2 - 1} (n_r - n).$$

Hence we obtain

$$n - n_l = n_r - n = \frac{(n^2 - 1)^2}{2n} \frac{\epsilon_0 B\omega}{Ne}. \tag{8–238}$$

From these results we recognize that left-handed and right-handed circularly polarized waves travel in the direction of the magnetic field with different velocities. As explained in Section 6–15, this is the characteristic property of optically active substances. Equations (8–238) show that the index of refraction of the left-handed circularly polarized wave is smaller than that of the right-handed wave if, as we have assumed, the light travels in the direction of the magnetic field. For the opposite direction of propagation, the index of refraction of the left-handed wave becomes larger than that of the right-handed wave. We thus conclude that the substance behaves as a levorotatory medium for a wave that travels in the direction of the magnetic field, and as a dextrorotatory medium for a wave that travels in the direction opposite to the field. This result is confirmed by experiment (see Section 6–16). It should be noted that naturally active substances *do not* change from levorotatory to dextrorotatory, or vice versa, when the direction of propagation of the wave is inverted.

8-1. A gaseous source emits light of wavelength 5000 A. Assuming that each molecule contains one linear atomic oscillator and that the amplitude of oscillation is 10^{-8} cm, compute the average power output of each molecule. If the total power output of the source is 1 watt, how many molecules are emitting simultaneously? If the gas has a pressure of 10^{-3} atm, a temperature of 70° C, and occupies a volume of 10 cm^3, what is the fraction of excited molecules? Loschmidt's number (the number of molecules per cm^3 of gas at 1 atm and 0°C) is 2.68×10^{19}.

8-2. Assume that each molecule of a certain gas contains two microscopic oscillators. For both oscillators, the ratio of the restoring force to the displacement is $k = 3 \times 10^5$ gm sec^{-2}. One of the oscillating particles is an electron (mass $m_e = 9 \times 10^{-28}$ gm); the other is a proton (mass $= 1836\ m_e$). For each oscillator, compute the characteristic frequency ν_0, the corresponding wavelength, and the time constant τ_r describing the radiation damping.

8-3. Assume that each molecule of a certain gas contains an oscillating electron of characteristic frequency ν_0 and an oscillating proton of characteristic frequency ν_0' corresponding to the same value of k. Take into account radiation damping, but no other forms of damping. Compute the relative amplitudes and the phases of the forced oscillations of the electron and proton in the field of an electromagnetic wave whose electric field at the point occupied by the molecule is represented by

$E = Ae^{2\pi i\nu t}$. Consider separately the following cases:

(a) $\nu = \nu_0$,

(b) $\nu = \nu_0 + \dfrac{1}{4\pi\ (\tau_r)_{\text{electron}}}$

(c) $\nu_0 \gg \nu \gg \nu_0'$.

8-4. Refer to Problem 8-3. Compute the amplitudes of oscillation of the electron and proton numerically, taking for ν_0, ν_0', and τ_r the values obtained from the solution of Problem 8-2, and assuming $A = 1$ volt/cm.

8-5. Neglecting damping, compute the index of refraction (at normal temperature and pressure) of the gas described in Problem 8-2 for the wavelengths $\lambda = 5000$ A and $\lambda = 1$ cm.

8-6. The index of refraction of hydrogen gas at 0° and 1 atm pressure is $n = 1 + 1.400 \times 10^{-4}$ at $\lambda = 5460$ A, and $n = 1 + 1.547 \times 10^{-4}$ at $\lambda = 2540$ A. Assuming a single resonant frequency, compute this frequency and the number of electronic oscillators per unit volume. Compare with the number of molecules per unit volume. For $\lambda = 4000$ A, compute the index of refraction of hydrogen gas at 10 atm pressure.

8-7. According to an early classical model, the hydrogen atom resembles a "planetary system," i.e., consists of a pointlike electron rotating about a pointlike proton under the action of the coulomb force. Assume that the proton is fixed in space and that the electron describes a circular orbit of radius r.

Show that the potential plus kinetic energy of the electron is

$$W = - e^2/8\pi\epsilon_0 r$$

(if the energy of the electron at rest at infinite distance from the proton is taken as zero). Assume $r = 10^{-8}$ cm at $t = 0$. Compute (a) the initial frequency and corresponding wavelength, (b) the time during which r decreases from 10^{-8} cm to 0.8×10^{-8} cm as a consequence of radiation loss, and (c) the change in wavelength during this time.

8–8. The "planetary" model of the hydrogen atom discussed in Problem 8-7 makes definite predictions about the optical properties of hydrogen, some of which are in qualitative disagreement with experiment. State the answers to the following questions, as obtained from the "planetary" model, and compare with the experimental facts.

(a) Does hydrogen emit monochromatic waves?

(b) What is the order of magnitude of the wavelength of the emitted radiation, if the linear dimensions of hydrogen atoms are of the order of 10^{-8} cm?

(c) Does a circularly polarized sinusoidal wave travel through hydrogen gas without changing its state of polarization?

(d) For a given frequency, does the velocity of propagation of the circularly polarized wave depend on its amplitude?

(e) The superposition principle states that two right-handed circularly polarized waves of amplitude A traveling with velocity v in a given direction add to a single right-handed circularly polarized wave of amplitude $2A$ traveling with velocity v in the same direction. Does the superposition principle hold according to the "planetary" model?

(*Hint:* Compute the steady state motion of the electron in the field of a circularly polarized wave, assuming a circular orbit.)

8–9. According to quantum mechanics, the electron of a hydrogen atom is not exactly localized in space. A classical model approaching the actual quantum mechanical description represents the hydrogen atom as a rigid spherical cloud of negative charge of total mass m_e and radius R with a positive point charge of mass m_p embedded in it (m_e is the mass of the electron and m_p the mass of the proton). Compute the *relative* motion of the positive charge and the negative cloud, assuming m_p to be infinitely large compared with m_e. Remembering that the radiation field depends only on this relative motion, show that the model accounts for the sinusoidal character of the waves emitted by the excited atom. Express the wavelength λ of the emitted wave in terms of R and the classical radius r_e of the electron. Compute λ for $R = 10^{-8}$ cm.

8–10. Using the model of the hydrogen atom discussed in Problem 8–9, determine the value of R that will give the correct value for the index of refraction of molecular hydrogen gas at $\lambda = 5460$ A ($n = 1 + 1.400 \times 10^{-4}$ at 0°C and 1 atm pressure).

8–11. Compute the index of refraction n of an ionized gas containing N free electrons per cm^3 (neglect the contribution of positive ions and non-ionized molecules, and express the result in terms of N, r_e, and λ). Determine the wavelength λ_m for which $n = 0$ (λ_m represents the maximum wavelength which can be propagated by the ionized gas, for when $n < 0$ no solution of Maxwell equations representing traveling waves exists).

8–12. The maximum density of ionization in the ionosphere corresponds to $N = 10^5$ free electrons per cm^3. Using the results of the preceding problem, compute the maximum wavelength of an electromagnetic wave that can traverse the ionosphere.

8–13. Compute the reflectance at normal incidence for yellow light of crown glass ($n = 1.520$) and flint glass ($n = 1.650$).

8–14. Deduce Eqs. (3–13 and (3–14) [Chapter 3] from Fresnel's formulas.

8–15. A plane linearly polarized light wave is incident from air upon a water surface. Determine the amplitudes and phases of the refracted and reflected waves relative to those of the incident wave for the following cases:

Angle of incidence	Angle between the plane of incidence and the plane of vibration
20°	0°
20°	90°
75°	0°
75°	90°

8–16. A plane linearly polarized light wave originating from under water is refracted at the boundary surface between water and air. Determine the amplitudes and phases of the refracted and reflected waves relative to those of the incident wave, for the following cases:

Angle of incidence	Angle between the plane of incidence and the plane of vibration
20°	0°
20°	90°
40°	0°
40°	90°

8–17. A beam of circularly polarized light is incident from air upon a glass surface at an angle of 45°. Describe in detail the state of polarization of the re-flected beam and of the refracted beam. The index of refraction of the glass is 1.52.

8–18. A beam of linearly polarized light originating from a source under water is refracted at the boundary surface between water and air. The angle of incidence is 40° and the plane of vibration forms an angle of 45° with plane of incidence. Compute the angles which the planes of vibration of the reflected and refracted rays form with the plane of incidence.

8–19. The light of the sun appears partially polarized to an underwater observer. Let I_1 and I_2 be the intensities of sunlight observed under water through a polarization filter perpendicular to the refracted ray whose transmission axis is (a) perpendicular and (b) parallel to the vertical plane passing through the sun. Determine the ratio I_1/I_2 as a function of the zenith angle θ of the sun.

8–20. A plane light wave is incident perpendicularly from air upon the plane surface of a glass block. Compute the Poynting vectors of the refracted wave ($\mathbf{S'}$) and of the reflected wave ($\mathbf{S''}$) in terms of the Poynting vector of the incident wave ($\mathbf{S}$) and of the index of refraction n of the glass. Show that $|\mathbf{S'}|_{av} + |\mathbf{S''}|_{av} = |\mathbf{S}|_{av}$.

8–21. A plane linearly polarized light wave is incident from air on a water surface at the Brewster angle. The electric vector of the incident wave lies in the plane of incidence; its amplitude of oscillation is A. Compute (a) the Poynting vector $\mathbf{S}$ of the incident wave, (b) the amplitude A' of the refracted wave and, (c) the Poynting vector $\mathbf{S'}$ of the refracted wave. Show that $|\mathbf{S'}|_{av} \neq |\mathbf{S}|_{av}$ and explain this result.

8–22. A sinusoidal wave of wavelength λ is incident perpendicularly from air upon a plane glass surface coated with a thin transparent film of thickness h. The index of refraction of the glass is n and that of the film is n_0. For what values of h and n_0 will the reflected intensity vanish? Consider only the first two reflected waves, and neglect the change of intensity at refraction.

8–23. Solve Problem 8–22 rigorously, taking multiple-wave interference into account (see Section 3–10).

8–24. A plane, sinusoidal, linearly polarized wave represented by

$$E_y = A \exp i[\omega t - 2\pi x/\lambda_0]$$

is incident perpendicularly upon a plane parallel glass plate of index of refraction n extending from $x = 0$ to $x = h$. It gives rise to a reflected wave (in the region of space defined by $x < 0$) and to a transmitted wave (in the region of space defined by $x > h$), while in the space between $x = 0$ and $x = h$ the electromagnetic field corresponds to that of two waves traveling in opposite directions. Write the boundary conditions at $x = 0$ and $x = h$ and use these conditions to determine the amplitudes of the reflected and transmitted waves. Compare with the results obtained from a consideration of the interference of the multiply reflected waves (Eqs. 3–50, 3–54).

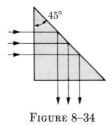

FIGURE 8–34

8–25. Consider a beam of light of wavelength 4500 A (in vacuum) which

is deflected through 90° by a totally reflecting prism of index of refraction $n = 1.6$ (Fig. 8–34). Compute the distance beyond the hypotenuse surface of the prism at which the mean square value of E is $1/e$ the mean square value of E in the air layer immediately adjacent to this surface.

8–26. The beam of light in the previous problem is linearly polarized, the plane of vibration being at 45° to the plane of incidence. Describe in detail the state of polarization of the totally reflected beam.

8–27. (a) Compute the scattering cross sections of the gas molecules described in Problem 8–2 for $\lambda = 7000$ A and $\lambda = 3500$ A. (b) Suppose that the gas is at normal pressure and temperature. Determine the fractional energy lost through scattering by two light beams of the above wavelengths traversing a gas layer 10 m thick.

8–28. A parallel beam of (a) linearly polarized light, and (b) circularly polarized light traverses a gas. Describe the state of polarization of the light scattered in the various directions (1) at 90° to the beam, (2) at 45° to the beam.

8–29. Two electronic oscillators, S_1 and S_2, of the same natural frequency ν_0 lie a distance h from each other on a line parallel to the direction of propagation of a linearly polarized wave of wavelength λ (Fig. 8–35) and intensity I. The resultant scattered radiation is observed at a point P in the plane perpendicular to the plane of vibration of the incident wave. The distance r of P from S_1 is very large compared with h. Let χ be the angle between the direction of propagation of the incident wave and the direction of observation.

(a) Write the equation giving the resultant scattered intensity I_s as a function of I, r, h, λ, and χ.

(b) Plot the intensity against h for

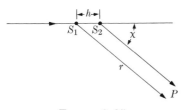

FIGURE 8–35

$\chi = 90°, \chi = 60°,$ and $\chi = 25.8°$; let h vary from 0 to 5λ.

(c) Suppose that one of the oscillators is fixed in space and the other moves back and forth between two points at $h = 0$ and $h = \lambda$, with a velocity w constant in absolute value and sufficiently small so that $\lambda/w \gg 2\pi/\omega$. The *average* intensity of the scattered radiation can then be obtained by averaging the result of (a) with respect to h. Compute this average for $\chi = 90°, \chi = 60°, \chi = 25.8°$.

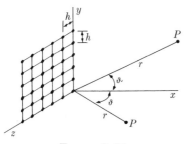

FIGURE 8–36

8–30. Consider an array of N^2 identical electronic oscillators forming a square two-dimensional lattice with sides parallel to the y- and z-axes (Fig. 8–36). Let h be the lattice distance. A plane linearly polarized wave of amplitude A and wavelength λ is incident upon the lattice in the x-direction, and its plane of vibration is parallel to the y-axis. (a) Compute the mean value of the Poynting vector of the scattered radiation at a distance r from the

origin in the xy- and xz-planes, as a function of the angle θ with respect to the x-axis. Assume that r is very large compared with the dimensions of the lattice. (b) Discuss the example: $h = 5$ A, $\lambda = 5000$ A, $N = 10^8$, and compare with the case of a single scattering center.

8–31. Suppose that a certain gas has a single absorption and emission line at a wavelength $\lambda_0 = 1612$ A. Its index of refraction at $\lambda = 5890$ A is $1 + 1.32 \times 10^{-4}$. Compute the scattering attenuation coefficient at $\lambda = 5890$ A.

8–32. Compute the radiation pressure on a reflecting surface 1 m from a 1000-watt incandescent lamp.

8–33. Compute the pressure of solar radiation at the surface of the earth, assuming complete absorption, and compare the total repulsion due to radiation pressure with the gravitational attraction. The energy flux of solar radiation at the earth is 1.34×10^3 watts/m², the radius of the earth is 6.36×10^6 m, the mass of the earth is 5.97×10^{24} kg, the mass of the sun is 1.99×10^{30} kg, the distance of the sun from the earth is 1.495×10^{11} m, and the gravitational constant is 6.67×10^{-5} m³ sec^{-2} kg^{-1}.

8–34. A plane elliptically polarized wave is incident perpendicularly on a thin conducting sheet such as that considered in Section 8–12. In the plane of the sheet, the electric field of the wave is represented by $E_y = A_y \cos \omega t$, $E_z = A_z \sin \omega t$. (a) Determine the motion of the electrons in the conducting sheet. (b) Compute the torque of the force acting upon an individual electron. (c) Show that the density of angular momentum in the field of the elliptically polarized wave is $\epsilon_0 A_y A_z/\omega$.

8–35. A plane linearly polarized wave is incident perpendicularly on a quarter-wave plate whose axes are at 45° to the plane of vibration. Compute the torque acting on the quarter-wave plate in terms of the mean energy flux per unit area, S_{av}, of the incident wave.

8–36. A light source has an emission line of wavelength $\lambda = 4000$ A which exhibits "normal" Zeeman effect. Compute the separation of the components of the triplet observed at 90° in a magnetic field of 0.1 weber/m^2 (1000 gauss). Estimate the minimum number of lines of a diffraction grating that can resolve such a triplet in the first order.

8–37. Excited atoms containing oscillators of a single frequency ν_0 are in a magnetic field **B**. Determine the fre-quencies, the relative intensities, and the states of polarization of the emission lines observed at 30° to the lines of force.

8–38. The index of refraction of a certain transparent material for $\lambda = 5000$ A is 1.5. The atoms of the material contain electronic oscillators of a single frequency, corresponding to a wavelength $\lambda_0 = 2000$ A. The material is immersed in a magnetic field of 1 weber/m^2. Compute the rotation of the plane of polarization of linearly polarized light of wavelength 5000 A traversing 1 cm of the material in the direction of the magnetic field.

CHAPTER 9

LIGHT QUANTA

9–1 The photoelectric effect. The theory developed in the two preceding chapters accounts in a very natural way for the two most fundamental properties of light, i.e., for the transverse character of light waves and for the numerical value of the velocity of light in empty space. It also explains very satisfactorily a large variety of optical phenomena and correctly predicts various relationships between optical and electric properties of matter.

True, the agreement between the theoretical predictions and the experimental data on the interactions of light with matter is not always perfect. However, we might be tempted to explain away these seemingly minor inconsistencies with the argument that, in developing the theory, we have used an admittedly crude model of matter. We might thus feel justified in thinking that we have obtained by now a final answer to our question as to the true physical nature of light; the answer, of course, is that light is an electromagnetic wave.

A single experimental fact, not included among those discussed previously, is sufficient to destroy our complacency and remind us once more of the limited validity of all our physical conceptions. To forestall possible misunderstanding, we hasten to state that we shall find no cause for questioning the electromagnetic character of light. What will need a drastic revision is the wave description of electromagnetic disturbances, and the conclusion, implicit in this description, that the electromagnetic energy is distributed in a continuous manner through space.

The phenomenon referred to is the *photoelectric effect*, which was discovered by Hertz in 1897 and which has received wide applications in modern technology through the development of phototubes.

We can demonstrate the photoelectric effect and study its characteristics with the experimental arrangement shown in Fig. 9–1. Two clean, insulated metal plates are mounted inside an evacuated tube and connected through a galvanometer to a variable voltage supply. Light of an appropriate wave-

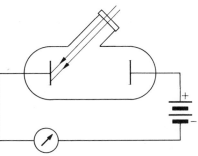

Fig. 9–1. Photoelectric effect.

length entering the tube through a quartz window (which is transparent to both visible and ultraviolet rays) strikes one of the plates. With zero voltage between the plates, the galvanometer records a certain current, which increases to a saturation value when the illuminated plate is brought to an increasingly high *negative* potential with respect to the other, and which decreases gradually when the illuminated plate is brought to a positive potential. The potential necessary to stop the photoelectric current completely is usually of the order of several volts.

The obvious interpretation of the photoelectric effect is that light striking a metal surface extracts electrically charged particles from it. Since the current increases when the illuminated plate is at a negative potential with respect to the other, we conclude that the particles carry a negative charge. It is thus natural to identify such particles with the conduction electrons. To check this assumption, we can determine the ratio e/m of the charge to the mass of the particles in question by accelerating them through an appropriate voltage difference and then measuring the curvature of their trajectories in a magnetic field. We find for this ratio a value equal to that which is characteristic of electrons.

Conduction electrons do not escape spontaneously from a metal even though they move freely within the metal, and it is apparent that in the immediate vicinity of the metal surface, an electron experiences a force directed toward the metal. To escape from the metal, the electron, then, must have an energy greater than a certain minimum amount, and light supplies the energy necessary for the escape. The electrons leave the illuminated plate with different velocities and in different directions. With no voltage difference between the plates, some of the electrons reach the collecting plate, thus establishing an electric current in the circuit.

If the collecting plate is brought to an increasingly high *positive* potential with respect to the illuminated plate, more and more of the electrons are attracted to the collecting plate, and the current increases until all of the electrons emitted by the illuminated plate reach the collecting plate. When this happens, a further increase of the voltage difference cannot produce further increase of the current: the current will have attained its saturation value.

If, on the other hand, the collecting plate is brought to an increasingly high *negative* potential with respect to the illuminated plate, fewer and fewer electrons will reach the collecting plate, and the current will decrease. Eventually, only the electrons emitted from the illuminated surface with the highest velocity will be able to overcome the retarding voltage, and the current will drop to zero at a value V_m of the retarding voltage such that eV_m represents the maximum energy E_m of the photoelectrons.

We obtain very important results by varying the *intensity* and the *frequency* of the incident light and investigating the corresponding change in the *number* per unit time of ejected electrons (as measured by the saturation current) and the change in their *maximum energy* E_m (as measured by the minimum retarding voltage necessary to stop the photoelectric current). Operating with light of a given frequency, we find that the *maximum energy* of the electrons *is independent of the light intensity* and that their *number* is *proportional to the intensity*. These results contradict the predictions of electromagnetic theory, according to which it is the electric field of the incident wave, acting upon the electrons near the metal surface, that supplies them with the energy necessary to break loose from the metal. The amplitude of oscillation of the electric field is proportional to the square root of the intensity and one would therefore expect that as the intensity increases, the electrons would be released from the metal surface with increasingly high energies. The contradiction becomes even more manifest if we note that photoelectric emission begins with no appreciable delay when light strikes the metal. Indeed, if any time lag exists at all, it is so short that the electron must be capable of absorbing the energy falling over an area enormously greater than the cross section of an atom in order to escape from the metal with the observed velocity.

If we now vary the frequency ν of the incident light, we observe the following. For each metal, the photoelectric effect occurs only when ν is *greater* than a certain characteristic value ν_0, called the *threshold frequency.* For example, the threshold frequency for tungsten corresponds to a wavelength of about 2800 A (ultraviolet light), and the threshold frequency for cesium corresponds to a wavelength of about 6500 A (visible light). The maximum energy E_m of the electrons released by light of a given frequency $\nu > \nu_0$ is proportional to the difference between ν and ν_0:

$$E_m = h(\nu - \nu_0). \qquad (9\text{--}1)$$

The proportionality constant h has the value

$$h = 6.623 \times 10^{-34} \text{ joule sec}, \qquad (9\text{--}2)$$

and is known as *Planck's constant.* The electromagnetic theory of light offers no explanation of this remarkable relationship between light frequency and electron energy.

9–2 Photons. The Compton effect. The experimental results described in the previous section become immediately understandable if we assume, as first suggested by Einstein in 1905, that light of a given frequency ν consists of discrete particles, each carrying an energy

$$E = h\nu. \qquad (9\text{--}3)$$

These particles are known as *light quanta,* or *photons.*

A photon falling upon a metal surface may disappear, transferring all of its energy E to a conduction electron. If this energy is sufficiently large, the electron may escape from the metal. Electrons in metals move about with various kinetic energies; hence different electrons, absorbing photons of the same energy, will escape from the metal with different kinetic energies. The maximum kinetic energy will be

$$E_m = E - E_0, \qquad (9\text{--}4)$$

where E_0 is the minimum energy that an electron must absorb before it can leave the metal. Obviously, the electrons with highest kinetic energy in the metal emerge from the metal with highest kinetic energy. E_0 represents also the minimum energy of photons capable of releasing electrons from the metal. The corresponding frequency ν_0, given by

$$E_0 = h\nu_0, \qquad (9\text{--}5)$$

is thus the "threshold frequency" defined previously. Equations (9–3), (9–4), and (9–5) yield Eq. (9–1), expressing the empirical relation between the light frequency and the energy of the photoelectrons.

It will be convenient here to measure energies in *electron volts* rather than joules. One electron volt (1 ev) is the kinetic energy of an electron accelerated from rest through a potential difference of one volt. The relation between electron volts and joules is

$$1 \text{ ev} = 1.6 \times 10^{-19} \text{ joule}. \qquad (9\text{--}6)$$

Note that the maximum energy of photoelectrons measured in ev is numerically equal to the retarding voltage V_0 necessary to stop the photoelectric current.

We now wish to inquire in more detail into the properties of photons, disregarding for the time being the apparent contradiction between the corpuscular character of light implicit in the photon hypothesis, and the wave character of light that is amply demonstrated by countless phenomena such as those of interference and diffraction.

The energy E of a photon of frequency ν is given by (9–3). In terms of the wavelength $\lambda = c/\nu$, E has the expression

$$E = \frac{ch}{\lambda} \qquad (9\text{--}7)$$

or, if E is measured in ev and λ in angstroms,

$$E \text{ (ev)} = \frac{12394}{\lambda \text{ (A)}}. \qquad (9\text{--}8)$$

We see that photons of visible light (for which λ is of the order of several thousand angstroms) have energies of the order of a few electron volts.*

We have seen in Section 8–12 that light has momentum as well as energy, as demonstrated experimentally by the observation of light pressure. The ratio between energy and momentum equals the velocity of light in vacuum, c. If light consists of a stream of photons, we must ascribe to each photon of energy $E = h\nu$ a momentum p given by

$$p = \frac{h\nu}{c} = \frac{h}{\lambda}. \tag{9–9}$$

In Section 8–12 we also showed that circularly polarized light carries an angular momentum equal to the energy divided by the angular frequency $\omega = 2\pi\nu$. Angular momentum can be represented by means of an "axial" vector, parallel to the axis of rotation, whose direction bears to the direction of rotation the same relation as the direction of advancement to the direction of rotation of a right-handed screw. Thus, as already mentioned, the vector representing the angular momentum of a beam of circularly polarized light is parallel or antiparallel to the direction of propagation depending on whether the polarization is left-handed or right-handed.

If we assume that all photons corresponding to light of a given frequency are identical, we must conclude that each photon of energy $E = h\nu$ carries an intrinsic angular momentum or *spin* **s** of magnitude $|\mathbf{s}| = h\nu/2\pi\nu$, or

$$|\mathbf{s}| = \frac{h}{2\pi}. \tag{9–10}$$

We must also assume that the vector **s** has only two possible orientations, either parallel or antiparallel to the direction of motion of the photon. Since a beam of linearly or elliptically polarized light may be regarded as the superposition of two light beams with opposite circular polarizations, we shall assume that a beam of linearly or elliptically polarized light con-

---

*Since the threshold frequency for most metals lies in the ultraviolet or in the visible region, we conclude that the energy E_0 required to extract electrons from metals is of the order of several electron volts. On the other hand, classical statistics predict that electrons in metals at normal temperature have an average kinetic energy of about 2×10^{-2} ev, and are distributed in energy according to a function that decreases gradually to zero as the energy increases. If this is so, we cannot speak of a "maximum kinetic energy" of the electrons in the metal, and it becomes difficult to understand why a sharply defined photoelectric threshold is found experimentally. The explanation of this contradiction lies in the failure of classical statistical theory as applied to metals. It is known that electrons in metals obey Fermi statistics, and this theory predicts an energy distribution that falls abruptly to zero at a given critical energy.

sists of photons with spins oriented in both possible directions. We shall return to this point later.

We mention here that according to the relativity theory, the kinetic energy E and the momentum p of a particle of rest mass m and velocity w are given by

$$E = \frac{mc^2}{\sqrt{1 - w^2/c^2}} - mc^2, \tag{9-11}$$

$$p = \frac{mw}{\sqrt{1 - w^2/c^2}}, \tag{9-12}$$

from which it follows that

$$p = \frac{w}{c^2}(E + mc^2). \tag{9-13}$$

Since the velocity of photons (in vacuum) is equal to c, we see from (9–11) and (9–12) that a photon can have a finite energy and a finite momentum only if $m = 0$. Thus we must ascribe to photons *zero rest mass*. Note that with $w = c$ and $m = 0$, Eq. (9–13) yields $p = E/c$, in agreement with (9–9).

Among the experimental facts that most clearly demonstrate the existence of photons is the *Compton effect*, which may be described as the collision of an individual photon of energy $h\nu$ with an individual electron at rest. In the collision, the electron acquires a certain amount of energy and momentum, and the photon flies off with a reduced energy $h\nu'$ in a direction different from that of the incident photon (Fig. 9–2). Measurements show that in this process both energy and momentum are conserved if Eqs. (9–3), (9–9), (9–11), and (9–12) are the correct expressions for the energy and momentum of the photon and of the electron, respectively.

The Compton effect occurs in the simple manner described above only if the energy of the photon is considerably greater than the binding energy of electrons in atoms, for otherwise electrons do not behave like free particles. Because the binding energies of electrons in outer shells of atoms are of the order of a few electron volts, the Compton effect cannot be demonstrated experimentally by means of visible or ultraviolet light, but only by means of x-rays or γ-rays. The details of such experiments will be omitted here.

It should be mentioned that the photon hypothesis is not based exclusively on the photoelectric and Compton effects; this hypothesis provides the most natural interpretation for many of the processes used for the detection of light. Very important among these is the photographic process, in which the absorption of a single light quantum by one of the molecules in a grain of emulsion produces a chemical change whereby

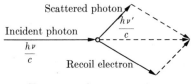

Fig. 9–2. Compton effect.

the grain is "developed" when the emulsion is placed subsequently in an appropriate solution. By means of the photographic technique or by means of sensitive phototubes it is perfectly possible to detect the arrival of individual photons and thus obtain direct proof of the corpuscular character of light.

9–3 The uncertainty principle. We are now faced with the problem of reconciling two apparently contradictory facts: (a) in its propagation through space, light behaves like a wave, and (b) in phenomena such as the photoelectric effect and the photographic process, light behaves like a stream of pointlike particles.

To begin with, we remark that from a purely logical point of view, statements (a) and (b) are not incompatible. Indeed, by accepting them both we can make perfectly unambiguous predictions and, moreover, these predictions will be in agreement with experimental observations. Specifically, given a source of light of a given frequency ν and a set of screens, mirrors, etc., we shall compute the distribution of light intensity I by means of the electromagnetic theory of light. We shall then state that the value of I at a given place and at a given time is proportional to the probability that a photon of energy $h\nu$ will manifest itself at the given place and at the given time (for example, by ejecting a photoelectron from a metal surface).

What, then, is the nature of the difficulty?

Let us consider a specific example. An opaque screen with two narrow parallel slits A and B, a small distance apart, is placed in front of a point source S of monochromatic light (Fig. 9–3). At some distance, on the other side of the screen, lies a metal plate from which the incident light may eject photoelectrons. We find that electrons are ejected most abundantly from the metal plate at those points where the interference theory predicts a maximum of light intensity. At points where the interference theory predicts zero intensity, no photoelectric effect occurs. Covering one of the two

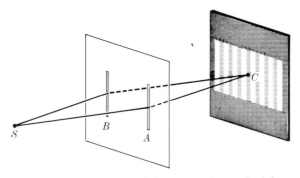

Fig. 9–3. Discussion of the uncertainty principle.

slits changes the situation drastically. In particular, with only one slit open, photons will be able to reach points of the photosensitive surface where no photons were observed when both slits were open.

We might think at first that perhaps, in the space beyond the slits, the photons that have passed through slit A interact with those that have passed through slit B, and that in such interactions the trajectories of the photons undergo certain deflections. We might then try to explain the observed distribution in the points of arrival of the photons on the photosensitive surface as a consequence of these deflections.

A very simple experimental argument shows that the above interpretation is wrong. For the *relative* probabilities of arrival of photons at various points of the photosensitive surface are completely independent of light intensity. In particular, they remain unchanged when the light intensity is reduced to such a low value that there is practically never more than a single photon at any one time in the space between the slits and the photosensitive surface. Thus we cannot invoke interaction between different photons to explain interference phenomena.

But now we come to the following paradox. Let C be a point of the photosensitive surface where the interference theory predicts zero intensity. With *either A or B* open, photons will arrive at C from the source. With *both A and B* open, no photons will arrive at C. Thus a photon which has gone through A will be able to reach C if B is closed, but will not be able to reach C if B is open. This conclusion is absurd, because the distance between the slits is enormously greater than whatever "dimensions" one might reasonably ascribe to photons, so that a photon that has gone through A has no way of knowing whether B is open or closed.

The solution of the difficulty is a very simple one, but has far-reaching consequences and requires the repudiation of certain notions that until recently were regarded as logical necessities. It may be formulated as follows. Photons behave in *some* respects like pointlike particles; for example, a photon is capable of transferring its whole energy to an electron instantaneously. However, photons do not possess *all* the properties which we intuitively ascribe to particles. In particular, *a photon does not have a definite position in space except at the instant when it interacts with matter* (e.g., when it is absorbed by photoelectric effect). Thus the statement made previously, "a photon which has gone through A can reach C if B is closed but cannot reach C if B is open," is deprived of any physical meaning. Since the photon does not have a definite position in space until it ejects an electron from the photosensitive surface, we cannot say that it has gone through either A or B.

We now wish to discuss some quantitative consequences of the point of view presented here.

We consider first a parallel beam of monochromatic light entering the observation room through a hole of sufficiently large dimensions so that diffraction phenomena may be neglected. The light beam may then be regarded as a stream of photons, all of the same energy $h\nu$, moving along parallel lines, say in the x-direction. Suppose, for the sake of simplicity, that the beam is very weak. We now try to isolate an individual photon by means of a very fast shutter that leaves the hole open for a short interval of time, Δt. From the point of view of the wave model of light, we have thus admitted into the observation room a wave train of length $c\,\Delta t$ which travels with a velocity c. Suppose that we detect the light with a photocell. At a given instant, a photoelectron may be ejected from the sensitive surface if this surface is located anywhere in the cylindrical volume of length $c\,\Delta t$ occupied by the wave train. The square of the amplitude of the wave determines the probability for the occurrence of photoemission, and we can thus say that there is an *uncertainty*

$$\Delta x \;=\; c\,\Delta t \qquad\qquad (9\text{–}14)$$

in the position of the photon at any given time.

Suppose now that we pass the light entering the observation room through a spectroscope to determine its frequency and, therefore, the energy of the photon. We find that the light is not monochromatic because (Sections 3–14 and 3–15) a wave train of finite duration is equivalent to the superposition of an infinite number of sinusoidal waves with frequencies distributed within a finite interval $\Delta\nu$. This frequency interval is related to the duration of the wave train, Δt, by

$$\Delta t \cdot \Delta\nu \;\approx\; 1 \qquad\qquad (9\text{–}15)$$

(see Eq. 3–72). It follows that there is now an *uncertainty* ΔE in the energy of the photon, and that ΔE is given by

$$\Delta E \;=\; h\,\Delta\nu \;\approx\; h/\Delta t. \qquad\qquad (9\text{–}16)$$

It is thus evident that if a photon of the originally monochromatic and parallel light beam has been admitted into the observation room during a given time interval Δt, we shall know, at all subsequent times, its x-coordinate with an uncertainty Δx given by (9–14), and its energy with an uncertainty ΔE given by (9–16). The momentum of the photon will be parallel to the direction of the incident beam (i.e., to the x-axis) and its magnitude will be known with an uncertainty

$$\Delta p_x \;=\; \frac{\Delta E}{c} \;=\; \frac{h\,\Delta\nu}{c} \;\approx\; \frac{h}{c\,\Delta t}.$$

Remembering that $c \, \Delta t = \Delta x$, we obtain the following relation between Δx and Δp_x:

$$\Delta x \cdot \Delta p_x \approx h. \tag{9–17}$$

We now see that while we can determine *either* the position *or* the momentum of a photon to any desired degree of accuracy, we cannot determine *both* quantities simultaneously with arbitrary accuracy. If, in an effort to reduce the uncertainty in the position, we decrease the time interval Δt during which the shutter is open, we simultaneously increase the uncertainty in the momentum in such a way that the product of the two uncertainties remains constant.

We obtain a similar result if we try to locate a photon in a direction perpendicular to the direction of the beam, which we shall call the y-direction. For this purpose we may admit the photons into the observation room through a narrow slit instead of a wide hole. The uncertainty in the y-coordinate of each photon, as it enters the observation room, is equal to the width Δy of the slit. But now diffraction phenomena will take place. On a distant screen there will appear a series of bright and dark fringes. Most of the light is concentrated in the central fringe, which subtends from the slit a half angle

$$\vartheta = \frac{\lambda}{\Delta y} \tag{9–18}$$

(see Section 4–14).

With the wide hole, all photons were moving in the direction of the x-axis, so that the y-component of their momentum was zero. However, the photons that have passed through the narrow slit no longer travel all in one direction. Since most of them will eventually arrive at the central fringe, we may say that, on the average, their trajectories form an angle with the x-axis of the order of ϑ, as given by (9–18). Thus the y-component of the momentum of a photon that has gone through the slit has an uncertainty

$$\Delta p_y \approx \frac{p\lambda}{\Delta y},$$

where p is the total momentum of the photon. From this equation, together with Eq. (9–9), we obtain

$$\Delta y \cdot \Delta p_y \approx h. \tag{9–19}$$

Thus the uncertainty in the value of the y-coordinate of the photon, times the uncertainty in the y-component of its momentum, is of the order of magnitude of Planck's constant h.

An analogous argument applied to a slit parallel to the z-direction yields the relation

$$\Delta z \cdot \Delta p_z \approx h. \tag{9–20}$$

It turns out that the order-of-magnitude relations (9–17), (9–19), and (9–20) have general validity, so that a given space coordinate of a photon and the corresponding component of its momentum are never known simultaneously with unlimited accuracy. Indeed, the product of the uncertainty in the value of the coordinate and the uncertainty in the value of the momentum component is always *of the order of magnitude of h or greater.*

This principle is known as the *uncertainty principle.* It may be well to state explicitly that it imposes no limitation on the accuracy that can be achieved by simultaneous measurement of two different space coordinates (say x and y), or two different components of the momentum (say p_x and p_y), or a space coordinate and the momentum component corresponding to a different coordinate (say x and p_y).

9–4 Complementarity. Experimental evidence has forced us to acknowledge the fact that light is a physical entity simultaneously endowed with *some* of the properties that we ordinarily ascribe to particles, and with *some* of the properties that we ordinarily ascribe to waves.

Light consists of individual photons, each carrying a finite amount of energy, as evidenced, e.g., by the photoelectric effect. Photons, however, are not particles in the ordinary sense of the word because it is impossible to simultaneously define the position and the momentum of a photon.

Light is a wave phenomenon, as shown by the occurrence of interference and diffraction effects. Light waves, however, are not waves in the ordinary sense of the word, for one cannot regard the light energy as distributed continuously in space.*

Thus both the particle model and the wave model of light have definite limitations. Because of these limitations, the two models are not mutually exclusive but rather are *complementary.* Each of them enables us to visualize a different aspect of the phenomenon of light. The uncertainty principle is a direct consequence of the dual character of light. It tells us how far we can push the particle model without bringing it into conflict with the wave aspect of light.

It should be noted that of the two complementary aspects of light, the particle aspect becomes dominant at high energies (or frequencies) and the wave aspect becomes dominant at low energies (or frequencies). For as the frequency increases, diffraction and interference phenomena become less and less noticeable. At the same time, the photon energy increases and therefore the interactions of individual photons become increasingly conspicuous. Thus γ-rays, for example, behave like particles in practically every way.

---

*Indeed, particles and waves "in the ordinary sense of the words" do not exist in nature! See Section 9–6.

On the other hand, as the frequency decreases, diffraction and interference phenomena become increasingly pronounced. At the same time, the photon energy decreases, and it becomes increasingly difficult to detect the effects of individual photons. For example, infrared light cannot produce photoelectric effect in the ordinary sense. However, in principle at least, an electron can acquire enough energy to escape from a metal surface if it happens to absorb in rapid succession several quanta of infrared light. This would be possible only under exceedingly strong illumination, and both the number and the average energy of the electrons would then increase with increasing intensity. This is exactly what the wave theory predicts, as pointed out in Section 9–1.

9–5 The "state" of a photon. We wish to discuss in more detail the concept of the "state" of a photon, and compare it with the concept of the state of a particle in classical mechanics.

To define the state of a particle in classical mechanics it is necessary to specify its *position* and its *momentum* at a given instant. If the particle moves in a known field of force, it is then possible to determine the position and the momentum of the particle at any other instant of time.

The mechanical concepts of position and momentum are meaningful also in the case of photons, for the position or the momentum of a photon can be determined experimentally, at least in principle, with any arbitrary degree of accuracy. However, we have seen that if the momentum of a photon is completely determined, its position is completely undetermined. A photon of a given momentum corresponds, of course, to a plane sinusoidal wave, for which the frequency and the direction of propagation are exactly determined, and for which the intensity is everywhere the same. Thus, for a photon, a precise knowledge of the momentum defines a state completely; it represents a *maximum amount of information.*

There are, however, states of the photon where the momentum is not exactly determined, but where some information is available concerning the position. The states represented by a wave train of finite length or by a wave of variable amplitude are examples. In the former case, the photon, at a given time, can be found only in a certain region of space; in the latter case the photon has a greater probability of being found in certain regions of space than in certain others.

As a simple example, consider a wave of periodically varying amplitude resulting from the superposition of two sinusoidal waves of slightly different frequencies. If we analyze the wave by means of a spectroscope, we shall find two lines, corresponding to the two frequencies of the component waves. The intensities of the lines will be proportional to the amplitudes squared of these two waves. The amplitudes squared thus represent the probabilities for the photon to be found in one or the other of the two momentum states.

Note that in this case, again, the state of the photon may be defined completely in terms of momentum, without explicit reference to position. However, for a complete definition of the state it is not sufficient to give the probabilities for the two possible values of the momentum. It is also necessary to assign the *phase difference* between the two corresponding waves at a given point and at a given instant, for obviously the probability distribution for the position of the photon at any instant of time depends on this phase difference.

We arrive at a similar conclusion if we analyze the state of a photon in relation to its spin.

We have seen that a beam of circularly polarized light may be described as a stream of photons with their spins parallel or antiparallel to the direction of propagation depending on whether the polarization is left-handed or right-handed. In other words, a photon belonging to a beam of circularly polarized light has a definite spin orientation.

Any experimental arrangement that distinguishes left-handed from right-handed circular polarization may be regarded as a device capable of separating photons with opposite spin orientations. A quarter-wave plate followed by an analyzer with the vibration axis in one of the two perpendicular directions at 45° to the axes of the plate is one such device. This system acts as a filter completely opaque to circularly polarized light of one kind, and completely transparent to circularly polarized light of the other kind, the selection being determined by the orientation of the analyzer (see Section 6–7).

A beam of linearly polarized light may be regarded as the superposition of two circularly polarized beams of equal intensities and opposite sense of rotation. Thus a photon of linearly polarized light is in a state for which the orientation of the spin is not determined. This does not mean that some of the photons have their spins parallel to and others their spins antiparallel to the direction of motion. It does mean that each photon is simultaneously and with equal probability in both states of opposite spin. This statement, however, does not define the state of the photon completely. For this purpose it is also necessary to specify the phase difference between the two circularly polarized waves that represent the two component states. Indeed, if we change this phase difference we also change the orientations of the plane of vibration of the wave representing the photon.

The state of a photon belonging to a beam of elliptically polarized light can also be regarded as a superposition of the two states with definite spin orientations. Here, however, the probability amplitudes of the two states are not equal, as they are in the case of linearly polarized light. In fact, an elliptically polarized wave can always be resolved into two circularly polarized waves of opposite sense of rotation and different amplitudes (see Section 6–2).

In conclusion, we recognize that in a beam of polarized light, irrespective of whether the polarization is circular, linear, or elliptical, all photons are in a single, completely determined state. Only in the case of circularly polarized light, however, is the state characterized by a definite orientation of the spin.

9–6 Wave mechanics. We have seen that the wave aspect and the particle aspect of light are compatible only if there is no conceivable experiment by which the position and the momentum of a photon can be simultaneously determined. To illustrate the far-reaching consequences of this requirement, let us consider the following event.

A photon in a parallel beam of monochromatic x-rays collides with an electron at rest at a given point of space. We know that the collision has occurred because, at a certain moment, we see the electron acquire a certain momentum. Before the collision, the photon had a perfectly determined momentum and a completely undetermined position. Immediately after the collision, it would seem that the position of the photon is accurately determined because we know the position of the electron with which it has collided. It would seem, also, that we can determine the exact momentum of the photon from the knowledge of its initial momentum and from a measurement of the momentum of the recoil electron.

This conclusion contradicts the uncertainty principle for photons and must thus be at fault if our previous results are correct. On examining the argument presented above, we recognize that it is based upon the hypothesis that both the position and the momentum of an electron can be determined with unlimited accuracy. To ensure the validity of the uncertainty principle for photons, we must thus assume that such a determination is physically impossible. In other words, we must assume that electrons as well as photons are subject to an uncertainty principle which limits the accuracy of measurements of position and momentum. By the same argument we can show that the uncertainty principle must hold for all kinds of material particles, and must thus be a general law of nature.

This means, however, that classical mechanics cannot be rigorously correct and, in particular, that it does not apply to microscopic systems such as atoms, for the uncertainty principle makes the very concept of the trajectory of an electron in an atom meaningless.

The uncertainty principle for photons is a consequence of the dual character of light. Since we have found that the same uncertainty principle holds for material particles, it is natural to assume that material particles, too, have some of the properties that are usually associated with waves. More specifically, we are led to the assumption that the motion of a material particle, like the motion of a photon, is describable in terms of a wave equation.

This is the basic idea of wave mechanics. That this idea is fundamentally correct has been proved by the outstanding success of wave mechanics in explaining atomic phenomena. Moreover, the wave properties of particles have been demonstrated directly through the observation of electron diffraction by crystals.

In a wave train, the length Δx and the spread in frequency, $\Delta \nu$, are related by

$$\Delta x \cdot \Delta \nu \approx c, \tag{9–21}$$

which follows immediately from Eq. (9–15). Δx represents the uncertainty in the position of the particle represented by the wave train. According to the uncertainty principle, the corresponding uncertainty, Δp, in the momentum satisfies the equation

$$\Delta x \cdot \Delta p \approx h. \tag{9–22}$$

Equations (9–21) and (9–22) become identical if we take

$$p = \frac{\nu h}{c} = \frac{h}{\lambda}.$$

Thus we are led to associate a particle of momentum p with a wave of wavelength

$$\lambda = \frac{h}{p}. \tag{9–23}$$

This relationship between the momentum and the wavelength of a particle is known as the *deBroglie equation*. It is identical to the relationship between the momentum and the wavelength of a photon (Eq. 9–9).

For particles of sufficiently small velocities, relativistic corrections may be neglected, and we can write

$$p = \sqrt{2mE},$$

where E is the kinetic energy of the particle. Equation (9–23) then becomes

$$\lambda = \frac{h}{\sqrt{2mE}}. \tag{9–24}$$

On the other hand, the wavelength corresponding to a photon of energy $E = h\nu$ is

$$\lambda = \frac{hc}{E}. \tag{9–25}$$

Thus the wavelengths λ_{part} and λ_{phot}, corresponding to a particle and to a photon of the same energy, are in the ratio

$$\frac{\lambda_{\text{part}}}{\lambda_{\text{phot}}} = \sqrt{\frac{E}{mc^2}} \, . \qquad\qquad (9\text{--}26)$$

The quantity mc^2 has the dimensions of energy, and is called the rest energy of the particle. For the electron, which is the lightest of all known material particles, $mc^2 = 0.51 \times 10^6$ ev.

Photons of visible light, as we have seen, have energies of the order of several ev and wavelengths of the order of several thousand angstroms. Equation (9–26) shows that electrons of several ev energy have wavelengths several hundred times smaller than photons of the same energy, i.e., they have wavelengths of the order of only 10 angstroms. Particles heavier than electrons have still smaller wavelengths. This is why the wave character of material particles is much less conspicuous than the wave character of photons.

The wave properties of matter, although they may not be as evident as the wave properties of light, provide a natural explanation of many striking phenomena. For example, one of the important results of wave mechanics (to be stated here without proof) is that the energy of atoms cannot vary in a continuous fashion, but can acquire only discrete values. The "quantization" of the energy of atoms has, of course, a direct relation to the existence of discrete light quanta. The transition from a quantum state of energy E_1 to a quantum state of lower energy E_2 may give rise to a photon of energy $E = E_1 - E_2$ and of frequency $\nu = (E_1 - E_2)/h$. Conversely, if the atom is in the quantum state of lower energy E_2, it may be raised to the quantum state of higher energy E_1 by absorption of a photon of energy $E_1 - E_2$.

The quantitative development of the general ideas presented in this section and, in particular, their applications to the interpretation of atomic spectra lie outside the scope of the present volume. Our only aim here was to show how the dual nature of light implies a corresponding dual nature of matter and forces upon us a drastic revision of the concepts of classical mechanics.

9–1. Compute the photon energies in ergs and electron volts corresponding to the following wavelengths: $\lambda = 10$ cm (short radio waves), $\lambda = 10^{-3}$ cm (infrared), $\lambda = 5000$ A (visible), $\lambda = 500$ A (ultraviolet), $\lambda = 1$ A (x-rays).

9–2. A light source of frequency ν, moving with a velocity $w \ll c$, emits a photon (a) in the direction of its motion, or (b) in the opposite direction. Using the conservation principles of energy and momentum, compute the energy and the corresponding frequency of the photon with respect to an observer at rest. Compare the results with the formula describing the Doppler effect.

9–3. The photoelectric threshold of sodium is 6800 A. Compute the minimum retarding voltage necessary to stop the photoelectric current in a photocell with sodium cathode illuminated by monochromatic light of wavelength $\lambda = 4000$ A.

9–4. Applying the laws of conservation of energy and momentum, prove that a photon scattered through an angle θ by collision with an electron (Compton effect) changes its wavelength by the amount

$$\Delta\lambda = (h/mc)(1 - \cos\theta),$$

where m is the electron mass.

9–5. It has been shown in the text that interference effects are compatible with the photon concept only if there is no way of determining the actual path of an individual photon. In the case of the Michelson interferometer (Section 3–12 and Fig. 3–31), it would

seem that it is possible to determine whether the photon has been reflected by the mirror M or by the mirror M' by observing the change of momentum of the mirror at which reflection occurs. Using the uncertainty principle, show that if the experiment is performed in such a way as to preserve the coherence of the two beams, it is intrinsically impossible to determine which path the photon has followed.

9–6. The following argument leads to the apparent conclusion that the concept of the photon is self-contradictory. Show that the fault of the argument lies in the implicit assumption that it is possible to determine simultaneously the angular position and the angular momentum of an object with unlimited precision, and that the contradiction disappears if we take into account the fact that the error in the angular position $\Delta\varphi$ and the error in the corresponding angular momentum ΔJ are related by the uncertainty relation

$$\Delta\varphi \cdot \Delta J \approx h.$$

(a) The angular momentum of a photon can be parallel or antiparallel to the direction of propagation. Upon absorption, the photon will transfer its angular momentum to the absorber. It is thus possible, at least ideally, to determine the sense of the angular momentum of a photon when the photon is absorbed.

(b) Consider a beam of linearly polarized light and a beam of natural light. Either beam may be regarded as the superposition of two circularly polarized beams of equal amplitude and opposite sense of rotation. Using particle description, we can say that the beam of natural light consists of photons of which half have their angular momentum parallel and half anti-parallel to the direction of propagation. In the linearly polarized beam, on the other hand, the angular momentum of each individual photon has an undetermined orientation until the time when the photon is absorbed. The differences between the behavior of linearly polarized light and that of natural light are compatible with the photon concept only because it is intrinsically impossible to determine the orientation of the angular momentum of a photon of linearly polarized light without absorbing the photon or destroying its state of polarization.

(c) Suppose now that a beam of linearly polarized light passes through a half-wave plate whose axes are at 45° to the plane of vibration of the incident beam. The emerging beam is linearly polarized, and its plane of vibration is at 90° to the plane of vibration of the incident beam. If we regard the incident beam as the superposition of two circularly polarized beams, we find that the half-wave plate has changed the right-handed beam into a left-handed beam, and vice versa. If we take the view that the beam consists of particle-like photons, we may say that the angular momentum of each photon traversing the plate has changed sign. By measuring the change of angular momentum of the plate due to the passage of an individual photon, we can determine the orientation of the angular momentum of each photon emerging from the plate in contradiction to the requirement stated under (b).

APPENDIX 1

MATHEMATICAL FORMULAS

(a) **Vectors.** Consider two vectors $\mathbf{u}$ and $\mathbf{v}$ of cartesian components u_x, u_y, u_z and v_x, v_y, v_z, respectively, forming an angle ϑ (Fig. A1–1). Let

$$|\mathbf{u}| = \sqrt{u_x^2 + u_y^2 + u_z^2},$$

$$|\mathbf{v}| = \sqrt{v_x^2 + v_y^2 + v_z^2}$$

be their lengths.

The *scalar* or *dot product* of $\mathbf{u}$ and $\mathbf{v}$, written $\mathbf{u} \cdot \mathbf{v}$, is the number defined by

$$\mathbf{u} \cdot \mathbf{v} = |\mathbf{u}|\,|\mathbf{v}|\cos\vartheta, \quad (A1\text{--}1)$$

or by the equivalent equation

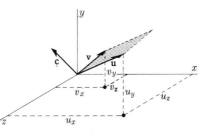

Fig. A1–1. Scalar and vector product of two vectors $\mathbf{u}$ and $\mathbf{v}$.

$$\mathbf{u} \cdot \mathbf{v} = u_x v_x + u_y v_y + u_z v_z. \quad (A1\text{--}2)$$

The *vector* or *cross product* of $\mathbf{u}$ and $\mathbf{v}$, written $\mathbf{u} \times \mathbf{v}$, is the vector $\mathbf{c}$ of magnitude

$$|\mathbf{u} \times \mathbf{v}| = |\mathbf{u}|\,|\mathbf{v}|\sin\vartheta. \quad (A1\text{--}3)$$

This vector lies in the direction perpendicular to the plane of the vectors $\mathbf{u}$ and $\mathbf{v}$. To determine its sense, we consider a right-handed screw rotated, through an angle of less than π, until the vector $\mathbf{u}$ overlaps the vector $\mathbf{v}$. The sense of advance of this screw determines the sense of the vector $\mathbf{u} \times \mathbf{v}$. Note that

$$\mathbf{v} \times \mathbf{u} = -\mathbf{u} \times \mathbf{v}. \quad (A1\text{--}4)$$

The components of $\mathbf{u} \times \mathbf{v}$ are

$$c_x = (\mathbf{u} \times \mathbf{v})_x = u_y v_z - v_y u_z,$$

$$c_y = (\mathbf{u} \times \mathbf{v})_y = u_z v_x - v_z u_x, \quad (A1\text{--}5)$$

$$c_z = (\mathbf{u} \times \mathbf{v})_z = u_x v_y - v_x u_y.$$

Consider a function $f(x, y, z)$, that is, a scalar quantity with a definite value at all points of a given region of space. In general, through each point P of this region we can draw a surface over which the function f has a constant value

$$f(P) = f(x, y, z) = \text{const.} \qquad (A1\text{--}6)$$

(Fig. A1–2). We can then define at the point P a vector called the *gradient of* f, indicated by the symbol grad f, with the following convention: the vector grad f is perpendiculr to the surface f = const. at P, it points in the direction in which f increases, and its magnitude is given by

$$|\text{grad } f| = \lim_{\delta s = 0} \frac{f(P') - f(P)}{\delta s}, \qquad (A1\text{--}7)$$

where P' is a point at the infinitesimal distance δs from P along the perpendicular to the surface f = const. The cartesian coordinates of grad f are

$$(\text{grad } f)_x = \frac{\partial f}{\partial x}, \qquad (\text{grad } f)_y = \frac{\partial f}{\partial y}, \qquad (\text{grad } f)_z = \frac{\partial f}{\partial z}. \qquad (A1\text{--}8)$$

(b) Complex numbers. A complex number $a + ib$ may be represented by a point in the complex plane, with the convention that the real part a is plotted as abscissa, and the coefficient of the imaginary part b is plotted as ordinate (Fig. A1–3). The quantity

$$\rho = \sqrt{a^2 + b^2} \qquad (A1\text{--}9)$$

is called the *absolute value* of the complex number; it represents the length of the vector of cartesian components a and b. The angle φ, defined by

$$\tan \varphi = \frac{b}{a}, \qquad (A1\text{--}10)$$

is called the *argument* or the *phase* of the complex number. It represents the angle formed with the real axis by the vector of components a, b.

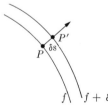

FIG. A1–2. Definition of grad f.   FIG. A1–3. Complex numbers.

The sum of several complex numbers $a_1 + ib_1$, $a_2 + ib_2$, $a_3 + ib_3$, $\cdots$ is defined as

$$(a_1 + ib_1) + (a_2 + ib_2) + (a_3 + ib_3) + \ldots$$
$$= (a_1 + a_2 + a_3 + \ldots) + i(b_1 + b_2 + b_3 + \ldots). \quad \text{(A1–11)}$$

In the complex plane, the vector representing this sum is the vector sum of the vectors representing the individual numbers.

The product of two complex numbers is

$$(a_1 + ib_1)(a_2 + ib_2) = (a_1a_2 - b_1b_2) + i(a_1b_2 + a_2b_1). \quad \text{(A1–12)}$$

The number $a - ib$ is called the *complex conjugate* of $a + ib$. The following equation holds:

$$(a + ib)(a - ib) = a^2 + b^2 = \rho^2. \quad \text{(A1–13)}$$

From the Taylor series expansions,

$$e^{i\varphi} = 1 + i\varphi - \frac{\varphi^2}{2} - \frac{i\varphi^3}{3!} + \ldots,$$

$$\cos \varphi = 1 - \frac{\varphi^2}{2} + \ldots,$$

$$\sin \varphi = \varphi - \frac{\varphi^3}{3!} + \ldots,$$

we obtain

$$e^{i\varphi} = \cos \varphi + i \sin \varphi \quad \text{(A1–14)}$$

or, changing φ into $-\varphi$,

$$e^{-i\varphi} = \cos \varphi - i \sin \varphi. \quad \text{(A1–15)}$$

Equations (A1–14) and (A1–15) yield

$$\cos \varphi = \frac{e^{i\varphi} + e^{-i\varphi}}{2}, \quad \text{(A1–16)}$$

$$\sin \varphi = \frac{e^{i\varphi} - e^{-i\varphi}}{2i}. \quad \text{(A1–17)}$$

From

$$\rho e^{i\varphi} = \rho \cos \varphi + i\rho \sin \varphi \quad \text{(A1–18)}$$

it follows that any complex number $a + ib$ may be written in the form $\rho e^{i\varphi}$ if we choose ρ and φ so as to satisfy

$$a = \rho \cos \varphi, \qquad b = \rho \sin \varphi.$$

These equations are equivalent to Eqs. (A1–9) and (A1–10).

The complex conjugate of the number $\rho e^{i\varphi}$ is $\rho e^{-i\varphi}$. The product of the complex numbers $\rho_1 e^{i\varphi_1}$, $\rho_2 e^{i\varphi_2}$, $\rho_3 e^{i\varphi_3}$, . . . is

$$(\rho_1 e^{i\varphi_1})(\rho_2 e^{i\varphi_2})(\rho_3 e^{i\varphi_3}) \cdots = (\rho_1 \rho_2 \rho_3 \cdots)e^{i(\varphi_1 + \varphi_2 + \varphi_3 + \cdots)}. \qquad \text{(A1–19)}$$

(c) **Sum of the geometric series.** Consider a geometric series of real or complex numbers

$$a, \, ac, \, ac^2, \, ac^3, \, \ldots, \, ac^n,$$

and let

$$S = a + ac + ac^2 + \cdots + ac^n \qquad \text{(A1–20)}$$

be its sum. To compute S, we multiply (A1–20) by c and obtain

$$cS = ac + ac^2 + \cdots + ac^n + ac^{n+1}. \qquad \text{(A1–21)}$$

By subtracting (A1–20) from (A1–21), we obtain

$$(c - 1)S = a(c^{n+1} - 1),$$

or

$$S = a\frac{c^{n+1} - 1}{c - 1}. \qquad \text{(A1–22)}$$

If, in particular, $c < 1$ and $n = \infty$, S acquires the value

$$S = \frac{a}{1 - c}. \qquad \text{(A1–23)}$$

(d) **The sagitta theorem.** Let AA' be the diameter of a circle (Fig. A1–4), H an arbitrary point of this circle, and K the foot of the perpendicular through H to AA'. AHA' is a right angle. Hence $\angle HAK = \angle A'HK$, since both angles are complementary to $\angle AHK$, and the triangles HAK and $A'HK$ are similar. It follows that

$$\overline{AK} : \overline{HK} = \overline{HK} : \overline{KA'},$$

and therefore

$$\overline{HK}^2 = \overline{AK} \cdot \overline{KA'}. \qquad \text{(A1–24)}$$

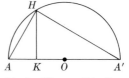

FIG. A1–4. The sagitta theorem.

APPENDIX 2

MECHANICAL WAVES

(a) **Waves on a string.** As in Section 1–3 (a), we let x be the abscissa of an arbitrary point P of the string, T the (constant) tension of the string, and $s(x,\ t)$ the lateral displacement of the point P at the time t. We assume that the displacement is everywhere sufficiently small so that the angles formed by the various elements of the string with the straight line representing the undisturbed position of the string are small fractions of a radian. In mathematical language, this means that

$$\frac{\partial s}{\partial x} \ll 1, \tag{A2-1}$$

where, of course, the partial derivative $\partial s/\partial x$ signifies the derivative of s with respect to x, computed for a fixed value of the time. Accordingly, in all our computations where there are terms containing the first power of $\partial s/\partial x$, we shall neglect terms containing powers of $\partial s/\partial x$ higher than the first.

To find the differential equation satisfied by s, we note that the portion of the string to the right of P acts upon the portion of the string to the left of this point with a force equal to T, tangent to the string and pointing toward the right (see Fig. A2–1). If α is the angle that the tangent makes with the x-axis, the component of this force in the direction perpendicular to the string is

$$T_y = T \sin \alpha.$$

Because of our assumption, we can write

$$\sin \alpha \approx \tan \alpha = \frac{\partial s}{\partial x},$$

and thus obtain

$$T_y = T \frac{\partial s}{\partial x}. \tag{A2-2}$$

The portion of the string to the left of P acts on the portion of the string to the right of this point with a force that is obviously equal and opposite to the one described above.

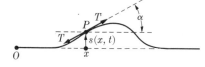

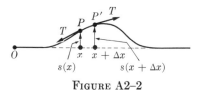

FIG. A2–1. Waves on a string.   FIGURE A2–2

We now ideally isolate a very short segment of the string extending from
x to $x + \Delta x$ (Fig. A2–2). The two forces acting at the two endpoints of this
segment have a resultant component in the direction perpendicular to the
x-axis equal to

$$\Delta T_y = (T_y)_{x+\Delta x} - (T_y)_x = \left(\frac{\partial T_y}{\partial x}\right) \Delta x,$$

or, from Eq. (A2–2),

$$\Delta T_y = T \frac{\partial^2 s}{\partial x^2} \Delta x. \tag{A2–3}$$

Since the string is inextensible, and since we consider only small disturbances, we may assume that each point of the string moves in a direction
perpendicular to the x-axis. Thus the acceleration of a point of the string
equals $\partial^2 s/\partial t^2$. Moreover, we can take the length of the segment of the
string between the abscissas x and $x + \Delta x$ as equal to Δx. If μ is the mass
of the string per unit length, and if we neglect gravitational forces, the second law of mechanics yields the following equation:

$$\mu \frac{\partial^2 s}{\partial t^2} \Delta x = \Delta T_y. \tag{A2–4}$$

From this equation, remembering (A2–3), we obtain

$$\frac{\partial^2 s}{\partial t^2} = \frac{T}{\mu} \frac{\partial^2 s}{\partial x^2}. \tag{A2–5}$$

This is the *differential equation of wave motion in one dimension.*

We shall now proceed to find the solutions of (A2–5). For this purpose
we denote by v a suitable constant, whose value will be determined later,
and define the quantity

$$t' = t - \frac{x}{v}. \tag{A2–6}$$

We then consider an arbitrary function of t':

$$f(t') = f\left(t - \frac{x}{v}\right).$$

If x is kept constant, f is a function of t through the auxiliary variable t'. According to a well-known rule, its derivative with respect to t equals the derivative of f with respect to t' times the derivative of t' with respect to t:

$$\frac{\partial f}{\partial t} = \frac{df}{dt'}\frac{\partial t'}{\partial t}.$$

This equation, together with (A2–6), yields

$$\frac{\partial f}{\partial t} = \frac{df}{dt'}. \tag{A2–7}$$

Similarly, *if t is kept constant, f is a function of x through the auxiliary variable t'.* We thus obtain

$$\frac{\partial f}{\partial x} = \frac{df}{dt'}\frac{\partial t'}{\partial x},$$

or, considering (A2–6),

$$\frac{\partial f}{\partial x} = -\frac{1}{v}\frac{df}{dt'}. \tag{A2–8}$$

By replacing the function f with the function df/dt' in (A2–7) and (A2–8), we obtain the following additional equations:

$$\frac{\partial}{\partial t}\left(\frac{df}{dt'}\right) = \frac{d^2f}{dt'^2},$$

$$\frac{\partial}{\partial x}\left(\frac{df}{dt'}\right) = -\frac{1}{v}\frac{d^2f}{dt'^2},$$

or, since $df/dt' = \partial f/\partial t = -v\partial f/\partial x$,

$$\frac{\partial^2 f}{\partial t^2} = \frac{d^2f}{dt'^2}, \qquad \frac{\partial^2 f}{\partial x^2} = \frac{1}{v^2}\frac{d^2f}{dt'^2}. \tag{A2–9}$$

If we now put

$$s(x, t) = f\left(t - \frac{x}{v}\right), \tag{A2–10}$$

and use (A2–9), we obtain from (A2–5)

$$\frac{d^2f}{dt'^2} = \frac{1}{v^2}\frac{T}{\mu}\frac{d^2f}{dt'^2}.$$

This equation becomes an identity if we choose for v the value

$$v = \sqrt{\frac{T}{\mu}}.\tag{A2-11}$$

We thus conclude that the function s defined by (A2–10) *is a solution of the differential wave equation* (A2–5).

The physical significance of this solution is discussed in Section 1–3(a), where it is shown that (A2–10) represents a wave traveling with velocity v in the direction of increasing x.

In a similar manner we find that if $g(t + x/v)$ represents an arbitrary function of the argument $t + x/v$, the equation

$$s(x, t) = g\left(t + \frac{x}{v}\right)\tag{A2-12}$$

yields another solution of the differential wave equation (A2–5). This solution represents a wave traveling with velocity v in the direction of decreasing x.

According to the theory of partial differential equations, the general solution of Eq. (A2–5) must contain two arbitrary functions. This general solution is found to have the form

$$s(x, t) = f\left(t - \frac{x}{v}\right) + g\left(t + \frac{x}{v}\right),\tag{A2-13}$$

and thus represents the superposition of two waves traveling in opposite directions.

Let u be the *transverse velocity* of an arbitrary point of the string; u is given by the equation

$$u(x, t) = \frac{\partial s}{\partial t}.\tag{A2-14}$$

Needless to say, this quantity should not be confused with the *velocity of propagation v of the wave* given by (A2–11). Note that if we differentiate (A2–2) with respect to t, remembering that

$$\frac{\partial^2 s}{\partial x \partial t} = \frac{\partial^2 s}{\partial t \partial x} = \frac{\partial u}{\partial x},$$

we obtain

$$\frac{\partial T_y}{\partial t} = T \frac{\partial u}{\partial x}.\tag{A2-15}$$

Note also that (A2–4) may be written as follows:

$$\frac{\partial u}{\partial t} = \frac{1}{\mu} \frac{\partial T_y}{\partial x}. \tag{A2–16}$$

From (A2–15) and (A2–16) we can easily verify that u and T_y satisfy a differential equation identical to that satisfied by s (Eq. A2–5) and are thus represented by functions of x and t similar to the functions representing the displacement. This result also follows immediately from (A2–2) and (A2–14). For example, in the case of a wave traveling in the positive direction, these equations yield

$$T_y = -\frac{T}{v} \dot{f}\left(t - \frac{x}{v}\right),$$

$$u = \dot{f}\left(t - \frac{x}{v}\right), \tag{A2–17}$$

where the symbol $\dot{f}$ stands for df/dt', the derivative of the function f with respect to its argument $t' = t - x/v$.

(b) **Sound waves in a pipe.** As in Section 1–3(b), we let x be the abscissa of an arbitrary element of the fluid in the unperturbed condition, s the longitudinal displacement of this element at the time t, and p the difference between the actual pressure and the pressure in the unperturbed condition. We again restrict our considerations to the case of small disturbances; i.e. we assume that the inequality (A2–1) is fulfilled, and, in addition, we assume that the pressure change p is small compared with the pressure p_0 in the undisturbed condition.

Consider a portion of the fluid which, in the undisturbed condition, lies between the sections of the pipe at x and $x + \Delta x$, respectively (Fig. A2–3). If A is the cross-sectional area of the pipe, the volume enclosed between these sections is $A \Delta x$. At a given instant of time t, let $s(x, t)$ be the displacement at x, and $s(x + \Delta x, t)$ the displacement at $x + \Delta x$. The volume of the gas has now become

$$A[x + \Delta x + s(x + \Delta x, t) - x - s(x, t)] = A[\Delta x + s(x + \Delta x, t) - s(x, t)].$$

With respect to the unperturbed state, there has been a change in volume given by

$$\Delta V = A[\Delta x + s(x + \Delta x, t) - s(x, t)] - A\,\Delta x = A[s(x + \Delta x, t) - s(x, t)].$$

The ratio of this quantity to the unperturbed volume $V_0 = A\,\Delta x$, that is, the fractional change of volume, is

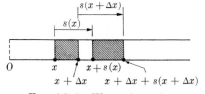
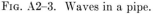

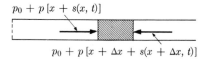

FIG. A2–3. Waves in a pipe.   FIGURE A2–4

$$\frac{\Delta V}{V_0} = \frac{s(x + \Delta x, t) - s(x, t)}{\Delta x},$$

or, if Δx is sufficiently small,

$$\frac{\Delta V}{V_0} = \frac{\partial s}{\partial x}.$$

To an increase of volume there corresponds a decrease of pressure, and vice versa. Because of our assumption, the fractional change of volume $\Delta V/V_0$ is small compared with unity; hence the corresponding change of pressure p may be regarded as proportional to $\Delta V/V_0$, and the following equation holds:

$$p = -\frac{1}{K}\frac{\partial s}{\partial x}, \qquad (A2\text{–}18)$$

where K is the compressibility of the gas.

If gravity and friction are neglected, the only forces to be taken into account are those due to the pressure. These act in opposite directions on the two end surfaces of the volume of gas here considered and their resultant is

$$\Delta F = -A\,\Delta p,$$

where Δp is the difference between the values of p at $x + \Delta x + s(x + \Delta x, t)$ and at $x + s(x, t)$ (see Fig. A2–4). Since Δx is a small length, ΔF becomes

$$\Delta F = -A\,\frac{\partial p}{\partial x}\,[x + \Delta x + s(x + \Delta x, t) - x - s(x, t)]$$

$$= -A\,\frac{\partial p}{\partial x}\left[1 + \frac{\partial s}{\partial x}\right]\Delta x.$$

Both $\partial p/\partial x$ and $\partial s/\partial x$ are small quantities; hence their product can be neglected, and we obtain

$$\Delta F = -A\,\frac{\partial p}{\partial x}\,\Delta x.$$

On the other hand, the mass of the volume of gas under consideration is $\rho_0 A \, \Delta x$, where ρ_0 is the density of the gas in the undisturbed condition. Thus, if we again denote by $u = \partial s/\partial t$ the velocity of the particles of the fluid,* and by $\partial u/\partial t$ their acceleration, the second law of dynamics yields the following equation:

$$\rho_0 A \, \frac{\partial u}{\partial t} \, \Delta x = \Delta F = -A \, \frac{\partial p}{\partial x} \, \Delta x,$$

or

$$\frac{\partial u}{\partial t} = - \frac{1}{\rho_0} \frac{\partial p}{\partial x}, \qquad (A2\text{–}19)$$

which is similar to (A2-16).

If we differentiate (A2–18) with respect to t, we obtain

$$\frac{\partial p}{\partial t} = - \frac{1}{K} \frac{\partial u}{\partial x}, \qquad (A2\text{–}20)$$

which is similar to (A2–15). We can now eliminate u between (A2–19) and (A2–20) by differentiating the first with respect to x and the second with respect to t. We obtain

$$\frac{\partial^2 p}{\partial t^2} = \frac{1}{K \rho_0} \frac{\partial^2 p}{\partial x^2}. \qquad (A2\text{–}21)$$

which has exactly the same form as (A2–5), with the constant $1/K\rho_0$ replacing the constant T/μ. We thus conclude that (A2–21) has solutions of the form

$$p(x, t) = F \left(t - \frac{x}{v} \right), \qquad (A2\text{–}22)$$

and

$$p(x, t) = G \left(t + \frac{x}{v} \right), \qquad (A2\text{–}23)$$

where F and G are arbitrary functions of the arguments $(t - x/v)$ and $(t + x/v)$, respectively, and v is given by the equation

$$v = \sqrt{\frac{1}{K\rho_0}}. \qquad (A2\text{–}24)$$

Equation (A2–22) represents a pressure wave traveling with velocity v in the direction of the positive x-axis, and (A2-23) represents a pressure wave

---

*Needless to say, the velocity u refers to the macroscopic motion of a small volume of fluid and must not be confused with the thermal velocity of the individual molecules.

traveling with the same velocity in the direction of the negative x-axis. The general solution (A2–21) is

$$p(x, t) = F\left(t - \frac{x}{v}\right) + G\left(t + \frac{x}{v}\right).\qquad (A2\text{–}25)$$

It is easily verified that the functions representing the displacement $s(x, t)$ and the velocity $u(x, t)$ in a given wave have a form similar to that of the function representing the corresponding pressure change $p(x, t)$. In the case of a wave traveling in the positive direction, for example, we can represent s and u by equations of the type

$$s = f\left(t - \frac{x}{v}\right),\qquad (A2\text{–}26)$$

$$u = \dot{f}\left(t - \frac{x}{v}\right).\qquad (A2\text{–}27)$$

From (A2–18) we then obtain

$$p = \frac{1}{Kv}\dot{f} = \frac{u}{Kv}.\qquad (A2\text{–}28)$$

(c) **Energy of waves.** Consider a wave traveling along a string and described by the equation

$$s(x, t) = f\left(t - \frac{x}{v}\right).\qquad (A2\text{–}29)$$

We assume that the wave has been produced by an external agency acting on the endpoint of the string at $x = 0$. The motion of this point is represented by the equation

$$s(0, t) = f(t).\qquad (A2\text{–}30)$$

The external force acting on the endpoint of the string has a component T_y perpendicular to the string, given by

$$-T_y = -T\frac{\partial s}{\partial x}\qquad (A2\text{–}31)$$

(see Eq. A2–2).

If we use, as before, the symbol $u(x, t) = \partial s/\partial t$ to indicate the transverse velocity, at the time t, of a point of the string of abscissa x, we find that in the time interval from t_0 to $t_0 + dt$ the point at $x = 0$ undergoes a transverse displacement $ds = u(0, t_0)\, dt$. Therefore the work done by the external force in this time is

$$-T_y\, ds = -T\frac{\partial s}{\partial x}\, u(0, t_0)\, dt = \frac{T}{v}\, u^2(0, t_0)\, dt,$$

where we have made use of the equation

$$\frac{\partial s}{\partial x} = -\frac{1}{v}\frac{\partial s}{\partial t} = -\frac{1}{v}u$$

obtained from (A2-29).

At the time $t > t_0$, the disturbance originating from 0 at the time t_0 has reached the point of abscissa

$$x = v(t - t_0), \tag{A2-32}$$

while the disturbance originating from 0 at the time $t_0 + dt$ has reached the point of abscissa $x - dx$, where

$$dx = v\, dt. \tag{A2-33}$$

Thus the energy $(T/v)u^2(0,\ t_0)dt$ delivered to the string in the time interval from t_0 to $t_0 + dt$ occupies, at the time t, the segment extending from $x - dx$ to x. During the subsequent time interval dt, the same energy passes through the point of abscissa x. Thus, if we denote by $U(x, t)$ the energy density per unit length, and by $\Phi(x, t)$ the energy flux per unit time at x and t, we obtain the equations

$$U(x, t)\, dx = \Phi(x, t)\, dt = \frac{T}{v}\, u^2(0, t_0)\, dt. \tag{A2-34}$$

We now note that the velocity $u(x, t)$, like the displacement $s(x, t)$, is a function of $t - x/v$, so that, if x, t and t_0 satisfy Eq. (A2-32),

$$u(0, t_0) = u(x, t).$$

Considering (A2-33) and remembering that $v^2 = T/\mu$, we then obtain from (A2-34)

$$U(x,\ t) = \mu u^2(x,\ t), \tag{A2-35}$$

$$\Phi(x, t) = vU(x, t). \tag{A2-36}$$

At any instant, the energy of the wave is partly potential energy and partly kinetic energy. Since the kinetic energy of an element dx equals $\frac{1}{2}\mu u^2\, dx$, Eq. (A2-35) shows that the total energy is *twice* the kinetic energy, or that the kinetic and potential energies are equal.

In a similar manner we can compute the energy density and the energy flux in a sound wave traveling in a pipe. We may think of this wave as produced by a piston that moves back and forth in the vicinity of the point $x = 0$. If p_0 is the pressure in the undisturbed gas, the actual pressure is $p_0 + p$. Hence, remembering Eq. (A2–18), we obtain for the force exerted by the piston on the fluid

$$(p_0 + p)A = p_0 A - \frac{A}{K} \frac{\partial s}{\partial x}.$$

The work done by this force in the time dt is

$$\left(p_0 A - \frac{A}{K} \frac{\partial s}{\partial x}\right) ds = p_0 A \, ds - \frac{A}{K} \frac{\partial s}{\partial x} u(0, t) \, dt,$$

or, since $\partial s/\partial x = -(1/v)\partial s/\partial t = -(u/v)$,

$$\left(p_0 A - \frac{A}{K} \frac{\partial s}{\partial x}\right) ds = p_0 A \, ds + \frac{A}{Kv} u^2(0, t) \, dt.$$

In the above expression, the first term is positive when the piston moves forward and negative when it moves backward; the total contribution of this term vanishes if the piston goes back to its original position. The second term is always positive and represents the energy transmitted by the piston to the wave. As in the previous example, it then follows that the energy U per unit length and the energy flux Φ are given by the equations

$$U(x, t) = \frac{A}{Kv^2} u^2(x, t) = \rho_0 A u^2(x, t), \qquad (\text{A2–37})$$

$$\Phi(x, t) = \frac{A}{Kv} u^2(x, t) = vU(x, t). \qquad (\text{A2–38})$$

As in the previous example, U is twice the kinetic energy per unit length.

With the help of Eq. (A2–28), U and Φ can be expressed in terms of the pressure change p as follows:

$$U(x, t) = KAp^2(x, t), \qquad (\text{A2–39})$$

$$\Phi(x, t) = KvAp^2(x, t). \qquad (\text{A2–40})$$

Note that, in both examples, if the expression for the disturbance is multiplied by a constant, the expressions for the energy density and the energy flux are multiplied by the square of the same constant.

In this sense, one can say that the energy density and the energy flux in a wave are proportional to the *square of the amplitude* of the disturbance. This important result applies to all wave phenomena.

(d) **A model of waves with frequency-dependent velocity.** We consider again a string of mass μ per unit length, subject to a uniform tension T. In addition, however, we now assume that the string is held by a large number of small springs (as shown in Fig. A2–5), which provide a restoring force proportional to the displacement and opposite to it. Since the restoring force is also proportional to the length Δx of the element, it can be expressed as $-ks\,\Delta x$, where k is a suitable proportionality factor. The restoring force is added to the force due to the tension: $T(\partial^2 s/\partial x^2)\,\Delta x$ (Eq. A2–3). Thus the equation of motion of the element Δx is

$$\mu \frac{\partial^2 s}{\partial t^2}\,\Delta x = T \frac{\partial^2 s}{\partial x^2}\,\Delta x - ks\,\Delta x,$$

or

$$\frac{\partial^2 s}{\partial t^2} = \frac{T}{\mu}\frac{\partial^2 s}{\partial x^2} - \frac{k}{\mu}\,s. \quad (\text{A2–41})$$

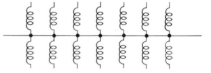

Fig. A2–5. Mechanical model of a dispersive medium.

This equation differs from the wave equation (A2–5) by the additional term $-ks/\mu$.

Equations (A2–10) and (A2–12), with f and g indicating arbitrary functions, are *not* solutions of the modified wave equation (A2–41). Thus a deformation of arbitrary shape will no longer travel along the string without change; however, it is easy to show that waves of special shapes will still do so. Let us assume that f in (A2–10) is a *sinusoidal* function of arbitrary angular frequency ω, amplitude A, and phase φ; that is, let us take

$$s = A \cos\left[\omega\left(t - \frac{x}{v}\right) + \varphi\right]. \quad (\text{A2–42})$$

We obtain

$$\frac{\partial s}{\partial t} = -\omega A \sin\left[\omega\left(t - \frac{x}{v}\right) + \varphi\right],$$

$$\frac{\partial^2 s}{\partial t^2} = -\omega^2 A \cos\left[\omega\left(t - \frac{x}{v}\right) + \varphi\right],$$

$$\frac{\partial s}{\partial x} = \frac{\omega}{v} A \sin\left[\omega\left(t - \frac{x}{v}\right) + \varphi\right],$$

$$\frac{\partial^2 s}{\partial x^2} = -\frac{\omega^2}{v^2} A \cos\left[\omega\left(t - \frac{x}{v}\right) + \varphi\right].$$

Substitution in (A2–41) then yields

$$-\omega^2 A \cos\left[\omega\left(t - \frac{x}{v}\right) + \varphi\right] = -\frac{\omega^2}{v^2}\frac{T}{\mu} A \cos\left[\omega\left(t - \frac{x}{v}\right) + \varphi\right]$$

$$-\frac{k}{\mu} A \cos\left[\omega\left(t - \frac{x}{v}\right) + \varphi\right].$$

With the notations

$$\frac{T}{\mu} = c^2, \tag{A2–43}$$

$$\frac{k}{\mu} = \omega_0^2, \tag{A2–44}$$

the above equation gives

$$\omega^2 = \omega^2 \frac{c^2}{v^2} + \omega_0^2,$$

or

$$v = \frac{c}{\sqrt{1 - (\omega_0^2/\omega^2)}}. \tag{A2–45}$$

This equation yields a real value of v only if $\omega > \omega_0$, indicating that solutions of the type represented by (A2–42) exist only for frequencies above a characteristic lower limit.

Equation (A2–42) represents a *sinusoidal wave* traveling in the *positive* x-direction with velocity v. One can easily show that a function such as

$$s(x, t) = A \cos\omega\left[\left(t + \frac{x}{v}\right) + \varphi\right], \tag{A2–46}$$

which represents a sinusoidal wave traveling in the *negative* x-direction, is also a solution of Eq. (A2–41).

In conclusion, the physical system described in this section is capable of propagating without deformation sinusoidal waves *of any frequency* $\omega > \omega_0$. The velocity of propagation is independent of the amplitude, but depends on the frequency, as shown by Eq. (A2–45).

(e) **A model of transverse waves with velocity dependent on the plane of vibration.** Consider a string kept under tension and, in addition, held by *two* sets of small springs arranged in two perpendicular planes that we may call the xy- and the xz-planes (see Fig. A2–6). Suppose that the two sets of springs are different, and thus give rise to different restoring forces, depending on whether the displacement of the string occurs in the y- or in the z-direction. Let $-k_y s_y \, \Delta x$ be the restoring force acting on the segment Δx when it is displaced by an amount s_y in the y-direction, and let $-k_z s_z \, \Delta x$ be

the restoring force acting on the
same segment when it is displaced
by an amount s_z in the z-direction.
Then the differential equation of a
wave vibrating in the xy-plane is

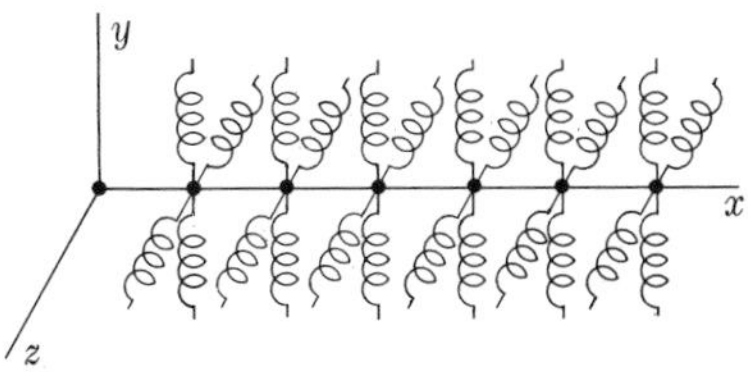

$$\frac{\partial^2 s_y}{\partial t^2} = \frac{T}{\mu} \frac{\partial^2 s_y}{\partial x^2} - \frac{k_y}{\mu} s_y, \quad \text{(A2–47)}$$

FIG. A2–6.   Mechanical model of double-refracting medium.

and that of a wave vibrating in the xz-plane is

$$\frac{\partial^2 s_z}{\partial t^2} = \frac{T}{\mu} \frac{\partial^2 s_z}{\partial x^2} - \frac{k_z}{\mu} s_z. \quad \text{(A2–48)}$$

These two equations have solutions of the form

$$s_y = A_y \cos\left[\omega\left(t - \frac{x}{v_y}\right) + \varphi_y\right],$$

$$s_z = A_z \cos\left[\omega\left(t - \frac{x}{v_z}\right) + \varphi_z\right], \quad \text{(A2–49)}$$

where v_y and v_z have the values

$$v_y = \frac{c}{\sqrt{1 - (\omega_{0y}^2/\omega^2)}}, \qquad v_z = \frac{c}{\sqrt{1 - (\omega_{0z}^2/\omega^2)}}. \quad \text{(A2–50)}$$

In the above equations, c is the constant $\sqrt{T/\mu}$ (see Eq. A2–43), and the
quantities ω_{0y} and ω_{0z} are defined by the equations

$$\omega_{0y} = \sqrt{\frac{k_y}{\mu}}, \qquad \omega_{0z} = \sqrt{\frac{k_z}{\mu}} \quad \text{(A2–51)}$$

(see Eq. A2–44).

We see that the system here considered will propagate unchanged any
sinusoidal wave of frequency $\omega > \omega_{0y}$ that vibrates in the xy-plane, or any
sinusoidal wave of frequency $\omega > \omega_{0z}$ that vibrates in the xz-plane. For a
given frequency, the velocity of propagation of the waves vibrating in the
two different planes will be different.

Suppose now that we excite the string by imparting to its endpoint a
sinusoidal motion in a direction *different* from either one of the two preferred directions, y or z. The wave that travels along the string will *not* be
a linearly polarized wave. Points at different positions along the string will

describe different trajectories and will not, in general, move along straight lines. We could compute the actual disturbance by considering it as the *superposition* of two waves, one vibrating in the xy-plane and one in the xz-plane, and traveling with different velocities, as given by Eqs. (A2–50). It is found that each point of the string describes, in general, an elliptical trajectory (see Section 6–2).

(f) **Reflection and transmission of waves at points of discontinuity.** Consider, as in Section 1–3(e), two pieces of string of different masses per unit length, joined to each other at a point O and kept under constant tension, T (Fig. A2–7). Let x be the distance from O, considered positive to the right of O and negative to the left. In the first string (i.e., for $x < 0$) the displacement satisfies the following differential equation (see Eq. A2–5):

$$\frac{\partial^2 s}{\partial t^2} = \frac{T}{\mu_1} \frac{\partial^2 s}{\partial x^2}, \quad \text{(A2–52)}$$

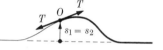

while in the second string (i.e., for $x > 0$) the displacement satisfies the equation

Fig. A2–7. Boundary conditions at a point of discontinuity.

$$\frac{\partial^2 s}{\partial t^2} = \frac{T}{\mu_2} \frac{\partial^2 s}{\partial x^2}. \quad \text{(A2–53)}$$

Let $s_1(x, t)$ be a solution of Eq. (A2–52) (valid for $x < 0$) and $s_2(x, t)$ a solution of (A2–53) (valid for $x > 0$). The two functions s_1 and s_2 represent a physically possible situation only if they satisfy certain *boundary conditions*. First, at the point where the two strings join, the displacements must be the same for both strings. Mathematically this means that, for $x = 0$, $s_1(x, t)$ and $s_2(x, t)$ must be equal at all times:

$$s_1(0, t) = s_2(0, t). \quad \text{(A2–54)}$$

Second, at the point of junction, the force exerted by the first string upon the second must be equal and directly opposite to the force exerted by the second string upon the first. Each force is equal in magnitude to the tension T, which is the same in the two strings, and is directed along the tangent to the string. We thus conclude that there cannot be a discontinuous change in the direction of the tangent at $x = 0$. Mathematically this means that

$$\left(\frac{\partial s_1}{\partial x}\right)_{x=0} = \left(\frac{\partial s_2}{\partial x}\right)_{x=0} \quad \text{(A2–55)}$$

Equations (A2–54) and (A2–55) represent the boundary conditions that must be satisfied by the functions s_1 and s_2.

In order to apply the above results to our problem, we begin by considering the fact that in the second string there is a wave traveling from O in the positive direction only. Thus, if v_2 is the velocity of propagation in the second medium,

$$v_2 = \sqrt{\frac{T}{\mu_2}},$$

$s_2(x, t)$ must have the following form:

$$s_2(x, t) = f_2 \left(t - \frac{x}{v_2} \right). \tag{A2–56}$$

The disturbance in the first string must satisfy Eq. (A2–52) whose general solution is

$$s_1(x, t) = f_1 \left(t - \frac{x}{v_1} \right) + g_1 \left(t + \frac{x}{v_1} \right), \tag{A2–57}$$

where

$$v_1 = \sqrt{\frac{T}{\mu_1}}$$

is the velocity of propagation in the first medium.

The boundary conditions (A2–54) and (A2–55) yield the following relations between the functions f_1, g_1, and f_2:

$$f_1(t) + g_1(t) = f_2(t), \tag{A2–58}$$

$$\frac{1}{v_1} \left[\dot{f}_1(t) - \dot{g}_1(t) \right] = \frac{1}{v_2} \dot{f}_2(t), \tag{A2–59}$$

where $\dot{f}_1$, $\dot{g}_1$, and $\dot{f}_2$ indicate the derivatives of the functions f_1, g_1, and f_2 with respect to their arguments.

Integration of (A2–59) gives

$$v_2[f_1(t) - g_1(t)] = v_1 f_2(t), \tag{A2–60}$$

where the constant of integration has been taken as equal to zero because, for sufficiently small or sufficiently large values of t, the functions f_1, g_1, and f_2 are known to be zero.

The function f_1 represents the incident wave and is therefore to be regarded as a datum of the problem. The function g_1 represents the reflected wave, and f_2 the transmitted wave. If $v_1 \neq v_2$, Eqs. (A2–58) and (A2–60) show that both g_1 and f_2 are different from zero. In other words, the boundary conditions at $x = 0$ *require the existence of a reflected as well as a transmitted wave.*

Solution of (A2–58) and (A2–60) with respect to g_1 and f_2 yields

$$g_1(t) = \frac{v_2 - v_1}{v_2 + v_1} f_1(t),$$

$$f_2(t) = \frac{2v_2}{v_2 + v_1} f_1(t).$$

Since g_1 is a function of $t + x/v_1$ and f_2 a function of $t - x/v_2$, the above equations give

$$g_1\left(t + \frac{x}{v_1}\right) = \frac{v_2 - v_1}{v_2 + v_1} f_1\left(t - \frac{x}{v_1}\right), \qquad (A2\text{–}61)$$

$$f_2\left(t - \frac{x}{v_2}\right) = \frac{2v_2}{v_2 + v_1} f_1\left(t - \frac{x}{v_2}\right). \qquad (A2\text{–}62)$$

From these equations we see that the reflected and transmitted waves have the same form as the incident wave. The functions f_2 and f_1 always have the same sign. The functions g_1 and f_1 have equal or opposite sign depending on whether v_2 is greater or smaller than v_1. Thus the reflection occurs with or without change of sign depending on whether the velocity in the second medium is smaller or greater than in the first.

Equation (A2–61) yields

at the limit for $\mu_2 = \infty$ (that is, for $v_2 = 0$):

$$g_1\left(t + \frac{x}{v_1}\right) = -f_1\left(t - \frac{x}{v_1}\right), \qquad (A2\text{–}63)$$

at the limit for $\mu_2 = 0$ (that is, for $v_2 = \infty$):

$$g_1\left(t + \frac{x}{v_1}\right) = f_1\left(t - \frac{x}{v_1}\right). \qquad (A2\text{–}64)$$

The assumption that the second string is infinitely heavy means physically that the endpoint O of the first string is rigidly attached to an immovable support. Equation (A2–63) indicates that in this case the reflected and the incident waves have identical amplitudes and opposite signs. The assumption that the second string is massless corresponds to a physical situation in which the endpoint O of the first string can move freely in the direction perpendicular to the string. Equation (A2–64) indicates that in this case the reflected and the incident waves have equal amplitudes and the same sign.

We can easily verify that our results are consistent with the principle of conservation of energy. The energy carried by the incident wave to the point O in the time interval from t to $t + dt$ is

$$\Phi_1 \, dt = \frac{T}{v_1} \dot{f}_1^2(t) \, dt$$

[see Eq. (A2–34)]. During the same time interval, the amounts of energy carried away from O by the reflected and transmitted waves are

$$\Phi_1' \, dt = \frac{T}{v_1} \dot{g}_1^2(t) \, dt,$$

and

$$\Phi_2 \, dt = \frac{T}{v_2} \dot{f}_2^2(t) \, dt,$$

respectively. From the above equations and from (A2–61) and (A2–62), we obtain

$$\Phi_1' + \Phi_2 = T \left[\frac{1}{v_1} \left(\frac{v_2 - v_1}{v_2 + v_1} \right)^2 + \frac{1}{v_2} \left(\frac{2v_2}{v_2 + v_1} \right)^2 \right] \dot{f}_1^2(t)$$

$$= \frac{T}{v_1} \frac{(v_2 - v_1)^2 + 4v_1 v_2}{(v_2 + v_1)^2} \dot{f}_1^2(t) = \frac{T}{v_1} \dot{f}_1^2 = \Phi_1.$$

(g) Spherical waves in a fluid. We propose first to find the differential equations satisfied by the pressure change p and the displacement s in a spherical sound wave [see Section 1–4(b)]. For this purpose we consider the layer of fluid which, in the undisturbed condition, lies between the spheres of radii r and $r + \Delta r$, where Δr is an infinitesimal quantity (Fig. A2–8). Let $s(r, t)$ and $s(r + \Delta r, t)$ be the displacements at time t of the points of the fluid that were originally at the distances r and $r + \Delta r$ from O. At time t, the radius of the inner sphere has become $r + s(r, t)$, and the radius of the outer sphere has become $r + \Delta r + s(r + \Delta r, t)$. We assume, as before, that the displacement s is a small quantity, and we consider only values of r very large compared with s. The volume changes of the two spheres are then:

$$4\pi r^2 s(r, t) \qquad\qquad \text{for the inner sphere,}$$

$$4\pi (r + \Delta r)^2 s(r + \Delta r, t) \qquad \text{for the outer sphere.}$$

The volume occupied by the fluid under consideration has therefore changed by the amount

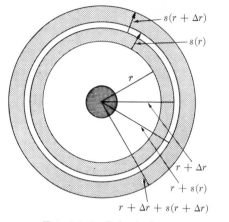

FIG. A2–8. Spherical wave.

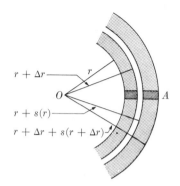

FIGURE A2–9

$$\Delta V = 4\pi[(r + \Delta r)^2 s(r + \Delta r, t) - r^2 s(r, t)] = 4\pi \frac{\partial(r^2 s)}{\partial r} \Delta r$$

Since the original volume was $4\pi r^2 \, \Delta r$, the *relative* volume change is

$$\frac{\Delta V}{V_0} = \frac{4\pi[\partial(r^2 s)/\partial r] \, \Delta r}{4\pi(r^2 \, \Delta r)} = \frac{1}{r^2} \frac{\partial(r^2 s)}{\partial r}.$$

If K is the compressibility of the fluid, the corresponding change of pressure p is given by

$$Kp = -\frac{1}{r^2} \frac{\partial(r^2 s)}{\partial r}.$$

or

$$Kp = -\frac{\partial s}{\partial r} - \frac{2s}{r}. \qquad (A2\text{–}65)$$

Consider next an element of volume of the fluid, in the shape of a cylinder of cross-sectional area A with its axis in the radial direction. In the undisturbed condition, the element extends from r to $r + \Delta r$ (Fig. A2–9). The volume is thus $A \, \Delta r$ and the corresponding mass is $\rho_0 A \, \Delta r$, where ρ_0 is the density of the undisturbed fluid.

The force acting on the volume element results from the pressure applied to the various points of its surface. At time t, the volume extends from $r + s(r)$ to $r + \Delta r + s(r + \Delta r)$. As in the one-dimensional case, however, we shall make no appreciable error if we disregard the displacement of the volume element in the computation of the force. The force due to the pressure applied to the lateral surface of the cylinder is zero for reasons of symmetry. The force applied to the end surface at r equals the pressure at r times the cross-sectional area A of the cylinder and acts in the positive r-direction. The force applied to the end surface at $r + \Delta r$ equals A times the pressure at $r + \Delta r$ and acts in the negative r-direction. Thus the net force applied to the element under consideration is

$$\Delta F = -\frac{\partial p}{\partial r} A \, \Delta r \cdot$$

If we now set this force equal to the product of the mass $\rho_0 A \, \Delta r$ and the acceleration, $\partial^2 s / \partial t^2$, we obtain

$$\frac{\partial p}{\partial r} = -\rho_0 \frac{\partial^2 s}{\partial t^2} . \tag{A2-66}$$

In order to eliminate s between Eqs. (A2–65) and (A2–66), we differentiate (A2–65) twice with respect to t:

$$K \frac{\partial^2 p}{\partial t^2} = -\frac{\partial^3 s}{\partial r \partial t^2} - \frac{2}{r} \frac{\partial^2 s}{\partial t^2} , \tag{A2-67}$$

and we differentiate (A2–66) once with respect to r:

$$\frac{\partial^2 p}{\partial r^2} = -\rho_0 \frac{\partial^3 s}{\partial t^2 \partial r} . \tag{A2-68}$$

Elimination of s between (A2–66), (A2–67), and (A2–68) yields

$$K \frac{\partial^2 p}{\partial t^2} = \frac{1}{\rho_0} \frac{\partial^2 p}{\partial r^2} + \frac{2}{\rho_0 r} \frac{\partial p}{\partial r} ,$$

or

$$r \frac{\partial^2 p}{\partial t^2} = \frac{1}{K\rho_0} \left(r \frac{\partial^2 p}{\partial r^2} + 2 \frac{\partial p}{\partial r} \right) .$$

This equation may be rewritten as follows:

$$\frac{\partial^2 (rp)}{\partial t^2} = \frac{1}{K\rho_0} \frac{\partial^2 (rp)}{\partial r^2} . \tag{A2-69}$$

We then see that the quantity rp (considered as a function of r and t) satisfies a differential equation of exactly the same form as the differential equation satisfied by $p(x, t)$ in the case of a one-dimensional wave (Eq.

A2–21). Since this equation is satisfied by any arbitrary function of $t - x/v$, it follows that (A2–69) has a solution of the form

$$rp = F\left(t - \frac{r}{v}\right),$$

or

$$p = \frac{F(t - r/v)}{r}, \tag{A2–70}$$

where

$$v = \sqrt{\frac{1}{K\rho_0}}, \tag{A2–71}$$

and F is an arbitrary function of the argument $t - r/v$.

Examination of Eq. (A2–70) shows that the curves representing p as a function of t for two different values r_1 and r_2 of r differ by a scale factor equal to r_1/r_2, and are shifted with respect to one another by an amount $\Delta t = (r_2 - r_1)/v$ along the time axis. Hence one can say that (A2–70) represents a pressure wave diverging from O with velocity v, whose amplitude varies in inverse proportion to the distance from O.

We note that the displacement s in a spherical sound wave has an expression of the form

$$s = \frac{f(t - r/v)}{r^2} + \frac{\dot{f}(t - r/v)}{vr}. \tag{A2–72}$$

The reader can easily verify that Eqs. (A2–70) and (A2–72) satisfy both (A2–65) and (A2–66) if v is given by (A2–71) and if the functions F and f are related to each other by the equation

$$\ddot{f} = Kv^2F = \frac{F}{\rho_0}. \tag{A2–73}$$

Differentiation of Eq. (A2–72) with respect to t yields

$$u = \frac{\partial s}{\partial t} = \frac{\dot{f}(t - r/v)}{r^2} + \frac{\ddot{f}(t - r/v)}{vr}. \tag{A2–74}$$

Equations (A2–72) and (A2–74) show that in a spherical sound wave the displacement s and the velocity u are not represented by functions of the same type as the function representing the pressure change p. Unlike the expression for p, the expressions for s and u contain two terms, of which one varies as $1/r$, the other as $1/r^2$. However, for sufficiently large values of r, the term proportional to $1/r^2$ becomes negligible compared with the term proportional to $1/r$. In this limit, the amplitudes of the displacement and velocity waves are inversely proportional to the distance from the origin, and Eqs. (A2–70), (A2–71), (A2–73), and (A2–74) provide the following relation between p and u:

$$p = \rho_0 v u = \frac{u}{Kv}. \qquad (A2\text{–}75)$$

This equation is identical to (A2–28), which gives the relation between p and u for one-dimensional sound waves.

(h) **The general differential equation of sound waves in a fluid.** To find the *general differential equation* satisfied by the pressure in a sound wave, we consider an infinitesimal volume of the fluid which, in the undisturbed condition, occupies a parallelepiped of sides Δx, Δy, Δz, parallel to the coordinate axes (see Fig. A2–10). At the time t, let $s_x(x, y, z, t)$, $s_y(x, y, z, t)$, and $s_z(x, y, z, t)$ be the cartesian components of the displacement of that point of the fluid which, in the undisturbed condition, was at the point having coordinates x, y, z. An argument similar to that developed in Section A2(b) shows that, at this time, the dimension of the volume element parallel to the x-axis has changed from Δx to $\Delta x + (\partial s/\partial x)\,\Delta x = (1 + \partial s_x/\partial x)\,\Delta x$. Similarly, the dimensions parallel to the y- and the z-axes have changed from Δy to $(1 + \partial s_y/\partial y)\Delta y$ and from Δz to $(1 + \partial s_z/\partial z)\,\Delta z$, respectively. The fractional change in the volume of the element is therefore

$$\frac{\Delta V}{V_0} = \frac{(1 + \partial s_x/\partial x)\,\Delta x \times (1 + \partial s_y/\partial y)\,\Delta y \times (1 + \partial s_z/\partial z)\,\Delta z - \Delta x\,\Delta y\,\Delta z}{\Delta x\,\Delta y\,\Delta z},$$

or, neglecting products of infinitesimal quantities,

$$\frac{\Delta V}{V_0} = \frac{\partial s_x}{\partial x} + \frac{\partial s_y}{\partial y} + \frac{\partial s_z}{\partial z}.$$

From this equation, and from the definition of the compressibility K, we obtain

$$Kp = -\left(\frac{\partial s_x}{\partial x} + \frac{\partial s_y}{\partial y} + \frac{\partial s_z}{\partial z}\right), \qquad (A2\text{–}76)$$

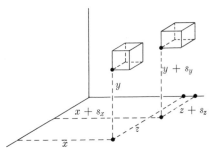

FIG. A2–10. Three-dimensional wave equation.

or, differentiating twice with respect to t,

$$K\frac{\partial^2 p}{\partial t^2} = -\left(\frac{\partial^3 s_x}{\partial x \partial t^2} + \frac{\partial^3 s_y}{\partial y \partial t^2} + \frac{\partial^3 s_z}{\partial z \partial t^2}\right). \qquad (A2\text{–}77)$$

We now note that the x-component of the force acting on the volume element under consideration is the resultant of the pressure applied at the two faces perpendicular to the x-axis, and has the value

$$\Delta F_x = - \Delta y\, \Delta z\, \frac{\partial p}{\partial x}\, \Delta x.$$

The x-component of the acceleration is therefore given by the equation

$$\rho_0\, \Delta x\, \Delta y\, \Delta z\, \frac{\partial^2 s_x}{\partial t^2} = - \frac{\partial p}{\partial x}\, \Delta x\, \Delta y\, \Delta z,$$

or

$$\frac{\partial^2 s_x}{\partial t^2} = - \frac{1}{\rho_0}\, \frac{\partial p}{\partial x} \tag{A2-78}$$

[compare Eq. (A2–19)]. Similarly, we obtain

$$\frac{\partial^2 s_y}{\partial t^2} = - \frac{1}{\rho_0}\, \frac{\partial p}{\partial y}, \tag{A2-79}$$

$$\frac{\partial^2 s_z}{\partial t^2} = - \frac{1}{\rho_0}\, \frac{\partial p}{\partial z}. \tag{A2-80}$$

Differentiation of the above equations with respect to x, y, and z, respectively, and substitution in (A2–77), yields

$$\frac{\partial^2 p}{\partial t^2} = \frac{1}{K\rho_0} \left(\frac{\partial^2 p}{\partial x^2} + \frac{\partial^2 p}{\partial y^2} + \frac{\partial^2 p}{\partial z^2} \right). \tag{A2-81}$$

By definition, in a *plane* wave p is a function of x and t alone, and (A2–81) reduces to

$$\frac{\partial^2 p}{\partial t^2} = \frac{1}{K\rho_0}\, \frac{\partial^2 p}{\partial x^2}. \tag{A2-82}$$

This equation is identical to the differential equation satisfied by the pressure wave in a pipe (Eq. A2–21).

APPENDIX 3

THE ELECTROMAGNETIC FIELD OF A POINT CHARGE MOVING WITH CONSTANT VELOCITY ON A STRAIGHT LINE

We take the trajectory of the point charge q as the z-axis, and let O be the instantaneous position of the charge, w its velocity. For reasons of symmetry, the magnetic lines of force are circles with their centers on the z-axis. We apply Eq. (7–16) to one of these circles and to the portion S of plane surface bounded by it (see Fig. A3–1), assuming that the charge q does not lie on this plane at the time under consideration. We obtain

$$\oint H_s \, ds = 2\pi R H_\varphi = \epsilon_0 \int \frac{\partial E_z}{\partial t} \, dS, \qquad (A3\text{–}1)$$

where R is the radius of the circle, E_z the component of **E** parallel to the z-axis, and H_φ is the magnitude of the magnetic field.

To evaluate the integral on the right side of (A3–1), consider that, since the charge moves with the constant velocity w, E_z must be a function of $t - z/w$:

$$E_z = f\left(t - \frac{z}{w}\right).$$

It follows that

$$\left(\frac{\partial E_z}{\partial t}\right)_z = -w\left(\frac{\partial E_z}{\partial z}\right)_t, \qquad (A3\text{–}2)$$

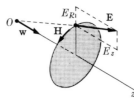

FIG. A3–1. Electromagnetic field of a moving charge.

where $(\partial E_z/\partial t)_z$ indicates the derivative of E_z with respect to t for constant z, and $(\partial E_z/\partial z)_t$ the derivative of E_z with respect to z for constant t. Thus Eq. (A3–1) becomes

$$2\pi R H_\varphi = -\epsilon_0 w \int \frac{\partial E_z}{\partial z} \, dS. \qquad (A3\text{–}3)$$

We now take a volume in the shape of a shallow cylindrical pillbox whose bases are circles of radius R located on planes perpendicular to the z-axis at

z and $z + dz$, respectively (see Fig. A3–2). Application of Gauss' theorem to this volume yields the equation

$$(\textstyle\int E_z \, dS)_{z+dz} - (\int E_z \, dS)_z + 2\pi R \, dzE_R = 0, \qquad (\text{A3–4})$$

where the first two terms represent the flux through the bases of the cylinder and the third term represents the flux through the lateral surface. In this term E_R indicates the component of **E** perpendicular to the z-axis.

Equation (A3–4) may be written as follows:

$$\int \frac{\partial E_z}{\partial z} \, dS = -2\pi RE_R, \qquad (\text{A3–5})$$

which, together with (A3–3), yields

$$H_\varphi = \epsilon_0 wE_R, \qquad B_\varphi = \frac{w}{c^2} E_R. \qquad (\text{A3–6})$$

Consider now an infinitesimal rectangle of sides dz and dR in a plane containing the z-axis (Fig. A3–3). We apply Faraday's induction law:

$$\oint E_s \, ds = -\int \frac{\partial B_n}{\partial t} \, dS,$$

to the perimeter of this rectangle. Considering that the electric field lies in the plane of the rectangle and the magnetic field is perpendicular to it, we obtain

$$E_z(R) \, dz + E_R(z + dz) \, dR - E_z(R + dR) \, dz - E_R(z) \, dR$$
$$= -\frac{\partial B_\varphi}{\partial t} \, dR \, dz,$$

or

$$\frac{\partial E_R}{\partial z} - \frac{\partial E_z}{\partial R} = -\frac{\partial B_\varphi}{\partial t}.$$

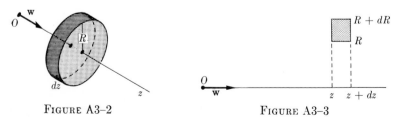

FIGURE A3–2   FIGURE A3–3

The magnetic field, like the electric field, is a function of $t - z/w$, and therefore

$$\frac{\partial B_\varphi}{\partial t} = -w \frac{\partial B_\varphi}{\partial z}.$$

Considering Eqs. (A3–6), we then obtain

$$\frac{\partial E_R}{\partial z} - \frac{\partial E_z}{\partial R} = \frac{w^2}{c^2} \frac{\partial E_R}{\partial z}. \tag{A3–7}$$

On the other hand, the components of the electric field $\mathbf{E}_0$ produced by the charge q at rest ($w = 0$) obey the equation

$$\frac{\partial E_R}{\partial z} - \frac{\partial E_z}{\partial R} = 0. \tag{A3–8}$$

Equations (A3–7) and (A3–8) are identical if w^2/c^2 is negligible compared with unity. These equations, together with Gauss' law (which states that the flux of $\mathbf{E}$ through a closed surface is q/ϵ_0 or zero depending on whether or not the surface encloses the charge q) determine the electric field completely. We thus conclude that the electric field of the moving charge differs from the electric field of the static charge by quantities of the order of w^2/c^2.

APPENDIX 4

NUMERICAL DATA

Wavelengths (in angstroms) of some spectral lines. Several of the lines listed appear as absorption lines in the solar spectrum (Fraunhofer lines); they are designated by the capital letters from C to K, as is customary.

Hydrogen	Helium	Sodium	Calcium (ionized)
6562.82(C)	6678.15	5895.92⎫(D)	3968.47(H)
4861.33(F)	5875.62	5889.95⎭	3933.67(K)
4340.46	5047.74		
4101.74	5015.67		
	4921.93		
	4713.14		
	4471.48		
	4437.55		
	4387.93		

Cadmium	Iron	Mercury
6438.47	5269.54(E)	5790.65
5085.82	4307.91(G)	5769.59
4799.92		5460.74
4678.16		4916.04
		4358.35
		4077.81
		4046.56

TABLE A4-2

INDICES OF REFRACTION OF SEVERAL SUBSTANCES FOR SODIUM LIGHT
($\lambda = 5893$ A).

Substance	Index of refraction, n
Quartz (fused)	1.458 (at 20°C)
Glass { zinc crown	1.517 "
high-dispersion crown	1.520 "
light flint	1.575 "
heavy flint	1.650 "
heaviest flint	1.890 "
Water	1.333 "
Ethyl alcohol	1.361 "
Carbon bisulfide	1.625 "
Solution of sucrose in water { 10% sugar	1.348 "
20% sugar	1.364 "
40% sugar	1.400 "
60% sugar	1.442 "
85% sugar (saturated)	1.503 "
Air	1.0002926 (at 0°C and 760 mm Hg pressure)
Carbon dioxide	1.000448–1.000454 "

TABLE A4-3

DEPENDENCE OF THE INDEX OF REFRACTION ON WAVELENGTH, FOR
SEVERAL KINDS OF GLASS AT 20°C.

Wavelength (angstroms)	Index of refraction		
	High-dispersion crown	Light flint	Heavy flint
3610	1.546	1.614	1.705
4340	1.533	1.594	1.675
5890	1.520	1.575	1.650
6560	1.517	1.571	1.644
7680	1.514	1.567	1.638

TABLE A4–4

PRINCIPAL INDICES OF REFRACTION OF SEVERAL CRYSTALS
FOR SODIUM LIGHT (λ = 5893 A).

(For uniaxial crystals, n_1 is the extraordinary and n_2 the ordinary index of refraction.)

	n_1	n_2	n_3
Uniaxial crystals:			
Apatite	1.64172	1.64607	
Calcite	1.4864	1.6583	
Quartz	1.5533	1.5442	
Zircon	1.9682	1.9239	
Biaxial Crystals:			
Aragonite	1.5301	1.6816	1.6859
Gypsum	1.5206	1.5227	1.5297
Mica	1.5692	1.6049	1.6117
Topaz	1.6155	1.6181	1.6250

TABLE A4–5

Specific rotation of quartz (angle of rotation in 1 millimeter thickness) and specific rotation of a solution of sucrose in water (angle of rotation produced by a 10-decimeter column of solution containing 1 gram of sucrose per cubic centimeter) for different wavelengths.

Wavelength (angstroms)	Specific rotation	
	Quartz deg/mm	Sucrose solution deg/dm
4358	41.55	128.49
4861	32.76	————
5086	29.78	91.16
5461	25.53	78.16
5893	21.72	66.45
6438	18.02	55.04
6708	16.53	50.51
7281	13.92	————

ANSWERS

TO

ODD-NUMBERED PROBLEMS

ANSWERS TO ODD-NUMBERED PROBLEMS

CHAPTER 1

1–1. (a) $\left(\dfrac{R_2}{D_2}\right) < \left(\dfrac{R_1}{D_1}\right)$; (b) 93 mi, 4300 mi.

1–5. (b) 0.145°.

1–7. Square pyramid with vertex 4.35 ft under center of raft.

1–9. (a) $n' = \dfrac{nx}{\sqrt{x^2 + y^2}}$; (b) $n' = \sqrt{n^2 - 1}$.

1–11. 18°32′, 32°4′, 42°55′, 48°30′.

1–13. (a) circular disk whose diameter subtends 0.4°; (b) flattened disk, width 0.4°, height 0.36°; (c) flattened disk, width 0.4°, height 0.10°; (d) flattened disk, width 0.4°, height 0.0028°.

1–15. $\mu u^2 v = 0.4\pi^2 \sin^2 \left[200\pi \left(t - \tfrac{1}{10}\right)\right]$ watts.

1–17. $p(r_2, t) = p_0 + p_1 \dfrac{r_1}{r_2} \sin\left[\omega\left(t - \dfrac{r_2 - r_1}{v}\right)\right]$.

1–19. (a) $E_P = \dfrac{2\pi R\,\Delta R}{x_0 v t_1} \sin\left[\dfrac{2\pi}{t_1}\left(t - \dfrac{x_0}{v} - \dfrac{1}{2}\dfrac{R^2}{x_0 v}\right)\right]$;

(b) $E_P = \dfrac{\pi}{4} 10^{-6} \sin\left[\dfrac{2\pi}{t_1}\left(t - 10^4 t_1\right)\right]$,

$$[\text{for } 10^4 t_1 < t < (10^4 + \tfrac{1}{2})\, t_1],$$

$$E_P = 0, \qquad\qquad [\text{for } (10^4 + \tfrac{1}{2})\, t_1 < t < (10^4 + 1)t_1] ,$$

$$E_P = \dfrac{\pi}{4} 10^{-6} \left\{\sin \dfrac{2\pi}{t_1} [t - (10^4 + \tfrac{1}{2})\, t_1]\right\},$$

$$[\text{for } (10^4 + 1)t_1 < t < (10^4 + \tfrac{3}{2})t_1].$$

1–21. $E_P = 0,$ $\qquad\qquad \left(\text{for } t < \dfrac{x_0}{v} + \dfrac{R^2}{2x_0 v}\right),$ *(cont.)*

489

$$E_P = 1 - \cos \frac{2\pi}{t_1}\left(t - \frac{x_0}{v} - \frac{R^2}{2x_0 v}\right),$$

$$\left(\text{for } \frac{x_0}{v} + \frac{R^2}{2x_0 v} < t < \frac{x_0}{v} + \frac{R^2}{2x_0 v} + t_1\right),$$

$$E_P = 0, \qquad \left(\text{for } t > \frac{x_0}{v} + \frac{R^2}{2x_0 v} + t_1\right).$$

1-23. (a) $E_P(t) = E\left(t - \dfrac{x_0}{v} - t_1\right),$ $\quad\left(\text{for } \dfrac{x_0}{v} + t_1 < t < \dfrac{x_0}{v} + 2t_1\right),$

$$E_P(t) = -E\left(t - \frac{x_0}{v} - 2t_1\right),$$

$$\left(\text{for } \frac{x_0}{v} + 2t_1 < t < \frac{x_0}{v} + 3t_1\right);$$

(b) $E_P(t) = \tfrac{1}{2} E\left(t - \dfrac{x_0}{v} - t_1\right),$ $\quad\left(\text{for } \dfrac{x_0}{v} + t_1 < t < \dfrac{x_0}{v} + 2t_1\right),$

$$E_P(t) = \tfrac{1}{2} E\left(t - \frac{x_0}{v} - 2t_1\right),$$

$$\left(\text{for } \frac{x_0}{v} + 2t_1 < t < \frac{x_0}{v} + 3t_1\right);$$

(c) $E_P(t) = E\left(t - \dfrac{x_0}{v}\right),$ $\quad\left(\text{for } \dfrac{x_0}{v} < t < \dfrac{x_0}{v} + t_1\right),$

$$E_P(t) = -\tfrac{1}{2} E\left(t - \frac{x_0}{v} - t_1\right),$$

$$\left(\text{for } \frac{x_0}{v} + t_1 < t < \frac{x_0}{v} + 2t_1\right),$$

$$E_P(t) = -\tfrac{1}{2} E\left(t - \frac{x_0}{v} - 2t_1\right),$$

$$\left(\text{for } \frac{x_0}{v} + 2t_1 < t < \frac{x_0}{v} + 3t_1\right);$$

(d) $E_P(t) = \dfrac{2A}{t_1}\left(t - \dfrac{x_0}{v}\right),$ $\quad\left(\text{for } \dfrac{x_0}{v} < t < \dfrac{x_0}{v} + \dfrac{t_1}{2}\right),$

$$E_P(t) = \frac{A}{t_1}\left[\frac{5}{2} t_1 - 3\left(t - \frac{x_0}{v}\right)\right],$$

$$\left(\text{for } \frac{x_0}{v} + \frac{t_1}{2} < t < \frac{x_0}{v} + t_1\right),$$

(*cont.*)

$$E_P(t) = -\frac{A}{2}, \qquad \left(\text{for } \frac{x_0}{v} + t_1 < t < \frac{x_0}{v} + \frac{3t_1}{2}\right),$$

$$E_P(t) = -\frac{A}{t_1}\left[2t_1 - \left(t - \frac{x_0}{v}\right)\right],$$

$$\left(\text{for } \frac{x_0}{v} + \frac{3t_1}{2} < t < \frac{x_0}{v} + 2t_1\right).$$

CHAPTER 2

2–1. (a) $\Delta\theta = 0.00029 \dfrac{p}{p_0} \dfrac{T_0}{T} \tan\theta$;   (b) $1'$.

2–3. $n^2 = \dfrac{n_0^2 B^2}{A^2 + B^2}\left[1 + \dfrac{A^2}{B^2} \cos^2\left(\dfrac{y}{B}\right)\right].$

2–7. 1.08 in.

2–11. (a) 1 m behind M_2; (b) $\frac{1}{2}$ m in front of M_2; (c) 0.3 m in front of M_1.

2–13. 5.32 ft.

2–17. 0.6 cm from center, magn. 1.2; 1 cm from center, magn. 2.

2–19. 30 cm to the right, 20 cm to the left of first surface; 60 cm to the left, 40 cm to the right of second surface.

2–21. (a) 200 cm, conv.; (b) 133 cm, conv.; (c) -500 cm, div.; (d) 400 cm, conv.; (e) -300 cm, div.

2–23. $s' = -0.375$ m, 1.5 mm, virt.,
$s' = -0.6$ m, 1.2 mm, virt.,
$s' = -1$ m, 0.66 mm, virt.

2–25. $46°16'$.

2–27. $0.02°$; $-0.05°$.

2–31. (c) $\Delta l/\epsilon = 0$.

2–33. $l = r - \sqrt{R^2 + (x')^2 - 2Rx'\cos\varphi} + n\sqrt{R^2 + x^2 - 2Rx\cos\varphi}$.

CHAPTER 3

3–1. $A = \sqrt{A_1^2 + A_2^2 + 2A_1 A_2 \cos(\alpha_1 - \alpha_2)}$;

$$\tan \alpha = \frac{A_1 \sin \alpha_1 + A_2 \sin \alpha_2}{A_1 \cos \alpha_1 + A_2 \cos \alpha_2}.$$

3–3. $(A_2 + 2A_1 \cos \alpha_1) \cos \omega t.$

3–5. $A = 2A_1 \left[\cos\left(\frac{\alpha_1}{2}\right) + \cos\left(\frac{3\alpha_1}{2}\right) \right]$; $\alpha = \frac{3}{2}\alpha_1.$

3–7. $\Delta x = 1.625$ mm; $\Delta x = 1.125$ mm.

3–9. $\alpha = 10^{-3}$ rad.

3–11. 0.3 mm.

3–13. (a) $\lambda = 5320$ A; (b) $\lambda = 6650$ A, $\lambda = 4433$ A.

3–15. $I_r = 4I\rho^2 \sin^2\left(\frac{2\pi nd}{\lambda}\right)$; $I_r \approx \frac{16\pi^2 n^2}{\lambda^2} \rho^2 d^2 I.$

3–17. 1110 A.

3–19. (a) $0.19 \sqrt{k}$ cm; (b) 110.

3–21. $I \approx \text{const.} \times \left[1 - \cos 4\pi \left(\frac{d_0}{\lambda} + \frac{r^2}{2R\lambda}\right) \cdot \cos\left(\frac{2\pi d_0 \Delta\lambda}{\lambda^2}\right) \right]$; fringes

disappear for $d_0 \Delta\lambda/\lambda^2 = (2k + 1)/4.$

3–23. (a) straight, equidistant, along lines of constant thickness; (b) 2×10^{-4} cm.

3–25. $I(\lambda) = I_0(\lambda)2\rho^2 \left[1 - \cos \frac{4\pi d\sqrt{n^2 - \sin^2 \theta}}{\lambda} \right].$

3–27. (a) 10^5; (b) 4.45×10^{-3}, $\sqrt{2} \times 4.45 \times 10^{-3}$, $\sqrt{3} \times 4.45 \times 10^{-3}$ rad; (c) 4.49×10^{-4} rad.

3–29. 1.6×10^{-4} rad.

3–31. $\lambda_1 - \lambda = \lambda - \lambda_2 = 0.04\lambda.$

3–33. Fringes contract or expand depending on whether evacuated tube is in the longer or shorter arm; intensity at center goes through a minimum 193 times.

CHAPTER 4

4-1. (a) minima: $r_0 = 8/2k$; maxima: $r_0 = 8/(2k + 1)$; (b) 4 m.

4-3. 0.09 cm.

4-5. 2 meters from plate.

4-7. (a) $\frac{3}{2}A$, $\frac{9}{4}I$; (b) 0.

4-9. Minima: 1.21, 1.77, . . . mm; maxima: 0.80, 1.52, . . . mm from edge of geometric shadow.

4-11. (a) Maxima at $Y = 0$, 1.24, 1.92, . . . mm; relative intensities: 1, 0.093, 0.032, . . . ; minima at $Y = 1.13$, 1.81, . . . mm; relative intensities: 0.0074, 0.0072, . . . ; (b) Maxima at $Y = 0.280$, 0.565, . . . mm; relative intensities: 1.76, 1.94, . . . ; minima at $Y = 0$, 0.396 mm; relative intensities: 1, 1.64.

4-13. (a) Central slit: from 0.9 to -0.9 mm; lateral slits: from 1.35 to 1.68 mm, from 1.94 to 2.2 mm, from -1.35 to -1.68 mm, from -1.94 to -2.2 mm; (b) 5.1.

4-15. Practically identical to that observed without wire, if $h \ll$ lens diameter.

4-19. Intensity $\dfrac{\sin^2 \alpha}{\alpha^2}$; phase $= \alpha$ for $\sin \alpha > 0$,

$$= \alpha + \pi \text{ for } \sin \alpha < 0.$$

4-21. $\dfrac{1}{Y^2 Z^2} [\sin (10c\,Y) \sin (10cZ) - \sin (2c\,Y) \sin (cZ)]^2$, $\left(c = \dfrac{\pi}{2.4} \text{ mm}^{-1} \right)$.

4-23. 7.9×10^{-7} rad, 4.9×10^{-4} rad; 7.9×10^{-4} cm, 4.9×10^{-4} cm.

4-25. (a) 3.9×10^{-5} rad; (b) 0.82 A.

4-27. 1.25×10^{-3} cm, 5×10^{-3} cm.

4-29. $I = (I_0/100\, \alpha^2 \beta^2)$
$[\sin^2 \alpha \sin^2 \beta + \sin^2 (3\alpha) \sin^2 (3\beta) + 2 \sin \alpha \sin (3\alpha) \sin \beta \times \sin (3\beta) \cos (8\alpha)]$,
$$(\alpha = \pi a Y / f\lambda, \beta = \pi aZ / f\lambda, I_0 = \text{intensity at } Y = Z = 0).$$

4-31. (a) $Y_0 = 0$, $Y_1 = \lambda f/h$, $Y_2 = 2\lambda f/h$, . . . ; (b) $Y_0 = Df\delta/h$, $Y_1 = Y_0 + \lambda f/h$, $Y_2 = Y_0 + 2\lambda f/h$, ...

4-33. Fringes become increasingly diffuse, disappear for $D \sim \lambda/\delta$.

4-35. $I = \dfrac{I_0}{16} \dfrac{\sin^2 \alpha}{\alpha^2} \dfrac{\sin^2 (16\alpha)}{\sin^2 (4\alpha)}$, $\left(\alpha = \dfrac{\pi a}{\lambda} \sin \theta \right)$.

4-37. (a) Slit width less than $\sim 10^{-3}$ cm; (b) orientation accurate to better than $\sim 10^{-3}$ rad.

4-39. $I = \text{const.} \times \left[\dfrac{\sin (3N + 1)\delta}{\sin \delta} - \dfrac{\sin 3(N + 1)\delta}{\sin 3\delta} \right]^2$. Maxima at

$\delta = k\pi$, intensity 4; maxima at $\delta = \dfrac{3k + 1}{3} \pi$,

$\delta = \dfrac{3k + 2}{3} \pi$, intensity 1 ($\delta$ defined by Eq. 4–73).

4-41. 430.

4-43. Image of linear grating with slits parallel to z- or to y-axis.

CHAPTER 5

5-1. 420.

5-3. (a) $\Delta\nu/\nu = 1 \times 10^{-5}$; (b) $\Delta\nu/\nu = 0.9 \times 10^{-5}$. ($\Delta\nu$ = frequency difference for atoms moving toward the observer and away from him, with the rms velocity corresponding to the given temperature.)

5-5. 1.97×10^8 m/sec; 1.71×10^8 m/sec.

CHAPTER 6

6-1. (a) Left-handed circular; (b) linear, plane of vibration at 135° to y-axis; (c) left-handed elliptical, major axis at 135° to y-axis; (d) right-handed elliptical, major axis at 45° to y-axis.

6-3. (a) $E_y = E_z = A \cos \omega[t - (x/v)]$; (b) $E_y = -A \cos \omega[t - (x/v)]$,
$E_z = \sqrt{3} A \cos \omega[t - (x/v)]$;   (c) $E_y = A \cos \omega[t - (x/v)]$,
$E_z = -A \sin \omega[t - (x/v)]$;   (d) $E_y = 2A \cos \omega[t - (x/v)]$,
$E_z = -A \sin \omega[t - (x/v)]$.

6-5. (a) Right-handed circular polarization, amplitude $3A$; (b) left-handed elliptical polarization, axes A and $3A$.

6–7. (a) At 45° to the y-axis; (b) 1.707.

6–9. (a) Left-handed circular; (b) linear; (c) right-handed circular.

6–11. 76° or 14°.

6–13. (a) 6050 A, 6300 A, 6560 A, 6840 A; (b) 6170 A , 6420 A, 6700 A, 7000 A, (c) 6050 A; 6560 A.

6–15. Ordinary wave: sphere of 1.809 cm radius; extraordinary wave: oblate ellipsoid, minor semiaxis 1.809 cm, equatorial section 2.018 cm radius.

6–17. (a) Both refracted rays in plane of incidence; angles of refraction 25°14′ for ordinary wave and ray, 28°24′ for extraordinary wave and ray; (b) 1 mm; both rays linearly polarized; ordinary ray vibrates in plane of incidence, extraordinary ray in plane perpendicular to it.

6–19. 37°5′ $< \alpha <$ 42°18′; plane of vibration contains optic axis.

6–21. $\sin \varphi' = (c/u) \sin \varphi$.

6–23. 3.10×10^{-7}, 2.37×10^{-7}, 1.88×10^{-7}.

6–25. 0.8×10^{-4}, 0.46.

6–27. (a) Fringes sharpest when transmission axis of F is parallel to one of the axes of the plate; fringes disappear when transmission axis of F is at 45° to the axes of the plates; (b) intensity constant. Plane of vibration rotates through 360°; (c) same as without any filter or quarter-wave plate, except for absolute intensity; (d) maxima and minima interchanged; (e) fringes disappear; (f) no fringes.

CHAPTER 7

7–1. 54.8 volts/m.

7–3. (a) $\lambda = 15$ m; left-handed circular polarization; x-direction;

    (b) $H_x = 0; H_y = -1.33 \times 10^{-3} \sin \{4\pi \times 10^7[t - (x/c)]\}$;
        $H_z = 1.33 \times 10^{-3} \cos \{4\pi \times 10^7[t - (x/c)]\}$;

    (c) 6.64×10^{-4} watt/m^2; 6.64×10^{-4} watt/m^2.

7-5. $E_x = 0$; $E_y = 0$; $E_z = 8.7 \cos\left\{12\pi \times 10^{14}\left[t - \dfrac{0.707}{c}(x+y)\right]\right\}$;

$H_x = -H_y = 0.016 \cos\left\{12\pi \times 10^{14}\left[t - \dfrac{0.707}{c}(x+y)\right]\right\}$, $H_z = 0$.

7-7. (a) $i = \dfrac{2aA}{R}\sin\dfrac{\pi b \cos\theta}{\lambda}\sin\left\{2\pi\left[\dfrac{t}{T} - \dfrac{x}{\lambda}\right]\right\}$ (x is the abscissa of the

center of the loop); (b) for $b < \dfrac{\lambda}{2}$, $\theta = 0$; for $b > \dfrac{\lambda}{2}$, $\cos\theta = \dfrac{\lambda}{2b}$.

7-9. (a) $E_x = 0$, $E_y = 2A \cos[2\pi(x/\lambda)]\cos(2\pi\nu t)$, $E_z = 0$ ($\lambda = c/\nu$);

(b) $H_x = 0$, $H_y = 0$, $H_z = 2\sqrt{\epsilon_0/\mu_0}\sin\left(2\pi\dfrac{x}{\lambda}\right)\sin(2\pi\nu t)$;

(c) $u = 2\epsilon_0 A^2\{\cos^2[2\pi(x/\lambda)]\cos^2(2\pi\nu t) + \sin^2[2\pi(x/\lambda)]\sin^2(2\pi\nu t)\}$;

(d) $S_x = \sqrt{\epsilon_0/\mu_0}\,A^2\sin[4\pi(x/\lambda)]\sin(4\pi\nu t)$, $S_y = 0$, $S_z = 0$;

(e) $(E^2)_{av} = 2A^2\cos^2[2\pi(x/\lambda)]$; (f) $(u)_{av} = \epsilon_0 A^2$; (g) $(\mathbf{S})_{av} = 0$.

7-11. (a) $E_x = 0$, $E_y = 0$, $E_z = A\{\cos 2\pi[\nu t - (x/\lambda)] + \cos 2\pi[\nu t - (y/\lambda)]\}$,

$(\lambda = c/\nu)$; (b) $H_x = \sqrt{\epsilon_0/\mu_0}\,A\cos 2\pi[\nu t - (y/\lambda)]$,

$H_y = -\sqrt{\epsilon_0/\mu_0}\,A\cos 2\pi[\nu t - (x/\lambda)]$, $H_z = 0$;

(c) $u = \epsilon_0 A^2\{\cos^2 2\pi[\nu t - (x/\lambda)] + \cos^2 2\pi[\nu t - (y/\lambda)]$

$+ \tfrac{1}{2}\cos[2\pi(x-y)/\lambda] + \tfrac{1}{2}\cos 2\pi[2\nu t - (x+y)/\lambda]\}$;

(d) $S_x = -E_z H_y$, $S_y = E_z H_x$, $S_z = 0$;

(e) $(u)_{av} = \epsilon_0 A^2\{1 + \tfrac{1}{2}\cos[2\pi(x-y)/\lambda]\}$,

$(S_x)_{av} = (S_y)_{av} = \tfrac{1}{2}\sqrt{\epsilon_0\mu_0}\,A^2\{1 + \cos[2\pi(x-y)/\lambda]\}$,

$(S_z)_{av} = 0$;

(f) maxima: $x - y = k\lambda$, minima: $x - y = (k + \tfrac{1}{2})\lambda$, ($k$ = integer);

(g) $x - y = (2k + 1)\dfrac{\lambda}{4}$.

7-13. (a) $E = 2A\cos\left(\dfrac{\pi h \sin\theta}{\lambda}\right)\cos 2\pi\left(\dfrac{t}{T} - \dfrac{r}{\lambda}\right)$;

(b) $H = 2A\sqrt{\epsilon_0/\mu_0}\cos(\pi h \sin\theta/\lambda)\cos 2\pi[(t/T) - (r/\lambda)]$;

(c) $S = 4\sqrt{\epsilon_0/\mu_0}\,A^2\cos^2(\pi h \sin\theta/\lambda)\cos^2 2\pi[(t/T) - (r/\lambda)]$.

7-15. (a) 4.1×10^{-18}; (b) 1.6×10^{10} sec.

7-17. (a) 3.72×10^{-15}; (b) 3.72×10^{-6}.

7-19. Equations (7-82), (7-83) with $|\mathbf{a}| = w(\Delta\alpha/\Delta t)$.

7-21. $I = \text{const.} \times \{1 + \rho^2 - 2|\rho| \cos[(4\pi h/\lambda)\sin\alpha]\}$; ($\lambda = 1.5$ m, $\rho^2 = $ reflectance).

7-23. $\text{Const.} \times \left| \dfrac{\sin(600\,\alpha)}{\sin\alpha} \right|$, ($\alpha = 0.76\pi \cos\theta$); limit of resolution:

$\Delta\theta \approx 1/450$.

CHAPTER 8

8-1. 5.7×10^{-12} watt; 1.74×10^{11} molecules; 8.1×10^{-7}.

8-3. (a) Amplitude ratio: $\dfrac{3 \times 1836}{4\pi} \dfrac{\lambda_0}{r_e}$; phase difference: $\dfrac{\pi}{2}$;

(b) amplitude ratio: $\dfrac{3 \times 1836}{4\sqrt{2}\pi} \dfrac{\lambda_0}{r_e}$; phase difference: $\dfrac{\pi}{4}$;

(c) amplitude ratio $1836 \left(\dfrac{\nu}{\nu_0}\right)^2$; phase difference: π.

8-5. $n = 1 + 1.3 \times 10^{-4}$; $n = 1 + 2.6 \times 10^{-4}$.

8-7. (a) $\nu = 2.527 \times 10^{15}$ sec^{-1}, $\lambda = 1187$ A; (b) 1.15×10^{-10} sec; (c) $\Delta\lambda = 342$ A.

8-9. $\lambda = 2\pi R \sqrt{R/r_e}$; for $R = 10^{-8}$ cm, $\lambda = 1187$ A.

8-11. $n^2 = 1 - (Nr_e\lambda^2/\pi)$; $\lambda_m = \sqrt{\pi/Nr_e}$.

8-13. $\rho^2 = 0.042$; $\rho^2 = 0.060$.

8-15.

	Refracted wave		Reflected wave	
Case	Amplitude	Phase	Amplitude	Phase
20°, 0°	0.85	0	0.13	π
20°, 90°	0.84	0	0.16	π
75°, 0°	0.50	0	0.33	0
75°, 90°	0.44	0	0.56	π

8-17. Elliptical polarization; reflected beam, major axis perpendicular to plane of incidence, ratio of axes 3.20; refracted beam; major axis in plane of incidence, ratio of axes 1.05.

8-19. $I_1/I_2 = \cos^2 (\theta - \theta')$, where $\sin \theta' = \sin \theta / 1.33$.

8-21. (a) $|S|_{av} = \frac{1}{2}\sqrt{\epsilon_0/\mu_0}\, A^2$; (b) $A' = A/n$; (c) $|S'|_{av} = (1/n)|S|_{av}$; cross sections of incident and refracted beams are in the ratio $1/n$.

8-23. $n_0 = \sqrt{n}$, $h = \dfrac{2k+1}{4} \dfrac{\lambda}{n_0}$.

8-25. 190 A.

8-27. (a) 3.23×10^{-28}, 5.98×10^{-27} cm^2; (b) 8.7×10^{-6}, 1.6×10^{-4}.

8-29. (a) $I_s = 4I_{s1} \cos^2 \left(2\pi \dfrac{h}{\lambda} \sin^2 \dfrac{\chi}{2} \right)$, with $I_{s1} = \dfrac{r_e^2}{r^2}\left(\dfrac{\nu_0^2}{\nu_0^2 - \nu^2} \right)^2 I$;

(c) $\chi = 90°$: $(I_s)_{av} = 2I_{s1}$; $\chi = 60°(I_s)_{av} = 2I_{s1}$;

$\chi = 25.8°$: $(I_s)_{av} = 3.88\, I_{s1}$.

8-31. $\mu = 4.5 \times 10^{-8}$ cm^{-1}.

8-33. Radiation pressure: 4.5×10^{-6} newton/m^2; radiation repulsion $= 1.6 \times 10^{-20}$ times gravitational attraction.

8–35. S_{av}/ω.

8–37. Line of frequency ν_0, linearly polarized, relative intensity 2; lines of frequencies $\nu_0 \pm eB/4\pi m_e$, elliptically polarized, relative intensity 7.

CHAPTER 9

9–1. 1.987×10^{-17}, 1.987×10^{-13}, 3.975×10^{-12}, 3.975×10^{-11}, 1.987×10^{-8} erg; 1.24×10^{-5}, 0.124, 2.48, 24.8, 1.24×10^4 ev.

9–3. 1.28 volts.

9–5. Uncertainty in position of mirror must be $\ll \lambda$; hence uncertainty in its momentum will be $\gg h/\lambda$, i.e., $\gg$ momentum of photon.

INDEX

INDEX